FISHES

of the
GREAT BARRIER REEF
and
CORAL SEA

FISHES

of the
GREAT BARRIER REEF
and
CORAL SEA

John E. Randall – Gerald R. Allen – Roger C. Steene

UNIVERSITY OF HAWAII PRESS
HONOLULU

A CHP Book

Copyright © John E. Randall, Gerald R. Allen, Roger C. Steene 1990

Published in North America by
University of Hawaii Press
2840 Kolowalu Street
Honolulu, Hawaii 96822

Designed, produced and published in Australia by
Crawford House Press
P.O. Box 143
Bathurst NSW 2795
Australia

Library of Congress Cataloguing-in-Publication Data

Randall, John E., 1924-
    Fishes of the Great Barrier Reef and Coral Sea / by John E.
Randall, Gerald R. Allen, and Roger C. Steene.
        p.   cm.
    Includes bibliographical references and index.
    ISBN 0-8248-1346-4
    1. Fishes--Australia--Great Barrier Reef (Qld)--Identification
2. Fishes--Coral Sea--Identification.   I. Allen, Gerald R.
II. Steene, Roger C. III. Title.
    QL636.R36 1990
    597.092'576--dc20   70406   90-38987
                                                                CIP

Printed in Singapore by Toppan Printing Co.

10 9 8 7 6 5 4 3 2 1

CONTENTS

ACKNOWLEDGEMENTS

We thank the following individuals who assisted this project either by lending logistic assistance during fieldwork, by sharing either their knowledge or photographs of the fishes of the Great Barrier Reef and Coral Sea region, or by rendering museum aid: Connie J. Allen, Anthony and Avril Ayling, Marie Louise Bauchot, Lori J. Bell, Eugenia B. Böhlke, Clay Bryce, Kent E. Carpenter, J. Howard Choat, Neville Coleman, Patrick L. Colin, Bruce B. Collette, Ian Croll, Jane B. Culp, Charles E. Dawson, Helmut Debelius (Ikan photo agency), John L. Earle, William N. Eschmeyer, W. I. Follett, Ronald Frick, Anthony C. Gill, Barry Gill, William Gladstone, Phillip C. Heemstra, Dannie A. Hensley, Douglass F. Hoese, J. Barry Hutchins, Walter Ivantsoff, Helmut Jesse, G. David Johnson, Patricia Kailola, Rudie H. Kuiter, Michel Kulbicki, Helen K. Larson, Mike and Jane Lark, Jeffrey M. Leis, John E. McCosker, R. J. McKay, Hajime Masuda, Joseph F. Nelson, Roy and Susan O'Connor, John R. Paxton, Theodore W. Pietsch, Stuart G. Poss, Richard L. Pyle, Robert M. Pyle, Helen A. Randall, Barry C. Russell, William F. Smith-Vaniz, Victor G. Springer, Lyle Squire, Walter A. Starck II, Wayne G. Starnes, Arnold Y. Suzumoto, Hugh Sweatman, Frank H. Talbot, Ron and Valerie Taylor, James M. Thomson, James C. Tyler, Dennis Wallace, Robin S. Waples, Paul Watson, Alwyne C. Wheeler, Jeffrey T. Williams, Richard Winterbottom, David J. Woodland and Tetsuo Yoshino.

Special thanks also to the Australian National Parks and Wildlife Service under the direction of Professor J. D. Ovington. This organisation funded a one month collecting trip to the Coral Sea for Gerald Allen in 1987. We are also grateful to the Western Australian Museum for permitting us to use seven plates of fish paintings by Roger Swainston that originally appeared in the Museum's publication *The Marine Fishes of North-Western Australia.*

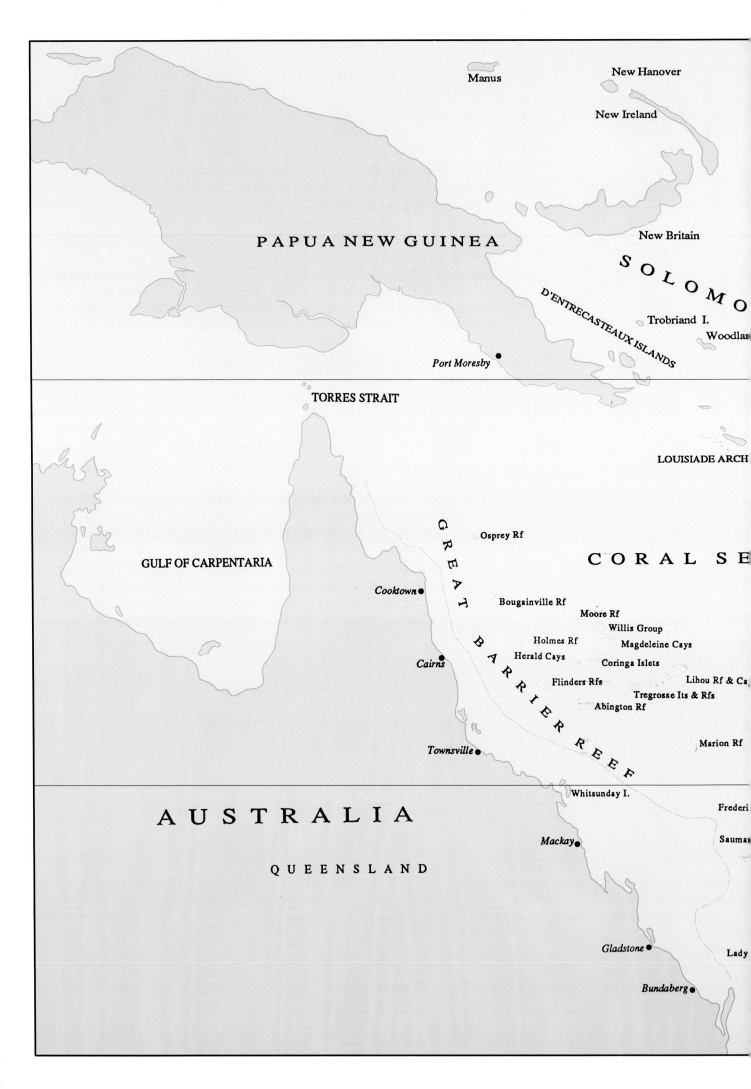

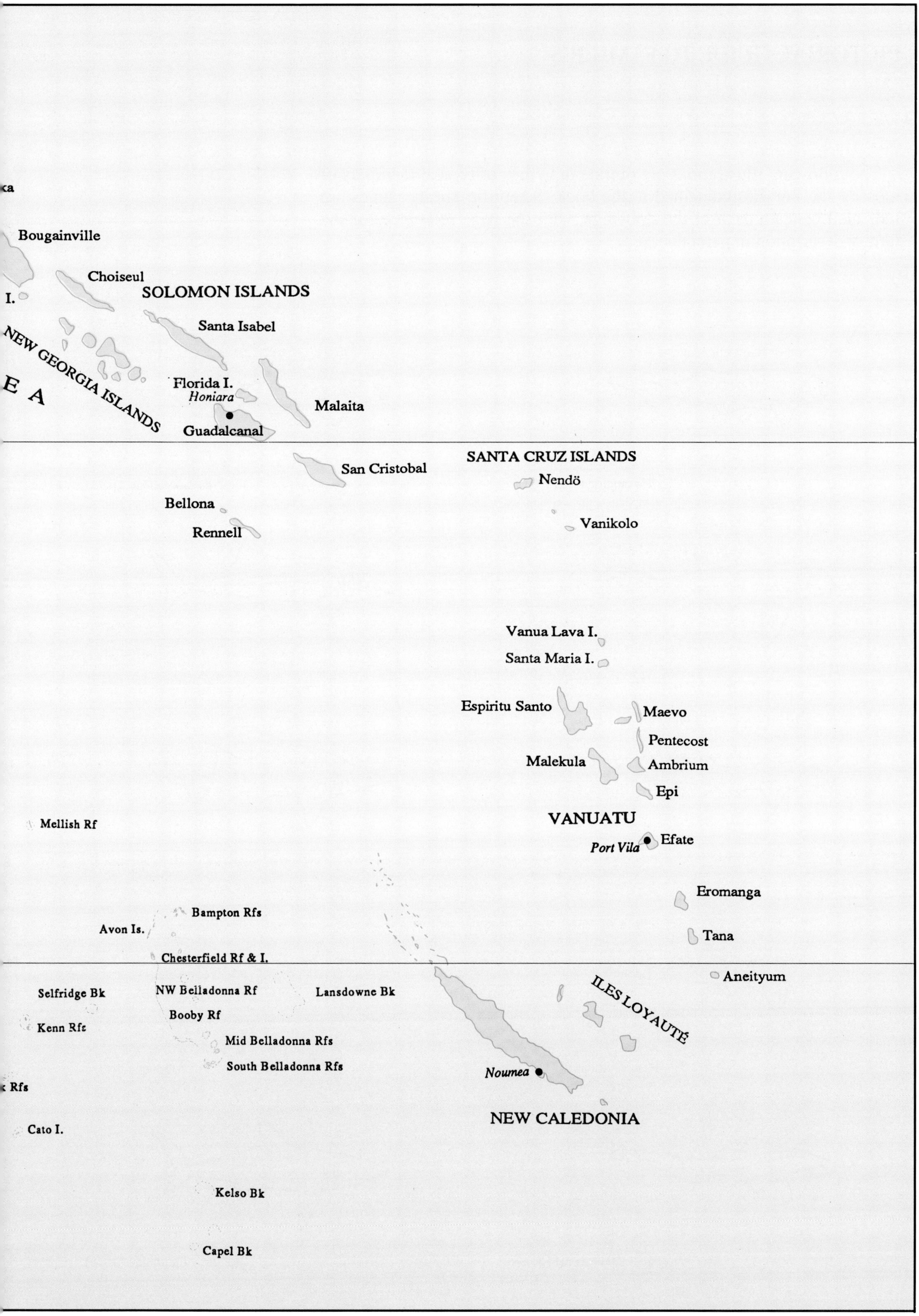

ka

Bougainville

Choiseul   SOLOMON ISLANDS

I.

Santa Isabel

NEW GEORGIA ISLANDS

E A

Florida I.
Honiara
Guadalcanal

Malaita

San Cristobal

SANTA CRUZ ISLANDS

Nendö

Bellona

Vanikolo

Rennell

Vanua Lava I.

Santa Maria I.

Espiritu Santo

Maevo

Pentecost

Malekula

Ambrium

Epi

VANUATU

Mellish Rf

Port Vila ● Efate

Eromanga

Bampton Rfs

Avon Is.

Tana

Chesterfield Rf & I.

Aneityum

Selfridge Bk   NW Belladonna Rf   Lansdowne Bk

ILES LOYAUTÉ

Booby Rf

Kenn Rfs

Mid Belladonna Rfs

South Belladonna Rfs

Noumea ●

Rfs

Cato I.

NEW CALEDONIA

Kelso Bk

Capel Bk

PICTORIAL GUIDE TO FAMILIES

The following illustrations are outline drawings of typical members of most of the families contained in the book. Scientific family names are indicated beneath each of the drawings, with the page reference for the family description in parentheses.

Hexanchidae (p 13)

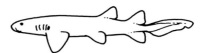

Ginglymostomatidae (p 15)

Heterodontidae (p 13)

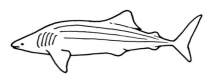

Rhincodontidae (p 15)

Orectolobidae (p 13)

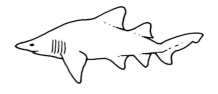

Odontaspidae (p 16)

Hemiscyllidae (p 14)

Alopiidae (p 16)

Stegostomatidae (p 15)

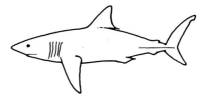

Lamnidae (p 16)

Scyliorhinidae (p 17)

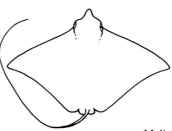

Myliobatidae (p 31)

Carcharhinidae (p 17)

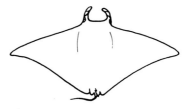

Mobulidae (p 31)

Hemigaleidae (p 22)

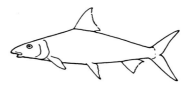

Albulidae (p 32)

Sphyrnidae (p 23)

Muraenidae (p 34)

Torpedinidae (p 28)

Ophichthidae (p 43)

Rhinobatidae (p 28)

Congridae (p 46)

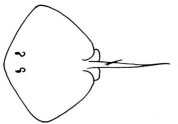

Dasyatidae (p 29)

Clupeidae (p 47)

xiii

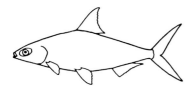

Chandidae (p 48)

Antennariidae (p 54)

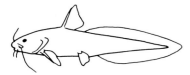

Plotosidae (p 48)

Gobiesocidae (p 56)

Synodontidae (p 49)

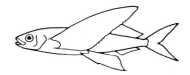

Exocoetidae (p 57)

Ophidiidae (p 52)

Hemiramphidae (p 57)

Carapidae (p 52)

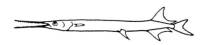

Belonidae (p 58)

Bythitidae (p 53)

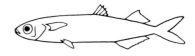

Atherinidae (p 59)

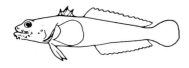

Batrachoididae (p 53)

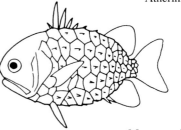

Monocentridae (p 59)

Holocentridae (p 60)

Dactylopteridae (p 76)

Aulostomidae (p 68)

Scorpaenidae (p 77)

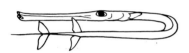

Fistulariidae (p 68)

Aploactinidae (p 86)

Centriscidae (p 70)

Platycephalidae (p 86)

Solenostomidae (p 71)

Centropomidae (p 88)

Syngnathidae (p 72)

Serranidae (p 89)

Syngnathidae (p 72)

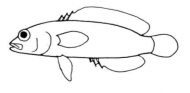

Pseudochromidae (p 124)

Plesiopidae (p 132)

Echeneidae (p 155)

Acanthoclinidae (p 134)

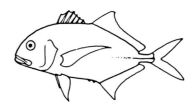

Carangidae (p 156)

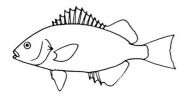

Teraponidae (p 134)

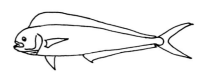

Coryphaenidae (p 168)

Kuhliidae (p 135)

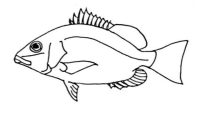

Lutjanidae (p 176)

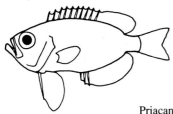

Priacanthidae (p 135)

Caesionidae (p 186)

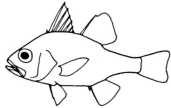

Apogonidae (p 137)

Lobotidae (p 189)

Malacanthidae (p 154)

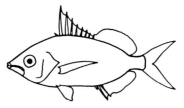

Gerreidae (p 189)

Haemulidae (p 190)

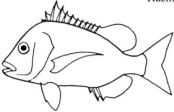

Sparidae (p 195)

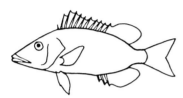

Lethrinidae (p 196)

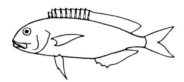

Nemipteridae (p 204)

Mullidae (p 208)

Pempheridae (p 213)

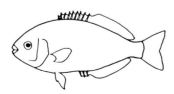

Kyphosidae (p 215)

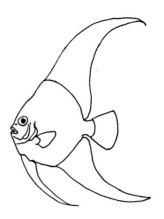

Ephippidae (p 216)

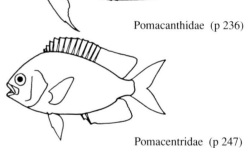

Chaetodontidae (p 220)

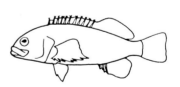

Pomacanthidae (p 236)

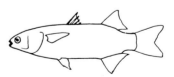

Pomacentridae (p 247)

Cirrhitidae (p 285)

Mugilidae (p 290)

Sphyraenidae (p 291)

xvii

Polynemidae (p 293)

Trypterygiidae (p 364)

Labridae (p 294)

Blenniidae (p 366)

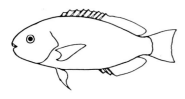

Scaridae (p 342)

Callionymidae (p 388)

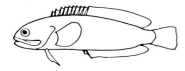

Opistognathidae (p 356)

Eleotridae (p 390)

Uranoscopidae (p 357)

Gobiidae (p 391)

Creedidae (p 359)

Acanthuridae (p 419)

Pinguipedidae (p 359)

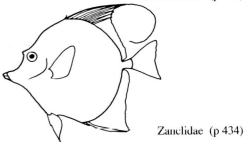

Zanclidae (p 434)

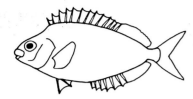

Siganidae (p 435

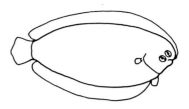

Soleidae (p 450)

Istiophoridae (p 441)

Balistidae (p 451)

Xiphiidae (p 441)

Monacanthidae (p 460)

Scombridae (p 442)

Ostraciidae (p 467)

Bothidae (p 449)

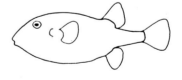

Tetraodontidae (p 472)

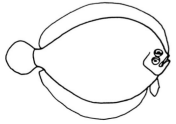

Pleuronectidae (p 450)

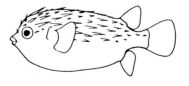

Diodontidae (p 478)

INTRODUCTION

(Opposite) The jetty at Green Island, a popular tourist destination, offers visitors an easy opportunity to observe marine life at close quarters.

Feeding time at the Cod Hole, Cormorant Pass, a popular dive destination near Lizard Island.

The Great Barrier Reef, the largest coral formation in the world, extends northward nearly to Papua New Guinea, from its southernmost outpost at Lady Elliott Island (24°F'S), a distance of 2300 kilometres (km). It is not a single continuous reef but a vast assemblage of reefs, shoals and islands. The outer barrier reef approximately follows the edge of the continental shelf (100-fathom line); it varies from 32 km to 260 km off the coast of Queensland. The huge lagoon area it protects, which is generally less than 60 meters (m) in depth, contains many inner reefs and islands, some of them high islands of continental origin. To the east lies the Coral Sea, rimmed on the north by Papua New Guinea and the Solomon Islands, and to the east by Vanuatu and New Caledonia. It contains a few scattered reefs which rise from depths of 700 to 1800 m. The clarity of the sea at these reefs is exceptional, making them popular destinations for dive boats from Queensland.

The Great Barrier Reef and its lagoon offer a wide variety of habitats for fishes and other marine organisms. The outer part of this massive reef, where the clearest water is generally found, is divisible into distinct zones. Typically there is a broad outer reef flat, the inner part of which may be covered with fleshy algae and the outer part with encrusting coralline algae. The reef flat is exposed during low spring tides. At the outer edge where the

surf breaks, there is a coralline algae rim, then the broad spur-and-groove zone subject to strong surge from incoming waves and the scouring action of sand and rubble in the grooves from powerful water movement. The grooves may extend as deep as 20 m. Below the spur-and-groove zone there is usually an abrupt vertical escarpment which drops to 30 m or more; this is followed by a gradual slope to the abyss. Each of these zones has its characteristic assemblage of corals, algae, and associated marine life. The channels and passages through the reef, both shallow and deep, provide still more habitats for which current is a major parameter.

On the sheltered side of the outer reef, as the water deepens slightly, there is a zone of elongate patches of coral and coralline algae, about 1-2 m wide and 20 m or more in length, separated by channels. Then a broad zone of sand grading into the depths of the lagoon. Isolated on the sand substratum there are usually many small coral heads (called bommies in Australia), each a microcosm of marine organisms. Within the deeper lagoon a variety of coral formations occur, some rising pinnacle-like from the deep water. Corals growing in the sheltered lagoon water are often delicately branched.

(Opposite) Escape Reef, on the outer edge of the Great Barrier Reef. A diver explores the reef top.

The past decade has seen a vast improvement in visitor facilities on the Great Barrier Reef such as this operation on Agincourt Reef off Port Douglas.

Myriads of small colourful fishes swarm around Pixie Bommie in the Ribbon Reef complex. Most of the fishes are basslets.

Also in the lagoon are broad expanses of seagrass beds. Moving toward the mainland of Queensland, silty sand and mud habitats tend to dominate the lagoon floor. The islets and larger islands of the Great Barrier Reef complex provide still more habitats such as rocky intertidal areas, sandy shores, and mangrove swamps. Just as the outer reef zones harbor characteristic fish communities, so also do the lagoon habitats, and many of the fishes seen there will not be found on exposed reefs.

In spite of their massive size and ability to withstand the forces of nature, coral reefs are not immune to depredations by man. Activities such as mining limestone or exploration for oil may cause rather obvious damage. Other more insidious human impacts, such as pollution, siltation, and enrichment of the sea from nutrients in run-off from the land, can cause more far-reaching deleterious effects. The nutrients can lead to an overgrowth of algae on reefs. Some scientists believe that the initial triggering of the huge infestations of the crown-of-thorns starfish on the Great Barrier Reef may have been from a pollutant which reduced the predators on larval starfish in the plankton. The fishing for the larger predaceous fishes on reefs is apt to result in a proliferation of their prey. If the prey were a sea urchin, for example, the effect of a great increase in the population of such an animal could be disastrous.

Because of increasing and unrestricted commercial and recreational pressure on the Great Barrier Reef, the Great Barrier Reef Marine Park Act was passed in 1975 and first implemented in 1979 for the southern part of the reef. In 1983 the Great Barrier Reef Marine Park was fully established from 24°30'S to the latitude of Cape York, 10°41'S. The Great Barrier Reef

Marine Park Authority has now developed zoning plans and regulations to protect this most valuable marine environment of Australia. The Australian National Parks and Wildlife Service has established nature reserves in the Coral Sea at Herald-Coringa Sand Cays and Lihou Reef.

New Guinea, Indonesia, and the Philippines collectively have the greatest number of species of marine plants and animals in the world. As would be expected from its proximity to New Guinea, the Great Barrier Reef also has an extremely rich marine fauna and flora, particularly in the northern part. Many plants and animals of the reef remain to be discovered and classified by marine biologists. For some of the better known groups, such as the corals and the fishes, our knowledge has reached a level to justify the preparation of guide books on these animals.

How to use the book

The present book is intended to provide for the identification of the 1111 species of fishes of the Great Barrier Reef and adjoining reefs of the Coral Sea (see map) which are most apt to be seen by snorkellers or divers. These fishes include not only those which live on or over coral reefs but ones which may be readily encountered in adjacent habitats such as sand flats or seagrass or algal beds. Fishes not included in the book are either rare or too small or cryptic to be noticed by the average diver. Because most of the species of fishes found on the Great Barrier Reef range widely in the rest of the western Pacific, and many extend their distributions west into the Indian Ocean and eastward to the islands of Oceania, this book will be useful for the identification of reef and shore fishes from regions beyond the Great Barrier Reef and Coral Sea.

Exposed corals at extreme low tide on Flynn Reef. These spectacular conditions only occur on a few days of the year.

5

The fishes are presented phylogenetically by family (the scientific names of which all end in IDAE); that is, the most primitive first and the most highly evolved last. We have followed the sequence given in Nelson's *Fishes of the World* (John Wiley & Sons, 2nd edition, 1984). There is a general discussion for each family to give characteristics and habits that apply to the group as a whole. Within each family the species accounts are given alphabetically by scientific name. This is the italicised name in two parts, the first being the generic name (capitalised) and the second the species name. Immediately following the species is the name of the author or authors who gave the fish its scientific name and the year in which the description was published. If the author's name appears in parentheses, he named the fish in a different genus from the one currently in use. A few species included herein are waiting their scientific names and descriptions; these are indicated by sp. following the generic name.

The common names of fishes used in this book are primarily the Australian names. These are often different from the fish names used in other parts of the English speaking world. Widely used equivalent English common names are also given.

Most of the fishes which occur in Australian waters were given their scientific names in the late 18th or 19th centuries. Many of the common wide-ranging fishes were named more than once by early naturalists. By the law of priority, the oldest name is the one to be accepted, provided it is binomial, was accompanied by a description, and was published on or after 1758, the date of the tenth edition of Carl Linnaeus' *Systema Naturae*, the starting point for our biological nomenclature. Subsequent names of the same organisms are called synonyms. Most of these synonyms have been

Lizard Island on the northern Great Barrier Reef is an isolated remnant of the mainland. Its unique position near the outer edge of the reef encompasses a wide range of habitats.

sorted out years ago, but some older names are still being unearthed which will replace names currently in use. We have listed synonyms in the species accounts which have been in widespread use in recent years.

In order to include 1100 species in a single book of reasonable size, the accounts of individual species must be brief. We are relying heavily on colour illustrations as the primary basis for identification, adding only a few remarks on the most important diagnostic characteristics. Often the number of spines and soft rays in the fins of fishes and the number of scales in a lengthwise series along the body (generally the pored scales of the lateral line) are of significance in determining the species.

We have listed the maximum length in centimetres (cm) attained by each species. This is frequently just an approximation. Good size records are maintained for the gamefishes, but data are often lacking in the literature for the largest of the many species of fishes that are not taken commercially or for sport.

The geographical distribution of each of the fishes is given in very general terms. If a species occurs broadly throughout the Indian and Pacific Oceans from the coast of East Africa to the easternmost islands of Oceania,

The outer edge of the Great Barrier Reef slopes away steeply to deep water.

Herald Cays, Coral Sea. Vegetated sand Cays such as this support huge bird populations and are important breeding grounds for turtles.

we state that it is Indo-Pacific in its distribution. If it ranges from southern Japan through the Philippines, Indonesia, and the islands of Melanesia to the Great Barrier Reef but not to the islands of Micronesia (except possibly nearby Palau) or Polynesia, we summarise this as Western Pacific.

Nearly all of the wrasses (Labridae) and parrotfishes (Scaridae), whose reproductive strategies have been determined, undergo a change in sex from female to male, often accompanied by a striking change in colour. For such species it is necessary to have two figures. The initial mature colour phase, often drab compared to that of the terminal male, can be either male or female for some species; for others only females are known in the initial phase. Some fishes have juvenile stages which are very different in colour from adults, and these may also be illustrated.

Most bony fishes have both spines and soft rays in their dorsal and anal fins. To differentiate these two kinds of fin rays, the count of the spines (not branched, not segmented, and usually sharp-tipped) is given in Roman numerals, and the count of soft rays (segmented, flexible, and often branched) is given in Arabic numerals. Thus a dorsal fin ray count of X,12 would indicate ten spines and twelve soft rays.

The scale count most often made on fishes is the number of pored scales of the lateral line from the upper end of the gill opening to the base of the caudal fin (tail). When the lateral line is not apparent, the longitudinal series of scales is counted between the same two points.

Occasionally the count of gill rakers is needed to differentiate closely related species. These are the protuberances along the inner edge of the first gill arch (opposite the red gill filaments where respiratory exchange takes place).

The shape of the trailing edge of the caudal fin is often useful in separating species. It may be forked, emarginate (inwardly concave), lunate (very deeply concave), truncate (the edge vertical), or rounded (outwardly convex).

Certain body and fin proportions are used to characterise a fish. These are presented as percentages of a larger measurement or more often as the number of times the smaller measurement can be divided into the larger. The depth of the body of a fish may be expressed as the number of times this measurement can be "stepped into" the standard length of the fish (standard length being the straight-line distance from the tip of the snout to the base of the caudal fin). A depth of 6 in the standard length would be that of an elongate fish, whereas a depth of 1.5 would indicate a high-bodied fish.

In describing bands of colour on a fish, a stripe refers to a horizontal marking and a bar to a vertical one.

Characteristics given in the first species account of a genus that apply to all the species in the genus are often not repeated in the subsequent accounts. Their occurrence in other species is indicated by parenthetical remarks.

The Coral Sea offers unsurpassed diving conditions. Visibility of 50 m is not uncommon.

External Features of Fishes

Cartilaginous Fishes (Sharks and Rays)

The two illustrations below and the four on the facing page are labelled to show the principal external parts of fishes.

Silvertip Shark
(*Carcharhinus albimarginatus*)

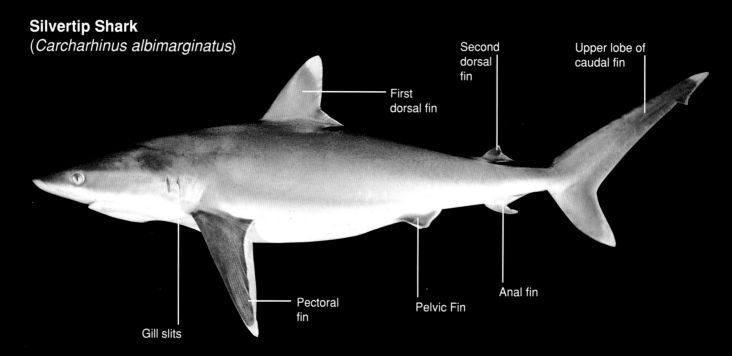

First dorsal fin

Second dorsal fin

Upper lobe of caudal fin

Pectoral fin

Gill slits

Pelvic Fin

Anal fin

Kuhl's Stingray
(*Dasyatis kuhlii*)

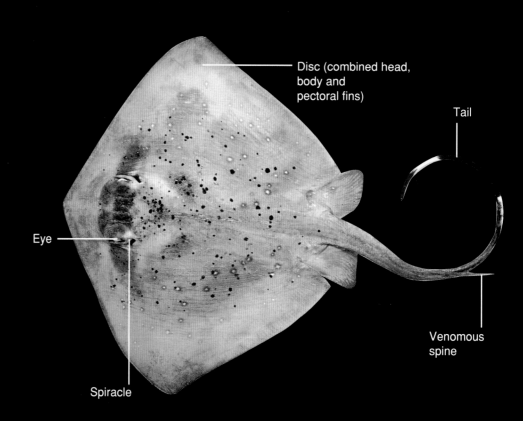

Disc (combined head, body and pectoral fins)

Tail

Eye

Spiracle

Venomous spine

Bony Fishes

Strawberry Rockcod
(*Cephalopholis spiloparaea*)

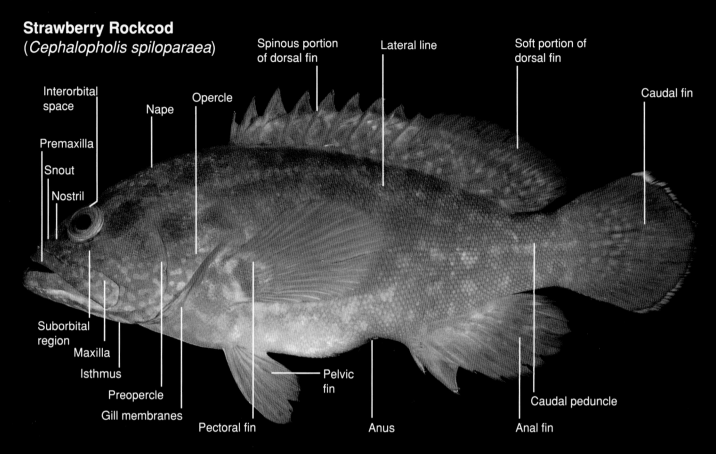

Interorbital space
Premaxilla
Snout
Nostril
Nape
Opercle
Spinous portion of dorsal fin
Lateral line
Soft portion of dorsal fin
Caudal fin
Suborbital region
Maxilla
Isthmus
Preopercle
Gill membranes
Pectoral fin
Pelvic fin
Anus
Anal fin
Caudal peduncle

A

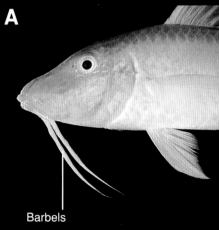

Barbels

B

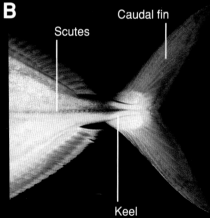

Scutes
Caudal fin
Keel

The picture labelled **A** is the head of a goatfish (Mullidae) and shows the pair of barbels on the chin. These are moved over the bottom or thrust into the sediment during feeding to assist the fish in finding its food.

B shows the tail of a trevally (Carangidae) which has a falcate caudal fin; this shape is often found on fishes capable of swimming very rapidly. Because of the stress placed on the narrow caudal peduncle, fishes such as jacks and tunas usually reinforce it with scutes and/or keels.

C depicts one of the gills (respiratory organs of fishes). The gill arch is the structural part. Gaseous exchange takes place in the gill filaments and the gill rakers keep food items from passing out of the gill opening along with expired water.

D is the roof of the mouth of a percomorph fish and shows the typical dentition of the premaxilla, vomer and palatine bones.

C

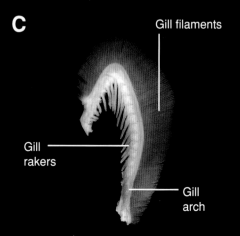

Gill filaments
Gill rakers
Gill arch

D

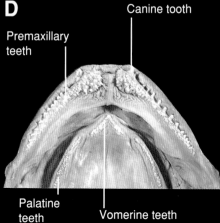

Canine tooth
Premaxillary teeth
Palatine teeth
Vomerine teeth

SHARKS

Perhaps no other group of fishes have captured the interest of humankind to the same extent as sharks. The habits and reputations of a relatively small number of species have shaped the popular notion that sharks are basically evil, menacing predators. This is definitely not true, as the majority of the approximately 340 species are no more threatening than most other fishes. Unfortunately a few species such as the Tiger Shark and White Pointer are known to fatally attack man. Even though the incidence of attacks is small, the danger represented by these animals is consistently blown out of proportion by over zealous journalists. Certainly the automobile is much more menacing than all the sharks in all the world's seas could ever be. A small sample of the amazing diversity of sharks is indicated in the plate that appears on the following page. They range in size from the gargantuan Whale Shark that grows to more than 15 m to species that are less than 0.5 m. Sharks are characterised by a cartilagenous skeleton; 5-7 lateral gill openings; upper jaw not fused to the cranium; usually numerous sharp conspicuous teeth in the jaws that are replaced when broken or worn by replacement teeth from intact rows behind; some short ribs present, but not protecting the body cavity as in most bony fishes; a spiracle opening usually present; males with claspers used to transfer sperm to the cloaca of females. The closely related rays share most of these features, but are generally separated by the body shape (disc-like in rays) and placement of the gill slits. The gill openings are located on the underside of the head, rather than on the sides of the head as in sharks. However, the differences are not absolute, and certain groups such as sawfishes, guitarfishes, sawsharks, and angel-sharks have intermediate

Grey Reef Shark (*Carcharhinus amblyrphnchos*)

characters. Sharks utilise a variety of reproductive modes; all fertilisation is internal. Depending on the species, the embryos may develop freely, attached to a placenta, or sealed in leathery egg cases. Relatively few species produce egg cases; these are generally deposited in bottom vegetation. Most species bear their young alive in broods that range from a few individuals to nearly 100. The newborn are called pups and usually have the appearance of miniature adults. Sharks are flesh eaters that feed mainly on fishes, crustaceans and molluscs. A few of the larger species take such prey as marine mammals, sea birds, sea turtles, and other sharks. Fish-eating species generally have well developed sharp teeth, often with lateral cusps or incisors, that are designed for seizing and tearing. The tooth shapes are very useful for helping to identify individual species. Some of these are shown below. Sharks have keen vision and an excellent sense of smell. Also their highly developed lateralis system (composed of special fluid-filled sensory canals) enables them to detect low frequency vibrations at considerable distances, thus facilitating prey detection and the avoidance of predation. They also have a sense to detect an electric field such as that which surrounds a sleeping fish at night. Sharks generally feed at night and have a remarkable adaptation called the tapetum lucidum that is also found in cats and other vertebrates that are nocturnal hunters. This structure, located behind the retina, increases the sensitivity of the shark's eye to the available light. Because sharks produce so few young and because we believe from limited data that they are, in general, slow growing, their populations may be greatly reduced by heavy fishing. When these top-level predators are removed from a community such as a coral reef, that community may be adversely affected.

SIXGILL AND SEVENGILL SHARKS
FAMILY HEXANCHIDAE

These are mainly deep-water sharks that live in all temperate and tropical seas. They are characterised by the presence of 6 or 7 gill slits (most sharks have 5), a single, relatively small dorsal fin that is situated well posteriorly near the tail base, and blade-like, comb-shaped teeth in the lower jaw. The family contains three genera and four known species. Most live in deeper sections of the continental shelf and slope. They generally occur near the bottom and range in size from about 1.4 to 4.8 metres. Reproduction is ovoviviparous, lacking a yolk-sac placenta. They feed on relatively large items including other sharks, rays, fishes, and crustaceans. Because of the occurrence in deep water, at least as adults, these sharks are not apt to encounter divers.

BLUNTNOSE SIXGILL SHARK
Hexanchus griseus (Bonnaterre, 1788)
(Plate I-8)

A large, cylindrical, heavy-bodied shark; head broad and rounded to bluntly pointed; six gill openings; a single dorsal fin; pelvic and anal fins of similar size, situated below dorsal fin; caudal peduncle short and stout; lower jaw with 6 rows of large comb-like teeth on each side; overall greyish, darker on back. Worldwide in tropical and temperate seas. Maximum size to at least 482 cm; at birth about 65-70 cm.

HORN OR BULLHEAD SHARKS
FAMILY HETERODONTIDAE

This family contains a single genus (*Heterodontus*) with eight species that occur in temperate and tropical seas along the fringe of the Indian and Pacific oceans. They are small, easily recognizable sharks distinguished by a squarish head and a stout, sharp spine at the beginning of each dorsal fin. They are slow mov-

ing animals, often seen resting on the bottom amongst rocks or weeds. Horn sharks are oviparous. They lay unusual, large, spiral-flanged egg cases, usually among rocky crevices. The young are generally over 14 cm long at hatching. The Port Jackson Shark of Australia breeds during late winter. Females lay 10 to 16 eggs on shallow reefs. The young hatch after about 9 to 12 months and move into nursery areas in bays and estuaries. The diet consists mainly of benthic invertebrates including sea urchins, crabs, prawns, abalone and other gastropods, oysters, polychaetes, and occasional small fishes. These sharks are generally harmless, but will pursue and bite if provoked by a diver.

ZEBRA BULLHEAD SHARK
Heterodontus zebra (Gray, 1831)
(Plate I-6)

A slender-bodied shark with an enlarged squarish head and pig-like snout; a low bony ridge above each eye; nostrils without barbels; with nasoral and circumnarial grooves that are connected to the mouth; anterior nasal flaps elongate posteriorly; small mouth with enlarged molariform teeth posteriorly; both dorsal fins with a sharp spine; tannish with striking pattern of narrow dark brown to blackish bars. Inhabits trawling grounds to at least 50 metres depth. Northern Australia to southern Japan. To about 125 cm.

WOBBEGONGS
FAMILY ORECTOLOBIDAE

These are distinctive flattened sharks with highly variegated patterns. Important characteristics include skin flaps and tassels on the side of the head, long nasal barbels, spiracles that are larger than the eyes, and a small, nearly terminal mouth with extremely sharp fang-like teeth. The family contains three genera and six species that are mainly confined to Australia, but three species range north to Japan. They are generally sluggish animals that are usually seen resting motionless, often among weeds. Reproduction is ovoviviparous, with large litters of 20 or more young. Wobbegongs are powerful bottom predators that feed on fishes, crabs, lobsters, octopuses, and other benthic invertebrates. They are not particularly aggressive and generally can be considered harmless. Nevertheless many attacks have occurred, some even fatal. These sharks will bite if accidentally trod on and may become aggressive if provoked.

Eucrossorhinus dasypogon

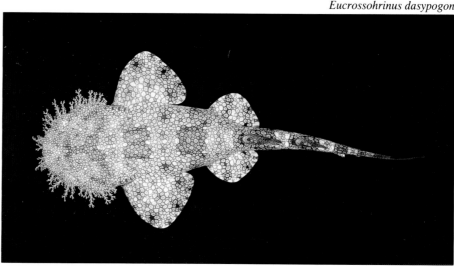

TASSELLED WOBBEGONG
Eucrossohrinus dasypogon Regan, 1908
(Plate I-16)

Head and body extremely broad, trunk width across pectoral insertions about equal to head length; highly branched skin flaps on side of head and on chin; dorsal fins situated well posteriorly, first dorsal fin slightly larger than second dorsal; pectoral and pelvic fins relatively large and broad; anal fin immediately anterior to caudal fin; tan or light grey with complex mottling and reticulated pattern of narrow dark lines and dark spots. Northern Australia and New Guinea. Reaches 360 cm, but most are 150-250 cm; size at birth about 22 cm.

BANDED WOBBEGONG
Orectolobus ornatus (De Vis, 1883)
(Plate I-14)

Head and body flattened; head with 5 skin flaps below and in front of eye on each side; additional broad skin flaps on side of head; chin without skin flaps; basally branched nasal barbels; nasoral and circumnarial grooves; two rows of enlarged fang-like teeth in upper jaw and three in lower jaw; dorsal fins situated well posteriorly, both dorsal fins about equal in size; pectoral and pelvic fins similar to dorsal fins in size; a small lobular anal fin in front of caudal fin; generally grey-brown with about 5-7 dark brown bars or saddles; variable brown mottling on head and body. Northern Australia, New Guinea, and southern Japan. To 288 cm; about 20 cm at birth.

NORTHERN WOBBEGONG
Orectolobus wardi Whitley, 1939
(Plate I-15)

Head and body flattened; head with 2 skin flaps below and in front of eye on each side; about 3-4 additional skin flaps on side of head; chin without skin flaps; basally branched nasal barbels; nasoral and circumnarial grooves; two rows of enlarged fang-like teeth in upper jaw and three in lower jaw; both dorsal fins about equal in size; pectoral and pelvic fins slightly broader than dorsal fins; a lobular anal fin in front of caudal fin; generally mottled brown with indication of darker brown bars or saddles. Northern Australia. Reaches at least 45 cm.

BAMBOO SHARKS
FAMILY HEMISCYLLIDAE

These are generally small, slender sharks characterised by the presence of both nasoral and perinasal grooves, short nasal barbels, a small transverse mouth, dorsolateral eyes, and a large spiracle below the eye. The family contains two genera and 11 species found in continental waters of the tropical western Pacific. The genus *Hemiscyllium* is restricted to Australia and neighbouring New Guinea. These sharks are commonly found in the intertidal zone, sometimes in tide pools, and on inshore rock or coral reefs. The biology of most of the species has not been studied in detail, but at

Hemiscyllium trispeculare

least some are oviparous, depositing eggs on the bottom in oval cases. Their diet consists primarily of small fishes and bottom-dwelling invertebrates. They are generally under 100 cm in length and are considered to be harmless.

BROWNBANDED BAMBOO SHARK
Chiloscyllium punctatum Müller & Henle, 1838
(Plate I-11)

Body slender; snout rounded; a short barbel next to each nasal opening; a pair of similar-sized dorsal fins without spines; dorsals with projecting free rear tips; no lateral ridges on side of body; adults often plain grey or brownish, young with dark

transverse bands and occasional spots. East coast of the Indian Peninsula to northern Australia & north to Japan. Attains 104 cm.

EPAULETTE SHARK
Hemiscyllium ocellatum (Bonnaterre, 1788)
(Plate I-10)

Body slender; snout blunt, somewhat swollen and elongate; a short barbel next to each nasal opening; eye and supraorbital ridge well elevated; mouth well in front of eyes; a pair of similar-sized dorsal fins without spines; dorsal with projecting free rear tips; no lateral ridges on side of body; tail very narrow, its base elongate and thick; a long low anal fin immediately in front of caudal fin; brownish with scattered dark spots; a large black spot ringed with white on side above pectoral fin. Northern Australia and New Guinea. Maximum size to 107 cm.

SPECKLED CATSHARK
Hemiscyllium trispeculare Richardson, 1843
(Plate I-9)

Body relatively stout and snout less swollen (compared to *H. ocellatum*); a short barbel next to each nasal opening; eye and supraorbital ridge well-elevated; mouth distinctly anterior to eyes; a pair of similar-sized dorsal fins without spines; dorsal fins without projecting free rear tips; no lateral ridges on side of body; tail very narrow, its base elongate and thick; a long low anal fin immediately in front of tail; light grey with densely clustered large and small dark spots forming a reticular pattern; a large black spot rimmed with white as in *H. ocellatum*, but this marking is rimmed posteriorly by a few large black spots. Northern Australia. Grows to 64 cm.

LEOPARD SHARKS
FAMILY STEGOSTOMATIDAE

See discussion of the single species of the family below.

LEOPARD SHARK
Stegostoma fasciatum (Hermann, 1783)
(Plate I-2)

Body somewhat cylindrical with prominent ridges on sides; head broadly conical, slightly flattened; snout broadly rounded or truncate; gill slits small, the fourth overlapping the fifth; nostrils with short pointed barbels; mouth moderately large, subterminal in position; teeth with an enlarged medial cusp and lateral cusplet on each side; caudal peduncle without lateral keels or precaudal pits; first dorsal fin larger than second dorsal and anal fins; anal fin larger than second dorsal fin; pectoral fins large and broadly rounded; caudal fin extremely long, about one-half of total length, without a ventral lobe; grey to yellow brown with scattered dark spots; young are dark brown to blackish with narrow yellow bars and yellow spots; East Africa and the Red Sea to Australia and New Caledonia; often seen on or adjacent to coral reefs, usually on sandy bottoms. The Leopard Shark is a sluggish, slow-swimming fish that feeds primarily on gastropod and bivalve molluscs with lesser amounts of crabs, shrimps, and small fishes. It is oviparous, laying large (17 cm in length), dark-coloured egg cases that have tufts of hair-like fibers which serve to anchor them to the bottom. Up to four fully formed egg cases have been found in the oviduct of an adult female. The young hatch at a size between 20 and 26 cm. This shark is unaggressive when approached underwater and is generally considered to be harmless. Maximum size to about 354 cm, but common between 150-250 cm. *Stegostoma varium* (Seba) is an earlier name but generally regarded as invalid.

NURSE SHARKS
FAMILY GINGLYMOSTOMATIDAE

This small family contains three species in two genera and has a circumglobal distribution in tropical and subtropical seas. These sharks occur on coral and rocky reefs, usually close to shore. Diagnostic features include two relatively close-set dorsal fins of about equal size on posterior half of body, a pair of barbels

Stegostoma fasciatum

Rhincodon typus

below the snout, and a groove between each nasal opening and the corner of the mouth. Knowledge of the reproduction is incomplete, but at least one species (*Ginglymostoma cirratum* from the Atlantic and eastern Pacific) is ovoviviparous with young that are nourished mainly by yolk while in the uterus; litters of 20-30 young have been reported. These sharks cruise around the bottom in search of food with their mouth and barbels close to the substrate. They are nocturnally active and ingest prey with a powerful sucking action. The diet includes mainly fishes, crabs, prawns, lobsters, other crustaceans, and cephalopods. Nurse sharks are generally considered to be harmless, but may bite and inflict serious injury if provoked.

TAWNY NURSE SHARK
Nebrius ferrugineus (Lesson, 1830)
(Plate I-3)

A large brownish shark with two dorsal fins of similar size; nasoral grooves present; a pair of barbels below snout; mouth infe-

rior with multi-cusped teeth; caudal fin moderately long, about one-fourth of total length; colour varies from tan or brown to dark grey brown. Often seen resting on sand in sheltered parts of the reef such as crevices and caves; found in depths to at least 70 m. Indo-West Pacific from East Africa and the Red Sea to the Society Islands. Grows to about 320 cm, but most seen are 150-250 cm; size at birth about 40 cm.

WHALE SHARKS
FAMILY RHINCODONTIDAE

See discussion of the single species of the family below.

WHALE SHARK
Rhincodon typus Smith, 1828
(Plate I-1)

Head broad and flat with terminal mouth situated just in front of eyes; minute, extremely numerous teeth; prominent ridges on sides of body with the lowermost expanding into a prominent keel on each side of caudal peduncle; first dorsal fin relatively large; a small second dorsal and anal fin; a somewhat lunate caudal fin without a prominent subterminal notch; colour generally blackish with "checkerboard" pattern of whitish spots, stripes, and bars; ventral parts whitish. Circumglobal in tropical and warm temperate seas; pelagic in habits and often seen far offshore, as well as inshore near coral reefs; encountered as single individuals, but aggregations are sometimes seen. Whale sharks appear to be highly migratory and may occur in certain areas at more or less predictable intervals. Their movements are probably dependent on availability of their planktonic food source and also by changes in sea temperatures. They are sometimes associated with schools of pelagic scombrids or other fishes. The exact mode of reproduction is unknown, but it is thought to be ovoviviparous, wherein the egg cases are retained in the uterus for most of the embryonic development. An adult female was recorded to have 16 egg cases in its uteri. Whale sharks are considered harmless and are often examined at close range by divers. They are suction filter feeders that consume a wide variety of organisms including small crustaceans, squids, and fishes, especially sardines, anchovies, mackerels, and tunas. Maximum size uncertain, perhaps to 18 m, but lengths above 12 m are rare; most reported specimens between 4-12 m. It is the world's largest fish; the smallest free-living whale sharks are about 55 cm in length.

SAND TIGER SHARKS
FAMILY ODONTASPIDAE

These are large, bulky sharks with a pointed snout, a long mouth extending well past the eyes, a pair of similar sized dorsal fins, and large dagger-like teeth. The family contains two genera, each with two species. They are distributed in all tropical and temperate seas. The best known member of the family is the Grey Nurse Shark (also called the Sand Tiger Shark). It is often common on rock and coral reefs, sometimes forming schools. The body is denser than water, but it swallows air at the surface to provide buoyancy. Normally there are two young per litter, one from each uterus, although considerably more egg cases are produced. It is believed that the larger embryo eats fertilized eggs and smaller embryos within the uterus until the time of birth. This shark is an active predator of a variety of

small to moderately large fishes, small sharks, rays, squids, crabs, and lobsters. Although it is mainly inoffensive and non-aggressive if left alone, it has a reputation as a maneater. It would appear this notoriety is undeserved and probably stems from confusion with certain whaler sharks (Carcharhinidae).

GREY NURSE SHARK
Eugomphodus taurus (Rafinesque, 1810)
(Plate I-4)

A large, robust body; head with a flattened, somewhat conical snout; eyes without nictitating eyelids; mouth long, extending well behind eyes; teeth large, with prominent dagger-like median cusp and small cusplet on each side; both dorsal fins about equal sized, situated on posterior half of body; pelvic and anal fins also similar sized and about equal in size to dorsals; caudal fin asymmetrical with prominent subterminal notch and strong ventral lobe; light brown, darker on back; frequently with darker reddish to brownish spots scattered on body; tropical and temperate waters of most seas, but absent from the eastern and central Pacific Ocean. Grows to 320 cm; size at birth 95-105 cm. Often classified in the genus *Carcharias*, now invalidated by the International Commission on Zoological Nomenclature.

THRESHER SHARKS
FAMILY ALOPIIDAE

These sharks are easily distinguished by their extremely elongate upper caudal lobe. Other features include long, narrow pectoral fins, a tall erect first dorsal fin situated above the middle of the body, minute second dorsal and anal fins, and a relatively large eye. The teeth are compressed and blade-like, in less than 60 rows in each jaw. The family contains three species, all in the genus *Alopias*. They are oceanic dwellers, occurring in all temperate and tropical seas. Thresher sharks use their long tails for herding prey. They swim in ever decreasing circles around a school of fishes or squids,

bunching the school with their elongate caudal fins. The tail is also used in whip-like fashion to stun or kill prey. Reproduction is ovoviviparous, with approximately 2-4 young per litter. The unborn sharks feed on smaller embryos within the uterus.

SMALL TOOTH THRESHER SHARK
Alopias pelagicus Nakamura, 1935
(Plate I-5)

Body slender; dorsal profile of head convex, and forehead moderately convex in lateral view; snout moderately long, conical shaped; teeth small, more than 29 rows in each jaw; eye moderately large; pectoral fins very elongate with straight anterior and posterior edges; upper lobe of caudal fin nearly as long as rest of shark; overall grey, darker on back, belly whitish. Primarily an oceanic, epipelagic shark. Circumtropical. Grows to at least 330 cm; size at birth about 96 cm.

MACKEREL OR MAKO SHARKS
FAMILY LAMNIDAE

This family is distributed in all temperate and tropical seas. It contains three genera and five species including the notorious Great White Shark or White Pointer. They are generally large, powerful sharks further distinguished by their spindle-shaped body, pointed snout, a slender, keeled caudal peduncle, lunate caudal fin, and sharp, dagger-like teeth (or in the case of the White Shark, triangular and serrate). Mackerel sharks are partly warm-blooded, and have a circulatory system that enables them to retain a body temperature that is warmer than the surrounding sea. Development of the young is ovoviviparous, without a yolk-sac placenta. They exhibit a remarkable phenomenon known as oophagy in which developing foetuses feed on fertilized eggs and possibly smaller siblings within the uterus. These rapid swimmers are capable of spectacular leaps when chasing their prey. They feed on a variety of fishes, other sharks, rays, sea birds, turtles, marine mammals, squids, and benthic crustaceans. They are aggressive, dangerous sharks that are sometimes responsible for fatal attacks on swimmers and surfers. The White Pointer (*Carcharodon carcharias*) probably ranges into the southern portion of our region, but is omitted because its main distribution lies in cooler seas.

SHORTFIN MAKO
Isurus oxyrinchus Rafinesque, 1809
(Plate I-7)

Body moderately slender; snout long and pointed; teeth smooth-edged, long and slender at front of jaws, blade-like and triangular posteriorly; a large first dorsal fin and very small second dorsal and anal fins positioned near base of caudal fin; pectoral fins relatively long and narrow; strong lateral keel on each side of caudal peduncle; caudal fin crescent-shaped; dark blue to nearly white on ventral parts. Circumglobal in tropical and temperate seas. Attains nearly 400 cm; size at birth between 60-70 cm.

CATSHARKS
FAMILY SCYLIORHINIDAE

This is the largest shark family with 15 genera and 89 species. They are generally less than 80 cm long and are characterized by elongate cat-like eyes, rudimentary nictitating eyelids, a long and arched mouth with small cuspidate teeth, nasal flaps variably shaped, but usually no barbels present, and caudal fin without a strong ventral lobe. Catsharks are distributed circumglobally in most cold and warm seas. They dwell in a wide variety of habitats from shallow inshore seas to great oceanic depths. Reproduction is either oviparous (lay egg cases) or ovoviviparous (retain eggs until the young are born). Some oviparous species have incubation periods of nearly a year. Catsharks feed on invertebrates and small fishes. They are generally harmless.

MARBLED CATSHARK
Atelomycterus macleayi Whitley, 1939
(Plate I-12)

Body long and slender; head narrow; anterior nasal flaps forming enlarged, very broad, triangular lobes; nasoral grooves present; eyes dorsolateral on head, elongated and slit-like; a pair of dorsal fins of about equal size on posterior half of body; pelvic and anal fins of similar size below first and second dorsal fins respectively; caudal fin relatively short with subterminal notch; colour highly variegated, light grey ground colour with darker bars and scattering of black spots. Northern Australia. Grows to 60 cm; oviparous, size at hatching about 10 cm.

RETICULATED SWELLSHARK
Cephaloscyllium fasciatum Chen, 1966
(Plate I-13)

Body stout and spindle-shaped; head very depressed and broad, narrowly rounded in lateral view; snout somewhat bulbous in lateral view; eye relatively large and slit-like with small spiracle just behind; anterior nasal flaps elongate, lobate, and not overlapping mouth posteriorly; gill slits relatively small; two dorsal fins situated well posteriorly, the second considerably smaller than the first; caudal fin short and broad; overall light brown or tan with striking pattern of darker open-centred saddles, loops, reticulations, and spots. Northern Australia and South China Sea; usually found in deep water (200-300 metres) on or near the bottom of the continental shelf. Maximum size to at least 42 cm.

WHALER SHARKS OR REQUIEM SHARKS
FAMILY CARCHARHINIDAE

The whalers (or requiem sharks) are one of the largest and best known family of sharks. Worldwide there are 48 species in 12 genera. However, relatively few species are on the Great Barrier Reef. Among the most common are the Silvertip Shark (*Carcharhinus albimarginatus*), Grey Reef Shark (*C. amblyrhynchos*), and Blacktip Reef Shark (*C. melanopterus*). The Whaler Sharks are active strong swimmers that occur singly or in small to large groups. They span a considerable range of

size. For example, some milk sharks (genus *Rhizoprionodon*) reach a maximum length of less than 100 cm, whereas the Tiger Shark (*Galeocerdo cuvier*) is among the largest of sharks with a maximum size of at least 7.4 m. Except for the Tiger Shark, which is ovoviviparous, all species are viviparous with a yolk sac placenta. They have litters of young that number from one or two to as many as 135. The pups resemble miniature versions of the adults and are able to fend for themselves moments after birth. Whaler sharks are responsible for about half of all reported shark attacks on humans. However, less than 100 attacks are reported each year worldwide and no more than 30 of these are fatal. Although attacks are extremely rare (largely because there are few divers and swimmers in northern Australian seas), people should recognize the potential danger of the more aggressive species such as the Tiger, Silvertip, and Bull. Spearfishermen are more prone to shark attack than other divers because fishes struggling on a spear emit low frequency vibrations which can attract sharks unerringly to the site. Once in the vicinity, the presence of blood, which is readily detected by the keen olfactory sense, is apt to add to their aggressive behaviour. A few species, in particular the grey reef shark, have been shown to exhibit threat posturing involving exaggerated lateral swimming movements (i.e. arc of movement of the head increases noticeably), arching the back, holding the pectoral fins downward, and snapping of jaws. If these motions are evident, one should move slowly away from the shark. Whalers are voracious predators that feed mainly on a variety of fishes, other sharks, rays, squid, octopuses, cuttlefish, crabs, lobsters, and prawns. Lesser items include sea birds, turtles, sea snakes, marine mammals, molluscs, carrion, and garbage.

SILVERTIP SHARK
Carcharhinus albimarginatus (Rüppell, 1837)
(Plate II-1)

Snout moderately long and broadly rounded, the preoral length 6.8-9.2 per cent of total length; interdorsal ridge present ; origin of first dorsal fin over or slightly anterior to inner pectoral corner; height of first dorsal 7.1-10.6 per cent of total length; apex of first dorsal obtusely pointed to acute; origin of second dorsal over or slightly behind origin of anal fin; grey, darker on back and shading to white ventrally; distinctive white tips or margins on first dorsal, caudal, and pectoral fins. Tropical Indo-Pacific, including eastern Pacific. Eats fish, may be aggressive; common on outer reef slopes below 18 m. Usually has 5 or 6, up to 11 pups per litter. Grows to 300 cm; size at birth 55-80 cm.

Carcharhinus albimarginatus

BIGNOSE SHARK
Carcharhinus altimus (Springer, 1950)
(Plate II-2)

Snout long and slightly pointed, the preoral length 7.5-10.0 per cent of total length; interdorsal ridge present on back; origin of first dorsal fin over pectoral axil or behind it to almost as far back as halfway along inner pectoral margin; height of first dorsal 8.3-11.9 per cent of total length; apex of first dorsal bluntly pointed; origin of second dorsal in front of anal fin origin; grey, becoming whitish below; distal ends of all fins except pelvics dusky (pigment on tips of pectorals darker on underside of fins). Circumglobal distribution in temperate and tropical seas. Feeds on fishes (including sharks and rays) and cephalopods; usually found between 90-430 metres depth. Has litters of 3-11 pups. Reaches 300 cm; size at birth 65-80 cm.

Carcharhinus amblyrhynchos

GREY REEF SHARK
Carcharhinus amblyrhynchos (Bleeker, 1856)
(Plate II-3)

Snout rounded, moderate to short in length, the preoral length 6.4-8.7 per cent of total length; no interdorsal ridge; origin of first dorsal fin over or just anterior to inner pectoral corner; height of first dorsal moderate, 8.6-11.3 per cent of total length; apex of first dorsal sharply rounded to acute; origin of second dorsal about over origin of anal fin; greyish brown to bronzy, shading to white ventrally; a broad black trailing edge on caudal fin, other fins without distinct white or dark markings. East Africa and Red Sea eastward to Hawaii and Pitcairn Island. Feeds mainly on bony fishes, occasionally on cephalopods and crustaceans; common on upper part of outer reef slopes, may be dangerous; wounds that are inflicted are often the result of divers not

heeding the shark's threat postures; generally there is just one slashing bite without the intent to feed. Has litters of 3-6 pups. Attains 255 cm; size at birth 60 cm. Sometimes misidentified as *C. menisorrah* (Valenciennes), a synonym of *C. falciformis*.

PIGEYE SHARK
Carcharhinus amboinensis (Müller & Henle, 1839)
(Plate II-4)

Snout very short and bluntly rounded, the preoral length 5.7 to 7.0 per cent of total length; no interdorsal ridge; origin of first dorsal fin over or just posterior to pectoral axil; height of first dorsal 11.0-12.0 per cent of total length; apex of first dorsal sharply rounded to pointed; origin of second dorsal fin in front of origin of anal fin; grey, darker on back and shading to whitish ventrally; juveniles with dusky tips to fins, adults plain. East Africa to Australia; an inshore species that sometimes ascends rivers. Maximum size to 280 cm.

BRONZE WHALER
Carcharhinus brachyurus (Günther, 1870)
(Plate II-5)

Snout of moderate length and sharply rounded to pointed, the preoral length 5.7-8.4 per cent of total length; usually no interdorsal ridge; origin of first dorsal fin over or slightly anterior to inner pectoral corner; height of first dorsal 6.8-9.7 per cent of total length; apex of first dorsal rounded to pointed; origin of second dorsal fin over or slightly behind anal fin origin; dark brownish grey shading to whitish ventrally, fins plain or with slightly dusky tips. Along continental margins in most tropical and temperate seas, apparently absent in the western Atlantic; more common in temperate areas. Feeds on other sharks, rays, bony fishes, and cephalopods; considered to be a dangerous species. Has litters of 13-20 pups. May reach 325 cm; 60-70 at birth.

Carcharhinus brevipinna

LONG-NOSE GREY SHARK
Carcharhinus brevipinna (Müller & Henle, 1839)
(Plate II-6)

Snout long and pointed, the preoral length 7.7-9.0 per cent of total length; no interdorsal ridge; origin of first dorsal fin over or behind inner pectoral corner; first dorsal fin relatively small, its height 6.0-10.2 per cent of total length; apex of first dorsal fin sharply rounded to pointed; origin of second dorsal over or slightly behind anal fin origin; grey, shading to white ventrally, sometimes with a faint white band on midside; fins of subadults and adults often dusky to black-tipped, especially the lower caudal lobe; margin of caudal fin narrowly blackish except leading edge of lower lobe. Continental margins of all tropical and warm temperate seas except the eastern Pacific. Feeds on small fishes; not considered dangerous. Has litters of 2-15 pups. Largest specimen 278 cm; 46-80 cm at birth.

WHITECHEEK SHARK
Carcharhinus dussumieri (Valenciennes, 1839)
(Plate II-9)

Snout moderately long and slightly pointed, the preoral length 5.8-7.9 per cent of total length; a low interdorsal ridge; origin of first dorsal fin over posterior half of inner pectoral margin; first dorsal fin moderately small, its height 8.0-10.7 per cent of total length; apex of first dorsal sharply rounded to pointed; origin of second dorsal over or slightly behind anal fin origin; grey, white below, with a conspicuous large black spot covering the distal part of the second dorsal; other fins unmarked. Continental margins from Arabian Gulf to northern Australia and north to Japan. Feeds mainly on small fishes, cephalopods, and crustaceans; a harmless species. Has litters of 2-4 pups. Maximum size to 78 cm; 38-39 cm at birth.

Carcharhinus falciformis

SILKY SHARK
Carcharhinus falciformis (Bibron, 1839)
(Plate II-8)

Slender-bodied, body depth 11.5-17.5 per cent of total length; snout moderately long and slightly pointed, the preoral length 6.9-9.3 per cent of total length; a low, narrow interdorsal ridge; origin of first dorsal fin behind inner pectoral corner by not less than one-third length of inner pectoral margin; first dorsal fin small, its height 5.2-9.9 per cent of total length; apex of first dorsal narrowly rounded; trailing edge of first dorsal very falcate; origin of second dorsal over or slightly behind anal origin; grey to dark grey dorsally, shading to white ventrally, sometimes with faint band of white invading grey on upper abdomen; first dorsal fin unmarked; second dorsal, anal, lower caudal lobe, and pectoral fins may have dusky tips. Circumtropical, oceanic and coastal; found inshore as shallow as 18 m, but more abundant offshore from the surface to at least 500 m. Eats mainly fishes; a potentially dangerous shark, but no attacks have been reported. Has litters of 2-14 pups. Grows to 230 cm; size at birth 70-87 cm. *C. floridanus* is a synonym.

BULL SHARK
Carcharhinus leucas (Valenciennes, 1839)
(Plate II-7)

Heavy-bodied; snout short and broadly rounded, the preoral length 4.6-6.7 per cent of total length; no interdorsal ridge; origin of first dorsal fin usually over or just posterior to pectoral axil; first dorsal fin moderately large, its height 7.0-11.3 per cent of total length; apex of first dorsal fairly pointed; origin of second dorsal distinctly in front of anal origin; grey, becoming white ventrally, often with faint pale grey horizontal band extending into the white of the upper abdomen; fins of small individuals with dusky tips or edges, adults plain. Continental coasts of all tropical and subtropical seas; often travels far up rivers. Feeds on about anything edible; a dangerous shark responsible for fatal attacks (most attacks attributed to the Grey Nurse Shark in Australia are actually this species). Has litters of 3-13 pups. May reach 300 cm; size at birth 56-81 cm.

BLACKTIP SHARK

Carcharhinus limbatus (Valenciennes, 1839)
(Plate II-10)

Snout moderately long and pointed, its preoral length 6.3-9.0 per cent of total length; no interdorsal ridge; origin of first dorsal fin over or slightly posterior to pectoral fin axil; first dorsal fin moderately large and falcate, its height 8.2-13.8 per cent of total length; apex of first dorsal acute; origin of second dorsal about over or slightly in front of anal fin origin; grey brown dorsally, shading to white ventrally with nearly horizontal band of grey on midside extending into white of upper abdomen; black tips on dorsal fins, lower lobe of caudal, pelvic fins, and pectoral fins. Feeds mainly on fishes, but also cephalopods and larger crustaceans; usually not aggressive, but has been known to attack. Has litters of 1-10 pups. Reported to reach 250 cm; size at birth 38-72 cm.

Carcharhinus limbatus

OCEANIC WHITETIP SHARK

Carcharhinus longimanus (Poey, 1861)
(Plate II-12)

Snout moderately short and broadly rounded, the preoral length 5.4-7.1 per cent of total length; interdorsal ridge usually present; origin of first dorsal fin slightly anterior to inner posterior corner of pectoral fins; first dorsal fin very large with apex broadly rounded, its height 9.2-15.2 per cent of total length; pectoral fins extremely long, broad, and distally rounded, length of anterior edge 20.2-27.1 per cent of total length; origin of second dorsal in front of or over anal fin origin; brownish grey on back, becoming white ventrally; tips of first dorsal fin, paired fins, and caudal fin lobes broadly mottled white; anal fin usually blackish at tip and second dorsal fin may be dusky at tip; juveniles with most fins tipped with black. Circumtropical; primarily oceanic-epipelagic. Feeds on fishes, squids, birds, turtles, pelagic crustaceans and gastropods, and occasional marine mammals; a dangerous species responsible for human attacks. Has litters of 1-15 pups. Grows to 396 cm; 60-65 cm at birth. *C. maou* (Lesson) is an earlier name but due to long-term usage, *longimanus* has been placed on the Official List of Specific Names in Zoology.

BLACKTIP REEF SHARK

Carcharhinus melanopterus (Quoy & Gaimard, 1824)
(Plate II-11)

Snout moderately short and rounded, its preoral length 5.6-7.3 per cent of total length;

no interdorsal ridge; origin of first dorsal fin over or slightly posterior to inner rear corner of pectoral fins; first dorsal fin of medium size and falcate, its height 8.0-11.4 per cent of total length; apex of first dorsal sharply rounded to pointed; origin of second dorsal about over anal fin origin; greyish to yellowish brown, white below, with a distinct slightly oblique brown band extending from above pectoral fin into whitish area of upper abdomen; all fins conspicuously black-tipped, most broadly on first

dorsal fin (where it is often accentuated by a broad submarginal whitish band). Indo-west and central Pacific from East Africa and the Red Sea to Hawaii and French Polynesia. Eats mainly small fishes; usually a timid species that is easily frightened away, but may bite spearfishermen, and has been known to bite the feet of persons wading in shallows. Has litters of 2-5 pups. Attains 180 cm; size at birth 33-52 cm.

Carcharhinus melanopterus

BLACK WHALER
Carcharhinus obscurus (Lesueur, 1818)
(Plate II-13)

Snout of moderate size, rounded, the preoral length 5.7-8.4 per cent of total length; interdorsal ridge present; origin of first dorsal fin over or slightly posterior to inner rear corner of pectoral fins; first dorsal fin of moderate size, the height 5.8-10.4 per cent of total length; apex of first dorsal pointed to narrowly rounded; origin of second dorsal above anal fin origin; grey, shading to white ventrally, with a faint, near-horizontal, grey band invading the white of upper abdomen; tips of fins dusky. Circumglobal in tropical and warm temperate seas; primarily on continental shelves from shallow water to 400 m. Feeds on wide variety of marine animals; a dangerous shark that has attacked humans. Has litters of 6-14 pups. Reaches 362 cm; size at birth 69-100 cm.

Carcharhinus plumbeus

SANDBAR SHARK
Carcharhinus plumbeus (Nardo, 1827)
(Plate II-14)

Body moderately heavy; snout rounded and of medium length, the preoral length 5.6-8.1 per cent of total length; interdorsal ridge present; origin of first dorsal fin over or slightly anterior to pectoral axil; first dorsal fin of mature adults very large, erect, slightly falcate, with a narrowly rounded to pointed tip, its height 13.6-16.5 per cent of total length; origin of second dorsal over or slightly anterior to anal fin origin; greyish brown dorsally, white ventrally, with a faint brown band in upper part of the white area on midside; tips and trailing edges of fins often dusky. Circumglobal in tropical and warm temperate seas; shallow reefs ranging down to 280 m. Feeds mainly on small fishes, also takes some molluscs and crustaceans; although large, this species is not known to attack humans. Has litters of 1-14 pups. Attains 300 cm; 56-75 cm at birth. *C. milberti* is a synonym.

BLACKSPOT SHARK
Carcharhinus sealei (Pietschmann, 1916)
(Plate II-15)

Snout moderately long and rounded, the preoral length 5.3-6.7 per cent of total length; interdorsal ridge reduced or absent; origin of first dorsal fin about over or slightly behind inner pectoral corner; first dorsal fin moderate in size, its height 8.8-11.0 per cent of total length; first dorsal falcate, its apex pointed; origin of second dorsal slightly to noticeably behind anal fin origin; grey, shading to whitish ventrally; a conspicuous black or dusky tip present on second dorsal fin, but other fins with pale posterior edges and no dark markings. East Africa to northern Australia; usually above 40 m depth. Eats small fishes, squids, and prawns; a harmless species. Has litters of 1-12 pups. May reach 95 cm; size at birth 35-45 cm.

SPOT-TAIL SHARK
Carcharhinus sorrah (Valenciennes, 1839)
(Plate II-16)

Snout moderately long and pointed, the preoral length 7.1-8.4 per cent of total length; interdorsal ridge present; origin of first dorsal fin over or slightly posterior to inner rear corner of pectoral fins; first dorsal fin of moderate size, falcate and apically pointed, the height 7.7-10.9 per cent of total length; origin of second dorsal fin distinctly posterior to anal fin origin; grey, shading to white ventrally; tips of second dorsal fin, lower caudal lobe, and pectoral fins black. East Africa and Red Sea to Solomon and Santa Cruz Islands; a shallow-water coastal species. Feeds mainly on fishes and cephalopods; not considered dangerous. Has litters of 2-6 pups. Grows to 160 cm; 45-60 cm at birth.

TIGER SHARK
Galeocerdo cuvier (Peron & Lesueur, 1822)

Head, thorax and abdomen stout, but body becoming very attenuate posteriorly, with a low lateral keel on each side of the narrow caudal peduncle; snout very short and slightly rounded, its preoral length 3.7-4.8 per cent of total length; spiracle a narrow slit behind eye; interdorsal ridge present; origin of dorsal fin over posterior corner of pectoral fin; first dorsal fin not very large, its height 7.5-9.3 per cent of total length; apex of first dorsal fin pointed; origin of second dorsal fin distinctly in front of anal fin origin; adults grey with vertical bars on upper half of sides (sometimes faint or

Carcharhinus sorrah

absent); young with large dark spots, some coalescing to form bars. Circumtropical; retires to deeper water during the day, but feeds on shallow reefs at night. Feeds on a wider variety of items than any other shark, including bony fishes, sharks, rays, turtles, birds, marine mammals, cephalopods, spiny lobsters, crabs, gastropods, jellyfishes, and carrion; an extremely dangerous shark responsible for attacks on divers and swimmers. Has 10 to over 80 pups per litter. Attains at least 7.4 m and possibly 9 m; size at birth 50-75 cm.

LEMON SHARK
Negaprion acutidens (Rüppell, 1837)

Body moderately stout; head broad and only slightly convex dorsally; snout broadly rounded to slightly wedge-shaped, and short, its preoral length 4.6-6.5 per cent of total length; spiracles usually absent (occasionally with very small spiracles); no interdorsal ridge; origin of first dorsal fin slightly posterior to inner rear corner of pectoral fins; first dorsal fin falcate, moderate in size, its height 6.9-10.9 per cent of total length; apex of first dorsal pointed; origin of second dorsal fin anterior to origin of anal fin; second dorsal fin about same size or slightly smaller than first dorsal fin; yellowish grey to yellowish brown, paler below, the fins more yellowish than body. East Africa and Red Sea to the Society Islands; frequently seen on shallow reefs. Eats mainly fishes; usually not considered dangerous, but has attacked humans especially following provocation or when aroused by spearfishing. Has litters of 1-13 pups. Maximum size to 310 cm; 45-80 cm at birth.

WEASEL SHARKS
FAMILY HEMIGALEIDAE

These are small to moderate-sized sharks that have a relatively slender body and horizontally oval eyes. Other features include absence of barbels, small to moderately large blade-like teeth usually with cusps (at least those in lower jaw), two dorsal fins of unequal size, the first dorsal base well ahead of the pelvic bases, and precaudal pit present. The members of this Indo-Pacific and eastern Atlantic family are often considered to be a subfamily of the

Galeocerdo cuvier

Negaprion acutidens

Carcharhinidae. Only one of the species, *Triaenodon obesus*, is commonly encountered on reefs in our area. Weasel sharks are viviparous and feed primarily on fishes and cephalopods. The largest species grows to about 250 cm.

WHITETIP REEF SHARK
Triaenodon obesus (Rüppell, 1837)

A slender shark, the depth about 11-16 per cent of total length; head depressed, about twice as broad as deep; very short and blunt snout; spiracles absent or minute; labial furrows very short; tubular anterior nasal flaps; small smooth-edged teeth with strong cusplets in both jaws; brownish grey, shading to whitish with a yellow cast ventrally, usually with a few scattered roundish dark grey spots on body (more on ventral half than dorsal); tips of first dorsal fin and upper caudal lobe broadly white; tips of second dorsal fin and lower lobe of caudal fin also often white. Indo-Pacific, including tropical eastern Pacific. Spends most of the day at rest on the bottom in caves or beneath ledges; a seemingly curious shark that often approaches divers at close range. Feeds mainly on fishes, also cephalopods; considered harmless, but a few attacks on spearfishermen have been reported. Has litters of 1-5 pups. Maximum size, 210 cm; 52-60 cm at birth. Randall (1977) reported tagging 124 *T. obesus* at Johnston Island. Seven from 81-105 cm precaudal length were recovered; they grew only 2.1-4.2 cm/year. The name *obesus* for this shark was a bad choice in view of its slender body.

Triaenodon obesus

HAMMERHEAD SHARKS
FAMILY SPHYRNIDAE

Hammerhead sharks are easily recognized by the hammer or mallet-shaped lateral expansions of the head. Otherwise the general body shape is very similar to that of the whaler sharks. The enlargement on either side of the head is thought to increase manoeuvring capabilities and also increases their sensory capacities related to vision, smell, and pressure detection. The family is distributed worldwide in tropical and temperate seas. There are nine species; all except one belong to the genus *Sphyrna*. They range in maximum size from about 140 to 600 cm. Some of the larger species have been responsible for attacks on humans, but recent studies indicate that they are not particularly aggressive unless provoked or baited. Their natural diet includes a variety of items such as fishes, sharks, cephalopods, crustaceans, and turtles.

SCALLOPED HAMMERHEAD
Sphyrna lewini (Griffith & Smith, 1834)

A large hammerhead shark with broad, narrow-blade lateral extensions on the head; width of hammer 24.0-30.0 per cent of total length; anterior margin of head broadly convex with a prominent median indentation and another more conspicuous notch laterally near the end, setting off the terminal lobe bearing the eye; a slight indentation in anterior margin between the median and lateral notches on each side, the overall effect being a scalloped edge; first dorsal fin moderately large and erect, outer posterior margin concave, the height 11.9-14.5 per cent of total length; free rear tip of second dorsal fin nearly reaching caudal fin; base of anal fin noticeably larger than that of second dorsal fin; brownish grey, shading to white ventrally; undersides of pectoral fins tipped with black. Worldwide in tropical and warm temperate seas. Has litters of 15-31 pups. Attains 420 cm; size at birth 42-55 cm. Other hammerheads occurring in the area are *S. mokarran*, distinguished by a nearly straight anterior margin on the head of adults, a tall, very falcate dorsal fin, and deeply notched pelvic and anal fins, and *Eusphyrna blochii* which has very long wing-like lateral blades of the head (nearly half the sharks total length from tip to tip).

Sphyrna lewini

PLATE I

1 **WHALE SHARK** (*Rhiniodon typus*)

2 **LEOPARD SHARK** (*Stegostoma fasciatum*)

3 **TAWNY NURSE SHARK** (*Nebrius ferrugineus*)

4 **GREY NURSE SHARK** (*Eugomphodus taurus*)

5 **SMALL TOOTH THRESHER SHARK** (*Alopias pelagicus*)

6 **BULLHEAD SHARK** (*Heterodontus zebra*)

7 **SHORTFIN MAKO** (*Isurus oxyrinchus*)

8 **BLUNTNOSE SIXGILL SHARK** (*Hexanchus griseus*)

9 **SPECKLED CATSHARK** (*Hemiscyllium trispeculare*)

10 **EPAULETTE SHARK** (*Hemiscyllium ocellatum*)

11 **BROWN-BANDED CATSHARK** (*Chiloscyllium punctatum*)

12 **MARBLED CATSHARK** (*Atelomycterus macleayi*)

13 **RETICULATED SWELLSHARK** (*Cephaloscyllium fasciatum*)

14 **BANDED WOBBEGONG** (*Orectolobus ornatus*)

15 **NORTHERN WOBBEGONG** (*Oretolobus wardi*)

16 **TASSELLED WOBBEGONG** (*Eucrossorhinus dasypogon*)

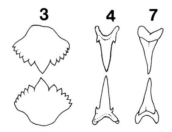

JUV.

1

2

3

4

5

6

7

8

9

10

11

12

13

14

15

16

PLATE II

1 **SILVERTIP SHARK** (*Carcharhinus albimarginatus*)

2 **BIGNOSE SHARK** (*Carcharhinus altimus*)

3 **GREY REEF SHARK** (*Carcharhinus amblyrhynchos*)

4 **PIGEYE SHARK** (*Carcharhinus amboinensis*)

5 **BRONZE WHALER** (*Carcharhinus brachyurus*)

6 **LONG NOSE GREY SHARK** (*Carcharhinus brevipinna*)

7 **BULL SHARK** (*Carcharhinus leucas*)

8 **SILKY SHARK** (*Carcharhinus falciformis*)

9 **WHITE CHEEK SHARK** (*Carcharhinus dussumieri*)

10 **BLACKTIP SHARK** (*Carcharhinus limbatus*)

11 **BLACKTIP REEF SHARK** (*Carcharhinus melanopterus*)

12 **OCEANIC WHITETIP SHARK** (*Carcharhinus longimanus*)

13 **BLACK WHALER** (*Carcharhinus obscurus*)

14 **SANDBAR SHARK** (*Carcharhinus plumbeus*)

15 **BLACKSPOT SHARK** (*Carcharhinus sealei*)

16 **SPOT-TAIL SHARK** (*Carcharhinus sorrah*)

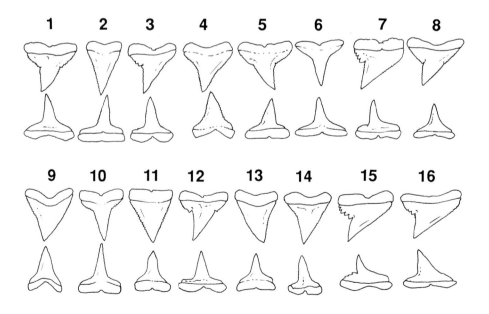

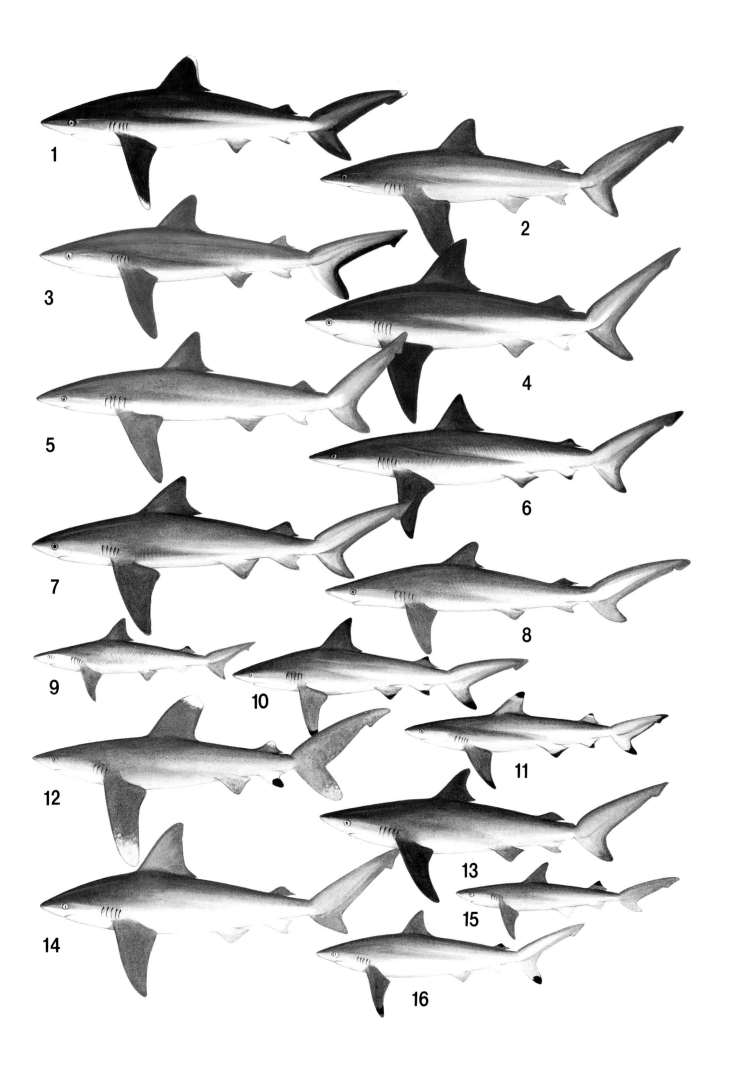

ELECTRIC RAYS
FAMILY TORPEDINIDAE

These rays generally have a rounded disc, soft and loose skin, small or vestigal eyes, and a pair of dorsal fins just before the small caudal fin. Their most noteworthy feature is the well-developed powerful electrical organs that are derived from branchial muscles. These are used to stun fish prey and also probably act as a defensive weapon against enemies, including man. Electric rays are generally sluggish fishes that occur in sandy or muddy areas. They sometimes conceal themselves by burying under the substratum. Young are born alive. The family is distributed in all tropical and temperate seas and contains about 11 genera and 42 species.

NUMBFISH
Hypnos monopterygium (Shaw & Nodder, 1795)

Rounded, ovate body with smaller rounded pelvic lobe at rear which bears the tail and a pair of small dorsal fins and a caudal fin; colour varies from light brown to blackish. Western Australia, South Australia and southeastern Australia, including southern Queensland and adjacent Great Barrier Reef; can produce an electric shock capable of causing severe cramping of an adult person's muscles. To 69 cm.

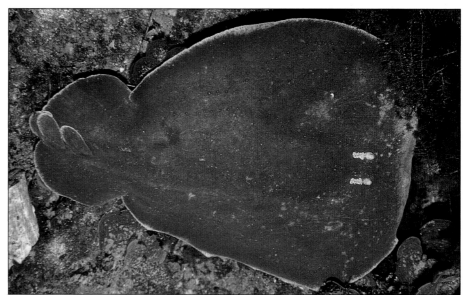

Hypnos monopterygium

Rhinobatos batillum

GUITARFISHES
FAMILY RHINOBATIDAE

The guitarfishes are a family of rays that have an elongate, rather shark-like body. The head and anterior part of the body is greatly flattened and like other rays the gill openings are ventrally located under the pectoral fins. The tail is relatively thick and carries two dorsal fins and a caudal fin with an expanded upper lobe. The snout is wedge-shaped to broadly rounded, and there are numerous small blunt teeth in the jaws. The family occurs in all tropical and warm temperate seas; about eight or nine genera and 52 species are known. These rays are generally encountered on soft sand or mud bottoms, often close to shore where they are sometimes hooked by anglers. The flesh is said to be of good quality, but they are seldom eaten. Guitarfishes give birth to live young. They feed on benthic invertebrates such as molluscs and crustaceans, and occasionally fishes. The largest guitarfishes grow to nearly 3 m, but are considered harmless.

COMMON SHOVELNOSED RAY
Rhinobatos batillum Whitley, 1939

Snout elongate and triangular, merging with pectoral-fin flaps; mid-dorsal ridge of back may have rough protruberances; two dorsal fins set well back on body, both about equal in size and also nearly equal to caudal fin; uniform olive yellow to light brown. Northern Australia between Shark Bay, Western Australia and the Capricorn Group, occasionally encountered near sand cays on the Great Barrier Reef. Reaches 240 cm.

STINGRAYS
FAMILY DASYATIDAE

These rays are characterised by an angular to rounded disc that is usually 1-2 times as wide as its length; the head is not separated or distinguishable from the rest of the disc; there are five pairs of gill openings on the underside of the disc; the jaws have small blunt or cuspidate teeth; the tail is moderately slender to very slender and whip-like, usually with a large venomous spine on its dorsal surface. Stingrays occur in all tropical and subtropical seas; about 10 genera and 90 species are known. Most species are found in coastal waters, in estuaries, off beaches and river mouths, and on flat "trawl ground" bottoms on sand or mud. Relatively few species occur in the vicinity of coral reefs. The tail spine is extremely dangerous and capable of delivering an excruciating wound. Human fatalities have been reported. Caution should be exercised when wading on sandy bottoms. If a ray is stepped on, it has the ability to thrust its tail upward and forward, impaling the victim with remarkable speed. Immersion of the injured limb in hot water (about 50°C) for 30-90 minutes will often dramatically relieve the pain, but medical assistance should be obtained. Stingrays feed on a variety of sand and mud-dwelling organisms, including crabs, prawns, worms, molluscs, and fishes. They are livebearers, the young resembling miniature adults.

KUHL'S STINGRAY
Dasyatis kuhlii (Müller & Henle, 1841)

Disc kite-shaped; snout gently rounded; tail about as long or longer than disc; a pair of sharp spines on upper surface of middle part of tail; pale brown or grey with small reddish to black spots and larger bluish-white blotches; tail posterior to spine with black and white bands. East Africa and Red Sea to Samoa and north to Japan; frequently seen resting or swimming in sandy areas adjacent to reefs. To 70 cm.

BLUE-SPOTTED STINGRAY
Taeniura lymma (Forsskål, 1775)

Disc ovate; snout rounded; tail slightly longer than body; a pair of sharp spines on upper surface of middle part of tail; tan or brownish with numerous blue spots. East Africa to the Western Pacific; often seen on the Great Barrier Reef, usually resting on sandy bottoms of caves or under ledges and coral bommies. Attains 240 cm.

Dasyatis kuhlii

Taeniura lymma

Taeniura melanospilos ▲ *Urogymnus africanus* ▼

BLACK-BLOTCHED STINGRAY
Taeniura melanospila Bleeker, 1853

Disc more or less round; snout rounded; tail about same length as body or slightly longer; a pair of sharp spines on upper surface of tail; grey with dense pattern of variable-sized black spots. Indo-Pacific, a large ray that is infrequently encountered in the vicinity of coral reefs or adjacent to sandy cays . Grows to 300 cm.

THORNY RAY
Urogymnus africanus (Bloch & Schneider, 1801)

Disc oval with central part of body mound-like and covered with bony tubercles; tail about same length as body, without sharp venomous spines; dark brown or greyish, tubercles whitish. East Africa to northern Australia and the Marshall Islands; sometimes seen resting on sandy bottoms, often in caves. To 300 cm. Often identified as *U. asperrimus* (Bloch & Schneider), but *africanus* is the correct name (Bernard Seret, pers. comm.).

EAGLE RAYS
FAMILY MYLIOBATIDIDAE

Eagle rays have a protruding head that is distinct from the disc; the eyes and spiracles are lateral on the head; the disc has triangular "wing" flaps; and the tail is much longer than the disc; most have one or more venomous spines near the tail base. They have powerful jaws equipped with large plate-like crushing teeth arranged in several rows. Eagle rays are usually found inshore near reefs. Like manta rays, a few species can leap high into the air from the water. Young eagle rays are born alive. The family occurs worldwide in tropical and warm temperate seas; there are five genera containing about 24 species.

SPOTTED EAGLE RAY
Aetobatus narinari (Euphrasen, 1790)

Head squarish with protruding, rounded snout; large triangular "wings" (pectoral fin flaps); tail very long and slender with 2-6 barbed spines at base; dark grey to black with numerous white spots dorsally, white ventrally. Cosmopolitan in tropical to warm temperate seas; feeds on molluscs, especially clams, mussels, and oysters; often sighted alone or in small groups cruising on the perimeter of coral reefs. Disc width to 250 cm. The Cownose Ray (*Rhinoptera javanica*) is also found in our area and somewhat resembles the Spotted Eagle Ray. However, its projecting head is divided into two rounded lobes.

MANTA OR DEVIL RAYS
FAMILY MOBULIDAE

These distinctive rays are easily recognised by the pair of large protruding flaps in front of the mouth, the lateral eyes and spiracles, large wing-like disc that is much wider than long, the ends pointed, no tail spine or only a rudimentary spine, and a small dorsal fin at the base of the tail. The cephalic flaps are used to direct planktonic food items into the mouth. Some mantas grow to a width of nearly 7 m and weigh more than 1300 kg; they are among the largest of fishes. Manta rays occur in all warm seas; the family contains two genera and about 10 species. They are frequently seen from boats far out to sea and also are encountered by divers in the vicinity of coral reefs. Mantas can make spectacular leaps above the water surface. The classification of the genus *Manta* is in great need of study.

MANTA RAY
Manta birostris (Donndorff, 1798)

Head projecting with pair of paddle-like extensions; large triangular "wings" (pectoral fin flaps); tail long and whip-like; disc above and below covered with small denticles; mouth terminal (at front of head); teeth in lower jaw only; dark grey to black, sometimes with white patches on shoulders; white on ventral surface. Circumtropical. To at least 6.7 m disc width and over two tonnes in weight.

Manta birostris

Aetobatus narinari

DEVIL RAY
Mobula tarapacana (Philippi, 1892)

Head projecting with pair of paddle-like extensions; large triangular "wings" (pectoral fin flaps); tail relatively short, without spine; skin smooth; mouth on underside of head; teeth in both jaws, relatively large and tassellated; colour of back brown to olivaceous green, ventral side white anteriorly and grey posteriorly. Indo-Pacific and eastern Atlantic, possibly circumtropical; not previously recorded from our area. Grows to a disc width of at least 305 cm and a weight of 350 kg. Also known as Box Ray.

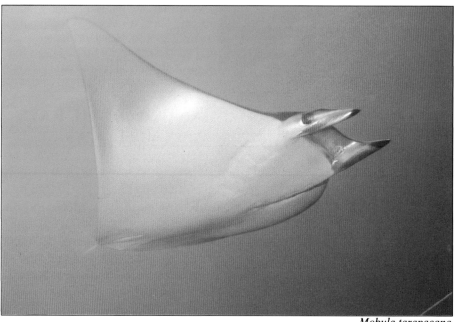

Mobula tarapacana

BONEFISHES
FAMILY ALBULIDAE

This small family of three genera is one of the most primitive of teleost fishes. The young pass through a late larval stage called the leptocephalus which is also found in other primitive Teleostei such as the ladyfish (*Elops*), the tarpon (*Megalops*), and true eels. This characteristic larva is transparent, ribbon-like, with a small head and forked tail. The body of bonefishes is elongate and only slightly compressed. Their most distinctive external feature is their overhanging snout and ventral mouth. There are very small teeth in bands anteriorly in the jaws and patches of small molariform teeth on the roof and floor of the mouth. The fins are all soft-rayed, the single dorsal in the middle of the body, and the anal fin far posterior; as in other primitive fishes, the pectoral fins are low on the body, and the pelvic fins abdominal in position; the caudal fin is deeply forked. Bonefishes get their name from the numerous fine bones in the flesh. It was long believed that there is a single circumtropical species of *Albula*, *A. vulpes* (type locality, Bahamas), but a recent electrophoretic study in Hawaii by Shaklee and Tamaru have shown that there are two Indo-Pacific species; as yet unpublished is the further finding that there are two other species in the western Atlantic and one in the eastern Atlantic. So there are five species of *Albula* in the world, not just one. Bonefishes root into sand with their conical snout for their usual food of small clams, various worms, and crustaceans; the hard parts of prey are crushed with their molariform teeth. These fishes are world-renown as hard-fighting gamefishes.

PACIFIC BONEFISH
Albula neoguinaica Valenciennes, 1846

Dorsal rays 18-19; anal rays 9; pectoral rays 16-18; lateral-line scales 62-72 (usually 67-70); body depth of adults about 4.5-5.5 in standard length; mouth distinctly ventral; silvery with a blackish spot at tip of snout. Indo-Pacific; typically found on sandy substrata, sometimes coming into very shallow water on sand flats. Attains at least 100 cm. The second Indo-Pacific species of bonefish, *A. glossodonta* (Forsskål), is difficult to distinguish from *neoguinaica*. Although not yet known from the Great Barrier Reef, it might be expected there. The tip of the lower jaw is more rounded and the median tooth patches on the roof and floor of the mouth are broader; there are 69-78 lateral-line scales (usually 72-75). In Hawaii, at least, there is a difference in vertebral counts, 65-69 for *neoguinaica* and 70-75 for *glossodonta*.

Albula neoguinaica

WORM EELS
FAMILY MORINGUIDAE

These sand-dwelling eels may reach a length of about 120 cm, but have a very small body diameter giving a worm-like appearance. The head shape, with a strongly protruding lower jaw is also diagnostic. These specialised eels live under the sand and are adept burrowers. Although they are relatively common, given the correct habitat conditions, they are never seen unless flushed from the sand by ichthyocides that are used by scientific collectors. These eels undergo significant changes in morphology with maturation. Immature eels are yellow to orange-brown and have tiny eyes with opaque tissue over them, and only rudimentary fin development. At maturity they develop larger functional eyes, larger fins, and change their colour to dark on the back, silvery below. They leave the sand and migrate to the surface to spawn (and presumably die). Females are larger than males and have higher vertebral and pore counts. About 10 species are known; most are found in the tropical Indo-Pacific region. Several occur in our area, one of which is discussed below. More research is needed on the classification of these unusual eels.

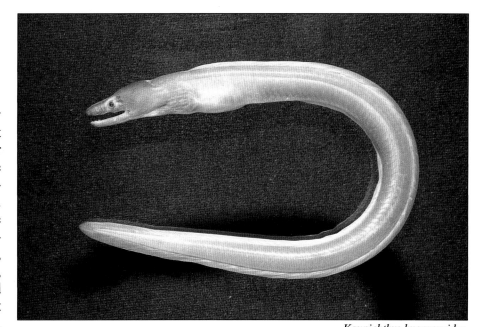

SLENDER WORM-EEL
Moringua ferruginea (Bliss, 1883)

Body worm-like; no fins, except rudimentary development around tail; head length 13-17 times in the total length; depth of body 45-70 times in total length; about 73 lateral-line pores before anus; vertebrae 115-132; yellow to reddish. East Africa to Easter Island, north to Ryukyu Islands. Attains 90 cm.

Moringua ferruginea

FALSE MORAYS
FAMILY CHLOPSIDAE

These small eels are characterised by having the dorsal fin originate above the gill opening or just behind, the median fins are continuous around the tail, the mouth reaches beyond the rear margin of the eye, and the posterior nostrils open downwards through the lip; pectoral fins present or absent. The teeth are small and pointed, in about three rows on the jaws and two separate rows on the vomer. Most species are small (less than 20 cm). They occur in all tropical seas, but are seldom seen due to their cryptic habits. Many of the species burrow in sand or are found deep in crevices of the reef. Most recent authors have classified the eels of this family in the Xenocongridae, now known to be a synonym of the Chlopsidae.

Kaupichthys hyoproroides

GREY REEF EEL
Kaupichthys hyoproroides (Strömann, 1896)

Dorsal and anal fins well-developed and confluent with caudal fin; pectoral fins larger than eye; eye 10-12.5 in head; snout blunt; anterior nostrils tubular; side of head (gill chamber) with longitudinal skin folds; vertebrae about 119; grey with pale fins. East Africa to Society and Hawaiian islands, also in tropical western Atlantic. Attains 15 cm. *K. atlanticus* Böhlke is a snynoym.

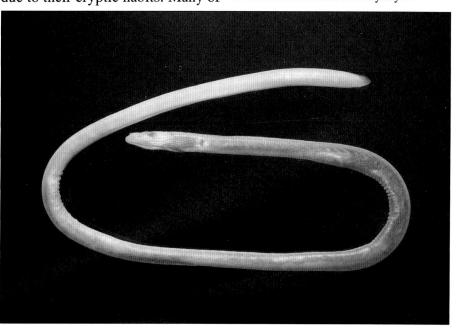

MORAYS
FAMILY MURAENIDAE

Moray eels are characterized by a very elongate muscular compressed body and large mouth; most species have long sharp canine teeth but some such as the species of *Echidna* have low nodular teeth. The gill opening is a small round aperture on the side of the body. Morays lack pectoral fins, and their dorsal and anal fins are confluent with the caudal fin. The genus *Uropterygius* is unusual in having rudimentary dorsal and anal fins which are confined to the tip of the tail. The largest genus is *Gymnothorax* (*Lycodontis* is a synonym), all species of which have sharply pointed teeth; their longest teeth are often fang-like depressible canines in one or three rows on the intermaxilla, a median bone on the roof of the mouth in front of the vomer. The morays with long canine teeth feed mainly on fishes, occasionally on octopuses and crustaceans. The species of *Echidna* prey principally on crustaceans, especially crabs, for which their blunt crushing teeth are well suited. The muraenid eels are often regarded as being nocturnal, but our observations indicate that only a few species actively forage for food at night. Morays are capable of inflicting painful wounds,

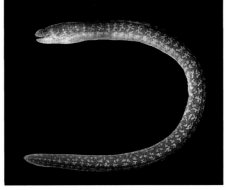

but the danger of being bitten by them is overstated; they are not apt to bite unless provoked or mistake a human hand or fingers as prey. A human hand thrust into a hole in the reef can easily be mistaken by a resident moray for an octopus. Recent studies have shown that morays begin mature life as males and change to females later in life. Like other eels, they have a relatively large transparent ribbon-like larva called the leptocephalus; it is long-lived in the pelagic realm, resulting in the broad distributions of many of the species. Young morays, in general, are more slender than adults; as they grow they tend to become stouter-bodied; this accounts for much of the variation given in the species accounts below in the ratio of body depth to total length. Some morays vary greatly in colour; in the brief description of colour in species accounts, only the most common pat-

tern is usually given. Not discussed below is the rare *Gymnothorax pindae* Smith which is all-brown, has triangular finely serrate teeth, and reaches about 40 cm.

SEYCHELLES MORAY
Anarchias seychellensis Smith, 1962

Body depth 20-25 in length; head length 8.1-9.6 in length; snout to anus 2.25-2.45 in length; teeth in jaws biserial, the outer row small, close-set, and curving backward (except anterior teeth); intermaxilla with three rows of needle-like canines, the outer rows continuous with four or five canines constituting an inner row on side of upper jaw; lower jaw with about seven canines in an inner row on anterior two-thirds of each side of jaw; posterior nostril above eye with an enlarged pore behind and medial to it; two large anterior lateral-line pores in front of gill opening; rayed portion of dorsal and anal fins restricted to end of tail; vertebrae 118-133; colour variable but frequently brown with three or four longitudinal rows of stellate whitish blotches; tip of tail yellow; posterior nostril and adjacent pore in a white spot; another phase is uniform brown. Indo-Pacific; a shallow-water species of exposed reef flats or rocky shores; often found in tidepools. Reaches about 29 cm. Three other species of the genus are known from Great Barrier Reef waters, all small and rarely seen: *A. allardicei* Jordan and Starks, *A. cantonensis* (Schultz), and *A. leucurus* (Snyder).

STARRY MORAY
Echidna nebulosa (Ahl, 1789)

Body slender, the depth 14-20 in length; head 8.5-9.5 in length; snout to anus 1.9-2.1 in length; short stout conical teeth at front of jaws; side of jaws with one to two rows of small close-set compressed nodular teeth; teeth on vomer nodular, in two rows; vertebrae 121-123; white with two rows of large dendritic black blotches containing small yellow spots; numerous small black spots between large blotches which become more numerous and irregularly linear with age. Indo-Pacific; usually seen on reef flats or rocky shores; feeds mainly on crabs. To 70 cm.

RINGED MORAY
Echidna polyzona (Richardson, 1844)

Body depth l2-16 in length; head 6.5-7.5 in length; snout to anus 2.0-2.15 in length; teeth in jaws in two rows, bluntly conical in young, nodular in adults; an elliptical patch of low nodular teeth on vomer; vertebrae 132-137; young with 25-30 dark brown bars separated by narrower white interspaces, the bars encircling body posterior to anus; bars progressively more obscure with age until in large adults the pattern is mottled brown; corner of mouth dark brown. Indo-Pacific; a shallow-water species. Attains 60 cm.

BAYER'S MORAY
Enchelycore bayeri (Schultz,1953)

Body elongate, the depth 12-27 in length; head 7-8.5 in length; snout to anus 2.4-2.55 in length; jaws long and slender with a broad gap showing along side when tips closed; extremely long canine teeth along entire lower jaw, front of upper jaw, on intermaxilla, and in an inner row on side of upper jaw; posterior nasal opening oval, small, above level of eye nearly an eye diameter in front of eye; vertebrae 146-153; brown with a yellowish green margin posteriorly on fins. Indo-Pacific; not common. Reaches 70 cm.

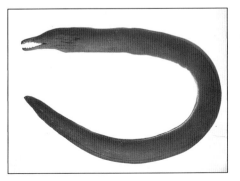

LONGFANG MORAY
Enchelynassa canina (Quoy & Gaimard, 1824)

Body depth 13-17 in length; head 7.5-8 in length; snout to anus 2.0-2.1 in length; jaws long, slender, and hooked as in *Enchelycore bayeri*; extremely long canine teeth at front of jaws, on intermaxilla, and inner row on side of upper jaw; anterior nostril a short tube with a long bilobed flap at posterior end; posterior nostril above front of eye, large and oval, with a raised rim; vertebrae 138-145; skin with narrow irregular vertical ridges; dark brownish grey with vertical thin blackish lines in grooves on skin; each pore along side of jaws in a whitish spot. Indo-Pacific; usual habitat, exposed outer reef areas in the depth range of less than one to 6 m; rarely seen by divers. Reported to 150 cm.

ZEBRA MORAY
Gymnomuraena zebra (Shaw, 1797)

Body depth 16-20 in length; head about 15 in length; snout to anus about 1.5 in length; dorsal and anal fins restricted to posterior part of tail; numerous molariform teeth (often with a diagonal ridge-like cusp) nearly covering jaws and palate like cobblestone pavement; chocolate brown to orangish brown with numerous narrow pale yellowish bars. Indo-Pacific and tropical eastern Pacific; limited data indicate that it feeds chiefly on crabs. Said to attain 150 cm, but rarely exceeds l m. Sometimes classified in *Echidna*.

LATTICETAIL MORAY
Gymnothorax buroensis (Bleeker,1857)

Body depth 11-16 in length; head 6-7 in length; snout to anus 2.15-2.3 in length; three rows of large canine teeth on intermaxilla; large canines on lower jaw in an inner row on front fourth of jaw; vertebrae 112-113; light brown anteriorly, finely mottled with dark brown, with four to six longitudinal rows of small black spots on body which are progressively larger posteriorly until on posterior third of body they interconnect to form irregular black bars, the pale interspaces as very narrow irregular bars; margin of fins yellow posteriorly. Indo-Pacific and Galapagos Islands. A small species, the largest recorded, 35 cm.

LIPSPOT MORAY
Gymnothorax chilospilus Bleeker, 1865

Body depth 15-19 in length; head 6.5-8 in length; snout to anus 2.1-2.3 in length; longest canines in the single row on intermaxilla; other long canines anteriorly in upper jaw and inner row at front of lower jaw; vertebrae 121-133; light brown, finely mottled with darker brown, with two or more rows of small dendritic dark brown blotches (sometimes forming short irregular dark bars); a dark brown spot at corner of mouth preceded on lower lip by a large white blotch and often followed by another above and behind corner of mouth; pores of upper and lower jaws usually in prominent white spots. Indo-Pacific; collected from less than one to 45 m, but usually found in less than 5 m. Largest, 50.5 cm.

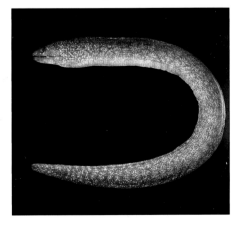

AUSTRALIAN MORAY
Gymnothorax cribroris Whitley, 1932

Body depth 16-18 in length; head 7.5-8.5 in length; snout to anus 2.1-2.2 in length; longest canines in the single row on intermaxilla; other long canines in the single row at front of both jaws; vertebrae 121-125; light brown anteriorly on body with a coarse reticulum of dark brown, gradually changing posteriorly to dark brown with irregular pale brown spots larger than eye; head whitish with irregular but well-defined dark brown spots behind eye, grading to very small spots dorsally on nape and on throat. Known only from the Great Barrier Reef and Western Australia; an inshore species often taken in tidepools. Reaches at least 35 cm.

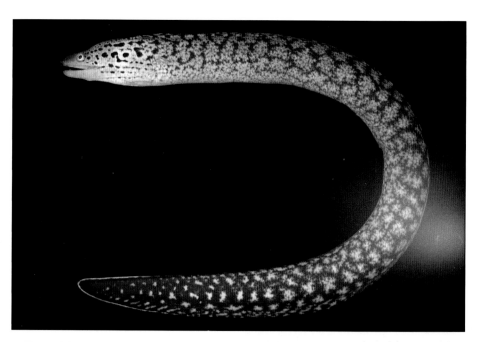

STOUT MORAY
Gymnothorax eurostus (Abbott, 1860)

Body depth 10-15 in length; head 7.5-9 in length; snout to anus 2.1-2.4 in length; three rows of long canines on intermaxilla in addition to canines in the outer row at front of jaw; teeth at side of upper jaw in two rows; vertebrae 120-123; highly variable in colour, but most often brown, becoming darker brown posteriorly, with numerous very small light yellow spots (more numerous anteriorly) and black spots about as large as eye in approximate longitudinal rows on anterior half of body; posterior end of tail edged in white. Indo-Pacific, but antitropical in distribution; found only in the southern part of the Great Barrier Reef; a common inshore reef species, though not often seen. Largest examined, 57 cm.

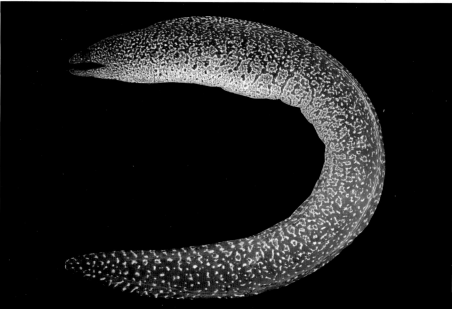

BLACKSPOTTED MORAY
Gymnothorax favagineus Bloch & Schneider, 1801

Body depth 13-17 in length; head 8-9 in length; snout to anus 2.1-2.2 in length; one row of long canine teeth on intermaxilla, longer than other canines at front of jaw; vomerine teeth of adults biserial; vertebrae 140-143; pale grey to pale brown with large roundish black spots which become relatively smaller, more numerous, and more close-set with growth. Western Pacific to East Africa. One of the two largest of Indo-Pacific morays. Reaches 180 cm; unconfirmed reports of still greater length.

DARKSPOTTED MORAY
Gymnothorax fimbriatus (Bennett, 1832)

Body depth 14-18 in length; head 6.5-8 in length; snout to anus 2.0-2.2 in length; a single row of canines on intermaxilla, much the longest in jaws; only a few enlarged canines in inner row on side of upper jaw; two pairs of long canines at front of lower jaw; vertebrae 131-136; grey with scattered round to irregular black spots on head and body, the pattern of spots and their shape variable from individual to individual. Indo-Pacific; not common. Reported to 80 cm.

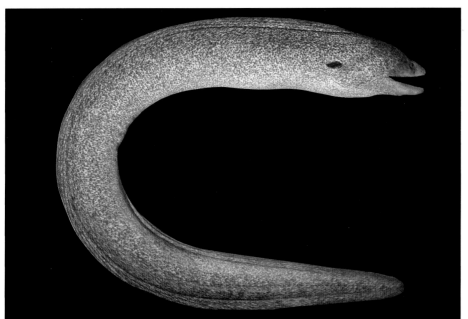

YELLOWMARGIN MORAY
Gymnothorax flavimarginatus (Rüppell, 1830)

Body depth 11-18 in length; head 6.5-10 in length; snout to anus 2.1-2.3 in length; large canines in one row on intermaxilla and in the single row at front of upper jaw; a pair of canines anteriorly in lower jaw; teeth on side of jaws in a single row; vertebrae 129-137; yellowish, densely mottled with dark brown; front of head purplish grey; a yellow-green margin posteriorly on fins; gill opening in a black blotch. Indo-Pacific; a common species; may be tamed to leave its refuge in the reef to take food from a diver's hand. Attains 120 cm.

FRECKLED MORAY
Gymnothorax fuscomaculatus (Schultz, 1953)

Body depth 16-19 in length; head 7-7.5 in length; snout to anus 2.0-2.3 in length; teeth in jaws conical and sharp but none as enlarged canines; teeth on side of upper jaw in two rows, the inner row larger; a double row of stout teeth anteriorly in lower jaw, and a single row of smaller teeth on side; origin of dorsal fin nearly a head length anterior to origin of anal fin; vertebrae 110-118; light brown with about four longitudinal rows of dark brown spots on body except anteriorly; pores on side of jaws and posterior nostrils each in a white spot. Indo-Pacific; few specimens in collections. Attains 20 cm.

SLENDERTAIL MORAY
Gymnothorax gracilicaudus Jenkins, 1903

Body depth 17-23 in length; head 7.5-9 in length; snout to anus 2.2-2.3 in length; the single row of canines on intermaxilla very long; other canines at front of upper jaw, in an inner row of two or three on side of jaw and two or three pairs at front of lower jaw; vertebrae 132-142; body whitish with narrow irregular dark brown bars which extend into dorsal fin or rows of vertically elongate dendritic dark brown blotches which tend to interconnect; two broader dark brown bars on upper half of postorbital head. Islands and reefs of Oceania to the Great Barrier Reef. Largest specimen, 32 cm.

GIANT MORAY
Gymnothorax javanicus (Bleeker, 1859)

Body depth 7-17 in length (large adults deep-bodied); head 6.5-9.5 in length; snout to anus 1.9-2.4 in length; two or three very large canines in a single row on intermaxilla; other long canines at front of jaws; teeth on side of jaws in one row; vomerine teeth biserial anteriorly; vertebrae 140-143; light brown with large subquadrate to irregular dark brown spots (spots on large eels may have irregular pale centres) in two to three irregular rows on body and smaller spots in fins; gill opening in a black blotch. Indo-Pacific; known from the depth range of 0.3-46 m; occurs in a variety of reef habitats. Attains at least 220 cm, thus the largest of Indo-Pacific morays; one of 216 cm from Hawaii (where rare) weighed 29 kg.

BLACKPEARL MORAY
Gymnothorax margaritophorus Bleeker, 1864

Body depth 18-22 in length; head 7-8 in length; snout to anus 2.2-2.3 in length; very long fang-like canines in one row on intermaxilla; other large canines at front of jaws and in an inner row on side of upper jaw; vertebrae 126-133; yellowish, finely mottled and irregularly barred with brown, shading to whitish ventrally on head and abdomen; a longitudinal row of round to oval black spots extending posteriorly from eye onto dorsal part of body. Indo-Pacific. Reported to 70 cm, but any over 40 cm are exceptional.

DWARF MORAY
Gymnothorax melatremus Schultz, 1953

Body depth 15-20 in length; head 7-9.5 in length; snout to anus 2.2-2.3 in length; no teeth of canine proportions in jaws; seven teeth on each side at front of upper jaw, conical anteriorly, becoming more compressed and recurved posteriorly; two stout conical teeth on intermaxilla; teeth in two rows on side of upper jaw and at front of lower jaw; vomerine teeth nodular, in one row; vertebrae 127-130; color variable, brown to yellow, sometimes with dark brown markings; a prominent black spot over gill opening; a black rim around eye. Indo-Pacific; common on reefs, but rarely seen by divers; collected from the depth range of 9-58 m. A very small species, the largest recorded, 26 cm.

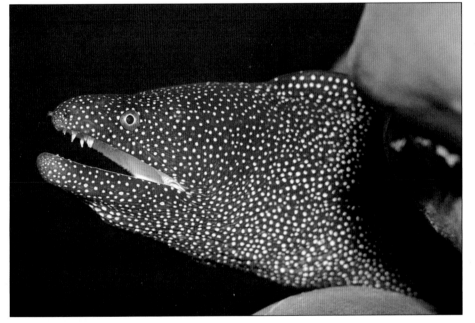

WHITEMOUTH MORAY
Gymnothorax meleagris (Shaw & Nodder, 1795)

Body depth 10-15 in length; head 7-8 in length; snout to anus 2.2-2.5 in length; three rows of fang-like canines on intermaxilla; canines also at front of upper jaw, in an inner row on side of jaw, and in an inner row at front of lower jaw; vertebrae 127-131; brown to yellowish brown with numerous small round dark-edged white spots; gill opening in a black blotch; tip of tail white; inside of mouth white. Indo-Pacific; common and often seen by divers. Reaches 100 cm.

YELLOWMOUTH MORAY
Gymnothorax nudivomer (Playfair & Günther, 1867)

Body depth 9-16 in length; head 8-9 in length; snout to anus 2.1-2.3 in length; compressed canine teeth, the edges sharp and finely serrate, in a single row in jaws; anterior six pairs of teeth in upper jaw enlarged; no teeth on vomer of adults; vertebrae 126-129; light brown anteriorly with numerous close-set very small irregular white spots, gradually becoming darker brown posteriorly, the spots progressively larger toward the tail and rimmed in dark brown; gill opening in a dark blotch; mouth bright yellow. Hawaii and western Pacific to East Africa; usually found in more than 30 m; often makes a threat display with widely open mouth; possesses a skin toxin. Attains 100 cm.

HIGHFIN MORAY
Gymnothorax pseudothyrsoideus (Bleeker, 1852)

Body depth 10-18 in length; head 6.5-7.5 in length; snout to anus 1.95-2.1 in length; dorsal fin well-developed, the height over anus about half body depth; vertebrae 127-135; pale yellowish, densely spotted with dark brown, the spots clustering to form dark spots larger than eye in about four irregular rows along body; juveniles with a white margin on fins, reduced to tip of tail in adults. Western Pacific; not common. Attains 80 cm.

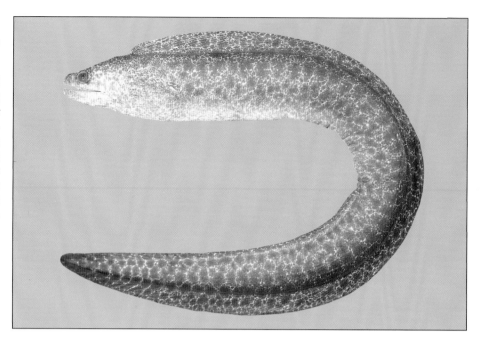

BANDED MORAY
Gymnothorax ruppelliae (McClelland, 1845)

Body depth 15-20 in length; head 7-8 in length; snout to anus 2.1-2.3 in length; teeth in jaws uniserial, the only canines at front of jaws and in a single row on intermaxilla; vertebrae 132-135; pale greyish brown with 16-21 dark bars about as wide as pale interspaces, these bars encircling body posterior to anus, some not meeting ventrally on trunk; bars becoming indistinct on large individuals; top of head yellow; a dark brown spot at corner of mouth. Indo-Pacific; nocturnal. Attains 80 cm. *G. petelli* (Bleeker) is a synonym.

UNDULATED MORAY
Gymnothorax undulatus (Lacepède, 1803)

Body depth 10-19 in length; head 6.5-8 in length; snout to anus 2.1-2.3 in length; a single row of long fang-like canines on intermaxilla and the usual canines anteriorly in jaws; young with a few canines in medial row on side of upper jaw; vertebrae 129-138; large close-set irregular dark brown blotches and small spots, the blotches tending to merge to form irregular bars posteriorly on body and fins, the narrow pale yellowish interspaces forming a very irregular reticulum; top of head yellowish green in life. Indo-Pacific; one of the most common morays at most localities; an aggressive species prone to bite; we have observed it actively hunting at night. Reaches at least 100 cm.

BARREDFIN MORAY
Gymnothorax zonipectis Seale, 1906

Body depth 15-21 in length; head 7-8 in length; snout to anus 2.2-2.3 in length; a single row of long canines on intermaxilla; lesser canines at front of jaws, sometimes with long teeth on inner row in upper jaw; vertebrae 122-126; brown with about four longitudinal rows of dendritic black blotches which are larger posteriorly; very fine whitish scribbling anteriorly on body and on fins; an irregular black spot behind eye broadly bordered above and below by white, the white extending to below corner of mouth; pores on side of jaws in large irregular white spots; fins with prominent diagonal black bars. Indo-Pacific; usually found in caves at depths greater than 20 m. Largest, 47 cm.

RIBBON EEL
Rhinomuraena quaesita Garman, 1888

Body extremely elongate, the depth 65-75 in length, and very compressed; head 18-21 in length; snout to anus 3.0-3.3 in length; teeth uniserial in jaws, intermaxilla, and vomer, all as small slender posteriorly slanted canines, those on intermaxilla longest; distal end of tubular nostrils of adults enormously expanded on posterior edge to a membranous scoop-like structure with jagged margin; a slender barbel-like appendage extending forward from front of upper jaw and three from lower; juveniles and subadults black with a yellow dorsal fin, the fin margins narrowly white; males become blue on the body, the snout, interorbital, and much of lower jaw yellow; mature females are entirely yellow except for black anal fin and white margin on fins. Central and western Pacific to islands of western Indian Ocean. Reaches at least 130 cm, the black and yellow immatures to 100 cm. *R. ambonensis* Barbour is a synonym based on the female form. Because of its striking colouration and unusual morphology, this muraenid eel is of value as an aquarium fish.

Rhinomuraena quaesita;
blue and black phases

LONGTAIL MORAY
Strophidon sathete (Hamilton 1822)

Body very elongate, the depth 38-47 in length; head 10-14 in length; tail about twice as long as head and trunk; teeth in jaws as small compressed canines, in two rows at side of upper jaw and front of lower jaw; longest teeth a series of about four depressible canines medially on intermaxilla; vertebrae 183-196; greyish brown, paler ventrally, the fins darker. Western Pacific to East Africa and the Red Sea; generally found in estuarine areas, sometimes from rivers. Largest reported, 375 cm, from Queensland. *Thyrsoidea macrura* (Bleeker) is a junior synonym (P.H.J. Castle, pers. comm.)

PEPPERED MORAY
Siderea picta (Ahl, 1789)

Body depth 10-20 in length (large adults deeper-bodied); head 6-8 in length; snout to anus 1.9-2.1 in length; teeth in jaws not of canine proportions, those in upper jaw in one row, conical at the very front, becoming compressed along side of jaw; a single conical tooth on intermaxilla; two rows of teeth at front of lower jaw, the outer row small; vertebrae 127-133; adults white, finely speckled with black, the dots sometimes grouped to form large diffuse spots; small juveniles with relatively larger black spots in about three longitudinal rows; larger juveniles may show pale centres to many of these spots. Indo-Pacific and islands of tropical eastern Pacific; a shallow reef-flat species that may be seen foraging for food in only a few cms of water, sometimes fully exposed as waves recede; feeds mainly on crabs, occasionally on fishes; has been observed to leap from the water to strike at grapsid crabs on rocks above the surface. Reaches at least 100 cm.

GREYFACE MORAY
Siderea thyrsoidea (Richardson, 1845)

Body depth 17-22 in length; head 9-10.5 in length; snout to anus 2.4-2.55 in length; teeth conical, none as canines, the two in the single row on intermaxilla the longest; teeth on side of jaws in two rows, the inner larger; teeth at front of lower jaw in two rows, those of the inner row longest; vomerine teeth small and blunt, in two rows which diverge anteriorly; vertebrae 127-136; pale yellowish, densely mottled with small dark brown spots; front half of head uniform dark purplish grey; gill opening in a dusky spot; iris white. Central and western Pacific; an inshore species. Largest reported, 66 cm, but usually less than 40 cm. *S. prosopeion* (Bleeker) is a synonym.

MARBLED MORAY
Uropterygius marmoratus (Lacepède, 1803)

Body depth 20-26 in length; head 9.5-11.5 in length; snout to anus 2.25-2.5 in length; needle-like teeth in three rows in jaws, those of inner row longest; intermaxilla with three rows of long depressible canines; vomerine teeth also sharp, in two or three rows anteriorly, narrowing to one posteriorly; gill opening on midside of body; vertebrae 133-138; whitish, densely mottled with roundish dark brown spots about size of eye or slightly larger. Central and western Pacific; generally found in shallow water on exposed rocky shores or reefs. Reported to 50 cm. Two other species of *Uropterygius* are known from the Great Barrier Reef or Coral Sea, *U. fuscoguttatus* Schultz and *U. micropterus* (Bleeker). Both are small (less than 30 cm) and rarely seen.

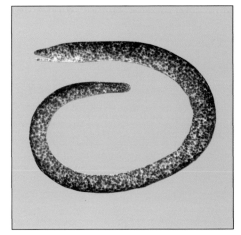

SNAKE EELS
FAMILY OPHICHTHIDAE

These fishes have a typical eel-shaped body that is more or less rounded in cross section. The body is scaleless, the eyes are usually small and situated just above the mouth; the snout is often pointed or nearly so; the lower jaw is frequently underslung; the posterior nostril is usually within or piercing the upper lip; the gill openings are midlateral to entirely ventral in position; the pectoral fins are present or absent; the tail tip is either hard and pointed or the caudal rays are conspicuous and confluent with the dorsal and anal fins. This large family is distributed in all tropical and temperate oceans; there are about 50 genera and approximately 240 species. Although they are very common, most people, including anglers and divers, are unaware of their presence. This is because they spend most of the time buried in the sand. The pointed snout is useful for burrowing. In addition, many have a bony, sharp tail and are equally adept at burrowing backwards and forward. The species that have conspicuous bands or spotting are sometimes mistaken for sea snakes, but they can be easily distinguished by their lack of scales and possession of a more or less pointed tail (paddle-like in sea snakes). The diet of most snake eels consists of small fishes, crabs, and prawns.

SHARPSNOUT SNAKE EEL
Apterichtus klazingai (Weber, 1913)

Head length 13-14, depth of body 60-72, tail length 1.8-1.9, all in total length; teeth uniserial on jaws and vomer; tail tip hard; no fins present; rear nostril opening outside, with a flap; front nostril tubular; head and snout covered with minute papillae; whitish with numerous small light brown spots. East Africa to the Marshall Islands. Reaches 40 cm.

STARGAZER SNAKE EEL
Brachysomophis cirrocheilos (Bleeker, 1857)

Head length about 8-9, depth of body 25-26, both in total length; head and body about equal to tail length or tail somewhat longer; teeth fang-like, biserial in upper jaw, uniserial on vomer and lower jaw; lips fringed with cirri; tail tip hard; a low dorsal fin present; pectoral fins present; the length of pectoral fin about 4-5 in head length; whitish to tan, often with tiny dark brown spots on upper surface. Indo Pacific, sometimes seen with only the head or snout protruding from the sand. Ambushes its prey of small fishes and crustaceans that venture near. To 125 cm.

CROCODILE SNAKE EEL
Brachysomophis crocodilinus (Bennett, 1833)

Head length about 7, depth of body 19, tail length 2.2, all in total length; teeth fanglike, biserial in upper jaw, the inner series larger; uniserial on vomer and lower jaw; lips fringed with cirri. Similar in appearance and habits to *B. cirrocheilos* (above), but has smaller pectoral fins, their length about 10-12 in head length; whitish to tan or brown. Indo-Pacific, including eastern Pacific. Attains 110 cm.

BLACK-STRIPED SNAKE EEL
Callechelys catostomus (Bloch & Schneider, 1801)

Head length 16-20, depth of body 60-75 both in total length; head and trunk about 2-3 times the length of the tail; posterior nostrils below front border of eye; teeth of upper and lower jaws uniserial, those on inner maxilla stout and biserial; tail tip hard; dorsal fin present, originating above rear end of mouth; no pectoral fins; colour whitish with a broad black stripe along upper side and black margin on dorsal fin. Indonesia to Society Islands. Reaches 60 cm. *C. melanotaenia* is a junior synonym.

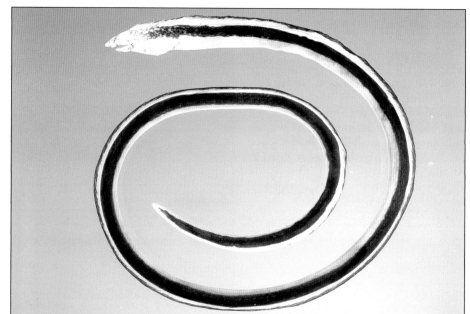

MARBLED SNAKE EEL
Callechelys marmorata (Bleeker, 1853)

Head length 10-14, depth of body 31-42, tail length 2.8, all in total length; teeth of upper and lower jaws uniserial; a few recurved conical teeth on intermaxilla; vomerine teeth biserial in front, then uniserial; tail tip hard; dorsal fin originating on nape; no pectoral fins; yellowish or cream colour with variable amount of black spotting and mottling. East Africa to Society Islands. To 57 cm.

CULVERIN
Leiuranus semicinctus (Lay & Bennett, 1839)

Head length 11-15, depth of body 33-70, tail length 1.9-2.1, all in total length; teeth of upper and lower jaws uniserial; a few teeth on intermaxilla and on vomer; tail tip hard; a low dorsal and anal fin present; dorsal fin origin above pectoral fin; a small pectoral fin present; no cirri on lips; white or yellowish with 20-30 black saddles, only those on tail forming complete rings. East Africa to Polynesia. To 60 cm.

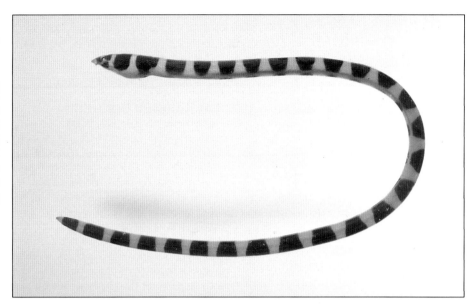

SLENDER SNAKE EEL
Muraenichthys macropterus Bleeker, 1857

Head length 7-8, depth of body 30-40, both in total length; head and trunk about 1.3-1.5 times in tail length; teeth of upper and lower jaws small and biserial, those on the vomer larger and more granular, arranged in two rows; origin of dorsal fin closer to anus than to gill openings; caudal fin rays conspicuous, tail tip flexible; no pectoral fins; olive on back, lighter below. East Africa to Society Islands. To 17 cm. Several species of *Muraenichthys* occur in the area, but they are very similar in appearance and require microscopic examination by museum specialists in order to identify them.

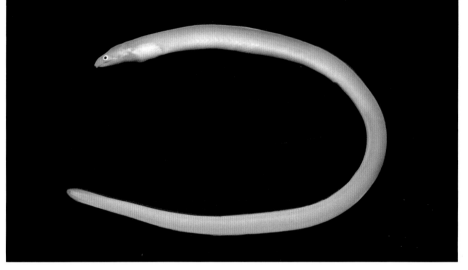

HARLEQUIN SNAKE EEL
Myrichthys colubrinus (Boddaert, 1781)

Head length 17.5-20, depth of body 48-55, tail length 1.8-1.9, all in total length; teeth of upper and lower jaws blunt and biserial; a few teeth on intermaxilla and 1-2 rows on vomer; dorsal fin origin on top of head. Yellowish white to white with 25-32 narrow black rings; black spots may develop between the rings with increasing age; colour pattern similar to that of *L. semicinctus* but black bars on body form complete rings rather than incomplete saddles. Red Sea to the Society Is. To 88 cm.

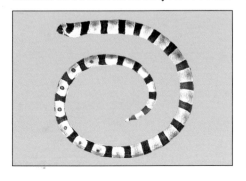

SPOTTED SNAKE EEL
Myrichthys maculosus (Cuvier, 1817)

Head length 12-16, depth of body 35-50, tail length 1.7, all in total length; teeth of upper and lower jaws blunt and biserial; a few teeth on intermaxilla; teeth of vomer biserial; dorsal fin origin on top of head. Colour pattern consisting of large to small oval black spots on cream-coloured background. East Africa and Red Sea to Polynesia; sometimes seen in the open over sandy bottoms or in weedy areas. Grows to 50 cm.

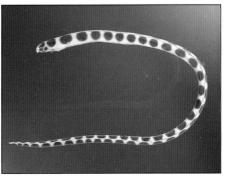

JOHNSTON SNAKE EEL
Schultzidia johnstonianus (Schultz & Woods, 1949)

Head length 7.9-10.2, depth of body 24-30, tail length 1.7-1.8, all in total length; teeth absent on vomer, absent or embedded on intermaxillary, those on maxilla and dentary minute or villiform. Caudal fin rays conspicuous, joined to dorsal and anal fins; tail tip flexible; gill openings midlateral; pectoral fins absent; dorsal fin origin behind anus; Cocos-Keeling Atoll in the eastern Indian Ocean to Polynesia. Reaches 35 cm.

CONGER EELS
FAMILY CONGRIDAE

Congers have a typical eel-shaped body with a small gill opening, and the caudal fin is continuous with the dorsal and anal fins. They differ noticeably from the more speciose moray eels in having pectoral fins and their body is nearly round anteriorly rather than compressed. The family is divisible into two subfamilies, the Congrinae (most of these are found in deep water rather than around reefs), and the Heterocongrinae, commonly known as garden eels. The reef-dwelling congers are generally nocturnal predators of fishes and crustaceans. The garden eels are found in large colonies that feed exclusively on plankton that is picked from passing currents. The flesh of conger eels is considered good eating.

SPECKLED GARDEN-EEL
Gorgasia sp.

Head length 19-24, depth 64-86, both in total length; lateral-line pores before anus 35-40; origin of dorsal fin just behind pectoral fin; pectoral fins small; overall pale grey with brownish yellow speckling. An undescribed species which will be named by P. Castle and J. Randall in a revision of Indo-Pacific Itetero congrinae. Western Pacific, including Coral Sea, Guam, and Marshall Islands; found in large colonies on clean sandy slopes below about 18 m. Reaches 46 cm.

BLACK-EDGED CONGER
Conger cinereus Rüppell, 1830

Head length 7.5-8.5, depth 16-23, both in total length; lateral-line pores before anus 37-41; pectoral fins well developed with 16-18 rays; origin of dorsal fin above anterior half of pectoral fin; teeth at edge of jaws compressed, close-set, forming a shearing edge; grey-brown, yellowish white ventrally; edges of dorsal and anal fins black; a blackish streak below eye and a large blackish patch on pectoral fins; body with dark bars while foraging for prey at night. East Africa and Red Sea to Easter Island. Up to 103 cm.

SPOTTED GARDEN-EEL
Heteroconger hassi (Klausewitz & Eibl-Eibesfeldt, 1959)

Head length 16-17, depth 38-55, both in total length; origin of dorsal fin just in front of pectoral fin; pectoral fins minute; white with numerous small black spots, a large black blotch on anterior one-third of body and a slightly smaller one covering pectoral region. Red Sea to Samoa and Line Islands, north to Ryukyu Islands; often encountered on sandy slopes below 15 m depth, usually in colonies containing up to several hundred individuals. They withdraw into their burrows at the approach of divers. To 40 cm.

HERRINGS AND SARDINES
FAMILY CLUPEIDAE

Clupeids are generally small silvery fishes that are easily recognised by their keel of scutes (special spiny scales) along the belly, and small, often poorly toothed mouths. Other features include a single dorsal fin that is located over the middle of the body, a forked caudal fin, usually a short anal fin located well posteriorly; pelvic fins on abdomen below dorsal fin, pectoral fins low on the side just behind the head, and no fin spines. Herrings and their relatives are of major importance to fisheries; they constitute about half of the world's catch of fishes. Clupeids are found in most shallow-water habitats including fresh water, brackish estuaries, coastal embayments, and oceanic reefs. They occur in all warm and cold seas. Most are found in schools that may contain hundreds or thousands of individuals. Zooplankton, often crustaceans, is the major dietary item for most clupeids. These fishes are very important as prey for larger fishes, particularly trevallies and tunas.

FOURSPOT HERRING
Herklotsichthys quadrimaculatus (Rüppell, 1837)

Dorsal rays 17-20; anal rays 17-19; pectoral rays 15 or 16; depth of body 3.3-5.5 in standard length; eye 2.3-3.7 in head length; wing-shaped median predorsal scales hidden under the normal paired and overlapping median scales; scales toothed posteriorly; silvery blue-green on back, silvery below, with a yellow stripe on body at eye level and a small yellowish spot above and below it just behind the gill opening. East Africa to Samoa and Marshall Islands. Used as tuna bait. Recently discovered in Hawaii; probably the result of an unintentional introduction. Reaches 15 cm.

BLUE-BACKED SPRAT
Spratelloides delicatulus (Bennett, 1831)

Dorsal rays 11-13; anal rays 10-11; pectoral rays 11-13; lower gill rakers 26-32; predorsal scales 8-13; scales in midlateral series 35-41; back blue, lower sides silver; pair of prominent dark streaks on caudal fin base. East Africa and Red Sea to the Society Islands; sometimes used as tuna bait. Attains 7 cm. A second species of *Spratelloides*, *S. gracilis*, has a distinct silver stripe along the middle of the side.

MILKFISH
FAMILY CHANDIDAE

See discussion of the single species of the family below.

MILKFISH
Chanos chanos (Forsskål, 1775)

Dorsal rays 13-17; anal rays 8-10; pectoral rays 15-17; pelvic rays 10-12; lateral-line scales 78-90; gill rakers on first arch 147-160 + 107-165; caudal fin strongly forked; scales cycloid except head scaleless; a large axillary scale above pectoral and pelvic fins; no fin spines; mouth small without teeth; eye covered with thick layer of gelatinous tissue; silvery blue-green on back, silvery on sides, and white below. East Africa to Polynesia. Spawns in the sea, the larval stage is transparent and ribbon-like (called the leptochpahlus); spends part of the life cycle in estuaries; highly esteemed as food in several regions; form the basis of an extensive fish-farming industry in south-eastern Asia; often encountered in schools. Grows to 180 cm.

EELTAIL CATFISHES
FAMILY PLOTOSIDAE

These catfishes have a slender, tapering eel-like body; there are usually four pairs of barbels around the mouth; first dorsal fin short with a stiff spine anteriorly; second dorsal fin continuous with the caudal and anal fins, consisting of numerous rays and no spines; the pectoral fin is situated just behind the head and has a sharp stiff spine on its anterior edge; both dorsal and pectoral fin spines are venomous and usually serrate; stab wounds from them are extremely painful. Plotosids are confined to the Indo-Pacific region. There are about eight genera and approximately 40 species. Over half of these are fresh-water inhabitants of Australia and New Guinea. Many of the marine plotosids are estuarine dwellers or occur on soft bottoms of commercial trawling grounds. Only the genera *Plotosus* and *Paraplotosus* are common on coral reefs.

WHITE-LIPPED CATFISH
Paraplotosus albilabrus (Valenciennes, 1840)

Dorsal rays I,4; total second dorsal-caudal-anal rays about 185-210; pectoral rays I,12 or 13; pelvic rays 12 or 13; brown, darker on back and lighter on belly. Indonesia, Melanesia and northern Australia; usually occurs solitarily; frequently seen resting on sand bottoms under ledges or around coral bommies. Reaches 134 cm, but most are under 40 cm.

STRIPED CATFISH
Plotosus lineatus (Thunberg, 1787)

Dorsal rays I,4; total second dorsal-caudal-anal rays 139-200; pectoral rays I,9-13; pelvic rays 10-13; brown to black, shading to white on ventral surface, with two narrow white stripes on side. East Africa and Red Sea to Samoa; juveniles are frequently encountered in tightly packed groups that swarm across the reef. To 32 cm. *P. anguillaris* (Bloch) is a synonym.

LIZARDFISHES
FAMILY SYNODONTIDAE

Lizardfishes have a reptile-like head with a large mouth and numerous slender sharp teeth; even the tongue has inward-directed teeth; the body is cylindrical and moderately elongate; the fins lack spines; there is a single relatively high dorsal fin of 10-14 rays and an adipose fin (small fleshy rayless fin on back between dorsal and caudal fins); the pelvic fins are large, with 8 or 9 rays; caudal fin forked; scales cycloid. Most of the species have a series of irregular dark blotches on the side, often interconnected and linked with dark blotches on the back, and usually with extensions to ventral part of body. Lizardfishes generally live on sedimentary bottoms, but some occur on reefs; they are able to bury themselves in sand or mud with only their eyes showing. All are voracious carnivores, darting upward with great rapidity to seize small fishes or shrimps that venture near. The late larval stage, which may reach more than 5 cm in length, is slender and transparent with a row of prominent internal black spots ventrally on the body; the number of these spots is helpful in determining the species. There are three genera of lizardfishes in our area, *Synodus* with 25 Indo-Pacific species, *Saurida* with 11 Indo-Pacific species, and the monotypic *Trachinocephalus* which is found in both the Atlantic and Indo-Pacific.

SLENDER LIZARDFISH
Saurida gracilis (Quoy & Gaimard, 1824)

Dorsal rays 11-12 (rarely 12); anal rays 9-10; pectoral rays 12-14 (usually 13); pelvic rays 9, the outer rays longer than inner; lateral-line scales 49-52; numerous small teeth exposed on side of jaws when mouth closed; palatine teeth in two rows on each side; small teeth on vomer (vomer absent in *Synodus*); origin of dorsal fin posterior to midpoint of distance from snout to adipose fin; whitish finely mottled with brown dorsally white below with black spots on lower side; three diffuse blackish blotches dorsally on posterior half of body, the largest behind dorsal fin. Indo-Pacific; usually found on sand in silty reef areas. To 28 cm..

TWOSPOT LIZARDFISH
Synodus binotatus Schultz, 1953

Dorsal rays 12-14 (usually 13); anal rays 8-10; pectoral rays 12 (rarely 11); pelvic rays 8, the inner rays longer than the outer (true of all *Synodus*) lateral-line scales 53-55; 3.5 rows of scales above lateral line to dorsal fin; cheek behind mouth scaled; palatine teeth in a single band on each side (characteristic of the genus), those anteriorly in a discrete group, longer than the posterior teeth; membranous flap on anterior nostrils long and broad; pectoral fins reaching beyond a line connecting origins of dorsal and pelvic fins; dorsal tip of snout with a pair of small but prominent black spots; all fins with dark spots on rays forming transverse bands, two on adipose fin. Indo-Pacific; usually found in less than 10 m. Reaches about 17 cm.

CLEARFIN LIZARDFISH
Synodus dermatogenys Fowler, 1912

Dorsal rays 11-13 (rarely 13); anal rays 8-10; pectoral rays 11-13; lateral-line scales 59-62; scale rows above lateral line 5.5; cheek usually not scaled to preopercular margin; palatine teeth as in *S. binotatus*; membranous flap on anterior nostrils long and slender; pectoral fins not reaching a line connecting origins of dorsal and pelvic fins; pelvic and anal fins without dark spots. Indo-Pacific; a common species on shallow sand or sand-rubble areas near coral reefs. Largest, 23 cm. Most authors have misidentified this species as *S. variegatus* (Lacepède)

ARROWTOOTH LIZARDFISH
Synodus doaki Russell & Cressey, 1979

Dorsal rays 13-15; anal rays 8-9; pectoral rays 12-13 (usually 13); lateral-line scales 57-60; 3.5 scale rows above lateral line; cheek scaled to margin of preopercle; larger teeth with arrow-shaped tips; palatine teeth as in *S. binotatus*; flap on anterior nostrils very long and rounded; pectoral fins reaching a line connecting origins of dorsal and pelvic fins; irregular bars and spots on body red, the centres of larger markings sometimes yellow; all fins with transverse red bands. Known from Hawaii, New Zealand, eastern Australia, Japan, and East Africa; usually found in relatively deep water (to 200 m), but has been observed in as little as 9 m. Reaches 28 cm.

JAVELINFISH
Synodus jaculum Russell & Cressey, 1979

Dorsal rays ll-13; anal rays 8-10; pectoral rays 12-13; lateral-line scales 59-62; scale rows above lateral line 5.5 (occasionally 6.5); no scales on cheek behind mouth; palatine teeth as in *S. binotatus*; nasal flap short and triangular; pectoral fins reaching a line connecting origins of dorsal and pelvic fins; a large black blotch nearly covering base of caudal fin; irregular vertical dark bars and stripes on body tending to form a cross-hatch pattern. Scattered records from Line Islands in the Central Pacific to Natal and the Comoro Is.; occurs in shallow water as well as moderate depths (to 88 m); generally found on sand or rubble near coral heads; unusual for a lizardfish in making frequent prolonged forays well above the bottom in quest of prey. Attains about 20cm.

REDMARBLED LIZARDFISH
Synodus rubromarmoratus Russell &
Cressey, 1979

Dorsal rays 10-12; anal rays 9; pectoral
rays 11-12; lateral-line scales 54-55; scale
rows above lateral line 3.5; cheek behind
mouth fully scaled; anterior palatine teeth
not longer than more posterior teeth and not
in a discrete group; nasal flap long and
blunt-tipped; pectoral fins not reaching a
line between origins of dorsal and anal fins;
blotches on body red. Known only from
Taiwan, Philippines, and the Great Barrier
Reef; recorded on the Great Barrier Reef
from depths of 15 m or more. Evidently a
small species; reaches about 12 cm.

REEF LIZARDFISH
Synodus variegatus (Lacepède, 1803)

Dorsal rays 12-14; anal rays 8-10; pectoral rays 12-13; lateral-line scales 61-63; scale
rows above lateral line 5.5; cheek behind
mouth fully scaled to preopercular margin;
palatine teeth as in *S. binotatus*; nasal flap
short and triangular; pectoral fins not reaching a line connecting origins of dorsal and
pelvic fins; markings on body varying from
brown to greenish or reddish; a dark midlateral stripe nearly as broad as eye linking
lateral row of dark blotches. Indo-Pacific;
the most reef-oriented species of the genus;
often found at rest on hard substratum, including live coral. Largest specimen, 28.3
cm. Most recent authors have misidentified
this species as *S. englemani* Schultz, now
known to be a junior synonym.

SNAKEFISH
Trachinocephalus myops (Bloch &
Schneider, 1801)

Dorsal rays 11-14; anal rays 13-18; pectoral rays 11-13; pelvic rays 8, the inner rays
longer than outer; lateral-line scales 51-61;
scale rows above lateral line 3.5; snout very
short, equal to or shorter than eye diameter;
mouth very oblique; interorbital space deeply
concave; body with alternating narrow dark-
edged pale blue and yellow stripes; an
oblique black spot at upper end of gill opening. Indo-Pacific and Atlantic, tropical to
warm temperate; occurs from the shallows
to 400 m on sand bottom, into which it
buries itself (except for its eyes) almost
instantly; rarely seen exposed. Reported to
33 cm.

BROTULAS
FAMILY OPHIDIIDAE

These fishes have an elongate, more or less eel-like body with the long-based dorsal and anal fins continuous with the caudal fin; the pelvic fins are either absent or consist of one or two slender filamentous rays; some species have barbels around the mouth. Unlike the similar-appearing cuskeels (family Bythitidae), brotulas are egg layers, and males therefore lack specialised copulatory organs. The family occurs worldwide in both shallow and deep seas. Only one species, *Brotula multibarbata,* is generally encountered on reefs in our area, but it is rarely seen because of its cryptic habits. It lives in caves and crevices during the day and periodically emerges from cover at night to feed on crustaceans (mainly crabs) and fishes.

BEARDED BROTULA
Brotula multibarbata Temminck & Schlegel, 1846

Dorsal rays 117-123; anal rays 88-100; pectoral rays 22-26; pelvic rays 2; barbels present on snout and chin; dusky brown to grey, dorsal and anal fins paler with black submarginal band; juveniles generally lighter, sometimes with scattered small black spots on head and body. Christmas Island (Indian Ocean) to Polynesia. To 60 cm.

PEARLFISHES
FAMILY CARAPIDAE

This family consists of two subfamilies, seven genera, and 31 species of small slender fishes of tropical to temperate seas. Some species are free-living, others are commensal in sea cucumbers, bivalves, starfishes, and tunicates; and some have been shown to be parasitic, feeding on the gonads and gills of their hosts. The common name pearlfishes is derived from species which have been found in pearl shells. Carapids are sometimes called fierasfers or glass eels, the latter name alluding to the transparent body of many species. These fishes are very elongate, the body tapering to a slender pointed tail. Those that live in sea cucumbers which are able to freely leave the host, enter tail-first through the cloacal opening. There is no caudal fin; the dorsal and anal fins lack spines and are confluent around the tip of the tail; pelvic fins absent

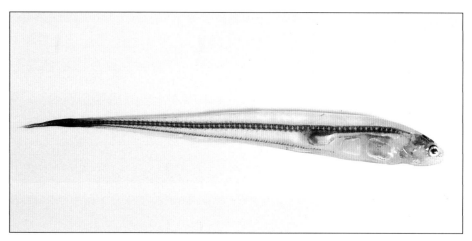

(except in the four free-living species of *Pyramodon*); pectoral fins may be reduced or absent; there are no scales; most unusual is the position of the anus of adults far forward on the throat. There are two larval stages, the planktonic vexillifer with a long predorsal filament, and the benthic tenuis. As pearlfishes spend most or all of their adult life within their host, they are not apt to be seen by divers. We present below an illustration and account of one species to represent the group.

FOWLER'S PEARLFISH
Onuxodon fowleri (Smith, 1955)

Pectoral rays 16; precaudal vertebrae 19-22; pectoral fins relatively long, usually slightly less than half head length; a pair of prominent incurved canine teeth anteriorly in jaws separated by a gap from small teeth posteriorly in jaws; body compressed; origin of dorsal fin slightly posterior to anal-fin origin; eye relatively large, about equal to snout length; transparent with some blackish distally on tail. Indo-Pacific; lives in clams, rock oysters, and pearl shells. Attains 9 cm.

CUSKEELS
FAMILY BYTHITIDAE

These are long slender fishes with a long dorsal fin that is sometimes continuous with the caudal and anal fins; there are no fin spines; scales are usually present, although they may be embedded; there is usually a strong opercular spine; the eyes are small, sometimes vestigal. These fishes bear their young alive; the males have an external intromittent organ. About 85 species are known including some from fresh and brackish waters and others from deepsea habitats. The reef species live deep in cracks and crevices. They are never seen unless flushed from their lairs with chemical ichthyocides (used by scientific collectors).

SLIMY CUSKEEL
Brosmophyciops pautzkei Schultz, 1960

Dorsal rays 78-81; anal rays 58-60; pectoral rays 25-29; body eel-like, laterally compressed; long-based dorsal and anal fins without spines; tail not connected to dorsal and anal fins; a pair of thread-like pelvic fins; body covered with heavy coating of mucus; generally grey. Red Sea to Samoa, north to the Ryukyu Islands. Attains 7 cm.

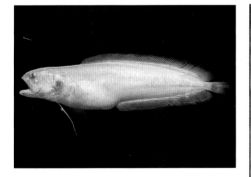

YELLOW CUSKEEL
Dinematichthys sp.

Dorsal rays 83-88; anal rays 64-68; pectoral rays 20-23; body moderately elongate; long-based dorsal and anal fins without spines; small caudal fin not connected to dorsal and anal fins; a pair of thread-like pelvic fins; colour yellow. Distributional limits uncertain. Reaches 6 cm. Judging from different-coloured individuals, there are several species in the Indo-Pacific re-

gion. Attempts to distinguish them on some basis other than colour have not been successful though the structure of the male genitalia is promising. Clearly a major study of this genus and the related *Ogilbia* is needed.

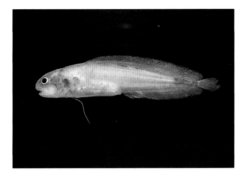

TOADFISHES
FAMILY BATRACHOIDIDAE

These fishes are characterised by a relatively large head and mouth with the eyes positioned more dorsally than laterally. There are III stout dorsal spines followed by a separate, long second dorsal fin; both second dorsal and anal fins without spines; head spines present on opercle and subopercle; body with or without scales; no canine teeth; usually one or three lateral lines.

Toadfishes, usually known as frogfishes in Australia, are bottom dwellers that shelter under rocks, in crevices, or bury themselves in sand or mud. They occur in brackish coastal estuaries as well as to depths of at least 180 m. The diet consists of crabs, prawns, molluscs (bivalves, gastropods, chitons, and octopus), echinoderms and fishes. Food is generally consumed whole; the stomach is capable of considerable expansion. Although the spines are not known to have venom, these fishes are greatly respected by New Guinean fishermen who claim that stab wounds result in severe pain.

BANDED FROGFISH
Halophryne diemensis (Lesueur, 1824)

Dorsal rays III,19-21; anal rays 16-18; pectoral rays 22-24; gill slit on upper 1/2-2/3 of pectoral fin base; four spines on gill cover; short tentacles on head; mottled brown with paler cross bars on body. Northern Australia from Shark Bay, Western Australia to Heron Is. Queensland; also throughout the Indo-Malayan Archipelago; a well camouflaged fish at times seen in crevices mainly on inner sections of the Great Barrier Reef or on coastal reefs. Attains 26 cm.

ANGLERFISHES OR FROG-FISHES

FAMILY ANTENNARIIDAE

These unusual fishes have globular somewhat compressed bodies, limb-like pectoral fins with an "elbow" joint, a small round gill opening, a very large, upward directed mouth, and a greatly modified first dorsal spine, termed the illicium, anteriorly on top of the head. The illicium forms a moveable "fishing rod" tipped with an enticing lure (esca). The rod is wiggled vigorously to attract fish prey that are swallowed whole. However, they do not always use their luring apparatus and are able to slowly stalk fishes or crustaceans. Anglerfishes can engulf prey longer than themselves as their abdomen can expand enormously. They are masters of camouflage, their colours closely corresponding to that of their surroundings such as bright coloured encrusting sponges. Gravid females expel a buoyant "raft" of up to 300,000 eggs. The "raft" remains afloat and intact for several days until hatching.

FRECKLED ANGLERFISH
Antennarius coccineus (Lesson, 1830)

Dorsal rays I+I+I,12 (rarely 13); anal rays 7 (rarely 8); pectoral rays 9-12 (rarely 9); last ray of pelvic fin bifurcate; illicium about as long as second dorsal spine; esca globular or filamentous; caudal peduncle absent; colour variable, usually yellow, red, or pale tan, often with a weakly pigmented dark spot at base of posterior dorsal rays. Indo-Pacific eastward to the Americas. Reaches 13 cm.

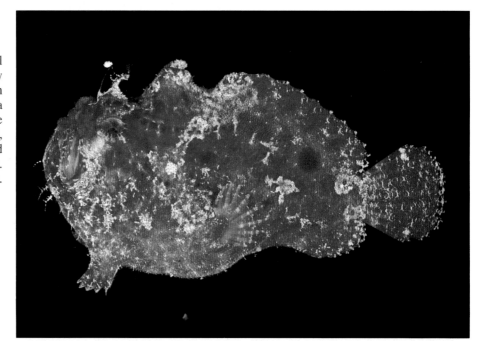

WHITE-FINGER ANGLERFISH
Antennarius nummifer (Cuvier, 1817)

Dorsal rays I+I+I,12 (rarely 13); anal rays 7 (rarely 8); pectoral rays 10 or 11; last ray of pelvic fin bifurcate; illicium about equal to length of second dorsal spine; esca filamentous; caudal peduncle present; colour variable, often yellow, pink, red, brown, or black; a darkly pigmented spot at base of posterior dorsal rays. East Africa and Red Sea to the Society Islands and north to Japan. To 13 cm.

PAINTED ANGLERFISH
Antennarius pictus (Shaw & Nodder, 1794)

Dorsal rays I+I+I,11-13 (usually 12); anal rays 7 (rarely 6); pectoral rays 9-11 (usually 10); illicium nearly twice length of second dorsal spine; esca filamentous; sometimes head and body with low wart-like swellings; colour variable, often tan, yellow, red, brown, or black, body colour solid or with dark (on light background) or light (on dark background) spots. East Africa to the Hawaiian and Society islands. Reaches 24 cm. *A. chironectes* (Latreille) is a synonym.

STRIPED ANGLERFISH
Antennarius striatus Shaw & Nodder, 1794

Dorsal rays I+I+I,11 or 12; anal rays 7; pectoral rays 9-12; illicium about equal to length of second dorsal spine; esca consisting of 2-7 elongate, worm-like appendages; colour variable, often light yellow, orange, green, grey or brown with black stripes or elongate blotches, sometimes solid black. Circumtropical, except absent from the eastern Pacific. To 22 cm.

TUBERCULATED ANGLERFISH
Antennatus tuberosus (Cuvier, 1817)

Dorsal rays I+I+I,12; anal rays 7; pectoral rays 9-12 (usually 11); illicium about 1.5-2 times length of second dorsal spine; distinct esca lacking; colour variable, grey, cream or yellow with dark brown marbling and reticulations, a dark brown band on caudal fin. East Africa to Samoa and the Hawaiian Islands. Attains 6.5 cm. *Antennarius bigibbus* Günther is a snynoym.

SARGASSUMFISH
Histrio histrio (Linnaeus, 1758)

Dorsal rays I+I+I,13; anal rays 13; pectoral rays 9-11; illicium much shorter than second dorsal spine; esca globular with short filaments; colour generally mottled green, brown, and yellow effectively blending with the floating *Sargassum* weed in which it is usually found. Indo-West Pacific and tropical Atlantic. Grows to 19 cm.

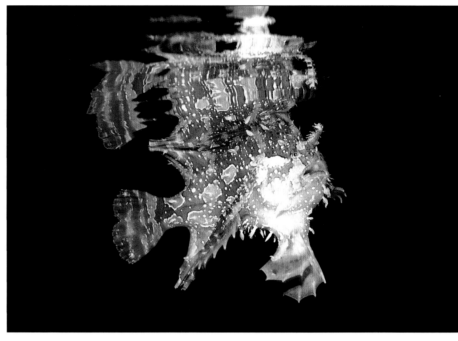

CLINGFISHES
FAMILY GOBIESOCIDAE

These small fishes are distinguished by their thoracic sucking disc which includes the modified pelvic fins of 4 rays. There is a single dorsal fin without spines; there are no scales, and the body is generally elongate. The family occurs worldwide and is represented by numerous species (many of them undescribed) in cool waters of Australia's southern half, but only a few inhabit tropical seas. Two are commonly encountered in our area. The thoracic disc, which is supported by highly modified pectoral and pelvic bones, is used to cling to rocks, weeds, sessile invertebrates, and a few species can adhere to the surface of larger fishes. They feed on zooplankton, algae, and small benthic invertebrates. A skin toxin was discovered by J. Randall in two species of clingfishes (reported by Hori et al., 1979), and it is expected that it will be found in other species of the family.

URCHIN CLINGFISH
Diademichthys lineatus (Sauvage, 1883)

Dorsal rays 13-15; anal rays 12-14; pectoral rays 25-26; distinguished by its long spatulate snout and slender shape; reddish or red brown with a pair of yellow stripes on upper half of head and body. Indo Pacific; shelters among spines of sea urchins or in branching corals. To 5 cm.

CRINOID CLINGFISH
Discotrema echinophila Briggs, 1976

Dorsal rays 8 or 9; anal rays 7 or 8; pectoral rays 25-27; reddish brown to nearly black with a conspicuous yellow stripe from snout to base of caudal fin. Indo-Pacific; found among the arms of crinoids (sea-lilies). Attains 3 cm.

FLYINGFISHES
FAMILY EXOCOETIDAE

Flying fishes are aptly named for their habit of emerging quickly from the water and gliding for long distances (up to 200-300 m) with their outstretched pectoral fins. These function as wings and are held rigid, without any flapping movements. When swimming the pectorals are held flat against the body. Flying fishes are primarily inhabitants of the open sea, but are often seen close to the outer edge of coral reefs over deep water. They feed mostly on planktonic organisms. Their eggs have sticky filaments that attach to floating and benthic weeds. The family includes eight genera and at least 50 species, many of which are found in our area; we include only one representative.

GARFISHES OR HALFBEAKS
FAMILY HEMIRAMPHIDAE

The garfishes, also known as halfbeaks, are elongate slender fishes that characteristically have the lower jaw extended into a long beak (except in a few species); the upper jaw is short and triangular in shape. There are no spines in the fins; the dorsal and anal fins are posteriorly located with their bases about opposite one another; the pelvic fins are abdominal in position; the pectoral fins are high on the sides and of variable length; the caudal fin is usually forked or emarginate. Most species live near the surface, frequently occurring in schools. There are also a number of estuarine and freshwater species. They sometimes leap from the water and skitter across the surface. Garfishes exhibit diverse feeding habits, some are herbivores, others are omnivores or carnivores, feeding on crustaceans and small fishes. Although bony, the flesh of garfishes is considered good eating in some regions.

SUTTON'S FLYINGFISH
Cypselurus suttoni (Whitley & Colefax, 1938)

Dorsal rays 12-13, the fin very high; anal rays 10-13; pectoral rays 13-14, the longest extending to or beyond rear base of dorsal fin; predorsal scales 40-41; longitudinal scale series 58-59; anal fin origin below base of fifth dorsal ray; origin of pelvic fins midway between posterior edge of head and origin of lower lobe of caudal fin; deep blue on back, shading to silvery white on side and ventrally; a large black spot on middle and outer part of dorsal fin; pectoral fins with brownish grey membranes and small dark spots, the posterior margin clear. Common in central and western Oceania; illustrated fish from Osprey Reef, Coral Sea. Attains at least 30 cm.

BARRED GARFISH
Hemiramphus far (Forsskål, 1775)

Dorsal rays 13-15; anal rays 11-13; pectoral rays 11-12; predorsal scales 36-41; lower jaw 2.6-4.3 in the standard length; pectoral fins 5.3-7.1 in standard length; lower lobe of caudal fin longer than upper lobe; about four blackish spots on upper sides (4-6 dark vertical bars on juveniles under about 10 cm), otherwise bluish on back and silvery on sides. East Africa and Red Sea to Samoa. Attains 35 cm.

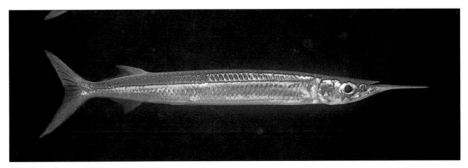

DUSSUMIER'S GARFISH
Hyporhamphus dussumieri (Valenciennes, 1846)

Dorsal rays 15-17; anal rays 15-17; pectoral rays 11 or 12; predorsal scales 34-37; lower jaw 4.5-5.2 in standard length; lower lobe of caudal fin slightly longer than upper lobe; olive to bluish on back, silvery on sides. Seychelles to the Tuamotu Archipelago. Reported to 28 cm.

LONGTOMS OR NEEDLE-FISHES
FAMILY BELONIDAE

The longtoms (also known as needlefishes in some regions) have very slender bodies and extremely elongate jaws with numerous needle-like teeth. The fins lack spines; the dorsal and anal fins are posterior in position, and the pelvics occur toward the end of the abdomen and contain six rays. The lateral line is low on the body, and the scales are small. These fishes live at the surface and are protectively coloured for this mode of life - green or blue on the back and silvery white on the sides and ventrally. When frightened (for example, by a light at night) they may leap from the water and skip at the surface. They have been known to injure people who lie in their path at this time, and fatalities have resulted. Longtoms feed mainly on small pelagic fishes. Their eggs are large and have adhesive filaments that attach to floating objects. The bones of some species are green, and the flesh may be greenish, but this does not affect the edibility of these fishes.

FLAT-TAILED LONGTOM
Platybelone argalus platyura (Bennett, 1832)

Dorsal rays 13-15; anal rays 17-19; pectoral rays 10 or 11; predorsal scales 95-130; gill rakers 4 or 5 + 6 or 7; caudal fin base greatly flattened, its width greater than the depth; greenish to bluish on back, silvery on sides. Circumtropical; the subspecies *P. argalus argalus* occurs in the tropical Atlantic. Grows to about 45 cm. Often occurs in small aggregations.

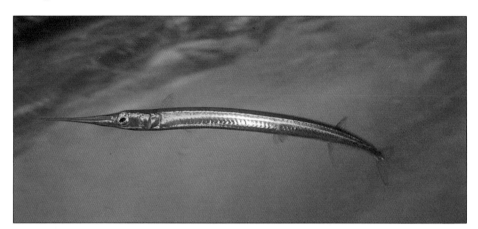

SLENDER LONGTOM
Strongylura leiura (Bleeker, 1851)

Dorsal rays 18-20; anal rays 22-26; pectoral rays 11 or 12; predorsal scales 121-152; gill rakers absent; caudal fin subtruncate; a black bar on cheek between opercle and preopercle; top of head and back greenish; a silver stripe along sides becoming wider posteriorly; whitish on ventral surface. East Africa to Fiji. Reaches 90 cm. Parin (1967) regards the Australian population as a separate subspecies, *S. leiura ferox* (Günther).

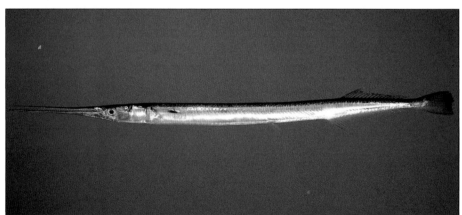

CROCODILE LONGTOM
Tylosurus crocodilus crocodilus (Peron & Lesueur, 1821)

Dorsal rays 21-24; anal rays 19-22; pectoral rays 14 or 15; predorsal scales 271-340; lower lobe of caudal fin much longer than upper lobe; prominent raised black keel on base of caudal fin; dark bluish green above, silvery below; a dark blue stripe on middle of sides. Tropical waters of Atlantic and Indo-Pacific; another subspecies, *T. crocodilus fodiator*, occurs in the tropical eastern Pacific. To 130 cm. Known as houndfish in American waters.

HARDYHEADS OR SILVERSIDES
FAMILY ATHERINIDAE

Hardyheads are small schooling fishes, usually found inshore and sometimes over reefs. There are also a number of freshwater and estuarine species. They have two dorsal fins, the first consisting of a few slender spines; the pelvic fins, which have one spine and five rays, are usually abdominal in position; there is no lateral line. Many atherinid fishes have a broad silvery stripe on the side and for this reason are called silversides in some regions. They are heavily preyed upon by other fishes such as trevallies. Although usually classified in the older literature with mullets and barracudas, recent studies suggest that hardyheads are allied to the halfbeaks (Hemiramphidae).

ROBUST HARDYHEAD
Atherinomorus lacunosus (Bloch & Schneider, 1801)

Dorsal rays IV-VII - I,8-11; anal rays I,12-16; pectoral rays 15-19; body robust, the depth 4.1-5.6 in standard length; eye large 2.4-3.1 in head length; origin of first dorsal fin posterior to middle of standard length; caudal fin forked; greenish grey on back, the scale edges dusky; a silvery stripe on the side, its upper edge with an iridescent blue line. Indo-Pacific; an inshore schooling species which feeds on zooplankton. Attains 13 cm. Often classified in the genus *Pranesus*. *Atherina pinguis* Lacepède and *A. forskalii* Rüppell are synonyms.

BARNES' HARDYHEAD
Hypoatherina barnesi Schultz, 1953

Dorsal rays V to VII-I,8-11; anal rays I,12-14; pectoral rays 13-16; midlateral scales 40-43; transverse scales 5; predorsal scales 16-19; first dorsal fin above middle of body; second dorsal fin originates behind beginning of anal fin; body depth 5.9-7.8 in standard length; olive on back, broad silvery stripe on sides. Western Pacific to Maldives. Attains 7 cm.

PINEAPPLEFISHES OR PINECONEFISHES
FAMILY MONOCENTRIDAE

These unusual fishes have the body covered with enlarged solid scales that form a rough armour; there are two separate dorsal fins, the first composed of V to VII strong spines; the pelvic fin has a strong spine on its anterior margin that can be locked erect; there are no anal fin spines. They have a light-producing organ located on the side or near the tip of the lower jaw. The light is actually produced by luminescent bacteria and the organ appears as an orange spot in daylight or a blue-green one at night. The family is confined to the Indo-Pacific region and consists of two genera, each with a single species.

KNIGHTFISH
Cleidopus gloriamaris De Vis, 1882

Dorsal rays V-VII,12; anal rays 11-12; pectoral rays 14-15; pelvic rays I,3-4; lateral-line scales 14-15; lower gill rakers 12; body depth 1.6-1.8 in standard length; upper jaw reaches level of rear edge of eye; head bones spiny and pitted; scales of body modified as armour of bony scutes; pale yellow to whitish with conspicuous black outlines on scales forming a network pattern; a pale luminescent organ on side of lower jaw. East and west coasts of Australia in rocky, occasionally coral-reef, habitats. Reaches 22 cm.

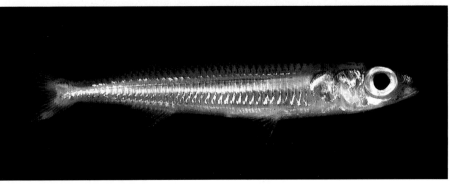

SQUIRRELFISHES AND SOLDIERFISHES
FAMILY HOLOCENTRIDAE

The fishes of this family are found on coral reefs or rocky bottom. They are very spiny, have large eyes, and most are red. All have I,7 pelvic fin rays, XI or XII dorsal spines, and IV anal spines. The mouth is moderately large, but the teeth are small. The caudal fin is forked. As their large eyes might suggest, these fishes are nocturnal; they tend to hide in caves or beneath ledges by day, coming out at night to forage for food. They feed mainly on crustaceans, the soldierfishes of the genus *Myripristis* on the larger elements of the plankton, such as crab larvae, and the squirrelfishes of the genera *Neoniphon* and *Sargocentron* mainly on benthic crabs and shrimps. In the earlier literature the fishes of the genus *Sargocentron* were usually classified in the genus *Holocentrus* (now restricted to the Atlantic) and later in *Adioryx* (a synonym), and species of *Neoniphon* in *Holocentrus* or *Flammeo* (a synonym). The squirrelfishes have a large spine at the corner of the preopercle which is lacking in the soldierfishes. This spine is venomous, and wounds from it may be very painful (though not as serious as those from scorpionfishes). The larger species of the family are good food fishes. Holocentrid fishes are classified in the order Beryciformes, most species of which occur in deep water.

Tailspot Squirrelfish
(*Sargocentron caudimaculatum*)

SHADOWFIN SOLDIERFISH
Myripristis adusta (Bleeker, 1853)

Dorsal rays X-I,14-16; anal rays IV,12-14; lateral-line scales 27-29; inner pectoral axil naked except for one (rarely two) moderate scales on lower half; pale salmon pink, the edges of the scales dorsally on body deep blue to black; median fins with a broad black outer border, broadest on the elevated parts of the dorsal and anal fins and ends of the caudal fin lobes. Indo-Pacific. The largest species of genus *Myripristis*; attains 32 cm.

BIGSCALE SOLDIERFISH
Myripristis berndti (Jordan & Evermann, 1903)

Dorsal rays X-I,13-15; anal rays IV,11-13; lateral-line scales 28-31; lower jaw of adults prominently projecting when mouth closed; vomerine teeth in a subtriangular patch; interorbital width 4.3-5.8 in head; lower half to three-fourths of inner pectoral axil with small scales; centres of scales silvery pink to pale yellowish, the edges red; black of opercular membrane extending below opercular spine; naked part of pectoral axil black; outer half of spinous dorsal fin yellow to orange-yellow, lower half and remaining fins red, the leading edges white (sometimes with a black submarginal streak). Indo-Pacific and tropical eastern Pacific. To 30 cm.

YELLOWFIN SOLDIERFISH
Myripristis chryseres (Jordan & Evermann, 1903)

Dorsal rays X-I,13-15; anal rays IV,11-13; lateral-line scales 32-38; front of lower jaw fitting into a deep notch in upper jaw when mouth closed; interorbital width 4.0-4.8 in head; no scales on inner pectoral axil; light red, the scale edges darker red; black of opercular membrane extending well below opercular spine; median and pelvic fins a mixture of yellow and red, usually with more yellow. Scattered records from Natal to Samoa and Hawaii; usually found at depths greater than 30 m. Reaches 25 cm.

DOUBLETOOTH SOLDIERFISH
Myripristis hexagona (Lacepède, 1802)

Dorsal rays X-I,13-15; anal rays IV,12-13; lateral-line scales 25-28; two pairs of tooth patches, one above the other, at front of lower jaw outside the gape (other *Myripristis* herein with a single pair); vomerine teeth in a broad V-shaped patch; interorbital width 4.1-5.1 in head; numerous small scales on inner pectoral axil; light red to yellowish, the scale edges red; black of opercular membrane extending to or nearly to level of upper pectoral base; fins red, the leading edges white without a submarginal black streak. East Africa to Samoa. Attains 20 cm.

EPAULETTE SOLDIERFISH
Myripristis kuntee Cuvier, 1831

Dorsal rays X-I,15-17; anal rays IV,14-16; lateral-line scales 37-44; no scales on inner pectoral axil; third anal spine shorter than fourth; red dorsally, shading to silvery pink below; a broad reddish brown bar from upper end of gill opening to pectoral-fin base; spinous dorsal fin translucent red basally, broadly yellow distally; remaining fins red, this colour brightest on elevated parts of soft dorsal and anal fins and the caudal fin; leading edges of fins narrowly white. Indo-Pacific. A small species, usually not exceeding 15 cm; largest, 19 cm.

BLOTCHEYE SOLDIERFISH
Myripristis murdjan (Forsskål, 1775)

Dorsal rays X-I,13-15; anal rays IV,11-13; lateral-line scales 27-32; lower jaw slightly projecting when mouth closed; vomerine teeth in a subtriangular patch; interorbital width 3.7-4.4 in head; numerous small scales on inner pectoral axil; third and fourth anal spines subequal; silvery pink, the scale edges red; black of opercular membrane extending a short distance below opercular spine; base of spinous dorsal fin whitish, the outer part broadly red; remaining fins red, this colour most dense on elevated part of soft dorsal and anal fins and a broad submarginal band in each caudal fin lobe; leading edges of fins white. Indo-Pacific. To 27 cm.

SCARLET SOLDIERFISH
Myripristis pralinia Cuvier, 1829

Dorsal rays X-I,14-16; anal rays IV,13-15; lateral-line scales 27-32; interorbital width 3.7-4.4 in head; no scales on inner pectoral axil; fourth anal spine slightly longer than third; red, the scale centres ventrally on body silvery pink; black of opercular membrane usually not extending below opercular spine; fins red except pelvics which are pale pink; tips of first few dorsal spines and leading edges of remaining median fins white. Society Islands to islands of western Indian Ocean. Maximum length, 20 cm.

LATTICE SOLDIERFISH
Myripristis violacea Bleeker, 1851

Dorsal rays X-I,14-16; anal rays IV,12-14; lateral-line scales 27-29; small scales usually present on inner pectoral axil; third and fourth anal spines subequal or fourth slightly longer; bluish silver, the scale edges dorsally on body broadly dark purplish to dark brown; scales on nape and interorbital almost completely dark; scale edges on side and ventrally on body brownish red to red; median fins light red, becoming red distally, the leading edges white; pelvic fins pale pink to white. Indo-Pacific; usually found on shallow protected reefs. Attains 20 cm.

WHITETIP SOLDIERFISH
Myripristis vittata Valenciennes, 1831

Dorsal rays X-I,13-15; anal rays IV,11-12; lateral-line scales 35-40; interorbital space broad, 3.3-4.0 in head; no scales on inner pectoral axil; third anal spine longer than fourth; reddish orange; no black on opercular membrane or pectoral axil; tips of dorsal spines and leading edges of fins white; a deep orange-red spot at pectoral-fin base. An insular species from western Indian Ocean to the islands of Oceania; usually seen in outer reef areas at depths greater than 15 m. To 20 cm.

YELLOWSTRIPED SQUIRRELFISH
Neoniphon aurolineatus (Liénard, 1839)

Dorsal rays XI,12-14; anal rays IV,8-9 (usually 9); pectoral rays 13-15; lateral-line scales 42-47; 3 1/2 rows of scales above lateral line to base of middle dorsal spines; lower jaw strongly projecting; last dorsal spine closer to first dorsal soft ray than penultimate spine (true of other *Neoniphon*); last dorsal spine shortest; silvery pink with yellow stripes on body. Indo-Pacific, from scattered insular localities. Generally found at depths greater than 40 m. Reaches 22 cm. *Flammeo scythrops* Jordan & Evermann is a synonym.

BLACKFIN SQUIRRELFISH
Neoniphon opercularis (Valenciennes, 1831)

Dorsal rays XI,12-14; anal rays IV,8-9 (usually 9); pectoral rays 13-15; lateral-line scales 36-41; 2 1/2 rows of scales above lateral line to base of middle dorsal spines; lower jaw strongly projecting; penultimate dorsal spine shortest; silvery with a dark red or black spot on each scale; spinous dorsal fin black except base and tips of membranes which are white. Indo-Pacific. Reaches about 35 cm.

SPOTFIN SQUIRRELFISH
Neoniphon sammara (Forsskål, 1775)

Dorsal rays XI,11-13; anal rays IV,8; pectoral rays 13-15; lateral-line scales 38-43; 2 1/2 rows of scales above lateral line to base of middle dorsal spines; lower jaw strongly projecting; penultimate dorsal spine shortest; pinkish silvery dorsally, silvery ventrally, with a dark red to black spot on each scale and a reddish stripe along lateral line; a large reddish black spot on first three dorsal fin membranes. Indo-Pacific; a common species of shallow, protected reefs. To 30 cm.

ROUGH SCALE SOLDIERFISH
Plectrypops lima (Valenciennes, 1831)

Dorsal rays XII,14-16; anal rays IV,10-12; lateral-line scales 39-42; scales above lateral line to base of middle dorsal spines 4 1/2; scales coarsely ctenoid; no pair of tooth patches at front of lower jaw outside gape; dorsal spines short, the longest about 3.0 in head length; uniform bright red. Indo-Pacific; hides in the deepest recesses of reefs by day and rarely ventures from caves at night. Maximum length, 16 cm. One other species of the genus, from the tropical western Atlantic.

TAILSPOT SQUIRRELFISH
Sargocentron caudimaculatum (Rüppell, 1838)

Dorsal rays XI,13-15; anal rays IV,8-9 (usually 9); pectoral rays 13-15; lateral-line scales 38-43; dorsal profile of head nearly straight; premaxillary groove not reaching or just reaching a vertical at front edge of eye; edge of nasal fossa often with one or more spinules; preopercular spine about equal to eye diameter; body red without stripes, the edges of the scales narrowly silver; a prominent silvery white spot behind rear base of dorsal fin (may disappear with death); some fish with posterior third of body silvery white. Indo-Pacific. Attains 21 cm.

THREESPOT SQUIRRELFISH
Sargocentron cornutum (Bleeker, 1853)

Dorsal rays XI,13; anal rays IV,9; pectoral rays 13; lateral-line scales 34-37; nasal fossa with three to five spinules on posterior edge and 0-1 on anterior (may be fewer on small fish); preopercular spine three-fourths to seven-eighths eye diameter; body with alternating broad deep red and narrow silvery white stripes, the red stripes converging posteriorly; a dark brown to black spot at base of caudal, soft dorsal and anal fins (may be small at anal base); spinous portion of dorsal fin blackish red with white triangular membrane tips and a vertically elongate white spot on each membrane except the first two and last. Indonesia, Philippines, Solomon Islands, and Great Barrier Reef. Largest specimen, 17.3 cm.

CROWN SQUIRRELFISH
Sargocentron diadema (Lacepède, 1801)

Dorsal rays XI,12-14; anal rays IV,8-10; pectoral rays 13-15; lateral-line scales 46-50; nasal fossa small, without spinules; preopercular spine small, 2.0-3.0 in eye; body with alternating broad red and narrow silvery white stripes; spinous dorsal fin deep red to black, the membrane tips white, with a pale band (often disjunct) in lower part of fin. Indo-Pacific; a common reef fish generally found in the depth range of 2-30 m. Recorded to 17 cm, but rarely exceeds 13 cm.

SAMURAI SQUIRRELFISH
Sargocentron ittodai (Jordan & Fowler, 1903)

Dorsal rays XI,13-14 (usually 13); anal rays IV,8-10; pectoral rays 14-16; lateral-line scales 43-47; preopercular spine about one-third eye diameter; longest dorsal spine 1.35-1.5 in head; body with alternating red and silvery white stripes of about equal width; spinous dorsal fin bright red with white tips, a series of white spots, one per membrane, in lower part of fin, and some blackish pigment on first two membranes. Known from scattered localities in the Indo-Pacific; depth range, 5-70 m. To 17 cm.

BLACKSPOT SQUIRRELFISH
Sargocentron melanospilos (Bleeker, 1858)

Dorsal rays XI,12-14; anal rays IV,9-10 (usually 9); pectoral rays 14; lateral-line scales 33-36; front of upper lip thickened and slightly protruding; nasal fossa with one to four spinules; body with alternating broad orange-red and narrow silvery white (brassy dorsally) stripes; a prominent black spot at base of soft dorsal, anal, and caudal fins; axil of pectoral fins black; spinous portion of dorsal fin red with white tips and a row of squarish white spots, one per membrane, in middle of fin. East Africa to Samoa. Reported to 25 cm. Often misidentified as *S. cornutum*.

SMALLMOUTH SQUIRRELFISH
Sargocentron microstoma (Günther, 1859)

Dorsal rays XI,12-14; anal rays IV,9-10 (usually 9); pectoral rays 14-15 (usually 15); lateral-line scales 48-55; preopercular spine small, 2.5-3.0 in eye diameter; nasal fossa small, without spinules; third anal spine very long, 1.1-1.2 in head length; body alternately striped with red and silvery white, the white stripes of unequal width (the one along lateral line narrow); spinous dorsal fin whitish with a broad irregular red submarginal zone. Islands of the western Indian Ocean to islands of Oceania except Hawaii; a shallow-water species. Largest reported, 19.3 cm.

PEPPERED SQUIRRELFISH
Sargocentron punctatissimum (Cuvier, 1829)

Dorsal rays XI,12-13 (usually 13); anal rays IV,9; pectoral rays 14-16; lateral-line scales 41-47; interorbital width greater than snout length; nasal fossa without spinules; preopercular spine about half eye diameter; body silvery red with bluish iridescence dorsally, usually with narrow red stripes, the scales finely dotted with blackish; outer part of spinous dorsal fin broadly red (except for white tips on anterior spines) with a white spot below on each membrane. Indo-Pacific; a common species on exposed rocky shores or reef fronts; found in shallower water than any other squirrelfish. *Holocentrum lacteoguttatum* Cuvier is a synonym.

REDCOAT
Sargocentron rubrum (Forsskål, 1775)

Dorsal rays XI,12-14; anal rays IV,8-10; pectoral rays 13-15; lateral-line scales 34-38; first suborbital bone with a short lateral spine; nasal fossa usually without spinules; preopercular spine about two-thirds eye diameter (nearly as long as eye on large fish); body with alternating brownish red and silvery white stripes of about equal width, the third and fourth and the fifth and sixth red stripes converging posteriorly; spinous dorsal fin red with white-tipped spines and a quadrangular whitish blotch on each membrane except the first. Red Sea and East Africa to the western Pacific, but absent from oceanic islands. Largest, 27 cm.

SABRE SQUIRRELFISH
Sargocentron spiniferum (Forsskål, 1775)

Dorsal rays XI,14-16; anal rays IV,9-10 (usually 10); pectoral rays 14-16; lateral-line scales 41-46; scale rows above lateral line to base of middle dorsal spines 3 1/2 (2 1/2 on other species of the genus herein); body deep, the depth 2.4-2.6 in standard length; dorsal profile of head nearly straight; lower jaw projecting when mouth closed; preopercular spine of adults longer than eye diameter; spinous dorsal membranes not incised; body red, the edges of the scales silvery white; a large vertically elongate crimson spot on head behind eye; spinous portion of dorsal fin solid deep red. Indo-Pacific. The largest of the squirrelfishes; attains 45 cm.

TAHITIAN SQUIRRELFISH
Sargocentron tiere (Cuvier, 1829)

Dorsal rays XI,13-15; anal rays IV,9; pectoral rays 13-15; lateral-line scales 46-52; body depth 2.7-3.0 in standard length; preopercular spine of adults nearly as long as eye diameter; dorsal spines short, the longest 2.6-3.4 in head; body red with silvery red stripes overlaid with blue iridescence (more evident ventrally); spinous portion of dorsal fin red with white-tipped spines and a white blotch in middle of each membrane (except first two where the spot is basal). Insular Indo-Pacific; more often seen on exposed than protected reefs; occurs at depths of 1 to at least 20 m. Reaches 33 cm.

PINK SQUIRRELFISH
Sargocentron tiereoides (Bleeker, 1853)

Dorsal rays XI,12-14; anal rays IV,9-10 (usually 9); pectoral rays 13-14 (usually 14); lateral-line scales 39-44; premaxillary groove reaching posterior to a vertical at front of eye; nasal fossa without spinules; preopercular spine about two-thirds eye diameter; body with alternating stripes of silvery pink and red of about equal width; spinous dorsal fin light red with white-tipped membranes and a deep red submarginal band. Indo-Pacific. To 16 cm.

VIOLET SQUIRRELFISH
Sargocentron violaceum (Bleeker, 1853)

Dorsal rays XI,13-14 (usually 14); anal rays IV,9; pectoral rays 13-14 (usually 14); lateral-line scales 33-37; body deep, the depth 2.3-2.6 in standard length; anterior and posterior margins of nasal fossa with one to three spinules; preopercular spine about equal to eye diameter; membranes of spinous dorsal fin not incised; body brownish to purplish red, each scale with a vertical silvery white line; head primarily red; upper part of opercular membrane blackish; spinous dorsal fin light red with white membrane tips and a narrow scarlet submarginal band. Indo-Pacific. Attains 25 cm.

TRUMPETFISHES
FAMILY AULOSTOMIDAE

See discussion of the single Indo-Pacific species of the family below.

TRUMPETFISH
Aulostomus chinensis (Linnaeus, 1758)

Dorsal rays VII-XII + 24-27; anal rays 26-29; pectoral rays 17; pelvic rays 6; generally brown or greenish with diffuse pale stripes and connecting bars on side, also white spots often pronounced on posterior part of body and on tail base; a small black spot near base of uppermost caudal fin rays; colour is variable, and sometimes a bright yellow variety is encountered.

Indo-Pacific, and eastern Pacific; common on coral reefs. Trumpetfishes are elongate with a tubular snout and minute teeth like members of the family Fistulariidae (see below), but their body and snout are laterally compressed, and they lack the elongate median tail filament found in fistulariids. In addition, they have a chin barbel and a series of short dorsal spines along the back. This slow-swimming predator relies partly on stealth and camouflage to sneak up on unsuspecting victims, usually small fishes, which it sucks into its mouth in pipette fashion. It often darts down on its prey from a vertical position. It sometimes hides by closely swimming beside larger fishes such as parrotfishes and goatfishes. It can quickly change its colour pattern to blend in with the surroundings. Also known as painted flutemouth in Australia. Grows to 80 cm.

Aulostomus chinensis Yellow phase ▲ Brown phase ▼

FLUTEMOUTHS
FAMILY FISTULARIIDAE

These extremely elongate fishes have a depressed body, a very long tubular snout with a short oblique mouth at the end, minute teeth, no fin spines, a single dorsal fin posteriorly on the body directly over the anal fin, and a forked caudal fin with a long median filament. They feed by sucking in small invertebrates and fishes in pipette fashion. Four species are known, one of which is common on shallow reefs in our area. Also known as cornetfishes in some regions.

SMOOTH FLUTEMOUTH
Fistularia commersonii Rüppell, 1838

Dorsal rays 15-17; anal rays 14-16; pectoral rays usually 15; greenish dorsally, shading to silvery white below, with two blue stripes or rows of blue spots on back; a free-swimming fish often seen over reefs and seagrass beds; it can quickly assume a dark-barred pattern when swimming close to the bottom. Circumtropical in distribution. Attains 150 cm. Sometimes misidentified as *F. petimba*, but this name applies to a deep-water species that possesses a row of narrow bony plates along the side of the body.

RAZORFISHES OR SHRIMPFISHES
FAMILY CENTRISCIDAE

These are small unusually shaped fishes that are related to the pipefishes and seahorses (family Syngnathidae). Their body is extremely thin or flattened, and nearly transparent. The body is encased in an integument of thin sutured plates. Adding to their bizarre appearance is the peculiar mode of swimming. They swim in small, synchronized groups, each fish in a vertical position with its snout pointing downwards. Two genera and four species occur in the Indo-Pacific. One is common on sections of the Great Barrier Reef.

RAZORFISH
Aeoliscus strigatus (Günther, 1860)

Dorsal rays III,9-10; anal rays 11-12; pectoral rays 11-12; pelvic rays 4; dorsal spine with a movable segment at its end; yellowish brown with a black stripe from snout through eye to base of caudal fin. Northern Indian Ocean and western Pacific; occurs in schools that frequently seek refuge among the spines of sea urchins (*Diadema*) or coral branches. Maximum size, 14 cm.

GHOST PIPEFISHES
FAMILY SOLENOSTOMIDAE

These are close relatives to pipefishes (Syngnathidae) which have their body similarly encased in segmented bony plates. The body is generally deeper than that of pipefishes and the pelvic fins are relatively large (absent in pipefishes). The elongate snout is used as a pipette to suck in the small invertebrates on which it feeds. These fishes are masters of camouflage. Their body shape and colouration blends in effectively with seaweeds and sessile invertebrate growths. Eggs are incubated by the female in a pouch that is formed by the enlarged pelvic fins.

GHOST PIPEFISH
Solenostomus cyanopterus Bleeker, 1852

Dorsal rays V + 18-20; anal rays 16-20; pectoral rays 24-27; pelvic rays 7; no skin flaps on head, body or fins; overall green to yellowish brown, sometimes with small black or white spots. Indo Pacific; usually encountered in weed beds or seagrass. Reaches 16 cm.

HARLEQUIN GHOST PIPEFISH
Solenostomus paradoxus (Pallas, 1870)

Dorsal rays V + 23; anal rays 22; pectoral rays 24; pelvic rays 7; numerous skin flaps on head, body and fins; colour variable from white or semi-transparent to black with intricate pattern of red, orange, or yellow lines and spots. Indo-West Pacific; sometimes found among branches of gorgonians or floating weed. To 12 cm.

Solenostomus paradoxus

Solenostomus cyanopterus

PIPEFISHES
FAMILY SYNGNATHIDAE

The pipefishes and their relatives the seahorses belong to the family Syngnathidae. They are characterised by a long, slender body that is composed of a series of ring-like, bony segments. They have a very small gill opening, no spines in the fins, no pelvic fins, a single dorsal fin, and a very small anal fin (dorsal, anal, and/or pectoral fins absent on a few species). Most species are seldom seen because of their habit of remaining in crevices, but members of the genus *Corythoichthys* are frequently encountered in the open. Perhaps the most unusual peculiarity displayed by this family is their habit of male egg incubation. The female deposits her eggs on the ventral surface of the male, usually in a pouch or on a specially vascularised surface. The "pregnant" male then carries these until hatching occurs.

SCULPTURED PIPEFISH
Choeroichthys sculptus (Günther, 1870)

Superior trunk and tail ridges continuous; inferior trunk ridge ends on anal ring; lateral trunk ridge continuous with inferior tail ridge; body rings 18-21; tail rings 21-25; dorsal rays 27-34; caudal fin present, but tiny; brown with several longitudinal rows of small white spots on side and larger white blotches on back; usually with dark stripe through eye and black spots on lower part of head. East Africa to Polynesia on shallow reefs. To 8.5 cm.

BROWN-BANDED PIPEFISH
Corythoichthys amplexus Dawson & Randall, 1975

Superior trunk and tail ridges discontinuous; lateral trunk ridge straight, ending near anal ring; inferior trunk and tail ridges continuous; body rings 14-16; tail rings 35-39; dorsal rays 23-30; caudal fin present; a series of broad brown bars encircling body with narrower white spaces between. Western Indian Ocean to Samoa, north to the Ryukyu Islands. Attains 9.5 cm.

BANDED PIPEFISH
Corythoichthys intestinalis (Ramsay, 1881)

Superior trunk and tail ridges discontinuous; lateral trunk ridge straight, ending near anal ring; inferior trunk and tail ridges continuous; body rings 15-17; tail rings 31-37; dorsal rays 26-32; caudal fin present; snout 2.0-2.1 in head length; overall whitish with diffuse brown bars on side and thin wavy brown to blackish stripes; black stripes usually present on head. Philippines to northern Australia, eastward to Samoa and Tonga. Reaches 16 cm.

SCHULTZ'S PIPEFISH
Corythoichthys schultzi Herald, 1953

Superior trunk and tail ridges discontinuous; lateral trunk ridge straight, ending near anal ring; inferior trunk and tail ridges continuous; body rings 15-17; tail rings 32-39; dorsal rays 25-31; caudal fin present; snout long and slender, 1.7-1.8 in head length; overall whitish with diffuse brown bars on side overlaid with relatively broad brown to reddish stripes and/or ocellated spots. Red Sea to Society Islands; to depths of 30 m. Maximum size, 16 cm.

RINGED PIPEFISH
Doryrhamphus dactyliophorus (Bleeker, 1853)

Superior trunk and tail ridges discontinuous; inferior trunk ridge ending on anal ring; lateral trunk ridge continuous with inferior tail ridge; body rings 15-17; tail rings 18-22; dorsal rays 20-26; caudal fin present; easily recognized by the distinct black to reddish cross bars and very elongate snout (1.4-1.8 in head length). East Africa and Red Sea to Samoa; inhabits caves and crevices. Reaches 18 cm. Often placed in the genus *Dunckerocampus*.

BLUESTRIPE PIPEFISH
Doryrhamphus excisus excisus Kaup, 1856

Superior trunk and tail ridges discontinuous; inferior trunk ridge ending on anal ring; lateral trunk ridge continuous with inferior tail ridge; body rings 17-19; tail rings 13-17; dorsal rays 21-29; caudal fin present; distinguished by bluish mid-lateral stripe on orange to reddish background and small fan-like tail. Indo-Pacific; inhabits reef crevices. To 7 cm. *D. melanopleura* (Bleeker) is a synonym. *D. excisus abbreviatus* is the Red Sea subspecies.

JANSS'S PIPEFISH
Doryrhamphus janssi (Herald & Randall, 1972)

Superior trunk and tail ridges discontinuous; inferior trunk ridge ending on anal ring; lateral trunk ridge continuous with inferior tail ridge; body rings 16; tail rings 21-23; dorsal rays 22-25; caudal fin present; distinguished by orange middle section of body with blue head and tail sections, caudal fin largely black with white centre. Northern Australia and Solomon Islands, north to Philippines and South China Sea; inhabits reef crevices. Attains 13 cm.

BROCK'S PIPEFISH
Halicampus brocki (Herald, 1953)

Superior trunk and tail ridges discontinuous; inferior trunk ridge ending at anal ring; lateral trunk ridge continuous with inferior tail ridge; body rings 14 + 33-37; dorsal rays 21-23; caudal fin present; head with filamentous dermal appendages, and dermal flaps often present along back; pale brown to tan; snout and suborbital region often with three brown bars; body usually with 10-11 diffuse pale bars. Western Pacific from northern Australia to the Ryukyu Islands and eastward to the Marshall and Mariana Islands. To 11.5 cm.

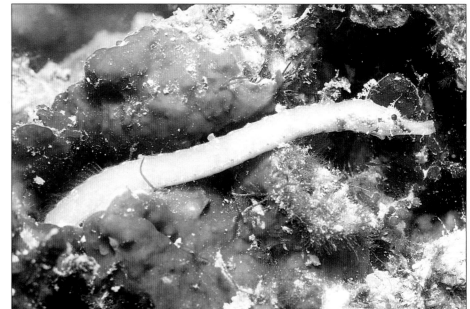

ORNATE PIPEFISH
Halicampus macrorhynchus Bamber, 1915

Superior trunk and tail ridges discontinuous; inferior trunk ridge ending at anal ring; lateral trunk ridge continuous with inferior tail ridge; body rings 14 or 15 + 25-27; dorsal rays 18 or 19; caudal fin present; dermal flaps well developed on head and body; colour variable, brown to pinkish red with whitish mottling or barring. Red Sea to northern Australia and Melanesia. Reaches 16 cm.

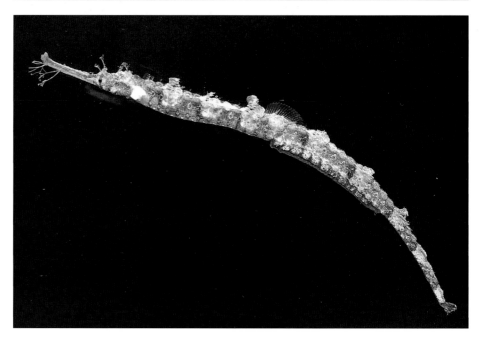

GLITTERING PIPEFISH
Halicampus nitidus (Günther, 1873)

Superior trunk and tail ridges discontinuous; inferior trunk ridge ending at anal ring; lateral trunk ridge continuous with inferior tail ridge; body rings 13-15 + 30-32; dorsal rays 18-22 (usually 20 or 21); caudal fin tiny; dermal flaps less developed than previous two species, usually unbranched; distinguished by its striking zebra-like pattern of white and dark brown bars. Northern Australia to the Ryukyu Islands and eastward to Fiji. To 7.5 cm.

SPOTTED SEAHORSE
Hippocampus kuda Bleeker, 1852

Body rings 11 +34-37; dorsal rays 15-18; coronet (crown-like structure on top of head) low, usually divided into two sections; caudal fin absent; colour variable depending on habitat, often brown or blackish. East Africa and Red Sea to the Hawaiian and Society islands; more common on coastal reefs and in estuaries. Attains 30 cm.

SHORTNOSE PIPEFISH
Micrognathus andersonii (Bleeker, 1858)

Superior trunk and tail ridges discontinuous, inferior trunk ridge ending on anal ring; lateral trunk ridge continuous with inferior tail ridge; body rings 15-17 + 27-32; dorsal rays 17-24; caudal fin present; colour brown, usually with white saddles across the back. East Africa and Red Sea to Samoa, north to Japan. To 8.5 cm.

SHORT-TAILED PIPEFISH
Trachyrhamphus bicoarctatus (Bleeker, 1857)

Superior trunk and tail ridges discontinuous; inferior trunk ridge ending at anal ring; lateral trunk ridge continuous with inferior tail ridge; body rings 21-24 + 55-63; dorsal rays 24-32; caudal fin long and rounded in juveniles, but vestigal or absent in adults; distinguished by long, narrow snout and slender, elongate body; overall light tan or brown to greenish with lighter cross bands. East Africa and Red Sea to New Caledonia, north to Japan; occurs on sand or rubble bottoms amongst sea grass. Reaches 39 cm.

FLYING GURNARDS
FAMILY DACTYLOPTERIDAE

These fishes are easily distinguished by the greatly enlarged, wing-like pectoral fins, and antenna-like isolated dorsal spine on top of the head. In addition, they have bony spikes and keels on the head and a long backward-directed spine arising from the lower corner of the cheek (preopercle). They can produce sounds by stridulation of the hyomandibular bone. Flying gurnards are usually encountered over sand or rubble bottoms. Slow locomotion is by "walking" with the pelvic fins. They are also capable of rapid bursts with the pectoral fins folded against the body. The pectoral fins are outstretched when the fish is alarmed. Known as searobins in Australia.

FLYING GURNARD
Dactyloptena orientalis (Cuvier, 1829)

Dorsal rays I - I - V - 9; anal rays 6; pectoral rays 32-35; pectoral fins wing-like with short filamentous extension of each ray beyond edge of fin; grey to light brown with large dark brown to blackish spots on back and upper sides; pectoral fins with numerous dark brown spots and wavy blue lines near margin. East Africa to Polynesia. Attains 38 cm.

SCORPIONFISHES
FAMILY SCORPAENIDAE

Scorpionfishes obtain their name from the venomous fin spines possessed by many of the species. Other characteristics include a bony ridge (suborbital stay) across the cheek; the head is relatively large and spiny, the cheek margin has 3-5 spines, there are one or two spines on the opercle, and other spines are scattered on the head. There is a single dorsal fin that is usually strongly notched at the rear of the spinous part and consists of VII-XVIII spines and 4-14 soft rays; the anal fin has II-IV spines and 5-14 soft rays. Scorpionfishes are bottom-living predators that occur in a variety of depths from shallow tide pools to the oceanic abyss. Most reef species are secretive, dwelling in caves and crevices. The spectacular firefishes (*Pterois*) and lionfishes (*Dendrochirus*) are often photographed by divers. They remain mostly stationary during daylight, but are nocturnally active. They feed mostly on crustaceans, but also consume fishes (including conspecific juveniles). Scorpaenids often exhibit variegated colour patterns that blend well with their surroundings, thus enabling them to remain undetected by their prey. The dorsal, anal, and pelvic spines are all venomous. Poison is produced by glandular tissue in longitudinal grooves on each side of the spine or (in stonefishes) a large oblong gland protruding from the side of the spine that is connected to the spine tip by a venom duct. Wounds from the spines vary from bee-sting intensity to unbelievable agony in *Synanceia* (stonefishes) and *Pterois*. Immersion of the injured limb in very hot water helps alleviate the pain, but treatment by a physician may be required. Scorpionfishes are found in all temperate and tropical seas and are commercially important in some areas. Most of the estimated 350 species and 70 genera occur in the Indo-Pacific; approximately 80 species are found in Australia.

Red Firefish *Pterois volitans*

COCKATOO WASPFISH
Ablabys taenianotus (Cuvier, 1829)

Dorsal rays XVII,7 or 8; anal rays III,5; pectoral rays 11 or 12; vertical scale rows about 90; sail-like dorsal fin; red-brown with white stripe down front of head. Andaman Sea to Fiji, north to Japan; a strongly compressed fish sometimes seen rocking back and forth on the bottom in response to surge; they are easily caught with a small hand net. To 10 cm.

DWARF LIONFISH
Dendrochirus brachypterus (Cuvier, 1829)

Dorsal rays XIII,9 or 10; anal rays III,5; pectoral rays 17 or 18; tentacles usually present above eye; lacks filaments on pectoral rays; dusky mottled brown to reddish with darker bars on body and pronounced banding on pectoral fins. East Africa and Red Sea to Samoa and Tonga, north to Philippines. Reaches 15 cm.

ZEBRA LIONFISH
Dendrochirus zebra (Cuvier, 1829)

Dorsal rays XIII,10 or 11; anal rays III,6 or 7; pectoral rays 17; tentacle usually present above eye; similar to *Pterois antennata* (below), but lacks filamentous rays on pectoral fin; head and body with red-brown bars alternating with narrower pink to whitish bars; most fins prominently striped or spotted; a dark brown or blackish blotch on lower edge of operculum. East Africa and Red Sea to Samoa. Attains 18 cm.

CALEDONIAN STINGER
Inimicus caledonicus (Sauvage, 1878)

Dorsal rays XVII,8 or 9 (usually 8); anal rays II,11 or 12 (usually 12); pectoral rays 12, lowermost 2 are free from main part of fin; overall brown, sometimes with pale spots or mottling; light and dark bars on inside of pectoral fin. Andaman Sea to Australia and New Caledonia; seldom noticed due to its efficient camouflage. To 25 cm.

MOZAMBIQUE SCORPIONFISH
Parascorpaena mossambica (Peters, 1855)

Dorsal rays XII,9; anal rays III,5; pectoral rays 14-16; rear spine of preorbital series strongly hooked forward; tentacle above eye well developed; overall brownish with strong mottling. East Africa to Society Islands. To 10 cm.

RAGGED-FINNED FIREFISH
Pterois antennata (Bloch, 1787)

Dorsal rays XII,11 or 12; anal rays III,6; pectoral rays 16 or 17; tips of pectoral rays long and filamentous; cross-banded supraorbital tentacle usually present; similar to *Dendrochirus zebra* (see above) with reddish brown bars and narrower white bars. East Africa to southeastern Polynesia. Reaches 20 cm.

RED FIREFISH
Pterois volitans (Linnaeus, 1758)

Dorsal rays XIII,11; anal rays III,6; pectoral rays 13-15; outer half of pectoral rays free with relatively broad membranes that are feather-like in appearance; supraorbital tentacle long, without cross bands; body with brown to blackish bars alternating with very narrow whitish to pale red interspaces; head with similar bands, those on posterior part diagonal and continuing onto breast. Western Australia and Malaysia to southeastern Polynesia, north to Japan; replaced by the similar *P. miles* in Indian Ocean. Attains 38 cm. Also known by the common name Turkeyfish.

WHITEFACE WASPFISH
Richardsonichthys leucogaster (Richardson, 1848)

Dorsal rays XIII,8; anal rays III,6; pectoral rays 15; mottled dark brown with a white stripe at front of head and small white spot on middle of side; similar markings to *Ablabys taenianotus* (above), but dorsal spine membranes deeply notched. India to northern Australia and Melanesia. To 8 cm.

WEEDY SCORPIONFISH
Rhinopias aphanes Eschmeyer, 1973

Dorsal rays XII,9; anal rays III,5; pectoral rays 16; distinctive head shape with upturned snout and oblique mouth; numerous branched tentacles on snout, lower jaw, above eye, and on median fins; also skin flaps present on side of body; overall velvety yellow to brown with an intricate maze pattern of black markings. Northeastern Australia, New Caledonia, New Guinea and north to Japan; rarely seen in our area. Reaches 24 cm.

LONGFINGERED SCORPIONFISH
Scorpaenodes albaiensis (Evermann & Seale, 1907)

Dorsal rays XIII or XIV,9 or 10; anal rays III,5; pectoral rays 16 or 17; vertical scale rows 40-43; middle pectoral rays much longer than those above; supraorbital tentacles present; overall brown to reddish with lighter mottlings; a brown spot at lower edge of operculum and another at base of pectoral fin. Western Pacific. Attains 8 cm.

GUAM SCORPIONFISH
Scorpaenodes guamensis (Quoy & Gaimard, 1824)

Dorsal rays XIII,8 or 9; anal rays III,4 or 5; pectoral rays 18 or 19; vertical scale rows about 42-44; overall brown with light and dark mottlings; fins with brown and white spots arranged in rows; a prominent black spot on upper edge of operculum (often surrounded by whitish area). East Africa and Red Sea to the Pitcairn Group. To 12 cm.

HAIRY SCORPIONFISH
Scorpaenodes hirsutus (Smith, 1957)

Dorsal rays XIII,8 or 9 (usually 8); anal rays III,5; pectoral rays 17-19; vertical scale rows about 30-32; 4 spines in a row below eye, and an extra spine below this row; tan or whitish mottling with irregular brown cross bars; dark brown spot on anterior part of pectoral fin and middle of pelvic fin; iris golden with red spoke-like markings. East Africa and Red Sea to Polynesia. Reaches 5 cm.

SHORTFINNED SCORPIONFISH
Scorpaenodes parvipinnis (Garrett, 1864)

Dorsal rays XIII,9; anal rays III,5; pectoral rays 17-19; vertical scale rows 48-50; at least 5 spines on ridge below eye, often 10 or more; small skin flaps on body; overall reddish to brown, often a large wedge-shaped whitish area covering rear part of head and anterior half of body. East Africa and Red Sea to Polynesia. Attains 13 cm.

PYGMY SCORPIONFISH
Scorpaenodes scaber (Ramsay & Ogilby, 1886)

Dorsal rays XIII,9; anal rays III,5; pectoral rays 17-19; vertical scale rows about 45; 3 or fewer spines in row under eye; few or no skin flaps on body; brilliant red to dark brown with whitish mottling or saddle-like patches; a conspicuous dark spot on lower part of operculum. Australia to Japan. To 8 cm.

BLOTCHFIN SCORPIONFISH
Scorpaenodes varipinnis Smith, 1957

Dorsal rays XIII,8; anal rays III,8; pectoral rays 17 or 18; vertical scale rows about 38-40; 3 or fewer spines in row under eye; few or no skin flaps on body; mottled red-orange to brown with irregular white to pink patches; sometimes a dark spot on rear of spinous dorsal fin and dark bar at base of pectoral fin. East Africa to Micronesia. Reaches 7 cm.

FALSE STONEFISH
Scorpaenopsis diabolus Cuvier, 1829

Dorsal rays XII,9; anal rays III,5; pectoral rays 17-19 (usually 18); vertical scale rows 43-48; palatine teeth absent; body humpbacked; usually mottled grey to whitish with irregular brown to reddish blotches; inner surface of pectoral fins orange-yellow with a black spot in upper part. When alarmed this fish moves its pectorals forward revealing the bright inner colour as a warning. East Africa and Red Sea to Polynesia. Attains 18 cm.

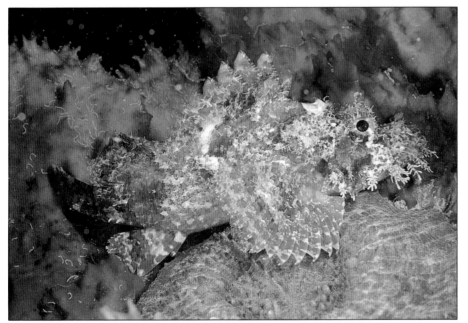

SMALLSCALE SCORPIONFISH
Scorpaenopsis oxycephala (Bleeker, 1849)

Dorsal rays XII,9; anal rays III,5; pectoral rays 19 or 20; vertical scale rows more than 60; palatine teeth absent; first dorsal spine short, second spine nearly as long as third spine and more than twice first spine; branched tentacles and skin flaps on head, body, and fins, particularly well developed on head; mottled red-brown to bright red. East Africa and Red Sea to central Pacific. To 30 cm.

RAGGY SCORPIONFISH
Scorpaenopsis venosa (Cuvier, 1829)

Dorsal rays XII,9; anal rays III,5; pectoral rays 16-18; vertical scale rows about 50; palatine teeth absent; first 3 dorsal spines increase in length evenly; branched tentacles and skin flaps on head, body, and fins; strongly mottled pattern of dark brown with whitish blotches; fins with dark spots arranged in rows. East Africa to central Pacific. Reaches 18 cm.

YELLOW-SPOTTED SCORPIONFISH
Sebastapistes cyanostigma (Bleeker, 1856)

Dorsal rays XII,9; anal rays III,5 or 6; pectoral rays 15 or 16; vertical scale rows about 42-45; palatine teeth present; preorbital bone usually with 5 spines; reddish or brown with large yellow blotches and numerous small white spots. Usually wedged in coral heads. East Africa and Red Sea to Samoa. Attains 7 cm. *Scorpaena albobrunnea* Günther is a synonym.

BARCHIN SCORPIONFISH
Sebastapistes strongia (Cuvier, 1829)

Dorsal rays XII,8 or 9; anal rays III,5; pectoral rays 14-17; vertical scale rows about 42-44; palatine teeth present; preorbital bone with 2 spines; a ridge present in front of lower opercular spine; supraorbital tentacles present; strongly mottled brown with dark bars on lower jaw and diffuse dark area usually at base of anteriormost dorsal spines. East Africa and Red Sea to Society Islands. To 6 cm. *Scorpaena tristis* Klunzinger is a synonym.

ESTUARINE STONEFISH
Synanceia horrida (Linnaeus, 1766)

Dorsal spines XIII,6 or 7; anal rays III (rarely II),5 or 6; pectoral rays 15-17 (usually 16); no overlapping scales on body; eyes somewhat elevated; a bony ridge present above and between eyes; prominent raised warts on sides; overall light to dark brown, sometimes mottled. India to Australia, north to China; fin spines extremely venomous. Reaches 30 cm.

REEF STONEFISH
Synanceia verrucosa Bloch & Schneider, 1801

Dorsal spines XIII,6 or 7; anal rays III,5 or 6; pectoral rays 18 or 19; no overlapping scales on body; eyes far apart with deep depression between them; colour highly variable according to surroundings, often mottled brown or grey with patches of red orange. East Africa and Red Sea to southeastern Polynesia; fin spines extremely venomous; occurs on rubble bottoms and coral reefs, often under rocks and ledges; also capable of burying in sand; extremely well-camouflaged. Attains 35 cm.

LEAF SCORPIONFISH
Taenianotus triacanthus Lacepède, 1802

Dorsal spines XII,10 or 11; anal rays III,5 or 6; pectoral rays 14 or 15; body extremely compressed laterally; scales modified into small spiny papillae; dorsal fin sail-like, the last soft rays partly attached to caudal fin; yellow, red, brown, or blackish. East Africa to the Galapagos; occasionally encountered on coral reefs, usually motionless on the bottom or rocking from side to side with the swell; they are poor swimmers and easily caught with a small hand net. Their skin is periodically shed. To 10 cm.

CROUCHERS OR ORBICULAR VELVETFISHES
FAMILY CARACANTHIDAE

Crouchers are small inconspicuous fishes that live among branches of *Acropora* and *Pocillopora* coral. They use their pectoral fins to tightly wedge themselves between the coral branches. Unless specifically searching for them, they are easily overlooked. The single genus and four known species are restricted to the Indo-Pacific. They are relatives of scorpionfishes (Scorpaenidae) and characterised by a nearly oval body that is covered with numerous papillae. The continuous dorsal fin contains VI to VIII spines and 11-14 soft rays; the anal fin has II spines and 11-13 soft rays. The pelvic fins are small with I spine and usually 2 soft rays. There are usually five or six spines on the edge of the cheek.

SPOTTED CROUCHER
Caracanthus maculatus (Gray, 1831)

Dorsal rays VI to VIII,12 or 13; anal rays II,11-14; pectoral rays 13 or 14; body covered with papillae, giving "furry" appearance; preorbital spine with two knobs; dorsal fin deeply notched; light grey with numerous, small red spots. East Indies and Australia to southeastern Polynesia, north to Japan. Up to 5 cm.

CORAL CROUCHER
Caracanthus unipinna (Gray, 1831)

Dorsal rays VII or VIII,12 or 13; anal rays II,11 or 12; pectoral rays 12 or 13; body covered with papillae, giving "furry" appearance; preorbital spine with one knob; dorsal fin not deeply notched; uniform grey-brown, darker on back. East Africa to Tuamotus, north to Japan. Attains 5 cm.

VELVETFISHES
FAMILY APLOACTINIDAE

Velvetfishes are closely related to scorpionfishes (Scorpaenidae), but instead of having small spinules on the head they possess knob-like projections. They also lack normal scales, these being replaced with microscopic bristles that give the skin the texture of fine sandpaper. Velvetfishes mainly inhabit rocky reefs and soft-bottom trawling grounds in the Indo-Pacific region. Most of the known species (40 estimated) occur in Australia; several are restricted to temperate or subtropical seas. Only one, *Neoaploactis tridorsalis* has been found on the Great Barrier Reef.

THREEFIN VELVETFISH
Neoaploactis tridorsalis Eschmeyer & Allen, 1978

Dorsal rays IV - VII - I,9 ; anal rays II,8; pectoral rays 12; pelvic rays I,3; caudal rays 16; dorsal fin begins above eye and is composed of three separate sections; scales highly modified, consisting of a spinous flange or shelf-like projection at right angles to the body, supported by an elongate diamond-shaped base embedded in the skin; head, body and fins strongly mottled with brown to dark grey, and white blotches. A rare species known only from Rottnest Island and Shark Bay in Western Australia and One Tree Is. in the Capricorn Group of the southern Great Barrier Reef. Grows to 5 cm.

FLATHEADS
FAMILY PLATYCEPHALIDAE

The flatheads have elongate, strongly depressed bodies. They are bottom-dwelling and occur primarily in the Indo-Pacific region (only two species outside this area). The group contains approximately 12 genera with 60 species. Although at least 10 species occur along the Queensland coast, only a few have been collected from the Great Barrier Reef and Coral Sea. As the common name suggests, these fishes

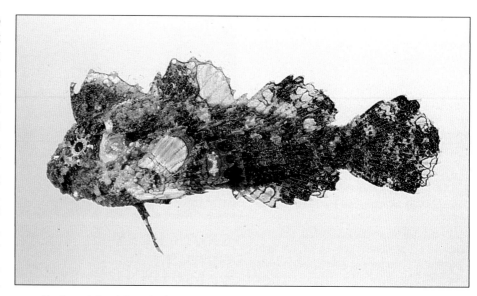

are distinguished by their flattened head shape. They are close relatives of scorpionfishes (Scorpaenidae); both groups are characterised by bony ridges and short spines on the head. Flatheads have two dorsal fins; the first with VIII-X spines usually has a slight connection to the second that contains 10-15 rays (as does the anal fin). These fishes are seldom noticed due to their protective colouration and habit of burying (often partially) themselves in the sand. They feed mainly on crabs and prawns, but fishes are also consumed.

Many of the temperate species are good-eating, but those from the Barrier Reef and Coral Sea are generally not used as table fishes.

DWARF FLATHEAD
Onigocia oligolepis (Regan, 1908)

Dorsal rays IX,11; anal rays 11; pectoral rays 18; lateral-line scales 34-36; overall white with conspicuous brown bars; head with brown and white mottling and brown bar through eye; fins white with brown mottling; occurs on fine sand bottoms, sometimes in caves. Indo-West Pacific. Grows to 10 cm.

SAND FLATHEAD
Thysanophrys arenicola Schultz, 1966

Dorsal rays IX,11-12; anal rays 12 (rarely 13); pectoral rays 19-22; lateral-line scales 51-54; interorbital space fits 1-2 times in eye diameter; overall tan or light brown, but strongly mottled and with numerous white flecks and spots on head and body; alternating brown and white bars on lips. East Africa to the Marshall Islands. Attains 23 cm.

LONGSNOUT FLATHEAD
Thysanophrys chiltonae Schultz, 1966

Dorsal rays IX,11; anal rays 12; pectoral rays 19-21; lateral-line scales 50-57; interorbital space fits 5-6 times in eye diameter; snout relatively long and spatulate; white with broad brown saddles across back and irregular brown mottling on head and side; fins with brown or white spotting. East Africa to Marquesas Islands. Maximum size, 23 cm.

FRINGELIP FLATHEAD
Thysanophrys otaitensis (Cuvier, 1829)

Dorsal rays IX,11-12; anal rays 12; pectoral rays 20-22; lateral-line scales 51-53; interorbital space 2-2.5 in eye diameter; papilla (skin flaps) on edges of lips; overall tan or light brown, but strongly mottled with brown and white; alternating brown and white bars on lips; fins mottled or spotted. East Africa to the Tuamotus. Reported to 25 cm. *I. papillolabium* Schultz is a synonym.

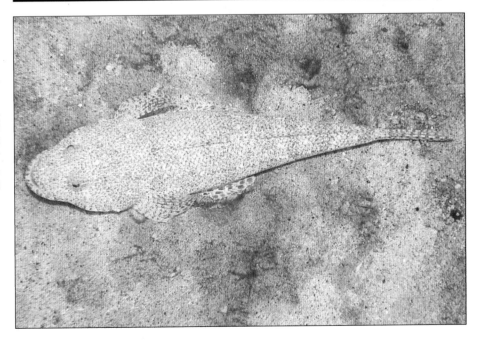

BARRAMUNDI
FAMILY CENTROPOMIDAE

The family Centropomidae is divisable into two subfamilies represented by the snooks of the Americas and the Barramundi and relatives of the Indo-Pacific region and African fresh waters. The Australian Barramundi is a popular table fish that inhabits mangrove estuaries and freshwater streams. It does not occur in clear offshore waters of the Great Barrier Reef and Coral Sea. However, a near look-alike, *Psammoperca waigiensis*, is found on inner reefs of the Great Barrier Reef system and also on coastal reefs.

SAND BASS
Psammoperca waigiensis (Cuvier, 1828)

Dorsal rays VII,I,12; anal rays III,8; pectoral rays 16-17; lateral-line scales 45-50; predorsal scales 23-24; depth of body 2.6-3.1 in standard length; colour varies from light silvery grey to dark brown; eye has glassy appearance with reddish glow; East Indies and northern Australia to China; inhabits rocky or coral reefs, frequently in weedy areas, usually in holes and crevices. Nocturnal. Reaches a length of 47 cm. Also known as Glasseye Perch.

ROCKCODS OR GROUPERS
FAMILY SERRANIDAE

The classification of fishes within the large family Serranidae has undergone major changes in recent years. Some groups which have at times been regarded as families, such as the Anthiidae (anthiases), Grammistidae (soapfishes), and Pseudogrammatidae (podges), as currently understood (Johnson, 1983, *Copeia*; Johnson and Baldwin, MS), are now regarded as serranids. In order to keep related genera in sequence, we present first the subfamily Anthiinae, followed by the tribes of the Epinephelinae: Epinephelini, Liopropomini, Diploprionini, Grammistini, and Pseudogrammatini. As a group, this family of fishes is difficult to define in terms of external characteristics. The majority of species have three spines on the opercle (main bone of the gill cover); the posterior border of the preopercle is almost always serrate or has small spines; the maxilla (posterior bone of the upper jaw) is fully exposed on the cheek when the mouth is closed; the mouth is large, and the jaws have more than one row of teeth (often a band of small teeth); most species have canine teeth at the front of the jaws; the scales are small and usually ctenoid (free edge with tiny spinules) or secondarily cycloid (smooth-edged); in addition to the count of lateral-line scales, the count of the diagonal scale rows in series from the upper end of the gill opening to the base of the caudal fin may be useful in distinguishing the rockcods of the genera *Cephalopholis* and *Epinephelus*; this count is called the longitudinal scale series; the pelvic fins of I,5 rays lie below or slightly in front of the base of the pectoral fins; there are nearly always III anal spines. The soapfishes are unique in possessing a skin toxin (grammistin) which makes them unpalatable to predators. All of the serranid fishes are carnivorous, feeding mainly on small fishes and crustaceans. The species of the anthiine genus *Pseudanthias* (often placed in *Anthias*, but the latter is now restricted to the Atlantic) feed on the small animals of the zooplankton a short distance above the bottom. Serranid fishes are hermaphroditic; the species of the two subfamilies included herein commence maturity as females and change sex to males later in life. The fishes of the genus *Pseudanthis* are haremic; that is, a single male (usually different in colour from the female) maintains a harem of females. If he dies, the ranking female soon changes sex to male and takes over the harem. A few rockcods of the genus *Epinephelus* are known to form large aggregations at spawning time. Some of the larger serranid fishes, particularly the coral trouts (*Plectropomus*) and the coronation trout (*Variola touti*) have been implicated in ciguatera fish poisoning.

Stocky Anthias (*Pseudanthias hypselosoma*)

SUBFAMILY ANTHIINAE

WAITE'S SPLITFIN
Luzonichthys waitei (Fowler, 1931)

Dorsal rays X-16, the two fins separate; anal rays III,7; pectoral rays 18-20; lateral-line scales 52-57; body slender, the depth 3.3-3.8 in standard length; papillae present on posterior margin of orbit; two opercular spines; fourth dorsal spine longest, but not prolonged; caudal fin deeply forked; pelvic fins short, 1.3-1.5 in head; yellow on back, pink to magenta on sides and ventrally; lobes of caudal fin deep magenta. Philippines, Indonesia, and Great Barrier Reef; usually found in aggregations on outer reef slopes in the depth range of about 10-50 m. Attains 7 cm. The identification of the Barrier Reef species as *waitei* is provisional; the genus *Luzonichthys* is in need of revision.

LONGFIN PERCHLET
Plectranthias longimanus (Weber,1913)

Dorsal rays X,13-15 (rarely 15), the fin divided to base between spinous and soft parts; anal rays III,6-7; pectoral rays 12-13 (usually 13, none branched or thickened); lateral line ending beneath soft portion of dorsal fin, the tubed scales 12-15; body depth 2.6-3.1 in standard length; two antrorse spines on lower margin of preopercle; posterior margin of preopercle and edge of subopercle and interopercle coarsely serrate; fourth dorsal spine longest; caudal fin slightly rounded; colour pattern mainly of large reddish brown blotches; three small white and five small dark brown spots on caudal peduncle. Western Pacific to East Africa; very cryptic; has been collected from the depth range of 6-73 m. To 3.5 cm.

DWARF PERCHLET
Plectranthias nanus Randall, 1980

Dorsal rays X,13-15 (rarely 13), the spinous and soft portions of fin almost completely divided; anal rays III,6-8 (nearly always 7); pectoral rays 14-16, none branched; lateral line ending beneath soft portion of dorsal fin, the tube-bearing scales 16-22; body depth 2.9-3.6 in standard length; lower margin of preopercle with two antrorse spines; posterior margin of preopercle and edge of subopercle coarsely serrate, the margin of interopercle smooth; fifth to seventh dorsal spines longest, subequal; caudal fin slightly rounded; colour nearly the same as *P. longimanus*. Islands of Oceania to Christmas and Cocos-Keeling Islands in the eastern Indian Ocean; no known continental shelf localities; taken in the depth range of 6-55 m; a secretive species. Maximum length, 4.8 cm.

REDBLOTCH PERCHLET
Plectranthias winniensis (Tyler, 1966)

Dorsal rays X,16-17 (modally 16), the fin deeply divided between spinous and soft portions; anal rays III,7; pectoral rays 16-18, none branched; lateral line ending beneath soft portion of dorsal fin, the tube-bearing scales 14-20; body depth 3.0-3.45 in standard length; lower margin of preopercle with two antrorse spines; posterior margin of preopercle with coarse serrae; subopercle with 0-2 weak serrae, and interopercle with none; fourth dorsal spine longest; caudal fin rounded; whitish, heavily blotched with brownish orange, becoming red-blotched posteriorly; a small white spot dorsally on caudal peduncle behind rear base of dorsal fin; a large red spot basally at front of dorsal fin. Indo-Pacific, depth range 23-58 m. Largest specimen, 4.8 cm.

BICOLOUR ANTHIAS
Pseudanthias bicolor (Randall, 1979)

Dorsal rays X,16-18 (rarely XI); anal rays III,7 (rarely 8); pectoral rays 19-21 (usually 20, rarely 21); lateral-line scales 57-64; body depth 2.75-3.05 in head; no fleshy papillae on edge of orbit; front of upper lip of males thickened and somewhat pointed; margin of subopercle and interopercle smooth; third dorsal spine of adult females prolonged; second and third dorsal spines of males prolonged; caudal fin of adults lunate; upper half of body orange-yellow, lower half abruptly lavender-pink; fleshy tips of elongate second and third dorsal spines of males yellow. Hawaii and New Caledonia to islands of the western Indian Ocean; usually in the depth range of 20-70 m. Attains 13 cm.

SILVERSTREAK ANTHIAS
Pseudanthias cooperi (Regan, 1902)

Dorsal rays X,15-17; anal rays III,7-8 (usually 7); pectoral rays 18-20; lateral-line scales 45-52; body depth 2.8-3.2 in SL; no fleshy papillae on edge of orbit; margin of subopercle and interopercle serrate; last dorsal spine longest; caudal fin of adults lunate, the lobe tips of males prolonged; a narrow whitish band from below eye to lower pectoral-fin base; females with red tips on caudal lobes; caudal fin of males red with narrow lavender upper and lower margins; males with a narrow red bar on side between lateral line and outer part of pectoral fin. Line Islands and Samoa west to East Africa. Reaches 14 cm. Often misidentified as *Anthias taeniatus* Klunzinger, a Red Sea species, or *A. kashiwae* Tanaka, a synonym.

REDFIN ANTHIAS
Pseudanthias dispar (Herre, 1955)

Dorsal rays X,16-18; anal rays III,7-8 (rarely 8); pectoral rays 18-20 (rarely 18); lateral-line scales 55-63; body depth 2.7-3.2 in standard length; no papillae on edge of orbit; front of upper lip of males thickened and pointed; two opercular spines; margin of subopercle and interopercle smooth; first dorsal spine very short, the second longest and slightly prolonged; caudal fin deeply forked; second pelvic soft ray slightly prolonged in females, greatly elongate in males; body orange-yellow above, pale lavender-pink below, the head of males largely violet; dorsal fin deep red, at least anteriorly. Western Pacific east to Samoa and the Line Islands, often in large aggregations; usual depth range 1-15 m. Largest specimen, 9.5 cm. Described in the genus *Mirolabrichthys*, now regarded as a subgenus of *Pseudanthias*.

Pseudanthias dispar Male ▲ Female ▼

BARRIER REEF ANTHIAS
Pseudanthias engelhardi (Allen & Starck, 1982)

Dorsal rays X,16; anal rays III,7; pectoral rays 17; lateral-line scales 42-45; body depth 2.55-2.6 in standard length; margin of subopercle and interopercle serrate; third dorsal spine longest, moderately prolonged in males; caudal fin deeply emarginate; pelvic fins reaching anal fin spines in females, anterior soft rays in males; light yellowish pink dorsally, the scales edged in orange, shading to pinkish white ventrally; snout and head above and behind eye orange-yellow; males with an orangish bar on side of body above outer part of pectoral fin. Known from only four specimens collected in 50-60 m on patch reefs at Escape Reef, Great Barrier Reef. Largest specimen, the male holotype, 10 cm.

Pseudanthias engelhardi Male ▲ Female ▼

STRIPED ANTHIAS
Pseudanthias fasciatus (Kamohara, 1954)

Dorsal rays X,16-17; anal rays III,7; pectoral rays 17-19; lateral-line scales 41-45; body depth 2.3-2.6 in standard length; no papilla on edge of orbit; margin of subopercle and interopercle serrate; third dorsal spine longest, slightly prolonged; caudal fin lunate, the lobes prolonged; pelvic fins not reaching anal fin; an orange-red stripe on body from opercular flap to upper caudal-fin base; orange-yellow spots on scales of lower half of body joining to form narrow stripes. Southern Japan to the Great Barrier Reef from the depth range of 20-68 m. Largest specimen, 21 cm.

Pseudanthias huchtii Male ▲ Female ▼

THREADFIN ANTHIAS
Pseudanthias huchtii (Bleeker, 1857)

Dorsal rays X,17; anal rays III,7; pectoral rays 17-18 (usually 17); lateral-line scales 36-40; auxiliary scales present on body; fins scaled basally; body depth 2.4-2.75 in standard length; no papillae on edge of orbit; margin of subopercle and interopercle serrate; third dorsal spine longest, greatly prolonged in males; caudal fin lunate, the lobes elongate in males; pelvic fins not reaching anal fin; females yellow with a deep yellow band from eye to pectoral base and submarginally in each caudal-fin lobe; males greenish dorsally, the scales with a yellow spot in centre, shading to pale blue-green ventrally; a deep orange band from eye to middle of pectoral fin; a maroon spot in outer upper part of pectoral fin, and a broad maroon submarginal band on pelvic fins. Philippines to Vanuatu and the northern Great Barrier Reef; depth range about 4-20 m. Reaches 12 cm. *Anthias mortoni* Macleay is regarded as a synonym.

STOCKY ANTHIAS
Pseudanthias hypselosoma Bleeker, 1878

Dorsal rays X,15-17 (usually 16, rarely 15); anal rays III,7; pectoral rays 18-20; lateral-line scales 44-48; body depth 2.5-3.0 in standard length; no papillae on margin of orbit; subopercle and interopercle serrate; fourth to tenth dorsal spines subequal; caudal fin of females slightly emarginate, of males truncate with slightly prolonged lobes at corners; pelvic fins not reaching anal fin; scales dorsally on body with yellow centres and magenta to lavender edges, nearly white ventrally; females with a bright red posterior margin on caudal fin which is broader at corners; males with a red blotch basally in dorsal fin between seventh and tenth spines. Samoa to Maldives; usually found on well-protected reefs of lagoons or bays at depths of 10-35 m. Reaches 19 cm. *Anthias truncatus* Katayama and Masuda is a synonym.

Pseudanthias hypselosoma Male ▲ Female ▼

LORI'S ANTHIAS
Pseudanthias lori (Lubbock & Randall, 1976)

Dorsal rays III,16-17 (rarely 17); anal rays III,7-8 (rarely 8); pectoral rays 16-18 (rarely 16); lateral-line scales 49-52; body elongate, the depth 3.4-4.0 in standard length; posterior edge of orbit with fleshy papillae; front of upper lip of males thickened and pointed; margin of subopercle and interopercle smooth; third dorsal spine of males prolonged; caudal fin lunate, the lobes more elongate in males; pelvic fins of females reaching slightly beyond anus, of males to or beyond origin of anal fin; pink, finely spotted with yellow, with a series of short red bars on back (progressively larger posteriorly) and a longitudinal red band on upper caudal peduncle; males may develop yellow areas within the red bars and band. French Polynesia to Christmas Island, Indian Ocean; usually seen in aggregations on drop-offs in 30-60 m. Reaches 12 cm.

Pseudanthias luzonensis Male ▼ Female ▲

YELLOWLINED ANTHIAS
Pseudanthias luzonensis (Katayama & Masuda, 1983)

Dorsal rays X,15-17; anal rays III,7; pectoral rays 17-19; lateral-line scales 44-48; body depth 2.5-2.8 in standard length; no papillae on margin of orbit; margin of subopercle and interopercle smooth or with a few small serrae; third dorsal spine longest, prolonged in males; caudal fin lunate; pelvic fins not reaching anal fin; females light orange-red, the scales with yellow centres, shading to white ventrally; a narrow lavender-edged orange-yellow band from eye to pectoral base (a comparable band seen on many species of the genus); males similar to females but with slightly irregular longitudinal yellow lines on side of body, and membranes between dorsal spines VI and IX largely bright red. Philippines, Indonesia, and the northern Great Barrier Reef; usual depth, 20-60 m. Largest specimen, 14.5 cm.

AMETHYST ANTHIAS
Pseudanthias pascalus (Jordan & Tanaka, 1927)

Dorsal rays X,15-17; anal rays III,7-8 (rarely 8); pectoral rays 16-19 (modally 18); lateral-line scales 48-52; auxiliary scales present; body depth 2.9-3.4 in standard length; prominent fleshy papillae on posterior edge of orbit; front of upper lip of males thickened and pointed; two opercular spines; margin of subopercle and interopercle smooth; fifth to tenth dorsal spines subequal (fifth generally longest in small fish and tenth in large adults); soft portion of dorsal fin of males elevated, often with some rays exserted; caudal fin deeply forked, the lobe tips of males prolonged; second soft ray of pelvic fins of males prolonged; purple, the ventral part of head and thorax light yellow; outer part of soft portion of dorsal fin of males red. French Polynesia west to Australia; in the North Pacific from the Marshall Islands to southern Japan; reported from outer reef areas in the depth range of 5-45 m. Largest specimen, 17 cm.

PAINTED ANTHIAS
Pseudanthias pictilis (Randall & Allen, 1978)

Dorsal rays X,15-16 (rarely 15); anal rays III,7; pectoral rays 18-19; lateral-line scales 46-50; auxiliary scales on head and anterior body; body depth 2.9-3.2 in standard length; no papillae on margin of orbit; margin of subopercle and interopercle smooth; first and tenth dorsal spines longest, but not prolonged; space between first two dorsal spines narrow; caudal fin emarginate; females heliotrope dorsally on body, shading to yellow on posterior third and to white ventrally; median fins yellow; males with a broad violet bar edged in orange below middle of soft portion of dorsal fin; body in front of bar similar in colour to females, posterior to bar orange, flecked with lavender; caudal fin deep orange with a large elliptical yellow area near base and pale lavender lobe tips. New Caledonia, Lord Howe Island, and the southern Great Barrier Reef; occurs in aggregations in a depth range of about 20-40 m. To 13.5 cm.

Pseudanthias pictilis Male ▲ Female ▼

SQUARESPOT ANTHIAS
Pseudanthias pleurotaenia (Bleeker, 1857)

Dorsal rays X,16-18; anal rays III,7; pectoral rays 17-19; lateral-line scales 45-50; body depth 2.4-2.7 in standard length; no papillae on edge of orbit; margin of subopercle and interopercle weakly serrate; third dorsal spine prolonged; caudal fin lunate; pelvic fins reaching to or beyond origin of anal fin; females yellow, the scales edged in orange except ventrally; a deep yellow band edged in lavender from eye to pectoral-fin base, and two parallel lavender lines passing from beneath pectoral fin to lower caudal peduncle; males orange-magenta with a very large, nearly square, violet spot anteriorly on side of body. Philippines south to northern Great Barrier Reef and east to the Marshall Islands and Samoa; generally found on steep outer reef slopes in 30-70 m (has been seen as shallow as 10 m). To 20 cm.

Pseudanthias pleurotaenia Male ▲ Female ▼

REDBAR ANTHIAS
Pseudanthias rubrizonatus (Randall, 1983)

Dorsal rays X,16; anal rays III,7; pectoral rays 18-20; lateral-line scales 42-47; body depth 2.7-3.05 in standard length; no papillae on edge of orbit; margin of subopercle and interopercle with a few serrae; fourth dorsal spine longest, but not prolonged; caudal fin deeply emarginate to lunate; pelvic fins reaching or extending beyond origin of anal fin (longest in large males); females light red with a yellow mark on each scale except ventrally where whitish, a narrow violet band from below eye to lower pectoral base, and red-tipped caudal lobes; males with a broad red bar below last four dorsal spines, the body before bar suffused with lavender and behind bar with yellow. Philippines, New Guinea, Solomon Islands, Fiji, and Great Barrier Reef; usual depth, 30-58 m, but recently observed in 10 m at Lady Elliot Island by the third author. Attains 10 cm. Specimens from 133 m off Barrow Island, Western Australia of the same colour pattern but 48-50 lateral-line scales and some different body proportions represent a probable subspecies of *P. rubrizonatus.*

PRINCESS ANTHIAS
Pseudanthias smithvanizi (Randall & Lubbock, 1981)

Dorsal rays X,15-17; anal rays III,7-8 (rarely 8); pectoral rays 16-18 (rarely 18); lateral-line scales 44-48; body depth 3.1-3.3 in standard length; posterior edge of orbit with papillae; front of upper lip of males thickened and pointed; three opercular spines; margin of subopercle and interopercle smooth; third dorsal spine of males prolonged; caudal fin lunate, the lobe tips of males very long; pelvic fins of females reaching anus, of males extending well beyond origin of anal fin; violet to magenta with a yellow spot on each scale except ventrally; a yellow line on side of snout and a median one on top of head continuing along back at base of dorsal fin; females with caudal-fin lobes broadly red; males with a broad band of pink on edge of upper lobe. Marshall Islands to Christmas and Cocos-Keeling Islands in the eastern Indian Ocean; known from the depth range of 10-70 m; forms large aggregations on steep outer reef slopes. To 9.5 cm.

SCALEFIN ANTHIAS
Pseudanthias squamipinnis (Peters, 1855)

Dorsal rays X,16-18; anal rays III,7; pectoral rays 16-18; lateral-line scales 37-43; auxiliary scales present; fins heavily scaled; no papillae on edge of orbit; margin of subopercle and interopercle serrate; third dorsal spine prolonged in adult females, greatly elongate in males; caudal fin lunate, the lobes of males very prolonged; pelvic fins of females not reaching origin of anal fin, of males extending well beyond; females orange-yellow, the scales rimmed with lavender except ventrally; males fuchsia, the scales on side of body with a yellow spot; a large deep orange to magenta spot on upper outer part of pectoral fins. Western Pacific to East Africa and Red Sea. Often the most common species of the genus on shallow reefs. Attains 15 cm.

Pseudanthias squamipinnis Male ▲ Female ▼

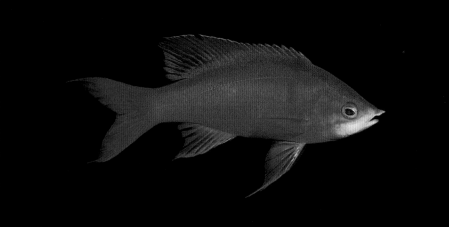

PURPLE ANTHIAS
Pseudanthias tuka (Herre & Montalban, 1927)

Dorsal rays X,15-17; anal rays III,7-8 (rarely 8); pectoral rays 15-17; lateral-line scales 45-49; body depth 2.8-3.3 in standard length; prominent papillae along posterior edge of orbit; front of upper lip of males thickened and strongly pointed; two opercular spines; margin of subopercle and interopercle smooth; fifth to tenth dorsal spines longest, subequal; soft portion of dorsal fin of males elevated; caudal fin lunate; pelvic fins of females reaching anus, of males extending beyond origin of anal fin; females purple with a bright yellow band on back, extending onto upper lobe of caudal fin; lower lobe also with a broad yellow band; males lacking yellow band on back and caudal lobes; ventral part of head pale yellow; a deep purple spot basally at rear of dorsal fin. Philippines to northern Great Barrier Reef; occurs in aggregations on outer reef slopes at depths from about 7 to 15 m. Attains 12 cm. The closely related *P. pascalus* is not known from the Philippines, Indonesia, and New Guinea where *tuka* is common; the two species occur together in Palau and the Great Barrier Reef.

Pseudanthias tuka Male ▲ Female ▼

LONGFIN ANTHIAS
Pseudanthias ventralis (Randall, 1979)

Dorsal rays X,16-18; anal rays III,9; pectoral rays 15; lateral-line scales 39-46; a few auxiliary scales dorsally on body; body depth 2.85-3.15 in standard length; no papillae at edge of orbit; margin of subopercle serrate, of interopercle smooth; fifth dorsal spine usually longest, not prolonged; caudal fin deeply emarginate; pelvic fins very long, reaching beyond spinous portion of anal fin; females pink to magenta, pale lavender to white ventrally, with a yellow band from upper part of eye along back at base of dorsal fin, and expanding onto caudal peduncle and fin; males irregularly spotted with magenta and yellow dorsally on head and body; males from New Caledonia and the Great Barrier Reef with a large red area in outer part of soft portion of dorsal fin and caudal fin. Islands of Oceania to the Great Barrier Reef; subspecifically different in Hawaii; known from the depth range of 26-68 m, but usually not found in less than 40 m. Reaches 7 cm.

Pseudanthias ventralisis   Male ▼   Female ▲

HAWK ANTHIAS
Serranocirrhitus latus Watanabe, 1949

Dorsal rays X,18-20; anal rays III,7; pectoral rays 13-14; lateral-line scales 33-38; body deep, the depth 1.9-2.2 in standard length; margin of subopercle and interopercle smooth; tenth dorsal spine slightly longer than preceding spines; caudal fin lunate; pelvic fins reaching origin of anal fin; deep pink, each scale with a yellow spot (spots large dorsally, progressively smaller ventrally); yellow bands radiating from eye. Southern Japan, Indonesia, Belau (Palau), Vanuatu, Fiji, New Caledonia, and northern Great Barrier Reef; usually found in caves or beneath ledges on outer reef drop-offs in the depth range of 15-70 m. Attains 13 cm.

SUBFAMILY EPINEPHELINAE

REDMOUTH ROCKCOD
Aethaloperca rogaa (Forsskål, 1775)

Dorsal rays IX,17-18 (usually 18); anal rays III,8-9 (rarely 8); pectoral rays 17-19; lateral-line scales 48-54; body deep, the depth 2.1-2.4 in standard length; fifth or sixth pectoral rays longest (middle pectoral rays longest on other species of Epinephelini); caudal fin truncate; dark brown, often with a whitish bar centered on abdomen; inside of mouth largely orange-red; juveniles with a broad white posterior border on caudal fin. Red Sea and coast of East Africa to Kiribati (Gilbert Islands); known from the depth range of 3 to 40 m; usually seen within or in the vicinity of caves. Reaches 60 cm.

WHITE-LINED ROCKCOD
Anyperodon leucogrammicus (Valenciennes, 1828)

Dorsal rays XI,14-16; anal rays III,8-9 (usually 9); pectoral rays 15-17 (rarely 17); lateral-line scales 63-72; body elongate, the depth 3.15-3.7 in standard length, and compressed, the width 2.3-2.8 in depth; no palatine teeth; posterior nostril of adults vertically elongate; caudal fin rounded; greenish to brownish grey with numerous orange-red spots on head, body, dorsal fin, and base of caudal fin; four longitudinal whitish streaks on posterior head and body, often broken into segments (may be lost in large adults); juveniles with orange-yellow and blue stripes and a blue-edged black spot at base of caudal fin, mimics of females of the wrasse *Halichoeres purpurescens* and allied species. Red Sea and East Africa to Samoa and the Marshall Islands. To 52 cm.

PEACOCK ROCKCOD
Cephalopholis argus Bloch & Schneider, 1801

Dorsal rays IX,15-17 (rarely 15); anal rays III,9; pectoral rays 16-18; lateral-line scales 46-51; longitudinal scale series 95-110; auxiliary scales (tiny scales at base of main scales) present on body; body depth 2.7-3.2 in standard length; teeth on midside of lower jaw of adults in five or six rows; dark brown with numerous small dark-edged blue spots on head, body, and fins; a large pale area often present on thorax; five or six pale bars on posterior half of body present or absent. Indo-Pacific; successfully introduced to the Hawaiian Islands. Found in a variety of coral reef habitats from shallow water to depths of at least 40 m; feeds mainly on fishes; has been implicated in ciguatera fish poisoning. Reaches 40 cm.

BROWN-BARRED ROCKCOD
Cephalopholis boenak (Bloch, 1790)

Dorsal rays IX,15-17; anal rays III,8; pectoral rays 15-17; lateral-line scales 46-5l; longitudinal scale series 86-100; body depth 2.6-3.05 in standard length; brown with eight slightly irregular dark brown bars on body; dark brown bands radiating from eye; a black spot on opercular membrane between upper two spines; a narrow bluish white margin posteriorly on median fins. Western Pacific to East Africa, but not reported from most oceanic islands; usual habitat shallow silty reefs in protected waters. Largest specimen, 24 cm. *C. pachycentron* (Valenciennes) is a synonym.

BLUE-SPOTTED ROCKCOD
Cephalopholis cyanostigma (Valenciennes, 1828)

Dorsal rays IX,15-17; anal rays III,8; pectoral rays 16-18 (rarely 18); lateral-line scales 47-49; longitudinal scale series 92-106; body depth 2.65-3.0 in standard length; brown to orangish brown with numerous black-edged light blue spots on head, body, and fins, those on thorax largest; pale spots larger than pupil, tending to form bars on body; outer third of pectoral fins orange-yellow with a narrow blackish margin (or blackish submarginal line). Philippines to Queensland, west to Thailand and Western Australia; usually found on shallow protected reefs or seagrass beds. Reported to 35 cm. *C. xanthoptera* Allen & Starck is a synonym; it was described from the subadult form with yellow on the median fans and no small blue spots.

Cephalopholis cyanostigma   Adult ▲   Juv. ▼

BLUE-LINED ROCKCOD
Cephalopholis formosa (Shaw, 1804)

Dorsal rays IX,15-17; anal rays III,7-8 (rarely 7); pectoral rays 16-18; lateral-line scales 47-51; longitudinal scale series 91-109; body depth 2.55-2.9 in standard length; yellowish brown with slightly irregular narrow blue stripes on head, body, and fins (those on dorsal fin mostly diagonal continuations of stripes from body); snout, lips, and ventral part of head and thorax with a variable number of small blue spots; a black spot on opercular membrane between upper two spines. Western Pacific to western India; typically found in shallow water on sheltered dead or silty reefs. Reaches 34 cm. Often misidentifed as *C. boenak.*

LEOPARD ROCKCOD
Cephalopholis leopardus (Lacepède, 1801)

Dorsal rays IX,13-15; anal rays III,9-10 (rarely 10); pectoral rays 16-18; lateral-line scales 47-50; longitudinal scale series 79-88; body depth 2.6-2.85 in standard length; head large, its length 2.15-2.35 in standard length; reddish brown, shading to whitish ventrally, with numerous red-orange spots (more evident ventrally); a saddle-like dark brown spot on caudal peduncle with a smaller dark spot behind it; a diagonal dark streak on upper outer part of caudal fin. Indo-Pacific; a secretive coral-reef species known from the depth range of 3-40 m. Maximum length, 20 cm.

DOTHEAD ROCKCOD
Cephalopholis microprion (Bleeker, 1852)

Dorsal rays IX,15-16 (rarely 16); anal rays III,8; pectoral rays 15-16 (usually 16); lateral-line scales 46-50; longitudinal scale series 84-98; pectoral fins moderately long, 1.4-1.55 in head; brown, the basal half of scales darker than outer half; six broad dark bars on body present or absent; head and anterior body with numerous small dark-edged blue spots; median fins dark brown with a blue-grey posterior margin (broadest at corners of caudal fin). Western Pacific to Andaman Sea; a shallow-water species usually found on silty reefs. To 23 cm.

CORAL COD
Cephalopholis miniata (Forsskål, 1775)

Dorsal rays IX,14-16; anal rays III,8-9 (rarely 8); pectoral rays 17-18 (usually 18); lateral-line scales 47-54; longitudinal scale series 94-114; snout anterior to nostrils scaleless; orange-red to reddish brown, often darker posteriorly, with numerous bright blue spots smaller than pupil on head, body, and median fins; capable of assuming a pattern of irregular diagonal bars; juveniles may be yellow with faint pale blue spots. Line Islands in the Central Pacific to East Africa and the Red Sea; generally found on well-developed coral reefs in clear water, more often on exposed than protected reefs; feeds more on small fishes than crustaceans. Largest reported, 41 cm.

SIXSPOT ROCKCOD
Cephalopholis sexmaculata (Rüppell, 1830)

Dorsal rays IX,14-16; anal rays III,9; pectoral rays 16-18; lateral-line scales 49-54; longitudinal scale series 95-108; body depth 2.65-3.05 in standard length; orange-red with numerous small blue spots on head, body, and median fins (short blue lines may also be present on head); six large quadrangular blackish blotches on back, the first four extending into dorsal fin; faint dark bars may extend ventrally from dark blotches on back. Indo-Pacific; known from the depth range of 10-150 m; usually found in caves. Largest specimen, 47 cm, but rarely exceeds 35 cm. *C. coatesi* Whitley is a synonym.

TOMATO ROCKCOD
Cephalopholis sonnerati (Valenciennes, 1828)

Dorsal rays IX,14-16; anal rays III,9; pectoral rays 18-20; lateral-line scales 66-76; longitudinal scale series 115-134; body depth 2.3-2.75 in standard length; nape of adults prominently convex; ventral margin of preopercle serrate or irregular; reddish to yellowish brown, darker posteriorly, with numerous small brownish red spots (these spots lacking on Indian Ocean specimens); juveniles dark reddish brown to black with a white posterior border on caudal fin (broadest at corners); larger juveniles lighter with scattered small pale greenish blotches. Line Islands and Kiribati in the Central Pacific to East Africa, usually at depths greater than 30 m; occurs to at least 100 m. Reported to 57 cm; largest examined 48.5 cm.

STRAWBERRY ROCKCOD
Cephalopholis spiloparaea (Valenciennes, 1828)

Dorsal rays IX,15-16 (usually 15); anal rays III,9; pectoral rays 17-19; lateral-line scales 47-52; longitudinal scale series 87-100; body depth 2.75-3.2 in standard length; margin of subopercle and interopercle usually smooth; pelvic fins short, not reaching anus, 1.9-2.15 in head; light red, mottled and blotched with brownish red; caudal fin with a bluish white posterior margin that becomes submarginal at corners; distal margin of soft portion of dorsal and anal fins usually with a pale bluish margin. Indo-Pacific; a common clear-water coral-reef species known from the depth range of 15-108 m, but usually more than 30 m. Largest, 21 cm. Has been misidentified as *C. analis* (Valenciennes), a synonym of the deep-water rockcod *C. aurantia* (Valenciennes).

FLAGTAIL ROCKCOD
Cephalopholis urodeta (Bloch & Schneider, 1801)

Dorsal rays IX,14-16; anal rays III,8-9 (rarely 8); pectoral rays 17-19; lateral-line scales 54-68; longitudinal scale series 88-108; body depth 2.75-3.1 in standard length; reddish brown, darker posteriorly, often with six faint irregular bars on body which bifurcate ventrally; numerous small orange-red spots on head and nape; a pair of dark spots at front of lower lip; caudal fin with two diagonal white bands which converge as they pass to posterior margin of fin. Central and western Pacific; a common coral-reef species which occurs at depths of 1-40 m. To 27 cm. Often misspelled *urodelus*. The Indian Ocean form, usually identified as *C. nigrippinis* (Valenciennes) lacks the two oblique white bands in the caudal fin.

BARRAMUNDI COD
Cromileptes altivelis (Valenciennes, 1828)

Dorsal rays X,17-19; anal rays III,9-10 (rarely 9); pectoral rays 17-18 (usually 18); lateral-line scales 54-62; body depth 2.5-3.0 in standard length; front part of head containing eye very small; dorsal profile of head nearly straight to above eye, then rising steeply to origin of dorsal fin; posterior nostril a vertical slit; greenish white to light greenish brown, with scattered large round black spots. Western Pacific to Nicobar Islands; more often found in silty reef areas than well-developed live reefs; may occur in very shallow water (even stranded in pools at low tide); very secretive. Reported to 66 cm in length and 3.5 kg in weight. A highly prized food fish.

AREOLATE ROCKCOD
Epinephelus areolatus (Forsskål, 1775)

Dorsal rays XI,15-17; anal rays III,8; pectoral rays 17-19 (modally 17, rarely 19); lateral-line scales 50-53; longitudinal scale series 97-115; body depth 3.0-3.3 in standard length; teeth on midside of lower jaw in two rows; rounded corner of preopercle with two to five enlarged serrae; caudal fin slightly emarginate to truncate; whitish with numerous close-set brown to brownish yellow spots on head, body, and fins (largest spots on adults approaching size of pupil); posterior border of caudal fin white. Western Pacific to East Africa and the Red Sea; depth range, 6-200 m; typical inshore habitat, small coral heads in silty sand or seagrass areas. Attains 45 cm.

WHITE-SPOTTED ROCKCOD
Epinephelus caeruleopunctatus (Bloch, 1790)

Dorsal rays XI,15-17; anal rays III,8; pectoral rays 17-19; lateral-line scales 51-61; longitudinal scale series 86-106; body depth 2.9-3.4 in standard length; dorsal profile of head nearly straight; teeth on midside of lower jaw of adults in three to five rows; posterior nostril of adults vertically elongate and enlarged; caudal fin rounded; grey-brown, the posterior head, body, and dorsal fin with scattered large white spots (some as large or larger than eye) and numerous small pale spots; a series of indistinct dark blotches on back at base of dorsal fin and one on caudal peduncle; a black streak above maxilla. Kiribati and Caroline Islands to East Africa; a shallow-water species of coral reefs and rocky substrata; stays close to shelter. To 60 cm.

ESTUARY COD
Epinephelus coioides (Hamilton, 1822)

Dorsal rays XI,14-16; anal rays III,8; pectoral rays 19-20 (usually 20); lateral-line scales 58-65, the anterior scales of large adults with branched tubules; longitudinal scale series 100-118; gill rakers 8-10 + 15-17; body depth 3.0-3.85 in standard length; teeth on midside of lower jaw in two to three rows; rounded corner of preopercle with enlarged serrae; nostrils subequal; caudal fin rounded; whitish or pale yellowish with five slightly diagonal brown bars on body that bifurcate ventrally and one on nape (bars on body above lateral line may be broken); brownish orange spots about the size of pupil or smaller on head and body, those on body tending to be in rows parallel to brown bars. Western Pacific to western Indian Ocean; common in the Persian Gulf; may occur on coral reefs in turbid areas; often encountered in brackish environments. Reaches at least 100 cm. Frequently misidentified as *E. tauvina* or *E. malabaricus. E. suillus* (Valenciennes) is a synonym.

CORAL ROCKCOD
Epinephelus corallicola (Valenciennes, 1828)

Dorsal rays XI,15-16; anal rays III,8; pectoral rays 18-20; lateral-line scales 54-63; longitudinal scale series 96-107; body depth 2.7-3.2 in standard length; dorsal profile of head nearly straight; teeth on midside of lower jaw in three to four rows; posterior nostril of adults vertically elongate; caudal fin rounded; brownish to greenish grey with widely scattered black spots smaller than pupil on head, body, and fins; three dusky to blackish spots on back at base of rear half of dorsal fin, the most anterior (at base of last two or three spines) largest and most distinct. Western Pacific; a shallow-water species of silty reefs; may occur in estuarine areas; cryptic. Largest examined, 31 cm.

BLUE MAORI
Epinephelus cyanopodus (Richardson, 1846)

Dorsal rays XI,16-17; anal rays III,8; pectoral rays 18-20; lateral-line scales 63-75; longitudinal scale series 130-147; body deep, the depth 2.4-2.65 in standard length; teeth on midside of lower jaw in two rows; posterior nostril of adults enlarged; membranes of spinous portion of dorsal fin not incised; caudal fin truncate; light bluish grey with numerous very small black spots and scattered larger blackish spots on head, body, and fins; subadults and large juveniles lack the larger dark spots and may have a broad submarginal black band posteriorly on the caudal fin and black-tipped pelvic fins; smaller juveniles may be mainly yellow. Western Pacific to Marshall Islands and Kiribati; reported from depths of 2-150 m; often found around isolated coral heads in lagoons. Reaches about 100 cm. *E. hoedtii* (Bleeker) and *E. kohleri* Schultz are synonyms. Very closely related to *E. flavocaeruleus* from the Indian Ocean.

BLACK-TIPPED ROCKCOD
Epinephelus fasciatus (Forsskål, 1775)

Dorsal rays XI,15-17; anal rays III,8; pectoral rays 18-20 (rarely 20); lateral-line scales 50-58 (61-68 in Oceania); longitudinal scale series 92-125 (114-135 in Oceania); body depth 2.9-3.3 in standard length; teeth on midside of lower jaw in two to three rows; caudal fin slightly rounded to truncate; light grey to pale yellowish red with five broad dusky to dark orange-red bars on body (more evident on dorsal half); tips of interspinous membranes of dorsal fin black (or red on deep-water fish). Wide-ranging throughout the Indo-Pacific; a common species of coral reefs or rocky bottom from the shallows to depths of 160 m. Reported to 40 cm; largest examined, 35 cm.

FLOWERY COD
Epinephelus fuscoguttatus (Forsskål, 1775)

Dorsal rays XI,14-15; anal rays III,8; pectoral rays 18-20; lateral-line scales 52-58; longitudinal scale series 102-115; gill rakers 10-12 + 18-21; scales on body cycloid (ctenoid on juveniles); body depth 2.6-2.9 in standard length; dorsal profile of head of adults above interorbital space convex; teeth on midside of lower jaw in three rows; posterior nostril of adults subtriangular, about four times larger than anterior nostril; caudal fin rounded; light yellowish brown with large irregular brown blotches on head and body, the darkest along back; a black saddle-like spot on caudal peduncle; head, body, and fins with numerous close-set small dark brown spots. Marshall Islands and Phoenix Islands to East Africa and the Red Sea; not common; a wary fish. Reaches at least 90 cm.

HEXAGON ROCKCOD
Epinephelus hexagonatus (Bloch & Schneider, 1801)

Dorsal rays XI,15-16 (usually 16); anal rays III,8; pectoral rays 18-19 (usually 18); lateral-line 61-68; longitudinal scale series 93-109; gill rakers 7-9 + 16-19; body depth 2.8-3.4 in standard length; teeth on midside of lower jaw in three to five rows; second anal spine longer than third, 2.1-2.35 in head; caudal fin rounded; head and body with dark brown polygonal spots about as large as pupil that merge or tend to merge on their sides, separated mainly by a triangular white dot at each angular corner of the spots; groups of spots darker than others forming a series of five dark blotches along back; a large yellow-brown spot behind eye, sometimes linked to a second horizontally elongate spot of the same colour on opercle; fins dark-spotted. Indo-Pacific; usually found in exposed outer-reef areas in relatively shallow water. Attains about 30 cm.

BLACKSADDLE ROCKCOD
Epinephelus howlandi (Günther, 1873)

Dorsal rays XI,15-17; anal rays III,8; pectoral rays 17-19 (rarely 19); lateral-line scales 49-52; longitudinal scale series 85-102; scales on body cycloid (ctenoid beneath pectoral fins); total gill rakers 23-26 (modally 25); body depth 2.9-3.3 in standard length; body width 1.7-2.1 in depth; teeth on midside of lower jaw in two rows; snout short, 4.25-5.0 in head; caudal fin rounded; whitish with numerous well-spaced small dark brown spots on head, body (except ventrally), and fins (only a few basally on pectorals); a blackish spot as large as eye on back and adjacent dorsal fin between last two spines; two lesser blackish spots may be present at base of soft portion of dorsal fin and one at top of caudal peduncle; a narrow white margin posteriorly on caudal fin, soft portions of dorsal and anal fins, and pectorals often with a blackish submarginal band; a black line usually present above maxilla. Western Pacific from Ryukyu Islands to Great Barrier Reef and east to the Marshalls and Samoa. Attains about 45 cm. Sometimes misidentified as *E. corallicola*, but more frequently confused with *E. macrospilos* which differs in lacking the large black spot on back, having fewer dark spots at a given size, a more projecting lower jaw, thicker body, lower average gill-raker count, and more often 19 than 18 pectoral rays.

Epinephelus howlandi

QUEENSLAND GROUPER
Epinephelus lanceolatus (Bloch, 1790)

Dorsal rays XI,14-16; anal rays III,8; pectoral rays 18-19; lateral-line scales 53-67, the tubes branched; longitudinal scale series 89-110; scales cycloid; body depth 2.5-3.4 in standard length; body thick, the width 1.55-1.75 in depth; teeth on midside of lower jaw in two rows in juveniles, at least seven rows in adults; eye small and interorbital space broad; dorsal spines short, the posterior spines longest on adults, 3.2-4.8 in head; caudal fin rounded; adults mottled dark greyish brown; juveniles irregularly barred with dark brown and yellow. Indo-Pacific; known from depths of a few to over 100 m; rare; spiny lobsters are a favorite item of diet. The largest Indo-Pacific reef fish; reported to 270 cm and weights of over 400 kg. Often classified in the genus *Promicrops*. There are reports of fatal attacks on humans, but none fully documented. Also called the giant grouper.

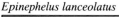
Epinephelus lanceolatus

SNUBNOSE ROCKCOD
Epinephelus macrospilos (Bleeker, 1855)

Dorsal rays XI,15-17; anal rays III,8; pectoral rays 18-19 (more often 19); lateral-line scales 48-52; longitudinal scale series 86-103; scales cycloid (ctenoid beneath pectoral fins); total gill rakers 21-24 (modally 23); body depth 3.0-3.4 in standard length; body robust, the width 1.4-1.85 in depth; teeth on midside of lower jaw in 2 rows; snout short, 4.25-5.3 in head; lower jaw strongly projecting; caudal fin rounded; whitish with well-separated small dark brown spots on head, body (except ventrally), and fins (except pectorals which may have a few spots basally); three spots (or pairs of spots) at base of dorsal fin and one at top of caudal peduncle may be darker than adjacent spots; a narrow white posterior margin on caudal fin (and often on soft portions of dorsal and anal fins, occasionally on pectorals); a narrow black streak above maxilla. Central western Pacific to Nicobar Islands. Largest, 43 cm. Very similar to *E. howlandi* (see account of *howlandi* for differences).

TROUT COD
Epinephelus maculatus (Bloch, 1790)

Dorsal rays XI,15-17; anal rays III,8; pectoral rays 17-18 (rarely 18); lateral-line scales 48-51; longitudinal scale series 103-120; gill rakers 8-10 + 15-17; body depth 2.75-3.1 in standard length; teeth on midside of lower jaw in two rows; spinous portion of dorsal fin high, the third or fourth spines longest, 2.2-2.7 in head; caudal fin rounded; light brown with numerous round to polygonal close-set dark brown spots, those on body about size of pupil; two very large dusky areas on back that extend broadly into dorsal fin where they are more heavily pigmented and separated by a whitish area; juveniles with these dark and white areas more evident; in addition, spotted with white. Western Pacific to Marshall Islands and Samoa; usually seen around coral heads in lagoons. Reaches 50 cm.

Epinephelus maculatus Adult ▲ Juv. ▼

MALABAR GROUPER
Epinephelus malabaricus (Bloch & Schneider, 1801)

Dorsal rays XI,14-16; anal rays III,8; pectoral rays 18-20; lateral-line scales 54-64, the anterior scales of large adults with branched tubules; longitudinal scale series 102-117; gill rakers 8-11 + 15-18; body depth 3.1-3.7 in standard length; teeth on midside of lower jaw of subadults in two rows, increasing to four or five rows in large adults; prominent rounded corner of preopercle with three to five enlarged serrae; caudal fin rounded; light greyish to yellowish brown with five slightly oblique broad dark bars on body that tend to bifurcate ventrally and may contain pale areas; head and body with numerous small well-separated black spots and scattered larger pale spots and blotches; a dark streak above maxilla; fins generally with small dark spots. Western Pacific to East Africa and Red Sea; occurs in various habitats, including estuaries, but not apt to be found in clear-water well-developed coral reefs. Probably exceeds 100 cm. *E. salmoides* (Lacepède) is a synonym.

DWARF SPOTTED ROCKCOD
Epinephelus merra Bloch, 1793

Dorsal rays XI,15-17; anal rays III,8; pectoral rays 16-18; lateral-line scales 48-52; body depth 2.9-3.2 in standard length; longitudinal scale series 100-114; gill rakers 6-8 + 14-16; teeth on midside of lower jaw in two rows; caudal fin rounded; whitish with numerous close-set round to hexagonal dark brown spots, a few of which are joined to form short bands; fins with dark brown spots that are progressively smaller distally except those of pectorals which are small throughout and largely confined to the rays. Indo-Pacific; a common species of protected reefs in lagoons and bays; feeds more on crustaceans than fishes. Largest examined, 27.5 cm. Also known as the honeycomb grouper.

SPECKLED-FIN ROCKCOD
Epinephelus ongus (Bloch, 1790)

Dorsal rays XI,15-16; anal rays III,8; pectoral rays 15-17; lateral-line scales 48-53; longitudinal scale series 90-109; body depth 2.5-3.2 in standard length; teeth in jaws small, those on midside of lower jaw in two rows; fleshy upper margin of opercle highly arched; caudal fin rounded; adults grey-brown with numerous small white spots which tend to join to form irregular longitudinal narrow white bands on body, especially posteriorly; pale spots larger than eye superimposed on this pattern; a black streak above maxilla; median fins with numerous small white spots and short dashes, a narrow white posterior margin, and broad black submarginal band; juveniles dark brown with well-separated white spots on head, body, and all fins. Caroline Islands and western Pacific to East Africa; a shallow-water species of coral reefs and rocky substrata. Reported to 40 cm. Often misidentified as *E. summana* (Rüppell) , a Red Sea endemic.

Epinephelus ongus Adult

Epinephelus ongus Juvenile

CAMOUFLAGE ROCKCOD
Epinephelus polyphekadion (Bleeker, 1849)

Dorsal rays XI,14-15; anal rays III,8; pectoral rays 16-17 (usually 17); lateral-line scales 47-52; longitudinal scale series 95-111; gill rakers 9-10 + 15-17; body depth 2.7-3.1 in standard length; teeth on midside of lower jaw in two or three rows; nostrils subequal; caudal fin rounded; light brown with large irregular brown blotches on head and body, overlaid by numerous small close-set dark brown spots; a prominent black saddle-like spot on caudal peduncle; all fins with many small dark brown spots. Indo-Pacific, generally on well-developed coral reefs; usually easy to approach underwater; feeds more on crustaceans than small fishes. Largest specimen, 61 cm. Often confused with *E. fuscoguttatus* due to similarity in colour pattern; *microdon* has lower pectoral-ray and gill-raker counts. *E. goldmanni* (Bleeker) and *E. microdon* (Bleeker) are synonyms.

Epinephelus polyphekadion

LONGFIN ROCKCOD
Epinephelus quoyanus (Valenciennes, 1830)

Dorsal rays XI,16-18; anal rays III,8; pectoral rays 17-19 (rarely 19); lateral-line scales 48-51; longitudinal scale series 86-96; gill rakers 7-8 + 14-16; body depth 2.9-3.5 in standard length; teeth on midside of lower jaw in two rows; snout short, 4.3-5.6 in head; pectoral fins long, 1.2-1.5 in head; whitish with numerous large close-set roundish to hexagonal dark brown spots on head and body (many on body as large or larger than eye); two dark brown diagonal bands on thorax (the upper sometimes divided into two spots); fins with dark brown spots, those on pectorals smaller and only on about basal half; median fins with narrow white margins, the anal with a dark brown submarginal band. Western Pacific to southwest coast of Thailand; in Queensland found mainly on coastal reefs and inner reefs of the Great Barrier Reef. Attains 35 cm. *E. megachir* (Richardson) is a synonym.

CHINAMAN ROCKCOD
Epinephelus rivulatus (Valenciennes, 1830)

Dorsal rays XI,16-18; anal rays III,8; pectoral rays 17-19; lateral-line scales 49-53; longitudinal scale series 86-102; scales on body largely ctenoid, but very small cycloid scales anteriorly on body above lateral line and on nape; body depth 2.6-3.3 in standard length; teeth on midside of lower jaw in two rows; light reddish to greenish brown with a whitish dot on each body scale; six irregular oblique brown bars on body, the first on nape, the last on caudal peduncle; a brownish red spot at base of pectoral fins; irregular broad brown bands on head. Western Pacific and Indian Ocean; known from the depth range of 1-150 m on coral reefs or rocky or weedy bottoms. Reaches 35 cm. *E. rhyncholepis* (Bleeker), *E. grammatohorus* Boulenger, and *E. homosinensis* Whitley are synonyms.

SIXBAR ROCKCOD
Epinephelus sexfasciatus (Valenciennes, 1828)

Dorsal rays XI,14-16; anal rays III,8; pectoral rays 17-19; lateral-line scales 46-51; longitudinal scale series 82-96; scales on body mainly ctenoid; body depth 2.65-3.2 in standard length; midside of lower jaw with 2 rows of teeth; corner of preopercle with 2 to 4 (usually 2) spines; caudal fin rounded; whitish with six slightly diagonal dark bars on body (first on nape, last on caudal peduncle); caudal fin and soft portions of dorsal and anal fins with black spots. Indo-Malayan region. Reaches 28 cm. Usually found on silty sand or mud bottoms at depths greater than 20 m.

FOUR-SADDLE ROCKCOD
Epinephelus spilotoceps Schultz, 1953

Dorsal rays XI,14-15 (rarely 14); anal rays III,8; pectoral rays 18-19 (usually 18); lateral-line scales 60-69; longitudinal scale series 86-100; gill rakers 7-8 + 15-18; body depth 3.1-3.5 in standard length; teeth on midside of lower jaw in three or four rows; second anal spine 2.5-3.2 in head; caudal fin rounded; whitish with numerous polygonal dark brown spots on head and body, those on body mostly smaller than pupil; spots so close together, especially dorsally, that intervening pale space is a network of white lines; a large black spot on back at base of last four dorsal spines and extending into fin; two simlar but smaller spots at base of soft portion of dorsal fin and one dorsally on caudal peduncle; dark spots on head progressively smaller anteriorly, those on snout very small (about size of nostrils); all fins dark-spotted. Line Islands in the Central Pacific to East Africa; a shallow-water coral-reef species. To about 35 cm. Often confused with *E. hexagonatus*, but *spilotoceps* has a shorter second anal spine, lacks the two large brownish yellow spots on the head behind eye, and its spots on the head are smaller.

GREASY ROCKCOD
Epinephelus tauvina (Forsskål, 1775)

Dorsal rays XI,14-16 (rarely 16); anal rays III,8; pectoral rays 18-19; lateral-line scales 65-74; longitudinal scale series 98-113; gill rakers 8-10 + 18-20; scales cycloid except for a ctenoid patch of variable size in pectoral region; body depth 3.1-3.8 in standard length; teeth on midside of lower jaw in three or four rows; mouth very large, the maxilla extending well beyond posterior edge of eye; posterior nostril of adults enlarged; caudal fin rounded; greenish grey to light brown dorsally, shading to white ventrally, with numerous well-spaced dull orange-red to brown spots on head, body, and fins (spots relatively smaller and more numerous on larger fish); five faint diagonal dark bars on body (may be result of darker spots); a large blackish spot often present at base of last four dorsal spines (more evident on small fish); three lesser blackish spots may be present at dorsal-fin base and one dorsally on caudal peduncle. Indo-Pacific; generally found on coral reefs in clear-water areas. Reported to 70 cm. *E. elongatus* Schultz and *E. chewa* Morgans are synonyms.

POTATO COD
Epinephelus tukula Morgans, 1959

Dorsal rays XI,14-15 (usually 15); anal rays III,7-9 (usually 8); pectoral rays 18-20; lateral-line scales 66-70; longitudinal scale series 113-135; teeth on midside of lower jaw in three to six rows; body depth 2.9-3.3 in standard length; caudal fin rounded; greyish brown with large widely spaced dark brown spots in about five longitudinal rows on body (most spots larger than eye); head with small dark spots and short dark bands radiating from posterior part of eye; fins with small dark spots. Western Pacific to East Africa and Red Sea, but unknown from many intervening localities such as islands of the western Indian Ocean; a bold species which readily approaches divers. Reported to 200 cm, 100 kg.

MAORI COD
Epinephelus undulatostriatus (Peters,1866)

Dorsal rays XI,15-16 (usually 16); anal rays III,8; pectoral rays 17-18 (usually 18); lateral-line scales 48-56; longitudinal scale series 96-110; body moderately deep, the depth 2.45-2.9 in standard length; teeth on midside of lower jaw in two rows; corner of preopercle with two to five enlarged serrae; caudal fin rounded; body with irregular slightly diagonal longitudinal pale bluish and brownish orange lines (the orange twice as broad); head greyish brown with numerous small close-set brownish orange spots; fins brown with faint brownish orange spots; median fins with a yellow margin. Southern Great Barrier Reef to New South Wales; from outer reef slopes in 5-73 m. Reaches nearly 50 cm.

THINSPINE ROCKCOD
Gracila albomarginata (Fowler and Bean, 1930)

Dorsal rays IX,14-15 (usually 15), the spines slender; anal rays III,9; pectoral rays 18-19 (usually 19); lateral-line scales 67-73; body depth 2.6-3.2 in standard length; head small, its length 3.0-3.2 in standard length; caudal fin slightly emarginate; adults greenish to brownish grey with 16-20 dark bars on side of body and a round dark spot about size of eye laterally at end of caudal peduncle; four or five narrow diagonal dark blue bands on head; a transient color phase in life shows a large white area on back flanked by black areas, and the caudal peduncle is whitish. Juveniles brown or violet with a broad red-orange stripe in dorsal and anal fins (more on soft portions); a similar band in each caudal lobe extending forward onto edges of peduncle. Indo-Pacific; usually in outer reef areas at depths greater than 15 m; an unusually active swimmer for a rockcod. To nearly 40 cm.

Gracila albomarginata Adult ▲ Juv. ▼

SQUARETAIL CORAL TROUT
Plectropomus areolatus (Rüppell, 1830)

Dorsal rays VIII,ll; anal rays III,8; pectoral rays 15-16 (rarely 15); lateral-line scales 83-97; small embedded scales on interorbital space; gill raker at angle of first gill arch clearly shorter than gill filaments at angle; body depth 3.15-3.7 in standard length; a pair of very large canine teeth anteriorly in jaws and one to four moderate canines on side of lower jaw (true of other *Plectropomus*); outer margin of anal fin slightly convex; caudal fin truncate to slightly emarginate; reddish brown with numerous round dark-edged blue spots on head and body, including ventrally; spots usually separated by about a spot diameter from adjacent spots; median fins with dark-edged blue spots notably smaller than those of body; paired fins without spots except basally on pectorals; caudal fin with a white posterior margin and broad blackish submarginal band. Marshall Islands and Samoa to the Maldives and Red Sea. Largest reported, 53 cm, but probably attains 70 cm. *P. truncatus* Fowler and Bean is a synonym.

CHINESE FOOTBALLER
Plectropomus laevis (Lacepède, 1802)

Dorsal rays VIII,ll; anal rays III,8; pectoral rays 16-18 (usually 17); lateral-line scales 92-115; interorbital space scaleless; body depth 2.95-3.65 in standard length; gill raker at angle of first gill arch shorter than gill filaments at angle; outer margin of anal fin straight; caudal fin slightly emarginate; two colour phases, one white with five chocolate brown bars on head and body which are broader dorsally, scattered small dark-edged blue spots, and yellow fins; second phase reddish brown with numerous small dark-edged blue spots on head, body, and fins; dark bars as in the first phase usually present but less conspicuous. Indo-Pacific (except Red Sea); this and other species of the genus prey mainly on reef fishes. Reaches at least 100 cm. *P. melanoleucus* (Lacepède) is a synonym. Although esteemed as food fishes, the species of *Plectropomus* are among the worst offenders in causing ciguatera fish poisoning.

Plectropomus laevis Dark phase ▼ Pale phase ▲

117

CORAL TROUT
Plectropomus leopardus (Lacepède, 1802)

Dorsal rays VIII,ll; anal rays III,8; pectoral rays 15-17 (usually 16); lateral-line scales 89-99; gill raker at angle of first gill arch longer than gill filaments at angle; interorbital space and top of snout scaleless; body depth 2.9-3.6 in standard length; outer margin of anal fin straight to slightly convex; caudal fin slightly emarginate; greenish to reddish brown with numerous dark-edged blue dots on head, body, and median fins, the dots generally not extending onto abdomen and thorax below level of lower edge of pectoral fins (dots on body of 25-45 cm fish less than 1 mm); caudal fin with a narrow whitish margin in the center, sometimes with a dark submarginal band. Fiji and Caroline Islands to Western Australia; the most common species of the genus on the Great Barrier Reef. Attains about 75 cm.

BARRED-CHEEK CORAL TROUT
Plectropomus maculatus (Bloch, 1790)

Dorsal rays VIII,ll; anal rays III,8; pectoral rays l6-17 (rarely 17); lateral-line scales 88-101; interorbital space and top of snout scaleless; gill raker at angle of first gill arch distinctly longer than longest gill filaments at angle; body depth 3.15-3.7 in standard length; outer margin of anal fin straight to concave; caudal fin slightly emarginate; pelvic fins 1.7-2.1 in head; greenish grey to brownish red with dark-edged blue spots (dark in preservative) of variable size, larger in general on head and anterior body; some spots, particularly on postorbital head and front of body, horizontally elongate; spots, especially anteriorly, widely separated (often fewer than l0 on operculum), and not extending onto lower fourth of body; median fins with small blue spots; a narrow whitish margin centroposteriorly on caudal fin; usually no blue spots on paired fins except one dorsally on pectoral base. Philippines, southeast Asia, Indonesia, and Australia; more common on coastal reefs of Queensland than the outer Great Barrier Reef. Reaches about 70 cm.

HIGHFIN CORAL TROUT
Plectropomus oligacanthus (Bleeker, 1854)

Dorsal rays VIII,ll; anal rays III,8; pectoral rays l4-16 (usually 15); lateral-line scales 66-96; interorbital space scaleless; body depth 3.l5-3.65 in standard length; third to fifth soft rays of dorsal fin and second to fourth rays of anal fin prolonged, thus forming an elevated anterior lobe to these fins; caudal fin emarginate; reddish brown to red with blue lines and small spots on head, vertical blue lines on side of body (may be broken into segments), and small blue spots dorsally, ventrally, and posteriorly on body and on caudal fin; spinous portion of dorsal fin with diagonal blue lines; soft portions of dorsal and anal fins with rows of blue dashes and small blue spots. Known only from the Philippines, Indonesia, New Guinea, Solomons, and northern Great Barrier Reef. Reaches about 65 cm.

LYRETAIL TROUT
Variola albimarginata Baissac, 1953

Dorsal rays IX,14; anal rays III,8; pectoral rays 18-19 (usually 18); lateral-line scales 64-75; gill rakers 7-9 + 13-16; body depth 3.0-3.4 in standard length; one or two large canines on side of lower jaw (in addition to anterior canines); anterior interspinous membranes of dorsal fin slightly incised; dorsal and anal fins pointed posteriorly; caudal fin of adults very lunate; light red with short irregular yellow lines and scattered small irregular red-edged bluish white to pale lavender spots on body; head orange-yellow, densely spotted with red; median fins with small pink and red spots, the caudal with a narrow white margin centroposteriorly and a dark submarginal band; paired fins yellowish, suffused with red. Western Pacific to western Indian Ocean; a coral reef species known from depths of l5-100 m. Attains 60 cm. Although adequately described by Baissac (1956), some authors have continued to misidentify this species as *V. louti*.

CORONATION TROUT
Variola louti (Forsskål, 1775)

Dorsal rays IX,l3-15 (nearly always l4); anal rays III,8; pectoral rays 17-19 (usually 18); lateral-line scales 64-78; gill rakers 7-10+15-18; body depth 2.85-3.25 in standard length; dentition as above; anterior interspinous membranes of dorsal fin slightly incised; posterior dorsal and anal fins pointed; caudal fin of adults very lunate; reddish brown to red, shading to orange-yellow ventrally on head and abdomen, with numerous small spots that may be pale blue, violet, or pink on head, body, and fins; fins with broad yellow posterior margins; juveniles with an irregular dark stripe from eye to upper caudal peduncle and a dark spot at upper base of caudal fin. Indo-Pacific; occurs on coral reefs from a few to at least 100 m; feeds primarily on fishes. Reaches 80 cm. Has been implicated in ciguatera fish poisoning.

Variola louti Adult ▼ Juv. ▲

SUBFAMILY GRAMMISTINAE

TRIBE LIOPROPOMINI

HEADBAND PERCH
Liopropoma mitratum Lubbock & Randall, 1978

Dorsal rays VI-I-I,ll-12 (rarely 11); anal rays III,8; pectoral rays 13-15; lateral-line scales 45-48, the lateral line highly arched over pectoral region (true of other *Liopropoma*); scales dorsally on snout reaching to or slightly in front of posterior nostrils; body elongate, the depth 3.2-4.l5 in standard length; head pointed (also characteristic of the genus); no large pores in interorbital space; posterior margin of preopercle with 19-30 serrae; caudal fin slightly emarginate, the corners of fin slightly rounded; red to reddish brown, often suffused with yellow posteriorly, usually with faint longitudinal dark lines following scale rows; a yellow band across front of interorbital space, one on side of snout, and one to three passing posteriorly from eye. Scattered localities throughout the Indo-Pacific in the depth range of 3-46 m; like others of the genus, very secretive. Attains 8.6 cm.

L. mitratum ▲ *L. multilineatum* ▼

MANYLINE PERCH
Liopropoma multilineatum Randall & Taylor, 1988

Dorsal rays VI-I-I,11-12 (rarely ll); anal rays III,8; pectoral rays 13-14 (rarely 13); lateral-line scales 46-47; scales dorsally on snout nearly reaching base of upper lip; body depth 2.95-3.45 in standard length; a pair of large pores in interorbital space (one on each side); posterior margin of preopercle with l0-16 small serrae; caudal fin emarginate, the lobes broadly rounded; body yellow with red longitudinal lines following scale rows, becoming red on caudal peduncle with a narrow white midlateral stripe; head light red, suffused with yellow posteriorly. Philippines to the Coral Sea and Fiji; depth of capture has ranged from 25-46 m; generally taken from caves. Reaches 8 cm.

METEOR PERCH
Liopropoma susumi (Jordan & Seale, 1906)

Dorsal rays VI-I-I,ll-12 (rarely 11); anal rays III,8; pectoral rays 15-16 (usually 15); lateral-line scales 44-47 (modally 46); scales dorsally on snout usually reaching to or slightly in front of nostrils; body depth 3.3-3.65 in standard length; no enlarged pores in interorbital space; posterior margin of preopercle with 6-17 serrae; caudal fin rounded to slightly emarginate in center, the corners broadly rounded; grey, shading to light red on caudal peduncle, with eight yellowish brown stripes; fins light red. Line Islands and Samoa to East Africa; occurs in caves or crevices in reefs; taken in the depth range of 2-34 m. The most common species of the genus. Largest, 9.2 cm. *Flagelloserranus meteori* Kotthaus is a synonym based on the late postlarval stage with greatly elongate and flexible second and third dorsal spines.

FLATHEAD PERCH
Rainfordia opercularis McCulloch, 1923

Dorsal rays IV-I,9, the two fins widely separated; anal rays II,8; pectoral rays 16-17; lateral-line scales 46-47; body elongate, the depth about 5.7-6.1 in standard length; dorsal part of head very flat; upper part of operculum joined by membrane to shoulder region; a series of spines at edge of opercle, subopercle, and interopercle; caudal fin rounded; dark orange with six narrow dark-edged light blue stripes and a small blue-edged black spot at midbase of caudal fin. Queensland to Western Australia; occurs in caves in coral reefs. To 15 cm.

TRIBE DIPLOPRIONI

ARROWHEAD SOAPFISH
Belonoperca chabanaudi Fowler and Bean, 1930

Dorsal rays VIII (rarely IX)-I,10; anal rays II,8; pectoral rays 13-15; lateral-line scales 69-76; scales ctenoid; body moderately elongate, the depth 3.5-3.7 in standard length; head pointed; upper edge of opercle joined to body by membrane (true of other soapfishes); preopercle coarsely serrate; caudal fin truncate; basal half of inner pelvic ray joined by membrane to abdomen (also characteristic of other soapfishes); bluish olive with numerous very small brown spots; a bright yellow spot dorsally on caudal peduncle; a large blue-edged black spot in spinous dorsal fin. Samoa and Marshall Islands to East Africa; a secretive fish which rarely ventures from the shelter of caves. Reaches 15 cm. Capable of producing the skin toxin grammistin.

TRIBE DIPLOPRIONI

BARRED SOAPFISH
Diploprion bifasciatum Cuvier, 1828

Dorsal rays VIII,13-16, deeply notched between spinous and soft portions; anal rays II,12-13; pectoral rays 17-18; lateral-line scales 80-88; scales on body mainly ctenoid; body deep, the depth 2.0-2.4 in standard length, and compressed, the width 3.3-4.0 in depth; preopercular margin coarsely serrate; caudal fin rounded; pelvic fins very long, reaching beyond spinous portion of anal fin; light yellow with two blackish bars, one on head through eye and a broader one on body and most of spinous portion of dorsal fin; occasional individuals entirely black. Western Pacific to India; secretes the skin toxin grammistin under stress. Reaches 25 cm. Also known in Australia as the Yellow Emperor.

TRIBE GRAMMISTINI

SIXLINE SOAPFISH
Grammistes sexlineatus (Thunberg, 1792)

Dorsal rays VII,13-14, the fin deeply divided between spinous and soft portions; anal rays II,9; pectoral rays 16-18; lateral-line scales 60-72; scales cycloid, embedded; body depth 2.3-2.8 in standard length; a small fleshy flap on tip of chin; posterior preopercular margin with two to four short broad-based spines; caudal fin rounded; adults black with six to eight yellow stripes (not counting one middorsally on head and nape); stripes on very large adults break up to series of dashes; juveniles with fewer stripes, and small juveniles with two series of large pale yellow spots. Indo-Pacific; a shallow-water reef fish that tends to be cryptic. Largest reported, 27 cm. Well known for producing the skin toxin grammistin which dissuades predators.

TRIBE PSEUDOGRAMMINI

OCELLATED PODGE
Grammistops ocellata Schultz, 1953

Dorsal rays VII,12-13 (rarely 13), the spinous and soft portions almost completely divided; anal rays III,8-9 (rarely 8); pectoral rays 14-15; lateral-line scales 58-67; scales cycloid, embedded; body depth 3.1-3.7 in standard length; head pointed; posterior preopercular margin smooth or with one or two short broad-based spines; grey-brown, the head yellowish with an ocellated black spot nearly as large as eye on opercle. Indo-Pacific, but known from few localities; never observed underwater by us; all specimens have been taken from caves with ichthyocides. Largest, 13.2 cm. Also produces a skin toxin, hence has been regarded as a soapfish, but it has more characters to ally it to *Pseudogramma* and related genera.

PORELESS PODGE
Aporops bilinearis Schultz, 1943

Dorsal rays VII,23-24; anal rays III,19-21; pectoral rays 16-18; longitudinal scale series 59-71; two lateral lines, the anterodorsal one ending below middle third of soft portion of dorsal fin, the midlateral posterior one commencing below or slightly in advance of it; scales ctenoid; body depth 3.1-3.6 in standard length; no large pores in interorbital space and no pores around edge of eye; a spine on upper part of preopercle pointing upward and backward; caudal fin small and rounded; pelvic fins small; yellowish brown with dark brown blotches smaller than pupil on body and dorsally on head. Indo-Pacific; cryptic. Reaches 11 cm.

PALESPOTTED PODGE
Pseudogramma polyacantha (Bleeker, 1856)

Dorsal rays VII-VIII (rarely VIII),19-22; anal rays III,15-18; pectoral rays 17-18; longitudinal scale series 50-54; a single dorsal lateral line ending beneath rear base of dorsal fin; scales ctenoid; body depth 3.3-3.5 in standard length; a pair of large pores in interorbital space, and other pores around edge of eye; a spine on upper part of preopercle pointing downward and backward; caudal fin small and rounded; pelvic fins small; yellowish brown with pale spots larger than pupil on body (the intervening spaces thus forming a darker brown reticulum); a dark brown spot nearly as large as eye on opercle. Indo-Pacific; one of the most common fishes taken in ichthyocide stations on coral reefs and adjacent rubble bottoms, yet we have never observed it while diving. Attains 8 cm.

DOTTYBACKS AND EEL BLENNIES

FAMILY PSEUDOCHROMIDAE

These are small, often brilliantly coloured fishes that are cryptic inhabitants of crevices and ledges. They have an elongate, compressed body; a single dorsal fin with I-III weak spines and 21-38 soft rays; anal fin with III spines and 11-21 soft rays; jaws and vomer with small, sharp teeth. The members of the genus *Pseudoplesiops* were formerly included in a separate family, Pseudoplesiopidae, but recent investigations have resulted in their inclusion in Pseudochromidae. They differ from other genera in the family by having a much-abbreviated lateral line, and I,3-I,4 pelvic rays (versus I,5). Typically the dottybacks spend much of their time hidden from view, but make brief forays into the open. The Royal Dottyback (*Pseudochromis paccagnellae*) has a particularly striking coloration and is a favourite of marine aquarists. The colour of dottybacks is often variable within a single species and is frequently related to sex (although data are lacking for several species). It appears that sex reversal is a common phenomenon in this group. The female deposits a ball of eggs that adheres to the substratum. It is guarded by the male who frequently picks it up with its mouth to shift the position. Hatching occurs after several days. Dottybacks feed on small benthic invertebrates such as crabs and prawns, and also small fishes. The eel blennies of the family Congrogadidae were formerly included in a separate family, but recent investigations indicate they should be classified as a subfamily within the Pseudochromidae. We are grateful to Anthony C. Gill of the Australian Museum for preparing the individual species accounts for this family.

SUBFAMILY CONGROGADINAE

CARPET EEL BLENNY
Congrogadus subducens (Richardson, 1843)

Dorsal rays 68-79; anal rays 57-66; pectoral rays 7-11; pelvic fin absent; no unbranched rays in caudal fin; generally brown to greenish brown with series of irregular yellow-white bars or rows of pale blotches along sides; usually an ocellated black spot present on the opercle; a cryptic species that lives in caves and rocky crevices. Malay Peninsula and Philippine Islands to Australia. Attains 45 cm.

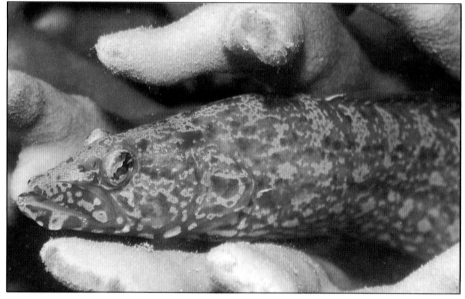

SUBFAMILY PSEUDOCHROMIDAE

OBLIQUE-LINED DOTTYBACK
Cypho purpurascens (De Vis, 1884)

Dorsal rays III,22-24; anal rays III,13-15; pectoral rays 17-19; pelvic rays I,5; scales in lateral series 30-37; anterior lateral-line scales 23-32; posterior lateral-line scales 3-9 + 0-2; circumpeduncular scales 16-17; gill rakers 4-7 + 10-13 = 14-19; overall red, except head orange; blue margins on scales and on dorsal and anal fins; a blue ring partially around eye; dorsal fin with an ocellated black spot. Southwestern Pacific. Grows to 7.5 cm.

MULTICOLOURED DOTTYBACK

Ogilbyina novaehollandiae (Steindachner, 1880)

Dorsal rays III,34-38; anal rays III,19-20; pectoral rays 17-19; pelvic rays I,5; scales in lateral series 47-54; anterior lateral-line scales 40-46; posterior lateral-line scales 8-15 + 1-3; circumpeduncular scales 22-25; gill rakers 5-8 + 10-12 = 16-20; juveniles pale pink, bright yellow on head and anterior part of dorsal fin; males greyish with reddish head, large specimens usually dark grey to black; females pinkish to bright yellow or greenish with short reddish bars below posterior dorsal fin; large females sometimes dark grey to black with red belly. Southern Great Barrier Reef. Maximum recorded size 10 cm.

Ogilbyina novaehollandiae Male ▲ Female ▼

QUEENSLAND DOTTYBACK

Ogilbyina queenslandiae (Saville-Kent, 1893)

Dorsal rays III,32-37; anal rays III,18-21; pectoral rays 18-20; pelvic rays I,5; scales in lateral series 43-56; anterior lateral-line scales 43-56; posterior lateral-line scales 38-50; circumpeduncular scales 24-26; gill rakers 5-8 + 11-13 = 16-20; colour variable, depending on sex; male mainly reddish anteriorly and purplish posteriorly; dorsal, anal, and caudal fins bluish except dorsal reddish on anterior part; female with a greyish head, largely yellow-orange on side, with 5-6 brown bars on upper half of anterior part of body; fins largely reddish. Great Barrier Reef. Attains 15 cm.

Ogilbyina queenslandiae Male ▲ Female ▼

SAILFIN DOTTYBACK
Ogilbyina velifera (Lubbock, 1980)

Dorsal rays II,25-26; anal rays III,16; pectoral rays 17-18; pelvic rays I,5; scales in lateral series 46-50; anterior lateral-line scales 30-39; posterior lateral-line scales 6-13 + 0-2; circumpeduncular scales 22-24; gill rakers 5-7 + 10-12 = 15-19; adults overall pale grey to yellowish with upper part of head bluish; a dark blue spot at front of dorsal fin; dorsal fin bluish, grading to yellow posteriorly; other fins yellowish; juveniles (and females?) light mauve to pinkish with top of head and front of dorsal fin yellowish; median fins bluish. Great Barrier Reef. Reported to 12 cm.

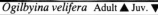
Ogilbyina velifera Adult ▲ Juv. ▼

DOUBLE-STRIPED DOTTYBACK
Pseudochromis bitaeniatus (Fowler, 1931)

Dorsal rays III,27; anal rays III,15; pectoral rays 18-19; pelvic rays I,5; anterior lateral-line scales 32-33; posterior lateral-line scales 8-10; gill rakers 4 + 12 = 16; head yellowish; body with two broad dark brown stripes with a band of white between. Indonesia to northeastern Queensland. Grows to 7 cm.

BLUE-BARRED DOTTYBACK
Pseudochromis cyanotaenia Bleeker, 1857

Dorsal rays III,22-23; anal rays III,13; pectoral rays 18-19; pelvic rays I,5; scales in lateral series 29-36; anterior lateral-line scales 23-31; posterior lateral-line scales 6-11 + 0-2; circumpeduncular scales 16; gill rakers 3-5 + 10-11 = 14-16; male purple except breast, belly, and side of head yellow, also anterior half of lateral line yellow; females brown except caudal fin red basally and yellow on outer portion. Eastern Indian Ocean to central Pacific. Reaches 6 cm. Has usually been referred to as *P. tapeinosoma*.

Pseudochromis cyanotaenia Male ▲ Female ▼

BROWN DOTTYBACK
Pseudochromis fuscus Müller & Troschel, 1849

Dorsal rays III,25-28; anal rays III,13-15; pectoral rays 17-20; pelvic rays I,5; scales in lateral series 34-43; anterior lateral-line scales 23-36; posterior lateral-line scales 4-14 + 0-3; circumpeduncular scales 19-21; gill rakers 5-9 + 11-15 + 17-21; two colour varieties are seen, one that is primarily brown and the other mainly yellow, both may have longitudinal rows of small blue spots. Central Indian Ocean to western Pacific. Attains 9 cm.

Pseudochromis fuscus Dark phase ▲ Pale phase ▼

FIRETAIL DOTTYBACK
Pseudochromis flammicauda Lubbock &
Goldman, 1976

Dorsal rays III,23-25; anal rays III,13-
14; pectoral rays 17-19; pelvic rays I,5;
scales in lateral series 36-40; anterior lateral-
line scales 24-30; posterior lateral-line scales
4-10 + 0; circumpeduncular scales 17-20;
gill rakers 4-6 + 10-12 = 14-18; overall light
blue grey except head yellowish tan and
caudal fin red orange. Great Barrier Reef.
Maximum size, 5.5 cm.

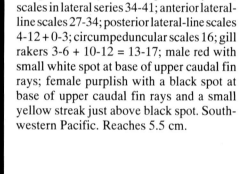

SPOT-TAILED DOTTYBACK
Pseudochromis jamesi Schultz, 1943

Dorsal rays III,24-26; anal rays III,13-
14; pectoral rays 18-20; pelvic rays I,5;
scales in lateral series 34-41; anterior lateral-
line scales 27-34; posterior lateral-line scales
4-12 + 0-3; circumpeduncular scales 16; gill
rakers 3-6 + 10-12 = 13-17; male red with
small white spot at base of upper caudal fin
rays; female purplish with a black spot at
base of upper caudal fin rays and a small
yellow streak just above black spot. Southwestern Pacific. Reaches 5.5 cm.

Pseudochromis jamesi **Male ▲ Female ▼**

ROYAL DOTTYBACK
Pseudochromis paccagnellae Axelrod, 1973

Dorsal rays III,21-22; anal rays III,11-13; pectoral rays 15-18; pelvic rays I,5; scales in lateral series 33-42; anterior lateral-line scales 17-28; posterior lateral-line scales 0-10 + 0-2; circumpeduncular scales 16-18; gill rakers 5-8 + 14-17 = 19-24; anterior half brilliant magenta, posterior half abruptly yellow. Indonesia to Melanesia and Australia. Attains 7 cm.

MIDNIGHT DOTTYBACK
Pseudochromis paranox Lubbock & Goldman, 1976

Dorsal rays III,28-31; anal rays III,16-18; pectoral rays 17-19; pelvic rays I,5; scales in lateral series 36-42; anterior lateral-line scales 22-34; posterior lateral-line scales 0-17 + 0-3; circumpeduncular scales 18-21; gill rakers 5-6 + 11-13 = 13-17; overall dark brown to black. Southwestern Pacific. Reported to reach 7 cm.

SPOTTED DOTTYBACK
Pseudochromis quinquedentatus McCulloch, 1926

Dorsal rays III,25-26; anal rays III,14; pectoral rays 17-20; pelvic rays I,5; scales in lateral series 39-47; anterior lateral-line scales 31-40; posterior lateral-line scales 6-14 + 0-1; circumpeduncular scales 20; gill rakers 5-7 + 10-12 = 16-18; yellow, tan, or brownish with longitudinal rows of small brown spots. Northern Australia. Attains 9.5 cm.

129

YELLOWFIN DOTTYBACK
Pseudochromis wilsoni (Whitley, 1929)

Dorsal rays III,25-27; anal rays III,13-15; pectoral rays 17-19; pelvic rays I,5; scales in lateral series 38-45; anterior lateral-line scales 28-37; posterior lateral-line scales 7-14 + 0-2; circumpeduncular scales 19-23; gill rakers 3-7 + 11-14 = 14-20; males purplish with yellow iris; females more brownish with yellow dorsal fin and yellow submarginal bands on caudal fin. Northern Australia. Maximum size, 8 cm.

Pseudochromis wilsoni Male ▲ Female ▼

BUG-EYED DOTTYBACK
Pseudoplesiops knighti Allen, 1987

Dorsal rays I,23; anal rays I-III,13-15; pectoral rays 16-18; pelvic rays I,4; transverse scale rows from upper edge of gill opening to caudal base 30-33; a single tubed lateral-line scale; predorsal scales 8-10, extending forward almost to above middle of eyes; scales with radii in anterior field only; posterior body scales ctenoid; gill rakers 3-5 + 10-12; colour varies from bright yellow to brown; perimeter of eye often narrowly blue or purple. Indonesia, Melanesia, and northern Australia. Largest specimen 4.5 cm.

FINE-SCALED DOTTYBACK
Pseudoplesiops multisquamatus Allen, 1987

Dorsal rays II,24-26; anal rays II,14-16; pectoral rays 16-18; pelvic rays I,4; transverse scale rows from upper edge of gill opening to caudal base 56-63; a single tubed lateral-line scale; predorsal scales 11-14, extending forward to midway between posterior edge of eyes and dorsal origin; scales with radii in anterior field only; posterior body scales cycloid; gill rakers 5 + 12-16 = 16-21; overall red, reddish brown, or pink; usually with yellow suffusion on head; fins mainly translucent except caudal fin yellow. Eastern Indian Ocean to central Pacific. Reaches 6 cm.

LARGE-SCALED DOTTYBACK
Pseudoplesiops rosae Schultz, 1943

Dorsal rays I,22-23; anal rays I,13-14; pectoral rays 16-18; pelvic rays I,3; transverse scale rows from upper edge of gill opening to caudal base 26-29; a single tubed lateral-line scale; predorsal scales 7-10, extending forward almost to above middle of eyes; scales with radii in all fields; posterior body scales ctenoid; gill rakers 2-4 + 7-9 = 9-12; head orange, grading to brown on body; iris red with perimeter of eye narrowly black. Eastern Indian Ocean to central Pacific. Attains 3 cm.

BEARDED DOTTYBACK
Pseudoplesiops sp.

Dorsal rays I,27-28; anal rays I-II,16-18; pectoral rays 16-18; pelvic rays I,4; transverse scale rows from upper edge of gill opening to caudal base 34-37; a single tubed lateral-line scale; predorsal scales 8-12, extending forward to midway between posterior edge of eyes and dorsal origin; scales with radii in anterior field only; posterior body scales ctenoid; gill rakers 2-4 + 7-10 = 10-13; a fleshy flap on chin; overall pale yellow to tan. Central Indian Ocean to western Pacific. To 4.5 cm. Closely related and similar in appearance to *P. revellei* from the central Pacific.

RING-EYED DOTTYBACK
Pseudoplesiops typus Bleeker, 1858

Dorsal rays II,24-26; anal rays II-III,14-16; pectoral rays 16-18; pelvic rays I,4; transverse scale rows from upper edge of gill opening to caudal base 33-39; a single tubed lateral-line scale; predorsal scales 10-16, extending forward to midway between posterior edge of eyes and dorsal origin; scales with radii in all fields; posterior body scales ctenoid in small (less than 3 cm SL) specimens, becoming cycloid in larger specimens; gill rakers 2-4 + 9-12 = 12-16; overall yellowish; narrow white or blue margin on dorsal and anal fins; perimeter of eye narrowly black. Eastern Indian Ocean to central Pacific. Grows to 7 cm.

LONGFINS
FAMILY PLESIOPIDAE

Longfins are mostly small cryptic fishes that dwell in rocky fissures and caves. The family contains about 17 species in six genera of which most occur in temperate and tropical seas of Australia. The family is characterised by a combination of features that include a single dorsal fin, the membranes often deeply incised between the spines; there are XI to XIV spines and 6-16 soft rays in the dorsal fin; III spines and 7-20 soft rays in the anal fin; the pelvic fin has one spine and four soft rays; lateral line in two parts. Most species have long pelvic fins, and the soft portions of the dorsal and anal fins may be prolonged posteriorly. Members of the genus *Assessor* are common in caves along the length of the Great Barrier Reef. They often swim upside down. Males of this genus (and possibly other plesiopids) incubate the egg mass in their mouth. Food items include small fishes, crabs, shrimps, copepods, amphipods, gastropods, and polychaetes. Also known as prettyfins.

YELLOW DEVILFISH
Assessor flavissimus Allen & Kuiter, 1976

Dorsal rays XI,8-10; anal rays III,9 or 10; pectoral rays 14-16; lateral-line scales 17-23 + 3-9; scales above lateral line finely ctenoid; caudal fin forked; bright yellow. Northern Great Barrier Reef. To 5.5 cm.

BLUE DEVILFISH
Assessor macneilli Whitley, 1935

Dorsal rays XI,8 or 9; anal rays III,9; pectoral rays 15; lateral-line scales 16-21 + 1-7; all scales cycloid; caudal fin forked; dark blue with light blue margin on all fins except pectorals. Great Barrier Reef and New Caledonia. Attains 6 cm.

COMET
Calloplesiops altivelis (Steindachner, 1903)

Dorsal rays XI,8 or 9; anal rays III,9; pectoral rays 18 or 19; lateral-line scales 19 or 20 + 9 or 10; dorsal and anal fins somewhat elevated and caudal fin elongate, lanceolate in shape; dark brown to blackish with numerous small white spots, a prominent ocellus at base of last dorsal rays. East Africa and Red Sea to Tonga and the Line Islands. Reaches 16 cm. When frightened, this fish moves head-first into the reef, leaving the posterior part of the body exposed. It then bears a resemblance to a white-spotted moray eel, the gap between the dorsal and anal fins appearing like the mouth, and the dorsal fin ocellus the eye (McCosker, 1977).

BLUE-TIP LONGFIN
Paraplesiops poweri Ogilby, 1908

Dorsal rays XII,9 or 10 (rarely 9); anal rays III,10; pectoral rays 18-20 (usually 19); lateral-line scales 28-32 + 9-13; caudal fin rounded; overall brownish with about 8-10 narrow dark bars on sides, margin of spinous dorsal fin blue. Central and southern Queensland and adjacent Great Barrier Reef. To 14 cm.

RED-TIPPED LONGFIN
Plesiops coeruleolineatus Rüppell, 1835

Dorsal rays X to XII,6-8 (frequently XI,8); anal rays III,8 or 9; pectoral rays 19-23; lateral-line scales 18-21 + 6-13; caudal fin rounded; brown to blackish with orange-red dorsal spine tips, faint orange submarginal band on caudal fin, and a blue line in the dorsal and anal fins. East Africa and Red Sea to Australia and the Marshall Islands. Reaches 8 cm.

BLUE-SPOTTED LONGFIN
Plesiops corallicola Bleeker, 1853

Dorsal rays XII,7; anal rays III,8; pectoral rays 20; lateral-line scales 17-18 + 13-14; caudal fin rounded; dark brown to blackish with lighter cross bars on sides, body and fins covered with small bluish or white spots; a large ocellated dark spot on gill cover. Madagascar to Tonga and the Line Islands. To 8 cm.

SPINY BASSLETS

FAMILY ACANTHOCLINIDAE

These small fishes are very similar in appearance to the dottybacks (Pseudochromidae), differing primarily by their greater number of spines in the dorsal and anal fins. The family contains three genera and five species that range from India to the Marshall Islands and New Zealand. They are secretive dwellers of reef crevices and therefore are seldom observed.

GRUNTERS

FAMILY TERAPONTIDAE

These are small, generalised percoid fishes with an oblong to ovate shape and somewhat compressed body; the opercle has two spines. The dorsal fin is notched and has XI to XIV stout spines and 8-14 soft rays; the anal fin has III spines and 7-12 soft rays; the caudal fin is rounded, truncate, or emarginate. The scales are small to moderate and ctenoid; the lateral line is complete and extends a short distance onto the caudal fin; the dorsal and anal fins

BANDED SPINY BASSLET
Belonepterygion fasciolatum (Ogilby, 1889)

Dorsal rays XVIII,6; anal rays X,5; pectoral rays 18-19; pelvic rays I,2; three lateral lines, uppermost along back, middle one from pectoral-fin axil to base of central caudal-fin rays, lower one from just above pelvic spine base to above last anal ray;

have a scaly sheath; the interorbital area, snout, preorbitals, and lower jaw are scaleless. The family contains approximately 45 species and is confined to the Indo-Pacific region. Aside from a few relatively widespread marine forms, most species (about 30) have evolved in fresh waters of Australia and New Guinea. Most marine species have colour patterns consisting of black stripes on a silvery ground. They are usually not seen around reefs; several are common among the catch of commercial trawlers, but are discarded as trash. The diet of

uppermost lateral-line scales 40-44; brown with series of narrow dark brown bars on sides; breast and lower half of head orange; a white stripe from below eye to upper pectoral fin base; fins mostly brown, the dorsal and anal becoming intensely dark posteriorly. West and east coasts of Australia in tropical and subtropical seas; also Lord Howe Island. Grows to 5 cm.

grunters is mixed, consisting of algae, insects, benthic invertebrates, and fishes.

CRESCENT GRUNTER
Terapon jarbua (Forsskål, 1775)

Dorsal rays XI-XII,9-11; anal rays III,7-10; pectoral rays 13-14; lateral-line scales 69-93; silvery white with three upward-curved stripes on sides; spinous dorsal fin with large black blotch; several black stripes on caudal fin. East Africa and Red Sea to Samoa; juveniles and adults frequently found in brackish or fresh waters, but spawning occurs in the sea; uncommon on the Great Barrier Reef except around some high islands with freshwater runoff. Reaches a maximum length of 32 cm.

FLAGTAILS
FAMILY KUHLIIDAE

These are small perch-like fishes that are usually silvery in colour and occur in either marine shallows or fresh water. The family contains two genera, *Parakuhlia* of West Africa with a single species and *Kuhlia* of the Indo-Pacific with about six species. They are characterised by a single dorsal fin that is deeply notched; a well-developed scaly sheath at the base of the dorsal and anal fins; III anal spines; fine teeth in the jaws arranged in bands; fine teeth also present on roof of mouth; caudal fin moderately forked and usually marked with black stripes or spots (thus the name flagtail). They are nocturnal predators that feed mainly on planktonic crustaceans. Juveniles and young adults frequently inhabit tidepools or form schools close to shore. Australian freshwater fishes of the genera *Edelia, Nannatherina,* and *Nannoperca* were formerly classified in the Kuhliidae, but recent studies indicate they should be placed in the Percichthyidae.

FIVEBAND FLAGTAIL
Kuhlia mugil (Bloch & Schneider, 1801)

Dorsal rays X,9-11; anal rays III,9-11; pectoral rays 14; lateral-line scales 48-56; caudal fin with five black bands, overall silvery. Indo-Pacific, including tropical eastern Pacific; frequently seen in large aggregatons in areas affected by surge. Reaches 20 cm.

BIGEYES
FAMILY PRIACANTHIDAE

This family consists of four genera and a total of 16 species, of which 13 occur in the Indo-Pacific region. Some such as *Cookeolus japonicus* (Cuvier) occur only in relatively deep water. In addition to their very large eye, the obvious basis for the common name of the group, they have a relatively deep and compressed body, very oblique mouth with strongly projecting lower jaw, small conical teeth in a narrow band in jaws, small rough scales, scaled head, and large pelvic fins which are joined to the abdomen by a membrane. They are all or partly red; some are able to quickly change their colour from solid red to blotched red and silver, or to silver. As their large eyes might suggest, they are nocturnal; food-habit data indicate that they feed primarily on larger zooplankton such as shrimp and crab larvae, larval fishes, larval polychaete worms, and small squids and octopuses.

GLASSEYE
Heteropriacanthus cruentatus (Lacepède, 1801)

Dorsal rays X,12-13 (usually 13); anal rays III,13-14 (usually 14); pectoral rays 17-19 (usually 18); lateral-line scales 63-81; gill rakers 21-25; border of preopercle broadly scaleless; a flat spine at corner of preopercle extending nearly to edge of operculum; body depth 2.3-2.7 in standard length; pelvic fins not very long, their length contained 1.4-1.8 in head length; caudal fin truncate, slightly rounded, or slightly double emarginate; colour variable, silvery pink, mottled red, or solid red; faint dark dots in median fins, most evident on the caudal. Circumglobal in tropical and subtropical seas, more often in insular than continental areas; inhabits shallow reefs, generally less than 20 m; usually seen in caves by day. Largest recorded, 32 cm.

BLOCH'S BIGEYE
Priacanthus blochii Bleeker, 1853

Dorsal rays X,12-14 (usually 13); anal rays III,13-15 (usually 14); pectoral rays 17-19 (usually 17); lateral-line scales 69-77; gill rakers 17-22; spine at corner of preopercle obsolescent in adults; body depth 2.6-2.9 in standard length; pectoral fins short,1.9-2.2 in head length; pelvic fins usually reaching beyond anal fin origin; caudal fin slightly rounded; red or pinkish silver blotched with red; usually with about l5 small dark spots along lateral line; pelvic fins dusky red with a small black basal spot. Samoa to the Gulf of Aden; usually from the depth range of l5-30 m on reefs. Attains about 35 cm.

CRESCENT-TAIL BIGEYE
Priacanthus hamrur (Forsskål, 1775)

Dorsal rays X,13-15 (usually 14); anal rays III,l3-16 (usually 14 or 15); pectoral rays 17-20 (usually 18 or 19); lateral-line scales 70-90; gill rakers 24-26; spine at corner of preopercle obsolescent in adults; body depth 2.5-2.9 in standard length; pectoral fins shorter than pelvic spine; pelvic fins long, reaching end of spinous portion of anal fin; caudal fin emarginate; usually uniform red to deep red with a series of about 15 small dark spots along lateral line; median and pelvic fins dusky red; a black spot at base of first three pelvic rays; capable of quickly altering to pinkish silver with six red bars on body and one extending ventrally from eye. Indo-Pacific; known from the depth range of about 15 to at least 250 m; easily approached underwater; sometimes seen in small groups. Reaches 40 cm. Closely related to the endemic *P. meeki* Jenkins of Hawaii and the Atlantic *P. arenatus* Cuvier.

CARDINALFISHES
FAMILY APOGONIDAE

These are small (usually under 10 cm), laterally compressed, often brightly coloured fishes. They have two separate dorsal fins, the first of six to eight spines, two anal spines, large eyes, a moderately large oblique mouth, and preopercle with a ridge preceding the margin. The Apogonidae is one of the largest coral fish families. They are represented in all tropical and warm temperate seas. The majority are distributed in the Indo-Pacific region. Worldwide there are an estimated 250 species in 21 genera; 94 species in 18 genera have been recorded from Australia. The common name is derived from the red coloration displayed by many of the species, but is somewhat misleading as shades of black, brown, yellow, and white are also well represented. Cardinalfishes occur in a diversity of habitats, but individual species are restricted to relatively narrow ecological zones. Some are found in sheltered sandy lagoons, often deep amongst the branches of coral formations. Others prefer caves and crevices of steep outer slopes. At dusk they emerge from these retreats for nocturnal feeding. Most species are seen as solitary individuals, in pairs, or in small aggregations. However, the semi-transparent species of *Rhabdamia* often occur in large aggregations that swarm above isolated coral bommies. Cardinalfishes are one of few marine fish families in which oral brooding is found. Courtship is often accompanied by flicking movements of the dorsal and pelvic fins. The prospective mates may also engage in chasing bouts and non-injurious nipping. During spawning the female releases a large gelatinous egg mass containing up to several hundred ova. The mass is summarily fertilised by the male who then engulfs it with his mouth. Egg-brooding males are easily distinguished by the swollen throat region, and the eggs can clearly be seen when the mouth is partially opened. Incubation lasts several days, during which time the male is unable to feed. Its main activity consists of periodically juggling the position of the egg mass. The larvae, measuring 2-4 mm, are planktonic for up to several weeks before settlement and subsequent transformation to the juvenile stage. Diet is variable according to species, but most consume some form of zooplankton (often copepods), and small benthic invertebrates such as crabs and prawns are also eaten.

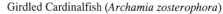

Girdled Cardinalfish (*Archamia zosterophora*)

GOLDBELLY CARDINALFISH
Apogon apogonides (Bleeker, 1856)

Dorsal rays VII-I,9; anal rays II,8; pectoral rays 14; lateral-line scales 28; gill rakers 5 + 15 or 16; mauve on back, becoming yellow on lower side with broken blue stripes or spots. East Africa to East Indies and northern Australia; generally uncommon, but sometimes seen around deep (over 30 m) bommies in the Coral Sea. To 10 cm.

STRIPED CARDINALFISH
Apogon angustatus (Smith & Radcliffe, 1911)

Dorsal rays VII-I,9; anal rays II,8; pectoral rays 14; lateral-line scales 28; gill rakers 5-6 + 13-15; overall whitish with five stripes on side which vary in colour from brassy to dark brown, and a dark spot at base of middle caudal fin rays; fin rays light red; similar to *A. nigrofasciatus* (see below), but has narrower dark stripes and usually 19 or 20 total gill rakers (versus 21-23). East Africa and Red Sea to Melanesia and Micronesia. Reaches 9 cm.

RING-TAILED CARDINALFISH
Apogon aureus (Lacepède, 1802)

Dorsal rays VII-I,9; anal rays II,8; pectoral rays 14; lateral-line scales 28; gill rakers 5-7 + 15-19; overall golden or bronzy with a black ring, which is broader dorsally and ventrally, around base of caudal fin; bright blue lines on head. East Africa to western Pacific; usually in small groups. Attains 12 cm.

THREE-SADDLE CARDINALFISH
Apogon bandanensis Bleeker, 1854

Dorsal rays VII-I,9; anal rays II,8; pectoral rays 13; lateral-line scales 28; total gill rakers usually 25-27; overall coppery or silvery with saddle or bar across base of caudal fin and wedge-shaped bar below eye; similar to *A. fuscus* (below), but usually has fewer gill rakers (25-27 vs 28-30, occasionally 26), and has faint saddles below the dorsal fins. East Indies to Samoa, north to Ryukyu Islands. To 10 cm.

RUBY CARDINALFISH
Apogon coccineus Rüppell, 1838

Dorsal rays VI-I,9; anal rays II,8; pectoral rays 13 or 14; lateral-line scales 25-26; gill rakers 3-4 + 11 or 12; overall semi-transparent and reddish. East Africa and Red Sea to Polynesia; found deep in caves and crevices during the day, therefore seldom seen. Attains 5 cm.

SPLIT-BANDED CARDINALFISH
Apogon compressus (Smith & Radcliffe, 1911)

Dorsal rays VI-I,9; anal rays II,9; pectoral rays 13 or 14; lateral-line scales 23-25; gill rakers 7 + 21; white or pinkish with about six red-brown stripes on side, the stripe originating at upper rear corner of eye split into two branches; 3-4 dark spots at base of caudal fin; eye blue. East Indies to Solomon Islands and north to Ryukyu Islands; usually in groups among branching corals; young fish bear a striking resemblance to *Cheilodipterus quinquelineatus*. Reaches 12 cm.

COOK'S CARDINALFISH
Apogon cookii Macleay, 1881

Dorsal rays VII-I,9; anal rays II,8; pectoral rays 15; lateral-line scales 28; gill rakers 4 or 5 + 12-14; whitish with 5-6 dark brown to yellowish brown stripes on side, the stripe originating at upper rear corner of eye incomplete; midlateral stripe ending in a distinct black spot at caudal-fin base. East Africa to Australia, north to Japan; occurs on coastal reefs and inner reefs of the Great Barrier Reef. To 10 cm.

YELLOW-STRIPED CARDINALFISH
Apogon cyanosoma Bleeker, 1853

Dorsal rays VII-I,9; anal rays II,8; pectoral rays 14; lateral-line scales 28; gill rakers 6 or 7 + 15 or 16; bluish silver with 6 orange-yellow stripes, including a short postocular stripe. East Africa and Red Sea to Australia and the Marshall Islands; sometimes in large aggregations around coral bommies. Attains 8 cm.

DOEDERLEIN'S CARDINALFISH
Apogon doederleini Jordan & Snyder, 1901

Dorsal rays VII-I,9; anal rays III,8 or 9; pectoral rays 14 or 15; lateral-line scales 28; gill rakers 2 or 3 + 10-12; whitish to pink with 4-5 narrow, brownish stripes on sides and large dark spot at base of caudal fin; fin rays light red. Western Pacific, but apparently antitropical. Southern Japan to Taiwan in the north and subtropical Australia to New Caledonia and the Kermadec Islands in the south. Attains 9 cm.

NARROWSTRIPE CARDINALFISH
Apogon exostigma (Jordan & Starks, 1906)

Dorsal rays VII-I,9; anal rays II,8; pectoral rays 12-14 (usually 13); lateral-line scales 23-25; gill rakers 2 + 8-11; light tan to whitish with blackish stripe through eye to base of caudal fin, tapering in width posteriorly; a small black spot immediately above lateral line at base of caudal fin. Red Sea to south-eastern Polynesia; usually seen in caves and under ledges. To 11 cm.

BROAD-BANDED CARDINALFISH
Apogon fasciatus (Shaw, 1790)

Dorsal rays VII-I,9; anal rays II,8; pectoral rays 15; lateral-line scales 27 or 28; gill rakers 5 + 16; tan or whitish with a broad, blackish, midlateral stripe which extends to end of caudal fin, and one or two narrow, dark stripes above; no black spot at caudal-fin base. East Africa and Red Sea to northern Australia, north to Japan; occurs in sandy or weedy areas, usually around inner reefs. Attains 10 cm. *A. quadrifasciatus* is a synonym.

SPUR-CHEEK CARDINALFISH
Apogon fraenatus Valenciennes, 1832

Dorsal rays VII-I,9; anal rays II,8; pectoral rays 13-16 (usually 14); lateral-line scales 23-25; gill rakers 2 or 3 + 7-11; tan to whitish with a blackish stripe through eye to base of caudal fin, tapering in width posteriorly; a black spot at base of caudal fin; similar to *A. kallopterus* (below), but basicaudal spot centred on lateral line rather than just above it. East Africa and Red Sea to the Line Islands and Tuamotu Archipelago; usually seen in caves and under ledges. Reaches 10 cm.

FRAGILE CARDINALFISH
Apogon fragilis Smith, 1961

Dorsal rays VI-I,9; anal rays II,9 or 10; pectoral rays 14; lateral-line scales 23 or 24; gill rakers 7 + 21 or 22; semi-transparent or whitish, often silvery on sides; sometimes with small blue spots on operculum and behind pectoral fins; a small black spot at base of caudal fin. East Africa to Samoa; forms large schools among reef crevices. To 5 cm.

SAMOAN CARDINALFISH
Apogon fuscus Quoy & Gaimard, 1824

Dorsal rays VII-I,9; anal rays II,8; pectoral rays 13; lateral-line scales 28; gill rakers 7 or 8 + 19-21; overall coppery or silvery with a dark saddle on upper half of caudal fin base and wedge-shaped bar below eye; similar to *A. bandanensis* (see above). East Africa and Red Sea to the Line Islands and Tuamotu Archipelago; often among staghorn corals. To 10 cm. Formerly known as *A. savayensis* Günther.

GUAM CARDINALFISH
Apogon guamensis Valenciennes, 1832

Dorsal rays VII-I,9; anal rays II,8; pectoral rays 13; lateral-line scales 26 or 27; gill rakers 7 or 8 + 17-19; overall coppery or silvery with a dark saddle on upper half of caudal-fin base and a narrow, oblique, dark band below eye; similar to *A. bandanensis* and *A. fuscus* (above), but band below eye much narrower. East Africa and Red Sea to Samoa. Attains 10 cm. *Apogon nubilus* Garman is a synonym.

FROSTFIN CARDINALFISH
Apogon hoeveni Bleeker, 1854

Dorsal rays VII-I,9; anal rays II,8; pectoral rays 12; lateral-line scales 24 or 25; gill rakers 5-6 + 20-21; yellow or tan with dusky brown speckling; first dorsal fin dark brown with white posterior margin. East Indies and northern Australia to Japan; usually seen with sponges, crinoids, or *Diadema* urchins in weedy areas. Reaches 5 cm.

IRIDESCENT CARDINALFISH
Apogon kallopterus Bleeker, 1856

Dorsal rays VII-I,9; anal rays II,8; pectoral rays 13; lateral-line scales 28; gill rakers 2 + 8-12; tan to light red-brown with dusky scale margins; a brown mid-lateral stripe and black spot at base of caudal fin. East Africa and Red Sea to Polynesia; ubiquitous and common. Attains 15 cm. The blue-green iridescence of this fish is evident mainly at night.

THREADFIN CARDINALFISH
Apogon leptacanthus Bleeker, 1856

Dorsal rays VI-I,9; anal rays II,9; pectoral rays 13; lateral-line scales 24; gill rakers 6 or 7 + 22 or 23; semi-transparent or whitish with several incomplete, narrow, orange bars on head and anterior part of body, also scattered blue spots; second dorsal spine filamentous. East Africa and Red Sea to Samoa; forms aggregations among branching corals. To 6 cm.

MOLUCCAN CARDINALFISH
Apogon moluccensis Valenciennes, 1832

Dorsal rays VII-I,9; anal rays II,8; pectoral rays 14; lateral-line scales 26 or 27; gill rakers 5-6 + 18-20; light brown or tan, often with a broad, yellow, midlateral stripe; a pearly white spot behind second dorsal fin. East Indies and northern Australia. Attains 9 cm.

BLACKSTRIPE CARDINALFISH
Apogon nigrofasciatus Lachner, 1953

Dorsal rays VII-I,9; anal rays II,8; pectoral rays 13 or 14 (usually 14); lateral-line scales 24 or 25; total gill rakers 20-24 (usually 21-23); white or yellow with five black stripes which are broader than pale interspaces; end of midlateral stripe slightly expanded to form a spot at caudal-fin base; fin rays light red. Similar to *A. angustatus*, but dark stripes broader and gill rakers more numerous. Red Sea to the Tuamotus; a reef species commonly seen in our area. Attains 10 cm.

SPOTNAPE CARDINALFISH
Apogon notatus (Houttuyn, 1782)

Dorsal rays VII-I,9; anal rays II,8; pectoral rays 15; lateral-line scales 26; gill rakers 7 + 21; mauve brownish with a black stripe from tip of lower jaw to eye, a vertically elongate black spot at base of caudal fin, and a black spot on each side of nape. Coral Sea to southern Japan; forms aggregations around coral bommies. To 10 cm.

NINE-BANDED CARDINALFISH
Apogon novemfasciatus Cuvier, 1828

Dorsal rays VII-I,9; anal rays II,8; pectoral rays 14; lateral-line scales 24-28; gill rakers 2-3 + 10-13; whitish with 4-5 black stripes; similar to *A. angustatus*, and *A. nigrofasciatus*, but lacks spot at base of caudal fin, and the stripes extend well onto basal half of caudal fin, the ones above and below midlateral stripe converging toward it on caudal fin. Cocos-Keeling Islands to Samoa, north to the Izu Islands; occurs on shallow reef flats. Reaches 9 cm.

CORAL CARDINALFISH
Apogon properupta (Whitley,1964)

Dorsal rays VII-I,9; anal rays II,8; pectoral rays 13; lateral-line scales 27; gill rakers 4 + 16; bluish silver with six yellow-orange stripes, including a short postocular stripe; very similar to and often confused with *A. cyanosoma*, which differs by having narrower yellow stripes. *A.properupta* is more common on inner and coastal reefs, whereas *A. cyanosoma* is more common on outer reefs of the Great Barrier Reef and in the Coral Sea. Known only from Queensland and the northern section of the Great Barrier Reef south to Montague Island, New South Wales. Maximum size, 6 cm.

SANGI CARDINALFISH
Apogon sangiensis Bleeker, 1857

Dorsal rays VI-I,9; anal rays II,8; pectoral rays 13 or 14; lateral-line scales 24; gill rakers 3 + 12; light grey-brown except breast region and lower half of head whitish, with a broad blackish stripe on head through eye, a small black spot at base of caudal fin, and a very small black spot on back between dorsal fins; front of first dorsal fin black. East Indies to Vanuatu, north to Japan. Attains 8 cm.

OBLIQUE-BANDED CARDINALFISH
Apogon semiornatus Peters, 1876

Dorsal rays VI-I,9; anal rays II,8; pectoral rays 12; lateral-line scales 27 or 28; gill rakers 3 or 4 + 12; semi-transparent red with three blackish stripes, the narrow first one on back at base of dorsal fins, the lowermost extending obliquely from eye to anal-fin base. East Africa to northern Australia, north to Japan; a secretive species that is seldom seen. To 7 cm.

REEF-FLAT CARDINALFISH
Apogon taeniophorus Regan, 1908

Dorsal rays VII-I,9; anal rays II,8; pectoral rays 14; lateral-line scales 28; gill rakers 4 or 5 + 12-14; whitish with five or six black stripes, the narrow third one extending a short distance posterior to upper edge of eye; similar to *A. cookii* (above), but no definite black spot at midbase of caudal fin. Mauritius to Polynesia; occurs on shallow reef flats. Reaches 8 cm.

FLAME CARDINALFISH
Apogon talboti Smith, 1961

Dorsal rays VI-I,9; anal rays II,8; pectoral rays 13; lateral-line scales 24; gill rakers 2 or 3 + 14; overall bright red; somewhat similar to *A. coccineus* (above), but not transparent red, has a longer caudal peduncle, straighter dorsal profile of head, and grows to a much larger size. Indo-Pacific; usually in caves and under ledges. Attains 14 cm.

TIMOR CARDINALFISH
Apogon timorensis Bleeker, 1854

Dorsal rays VII-I,9; anal rays II,8; pectoral rays 15 or 16; lateral-line scales 28; gill rakers 3 or 4 + 11 or 12; coppery brown to yellowish with an oblique black line below eye; sometimes three faint dark bars on sides. East Africa and Red Sea to northern Australia, north to Japan; occurs under boulders on shallow reef flats. To 8 cm. *Apogon fraxineus* Smith is a synonym.

THREE-SPOT CARDINALFISH
Apogon trimaculatus Cuvier, 1828

Dorsal rays VI-I,9; anal rays II,8; pectoral rays 14; lateral-line scales 25 or 26; gill rakers 2 or 3 + 10 or 11; reddish brown with a dark brown bar (may be broken) below each dorsal fin and a dark spot at base of caudal fin; juveniles with more intense dark markings, including a saddle at front of second dorsal fin and a pair of spots along middle of caudal peduncle. East Indies to Samoa, northwards to the Ryukyu Islands; generally found in rich coral areas. Attains 13 cm.

OCELLATED CARDINALFISH
Apogonichthys ocellatus (Weber, 1913)

Dorsal rays VII-I,9; anal rays II,8; pectoral rays 15; lateral-line scales 25; gill rakers 1 + 4 or 5; no palatine teeth; preopercle with both ridge and edge smooth; caudal fin rounded; brownish with faint dark stripes corresponding with scale rows, an oblique brown bar on cheek below eye, and a large ocellated black spot on first dorsal fin. East Africa to the Marquesas and Tuamotus; occurs under rocks on shallow reef flats. Reaches 6 cm.

NARROW-LINED CARDINALFISH
Archamia fucata (Cantor, 1850)

Dorsal rays VI-I,7 or 8; anal rays II,15-18; pectoral rays 14; lateral-line scales 28; gill rakers 5 or 6 + 14-16; silvery with numerous, vertical, orange lines on sides, an oblique brown bar below eye, and large diffuse black spot at base of caudal fin. East Africa and Red Sea to Samoa; forms schools among branching corals. To 9 cm.

LEA'S CARDINALFISH
Archamia leai Waite, 1916

Dorsal rays VI-I,8; anal rays II,13-16; pectoral rays 14; lateral-line scales 28; gill rakers 5 or 6 + 15 or 16; yellowish tan with a pair of silvery stripes through eye from snout tip and about five faint brown bars on anterior half of sides, the widest below second dorsal fin. Coral Sea and southern Great Barrier Reef. Attains 9 cm.

BLACKSPOT CARDINALFISH
Archamia melasma Lachner & Taylor, 1960

Dorsal rays VI-I,9; anal rays II,16-18; pectoral rays 13-15; lateral-line scales 24; gill rakers 4 + 16 or 17; silvery white with numerous vertical orange lines on side, an oblique blackish bar below eye and a blackish spot at upper end of gill opening, continuing faintly as a bar to lower edge of operculum; a yellow line on side of snout. Northern Australia and New Guinea. To 9 cm.

GIRDLED CARDINALFISH
Archamia zosterophora (Bleeker, 1856)

Dorsal rays VI-I,9; anal rays II,16 or 17; pectoral rays 14; lateral-line scales 26 or 27; gill rakers 6 + 16; slightly transparent and overall pinkish or greyish silvery with a pair of narrow orange bars on head behind eye, broad blackish bar below second dorsal fin, and a small black spot at base of caudal fin. Indonesia and Philippines to New Caledonia, north to Ryukyu Islands; commonly associated with branching *Acropora* corals. Attains 8 cm.

TIGER CARDINALFISH
Cheilodipterus macrodon (Lacepède, 1802)

Dorsal rays VI-I,9; anal rays II,8; pectoral rays usually 13; lateral-line scales usually 28; developed gill rakers 7-11; large canine teeth as in *C. artus*; whitish with 8-10 dark reddish brown stripes broader than pale interspaces; juveniles with a very large black spot midlaterally at caudal fin base, gradually expanding into a broad blackish bar; in very large fish bar may fade to a whitish zone. Indo-Pacific; commonly seen in caves. One of the largest cardinalfishes; attains at least 22 cm.

WOLF CARDINALFISH
Cheilodipterus artus Smith, 1961

Dorsal rays VI-I,9; anal rays,II,8; pectoral rays usually 13; lateral-line scales 27-28 (usually 28); developed gill rakers 11-17; large canine teeth at front of jaws and side of lower jaw; whitish with 8-10 dark yellowish brown stripes, slightly narrower than pale interspaces; a midlateral black spot at caudal fin base, becoming a broad diffuse blackish bar with age. East Africa to Tuamoto Archipelego; in the western Pacific from Ryukyu Islands to Great Barrier Reef, usually in sheltered water among branching corals. Reaches 12 cm.

FIVE-LINED CARDINALFISH
Cheilodipterus quinquelineatus Cuvier, 1828

Dorsal rays VI-I,9; anal rays II,8; pectoral rays 12 or 13 (usually 12); lateral-line scales usually 27; developed gill rakers 8-14; large canines present; white with five narrow black stripes on sides; base of caudal fin yellow with a black spot at base of middle rays. East Africa and Red Sea to southeastern Polynesia; usually in caves and under ledges. Attains 12 cm.

MIMIC CARDINALFISH
Cheilodipterus zonatus Smith & Radcliffe, 1912

Dorsal rays VI-I,8; anal rays II,8; pectoral rays 13; lateral-line scales 24; gill rakers 5 + 15; large canines present; whitish with a broad, midlateral, black stripe. Indonesia, Philippines, New Guinea, and Queensland; an effective mimic of the sabre-tooth blenny *Meiacanthus vittatus* (a New Guinea species with venomous fangs not yet recorded from our area). Reaches 8 cm.

WEED CARDINALFISH
Foa brachygramma (Jenkins, 1903)

Dorsal rays VII-I,9; anal rays II,8; pectoral rays 12; lateral-line scales 9 or 10; gill rakers 3 + 8-10 (developed rakers 7); palatine teeth present; preopercular ridge and margin smooth; body deep, the depth 2.2-2.5 in standard length; caudal fin rounded; mottled brown. East Africa to central Pacific, north to Japan; occurs under rocks and sponge in sandy or weedy areas. To 6 cm.

DWARF CARDINALFISH
Fowleria abocellata Goren & Karplus, 1980

Dorsal rays VII-I,9; anal rays II,8; pectoral rays 14; lateral-line scales 9 or 10; gill rakers 3 + 10 (developed rakers 5); no palatine teeth; preopercular ridge and margin smooth; caudal fin rounded; mottled brown with 6-8 narrow pale bars and 3-4 short, dark bands radiating from rear edge of eye. Red Sea to western Pacific. Attains 5 cm.

AURITA CARDINALFISH
Fowleria aurita (Valenciennes, 1831)

Dorsal rays VII-I,9; anal rays II,8; pectoral rays 14; lateral-line scales 10-13; gill rakers 3 or 4 + 12 (developed rakers 4-6); no palatine teeth; reddish brown with an ocellated black spot on operculum, without markings on body and fins. East Africa and Red Sea to western Pacific. Reaches 9 cm.

EARED CARDINALFISH
Fowleria marmorata (Alleyne & Macleay, 1877)

Dorsal rays VII-I,9; anal rays II,8; pectoral rays 14; lateral-line scales 10-13; gill rakers 3 + 12 (developed rakers 6); no palatine teeth; brown to reddish brown with about 10 darker red-brown bars on sides and a prominent ocellated black spot on operculum; fins red. Red Sea to southeastern Polynesia. To 6 cm.

PEPPERED CARDINALFISH
Fowleria punctulata (Rüppell, 1838)

Dorsal rays VII-I,9; anal rays II,8; pectoral rays 14; lateral-line scales 10-12; gill rakers 3 or 4 + 12 (developed rakers 6); no palatine teeth; reddish brown with black spots in longitudinal rows on sides, and an ocellated black spot on opercle. Red Sea to Central and South Pacific. Attains 6 cm. *Fowleria isostigma* (Jordan & Seale) is a synonym.

VARIEGATED CARDINALFISH
Fowleria variegata (Valenciennes, 1832)

Dorsal rays VII-I,9; anal rays II,8; pectoral rays 13; lateral-line scales 10 or 11; no palatine teeth; gill rakers 3 or 4 + 12 (developed rakers 6); brown mottling on body, black ocellated spot on opercle, and spotted fins. Red Sea to Samoa, north to Ryukyu Islands. Reaches 8 cm.

EIGHTSPINE CARDINALFISH
Neamia octospina Smith & Radcliffe, 1912

Dorsal rays VIII-I,9; anal rays II,8; pectoral rays 18; lateral-line scales 24; gill rakers 2 + 10-12 (developed rakers 6 or 7); no palatine teeth; caudal fin rounded; whitish with three short, brown bands radiating from rear edge of eye. Differs from all other apogonids in having VIII spines in the first dorsal fin. East Africa and Red Sea to Australia and Philippine Islands. To 5 cm.

GELATINOUS CARDINALFISH
Pseudamia gelatinosa Smith, 1955

Dorsal rays VI-I,8; anal rays II,8; pectoral rays 15-17 (usually 16); only first few scales of lateral line with pores, 39-43 scales in longitudinal series; gill rakers 3 or 4 + 11-14 (developed rakers 8 or 9); body elongate, the depth 4.0-4.7 in standard length; caudal fin large and rounded; translucent with light golden to silvery sheen, numerous tiny black spots arranged in longitudinal rows; caudal fin blackish. East Africa and Red Sea to the Society Islands, north to Japan; lives deep in coral thickets, hence is seldom seen by day. Reaches 10 cm.

SLENDER CARDINALFISH
Rhabdamia gracilis (Bleeker, 1856)

Dorsal rays VI-I,9; anal rays II,12 or 13; pectoral rays 13; lateral-line scales 23 or 24; gill rakers 6 + 21; preopercular ridge and margin smooth; body depth 3.4-3.7 in standard length; caudal fin well forked; translucent whitish or pink, silvery on head and abdomen; a small black spot sometimes present posteriorly on caudal peduncle before base of lower caudal rays. East Africa to the Marshall Islands; forms large aggregations above coral bommies. Attains 6 cm.

STRIPED SIPHONFISH
Siphamia majimai Matsubara & Iwai, 1958

Dorsal rays VI-I,9; anal rays II,8; pectoral rays 15; lateral-line scales 23 or 24; developed gill rakers 9; a luminous organ in translucent muscles of thorax; entirely dark brown or blackish, often with small white spot at base of each dorsal fin and on top of caudal peduncle. Northern Australia to Japan; commensal with sea urchins and crown-of-thorns starfish. To 3.5 cm.

CORAL CARDINALFISH
Sphaeramia nematoptera (Bleeker, 1856)

Dorsal rays VI-I,9; anal rays II,10; pectoral rays 12; lateral-line scales 24; total gill rakers 32-37; preopercular ridge smooth, the margin serrate; body deep, the depth 1.8-2.0 in standard length; caudal fin emarginate, the lobes broadly rounded; anterior rays of second dorsal fin filamentous; head yellowish; a broad blackish bar below first dorsal fin and large brown spots on posterior half of body. East Indies and northern Australia to Micronesia, north to Japan; occurs with branching corals on shallow protected reefs. Attains 8 cm.

153

SAND TILEFISHES
FAMILY MALACANTHIDAE

The sand tilefishes (also known as blanquillos) have elongate bodies (the depth 3.4 to 3.8 in standard length); a long unnotched dorsal fin consisting of I to X spines and 13-60 soft rays; anal fin of I or II spines and 12-56 soft rays; opercle with a single spine; jaws with both canine and villiform teeth; no teeth on roof of mouth; small scales, those on body ctenoid. They are closely related to, and sometimes classified in, the family Branchiostegidae. The latter consists of deeper bodied fishes with a median ridge in front of the dorsal fin. Sand tilefishes live on sandy or rubble bottoms, often at base of outer reef dropoffs. They seek refuge in burrows (except for one species that substitutes rubble mounds it constructs) and are often encountered in pairs. The species of *Hoplolatilus* feed mainly on zooplankton as they maintain a position of a metre or more above the bottom in the vicinity of their refuge.

GREY TILEFISH
Hoplolatilus cuniculus Randall & Dooley, 1974

Dorsal rays III-V,29-34; anal rays I,19 or 20; pectoral rays 16-18 (usually 17); lateral-line scales 116-140; body long and slender; caudal fin slightly forked; light olive brown on back, pale grey to yellowish white on lower sides, blue area on head around eye, caudal fin yellowish. Mauritius to the Society Islands; usually between 25-100 m in rubble or rubble-sand areas. Attains 15 cm.

BLUE TILEFISH
Hoplolatilus starcki Randall & Dooley, 1974

Dorsal rays VIII,21-23; anal rays II,15-16; pectoral rays 18 or 19; lateral-line scales 100-118; body long and slender; caudal fin deeply forked; olive brown on back, shading to yellowish on lower sides; head and pectoral-throat region bright blue, caudal fin yellow; young individuals entirely blue. Indonesia to Australia, Melanesia and Micronesia; usually below 20 m on outer reef slopes. To 15 cm.

FLAGTAIL BLANQUILLO
Malacanthus brevirostris Guichenot, 1848

Dorsal rays I-IV,52-60; anal rays I,46-53; pectoral rays 15-17; lateral-line scales 146-181; body long and slender; caudal fin truncate; light grey, yellowish above eye, two black stripes on caudal fin. East Africa and Red Sea to the Hawaiian Islands; occurs on open sand-rubble bottoms. Usually seen in pairs; live in a burrow of their own construction, often under a surface rock on sand. Reaches 30 cm. *M. hoedtii* Bleeker is a synonym.

BLUE BLANQUILLO
Malacanthus latovittatus (Lacepède, 1801)

Dorsal rays III-IV,43-47; anal rays I,37-40; pectoral rays 16 or 17; lateral-line scales 166-175; body long and slender; caudal fin truncate; head and anterior part of body blue, becoming whitish posteriorly with a broad midlateral black stripe on body, extending onto caudal fin. Juveniles bluish white with a more distinct black stripe which extends to front of head. East Africa and Red Sea to the Cook Islands, north to Japan; usually below 5 m in barren sandy areas or rubble near reefs. Reaches 35 cm.

Malacanthus latovittatus Juv.

Malacanthus latovittatus

SUCKERFISHES OR REMORAS
FAMILY ECHENEIDAE

These peculiar fishes are easily distinguished by the sucking-disc on top of the head which represents a modification of the spinous dorsal fin. The body is slender and somewhat rounded in cross section; the second dorsal and anal fins are similar in shape and opposite one another. These sea-going hitchhikers use their suction apparatus to attach themselves to large marine animals including sharks, rays, bony fishes, turtles, whales, and dolphins. Occasionally they latch on to boats or even unsuspecting divers. They feed on scraps that result from the feeding activities of their hosts; in addition they sometimes eat parasitic crustaceans that have attached to the hosts. Some species are restricted to specific hosts.

SLENDER SUCKERFISH
Echeneis naucrates Linnaeus, 1758

Dorsal rays 34-42; anal rays 32-38; pectoral rays 21-24; distinctive flat head with sucking disc of 21-27 transverse laminae; caudal fin slightly rounded; lower jaw projecting; grey with a white-edged black stripe on side from tip of lower jaw through eye to caudal fin, this stripe broadest anteriorly on body. Circumtropical; often seen on coral reefs. Attaches to a wide variety of hosts, but frequently encountered free living. Reaches 100 cm.

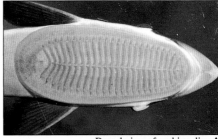

Dorsal view of sucking disc ▲

155

TREVALLIES

FAMILY CARANGIDAE

The trevallies (also known as jacks in some regions) are well represented in all tropical and subtropical seas. The family contains about 25 genera and approximately 140 species. The members of the family are generally silvery in colour and exhibit a wide size range: from the scads that attain about 30 cm to the Giant trevally (*Caranx ignobilis*) which grows to 170 cm and may weigh over 35 kg. Trevallies are powerful midwater swimmers characterised by a streamlined shape, laterally compressed body, slender tail base, and a strongly forked caudal fin. Most species have the posterior scales of the lateral line modified into spiny, plate-like structures known as scutes. The dorsal and anal fins are generally low, but often have elongated rays on their anterior portions. The first dorsal fin is composed of III-IX spines and the second of one spine and 18-37 soft rays. There are usually III anal spines with the first two detached from the rest of the anal fin, and usually 15-31 soft rays. One or more of the dorsal and anal spines are often obsolete or embedded in some species. Carangids are pelagic spawners that release large numbers of tiny, buoyant eggs. Judging from the widespread distribution of most species, the larvae may lead a pelagic existence for extended periods. The juveniles of several species, including the Giant trevally and the Bigeye trevally (*Caranx sexfasciatus*) are often found in brackish estuaries or in fresh water. Most of the trevallies are highly esteemed as food fishes and therefore they are targeted by both sport anglers and commercial fishermen. Trevallies frequently occur in large schools that roam for considerable distances. Although they are not strictly reef fishes, they are common on the edges of reefs, particularly along steep outer reef dropoffs. They are voracious

Bigeye Trevally *(Caranx sexfasciatus)*

predators that feed on a variety of fishes. Some species such as the Golden trevally (*Gnathanodon speciosus*) consume mainly molluscs and crustaceans, and the scads (genus *Decapterus*) eat mainly planktonic invertebrates. Some of the species of *Caranx* have been implicated in ciguatera fish poisoning when large. Much of the information in the individual species accounts that follow was taken from Smith-Vaniz, 1986 (in *Smiths' Sea Fishes,* M. Smith and P. Heemstra, eds.).

PENNANTFISH
Alectes ciliaris (Bloch, 1788)
(Plate III-1)

Dorsal rays VII (embedded and not apparent in adults) + I,18-22; anal rays II + I,18-20; gill rakers 4-6 + 12-17; anterior dorsal and anal rays extremely long and filamentous in juveniles; suborbital depth narrow, 1.7-3.0 in upper jaw length; body superficially naked, the scales minute and embedded; silvery with light metallic bluish tinge dorsally; a small, diffuse dark opercular spot; juveniles with 5 dark chevron-shaped bars on body. Worldwide in tropical seas; adults solitary in coastal waters to 100 m; young usually pelagic and drifting. It has been suggested that the juveniles with their filamentous dorsal and anal rays may be mistaken by predators for jellyfishes with long stinging tentacles. To 130 cm.

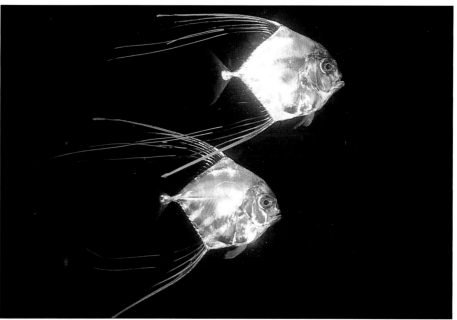
Alepes sp.

DIAMOND TREVALLY
Alectes indicus (Rüppell, 1830)
(Plate III-2)

Dorsal rays VI (embedded and not apparent in adults) + I,18-20; anal rays II + I,18-20; anterior dorsal and anal rays extremely long and filamentous in young; suborbital depth broad, 0.8-1.0 in upper jaw length; gill rakers 8-11 + 21-26; body superficially naked, scales minute and embedded; silvery, with dusky green tinge dorsally; a small, diffuse dark opercular spot; juveniles with 5-7 broad, dark bars. East Africa to Australia and the Ryukyu Islands. Grows to 44 cm.

FRINGE-FINNED TREVALLY
Absalom radiatus (Macleay, 1881)
(Plate III-3 and IV-17)

Dorsal rays VIII-I,22; anal rays II-I,19-20; dorsal and anal rays of males filamentous (Plate IV-34); breast scaly except for a very small scaleless area ventrally; strongly arched anterior part of lateral line fits twice in length of posterior straight part; scutes 38-45; olive green to bluish on back, silvery white below; often an indication of 6 or more dark bars on sides; operculum with a large black spot; dorsal fins sometimes orange; caudal fin yellow with black upper tip. Indonesia and northern Australia; coastal waters, sometimes entering river mouths. Reaches 40 cm.

SMALL MOUTH SCAD
Alepes sp.
(Plate III-4)

Dorsal rays VIII-I,24-26; anal rays II-I,20-22; gill rakers 8 - 10 + 18-21; body relatively slender and ovate, laterally compressed; dorsal and anal fins low; well-developed posterior and poorly developed anterior adipose eyelid; curved part of lateral line short and strongly arched, fits about twice in length of posterior straight part; scutes 51-70; blue-green on back, silvery below (juveniles with dark bars on body); operculum with a diffuse, dark blotch; dorsal, anal, and caudal fins dusky yellow-green; caudal lobes often with dark tips. Indonesia and northern Australia. To 35 cm.

YELLOWTAIL SCAD
Atule mate (Cuvier, 1833)
(Plate III-5)

Dorsal rays VIII + I,22-25; anal rays II + I,18-21; terminal dorsal and anal rays finlet-like in large adults but joined basally to adjacent rays by inter-radial membranes; gill rakers 10-13 + 26-31; both jaws with single series of small, conspicuous teeth; upper jaw (in large adults) with 2-3 rows of small canines anteriorly; adipose eyelid completely covering eye except for a vertical slit centred on pupil; straight lateral line with 0-10 scales and 36-39 scutes; olive green dorsally, shading to white ventrally; 9-10 grey bars, wider than pale interspaces, usually present dorsolaterally; black opercular spot; dorsal and caudal fins dusky greenish yellow. Widespread in Indo-West Pacific eastward to Hawaiian Islands; forms schools. Attains 30 cm.

Atule mate

ONION TREVALLY
Carangoides caeruleopinnatus (Rüppell, 1830)
(Plate III-7)

Dorsal rays VIII + I,20-23; anal rays II + I,16-20; gill rakers 6-8 + 15-18; breast naked to behind pelvic origin, and usually laterally to pectoral base; straight part of lateral line with 20-38 small scutes; soft dorsal lobe filamentous in juveniles, usually shorter than head in adults; bluish green above, silvery below; sides with numerous small yellow spots; a small black opercular blotch. East Africa to Japan and Australia. To 40 cm.

CLUB-NOSED TREVALLY
Carangoides chrysophrys (Cuvier, 1833)
(Plate III-6)

Dorsal rays VIII + I,18-20; anal rays II + I,14-17; gill rakers 5-9 + 15-18; straight part of lateral line with 20-37 weak scutes; breast naked to behind pelvic origin and laterally to pectoral base; dorsal profile of snout gently sloped, then abruptly vertical just above mouth cleft; soft dorsal lobe falcate in young, becoming shorter than head in adults; generally silvery, greenish above; a small black opercular spot. East Africa eastward to Japan and Australia. Grows to 60 cm.

WHITEFIN TREVALLY
Carangoides equula (Temminck & Schlegel, 1844)
(Plate III-10)

Dorsal rays VIII + I,23-25; anal rays II + I,21-24; gill rakers 7-10 + 18-23; straight part of lateral line with 0-6 scales + 22-23 scutes; breast completely scaled; spinous dorsal height equals or exceeds height of soft dorsal lobe; bluish grey to green above, silvery white below; soft dorsal and anal fins with submarginal brownish band, fin lobes white distally. East Africa, Gulf of Oman, Japan, Australia, New Zealand, Hawaii and Easter Island; a benthic species largely restricted to shelf/slope habitats in 100-200 m. Reaches 37 cm.

BLUE TREVALLY
Carangoides ferdau (Forsskål, 1775)
(Plate III-8)

Dorsal rays VIII + I,26-34; anal rays II + I,21-26; gill rakers 7-10 + 17-20; straight part of lateral line with 10-30 scales + 21-37 small scutes; breast naked ventrally to pelvic origin, this scaleless region separated from naked pectoral base by a broad band of scales; curved part of lateral line weakly arched; generally silvery, blue-green above, paler below; sides usually with 5-6 dusky bars; inconspicuous golden spots sometimes present. Indo-Pacific eastward to Hawaiian Islands. Attains 70 cm.

GOLD-SPOTTED TREVALLY
Carangoides fulvoguttatus (Forsskål, 1775)
(Plate III-9)

Dorsal rays VIII + I,25-30; anal rays II + I,21-26; gill rakers 6-8 + 17-21; straight part of lateral line with 18-27 scales + 15-21 scutes; breast naked to behind pelvic origin and variable laterally, extending uninterrupted to pectoral base or separated by a band of scales; adults with mouth cleft distinctly below level of lower margin of eye; blue-green above, silvery below, usually with many small brassy spots on sides; large adults often with 3 black blotches in a midlateral row on flanks. Indo-Pacific. To 100 cm.

BLUDGER TREVALLY
Carangoides gymnostethus (Cuvier, 1833)
(Plate III-15)

Dorsal rays VIII + I,28-32; anal rays II + I,24-26; gill rakers 7-9 + 19-22; straight part of lateral line with 14-25 scales + 20-31 scutes; breast naked to behind pelvic origin and laterally to pectoral base; adults with mouth cleft at level of lower margin of eye; olive green above, silvery white below; a few brown or golden spots sometimes present midlaterally; opercular spot dusky and usually inconspicuous. Indo-Pacific; most common over slightly deeper offshore reefs; larger individuals usually solitary, juveniles form small schools. Maximum length, 90 cm.

BUMP-NOSED TREVALLY
Carangoides hedlandensis (Whitley, 1934)
(Plate III-12)

Dorsal rays VIII + I,20-22; anal rays II + I,16-18, adult males with 3-8 central dorsal and anal rays filamentous; gill rakers 6-11 + 14-17; straight part of lateral line with 17-29 weak scutes; breast naked to behind pelvic origin and laterally to pectoral base; soft dorsal lobe longer than head length; adults with distinct bulge in interorbital region; greenish blue dorsally, silvery grey below; a blackish blotch on upper opercular margin; pelvics blackish in young, pale in adults; caudal fin yellowish. East Africa to Samoa and north to Japan; a coastal, demersal species. Attains 32 cm.

Carangoides hedlandensis

EPAULET TREVALLY
Carangoides humerosus (McCulloch, 1915)
(Plate III-11)

Dorsal rays VIII + I,19-21; anal rays II - I,18-19; gill rakers 6-7 + 16-17; naked area on breast extending to, but not above pectoral-fin base; curved portion of lateral line gently arched and equal to or slightly longer than straight portion; scutes weak to moderate, 26-30; pectoral fins long and falcate, almost reaching junction of straight and curved parts of lateral line; green to bluish on back, silvery below; a large diffuse black spot on operculum; spinous dorsal fin black. Indonesia, New Guinea, and northern Australia. Grows to 25 cm.

THICKLIP TREVALLY
Carangoides orthogrammus Jordan & Gilbert, 1881
(Plate III-14)

Dorsal rays VIII + I,28-31; anal rays II + I,24-26; gill rakers 8-10 + 20-23; lips noticeably fleshy in large adults; breast naked ventrally to origin of pelvic fins, occasionally with small patch of prepelvic scales; naked area of breast separated laterally from naked base of pectoral fin by a moderate band of scales; curved part of lateral line slightly longer to about equal to straight, posterior part; scutes 19-31; brassy to greenish blue above, silvery below; adults with several elliptical yellow spots on sides, often with dusky centres. Indo-Pacific, including eastern Pacific. Attains 70 cm.

WHITE-TONGUED TREVALLY
Carangoides talamparoides Bleeker, 1852
(Plate III-13)

Dorsal rays VIII + I,20-23; anal rays II + I,17-19; gill rakers 6-9 + 18-21; gill rakers visible, but not conspicuous when mouth is open; naked area on breast extending above pectoral fin base, often reaching lateral line; curved portion of lateral line slightly longer than straight portion; scutes weak, 21-32; silvery blue-grey on back, silvery white below (juveniles with 5-6 dark bars on body); a black spot on operculum; tongue white or pale grey; caudal fin with central ray dusky yellow with black distal margin. Gulf of Oman to northern Australia; inhabits waters of continental shelves. To 32 cm.

MALABAR TREVALLY
Carangoides malabaricus (Bloch & Schneider, 1801)
(Plate III-16)

Dorsal rays VIII + I,20-23; anal rays II + I,17-19; gill rakers 8-12 + 21-27; breast naked to behind pelvic origin and laterally to pectoral base, including small area anteriorly just above fin; straight part of lateral line with 19-36 weak scutes; soft dorsal lobe only slightly falcate, shorter than head; silvery, bluish grey above; small white spot often at base of anal rays; a small, black opercular spot. Tropical coastal waters of Indo-Pacific; a benthic, schooling species. Reaches 28 cm.

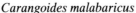

Carangoides malabaricus

JAPANESE TREVALLY
Carangoides uii Wakiya, 1924
(Plate III-17)

Dorsal rays VIII + I,21-23; anal rays II + I,18 or 19; gill rakers 6-7 + 16-18; lobe of second dorsal fin extremely elongate, (the length may exceed the length of the second dorsal base in large adults); breast naked ventrally to behind origin of pelvic fins; laterally, naked area of breast extending diagonally to naked base of pectoral fin; straight part of lateral line with 16-26 weak scutes; bluish grey above, silvery below; an indistinct, dark spot on opercle; spinous dorsal fin and lobe and margins of second dorsal fin dark. East Africa to Australia and Japan; inhabits coastal waters of continental shelves. Reaches 25 cm.

Caranx ignobilis

BLUE-SPOTTED TREVALLY
Caranx bucculentus Alleyne & Macleay, 1877
(Plate IV-7)

Dorsal rays VIII + I,17-18; anal rays II + I,16; naked area on breast extending to, but not above pectoral fin base; curved part of lateral line strongly arched and much shorter than straight posterior part; scutes strong, 35-38; body pale blue-green above, silvery white below; usually with blue spots on back and sides; juveniles with 6 dark bars on sides, developing with age into 3 horizontal rows of squarish blotches; a distinct black spot on operculum. Northern Australia and New Guinea; common in trawl catches. Maximum size, 66 cm.

Caranx lugubris ▲   *Caranx melampygus* ▼

GIANT TREVALLY
Caranx ignobilis (Forsskål, 1775)
(Plate IV-1)

Dorsal rays VIII + I,18-21; anal rays II + I,15-17; gill rakers 5-7 + 15-17; straight part of lateral line with 26-38 strong scutes; breast naked ventrally, typically with a small patch of prepelvic scales; adults mainly silvery grey to black above, usually paler below; no dark spot at upper end of opercle; fins usually uniformly pigmented grey to black. Widespread in Indo-West Pacific from East Africa to the Hawaiian and Marquesas Islands. Attains 170 cm and 53 kg.

BLACK TREVALLY
Caranx lugubris Poey, 1860
(Plate IV-2)

Dorsal rays VIII + I,20-22; anal rays II + I,16-19; gill rakers 6-8 + 17-22; straight part of lateral line with 26-32 strong scutes; breast completely scaled; body and fins mostly uniform grey to black; small dark spot at upper end of opercle, and scutes often black. Circumtropical; commonly seen on outer reef slopes. Grows to 80 cm.

BLUEFIN TREVALLY
Caranx melampygus Cuvier, 1833
(Plate IV-3)

Dorsal rays VIII + I,21-24; anal rays II + I,17-20; gill rakers 5-9 + 17-20; straight part of lateral line with 27-42 strong scutes; breast completely scaled; head and dorsal half of body brassy, suffused with blue and covered with small blue-black spots (forming at about 20 cm and increasing in number with size); second dorsal, anal, and caudal fins electric blue; fins of juveniles and young adults pale to dusky, except pectorals yellow. Tropical Indo-Pacific to the Americas; solitary or forms small schools around coral reefs. Reaches 100 cm.

BRASSY TREVALLY
Caranx papuensis Alleyne & Macleay, 1877
(Plate IV-4)

Dorsal rays VIII + I,21-23; anal rays II + I,16-19; gill rakers 7-9 + 18-21; straight part of lateral line with 31-39 strong scutes; breast naked ventrally, usually with a patch of prepelvic scales; brassy to yellowish green above, silvery below; conspicuous pale spot on shoulder just behind posterodorsal margin of opercle; small black spots scattered on head and body above lateral line (forming at about 30 cm and becoming more numerous with age); upper caudal lobe uniformly dark, lower lobe dusky to yellow with narrow white distal margin. Indo-Pacific eastward to Marquesas Islands. To 75 cm.

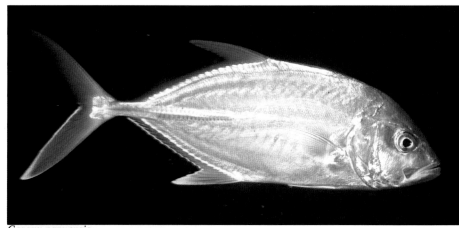

Caranx papuensis

BANDED SCAD
Caranx para Cuvier, 1833
(Plate IV-6)

Dorsal rays VIII + I,23-26; anal rays II + I,19-22; gill rakers 10-12 + 27-32; ventral profile of body distinctly more convex than dorsal profile; curved part of lateral line fits 1.5-2.2 times in straight posterior part; straight part of lateral line with 35-45 well-developed, broad scutes; bluish grey to green above, silvery below; a large, black spot on upper margin of opercle and adjacent area of shoulder; dark bars sometimes evident on sides above lateral line. East Africa to northern Australia and north to Japan; a coastal species of continental margins. Attains 18 cm.

Caranx sexfasciatus ▲   *Caranx tille* ▼

BIGEYE TREVALLY
Caranx sexfasciatus Quoy & Gaimard, 1824
(Plate IV-8)

Dorsal rays VIII + I,19-22; anal rays II + I, 14-17; gill rakers 6-8 + 15-19; straight part of lateral line with 27-36 strong scutes; breast completely scaled; eye large; adults iridescent blue-green above, shading to silvery white below; a small blackish spot near upper end of opercle (absent in young); soft dorsal lobe with white tip; caudal yellowish to black; lateral-line scutes dark to black. Widespread in tropical Indo-Pacific from East Africa to the Americas; nocturnal; usually seen by day in nearly stationary milling schools off reef escarpments. Reaches 78 cm.

TILLE TREVALLY
Caranx tille Cuvier, 1833
(Plate IV-5)

Dorsal rays VIII + I,20-22; anal rays II + I,16-18; gill rakers 6-8 + 15-17; straight part of lateral line with 33-42 strong scutes; breast completely scaled; adults dark olive green to bluish grey above, shading to silvery white below; a blackish spot, at least one-half pupil diameter, on upper part of opercle (absent in young); soft dorsal lobe olive grey to blackish; lateral-line scutes grey, except dark in caudal peduncle region. East Africa, Madagascar, Sri Lanka, Okinawa to Australia and Fiji; a coastal species preferring inshore waters. Attains at least 80 cm.

REDTAIL SCAD
Decapterus kurroides Bleeker, 1855
(Plate IV-10)

Dorsal rays VIII + I,28-29; anal rays II + I,22-25; curved part of lateral line with 47-55 scales and 0-2 scutes, straight part of lateral line with no scales and 31-36 scutes, total lateral-line scales 80-86; gill rakers 10-12 + 30-33; upper jaw with a narrow band of minute teeth anteriorly; margin of opercular membrane smooth; bluish green above, silvery white below; caudal bright red and dorsal lobe dark distally, sometimes with pale tip; small black opercular spot. East Africa to Australia and Japan; a schooling species taken by trawl in 100-300 m, but usually below 150 m. Reaches 50 cm.

MACKEREL SCAD
Decapterus macarellus (Cuvier, 1833)
(Plate IV-11)

Dorsal rays VIII + I,31-36 + 1; anal rays II + I,27-30 + 1; curved part of lateral line with 58-75 scales and no scutes, straight part of lateral line with 14-29 scales and 24-40 scutes, total lateral-line scales 110-138; gill rakers 10-13 + 34-38; rear end of upper jaw moderately rounded and slanted antero-ventrally; upper jaw without teeth; interorbital scales usually extending to above front margin of pupil; bluish green above, silvery below; caudal yellow green and dorsal lobe sometimes dark distally; small black opercular spot. Circumtropical; a schooling species, occurring mostly in open water and common in insular habitats; may be at surface but usually in 40-200 m. Grows to 32 cm.

LONG-BODIED SCAD
Decapterus macrosoma Bleeker, 1851
(Plate IV-13)

Dorsal rays VIII + I,33-38 + 1; anal rays II + I,27-30 + 1; curved part of lateral line with 58-72 scales and no scutes, straight part of lateral line with 14-29 scales and 24-40 scutes, total lateral-line scales 110-126; gill rakers 10-12 + 34-38; rear end of upper jaw concave above, rounded and produced below; upper jaw without teeth; interorbital scales not extending forward beyond rear margin of pupil; metallic blue above, silvery below; caudal hyaline to dusky, the dorsal lobe dark distally; a small black opercular spot. Widespread in Indo-Pacific; also occurs in the eastern Pacific; a schooling species usually taken by trawl in 30 to at least 170 m. Attains 32 cm.

RUSSELL'S MACKEREL SCAD
Decapterus russelli (Rüppell, 1830)
(Plate IV-12)

Dorsal rays VIII + I,28-31 + 1; anal rays II + I,25-28 + 1; curved part of lateral line with 42-62 scales and 0-4 scutes, straight part of lateral line with 0-4 scales and 30-40 scutes; total lateral-line scales 77-102; gill rakers 10-14 + 30-39; upper jaw with a single series of minute teeth; margin of opercular membrane smooth; bluish green above, silvery below; caudal fin hyaline to dusky yellow, and dorsal fins hyaline basally, light dusky distally; a small black opercular spot. East Africa to Japan and Australia. Grows to 38 cm.

ROUGH-EAR SCAD
Decapterus tabl Berry, 1968
(Plate IV-9)

Dorsal rays VIII + I,30-31 + 1; anal rays II + I,24-25 + 1; curved part of lateral line with 61-71 scales and no scutes, straight part of lateral line with 4-10 scales and 30-40 scutes; total lateral-line scales 103-113; gill rakers 10-12 + 30-33; upper jaw with a single series of minute teeth; margin of opercular membrane minutely serrated; blue to greenish above, silvery below; caudal fin bright red, and tips of dorsal rays reddish; a small black opercular spot. Indo-Pacific eastward to Hawaiian Islands, also tropical Atlantic; a schooling species usually taken by trawl in 200-360 m. To 50 cm.

RAINBOW RUNNER
Elagatis bipinnulata (Quoy & Gaimard, 1825)
(Plate V-2)

Dorsal rays VI + I,25-28 + 2; anal rays I + I,18-20 + 2; end of upper jaw terminating distinctly before eye (to below front margin of eye in young); anal fin base relatively short, about 1.5 times soft-dorsal base; no scutes; caudal peduncle grooves present dorsally and ventrally; dark olive green or blue above, white below; 2 narrow light blue or bluish white stripes along sides, with a broader olive or yellowish stripe between them; fins with an olive or yellow tint. Circumtropical; a pelagic species, usually found near the surface, sometimes far offshore. Up to 120 cm; common to 80 cm.

Elagatis bipinnulata

GOLDEN TREVALLY
Gnathanodon speciosus (Forsskål, 1775)
(Plate IV-14)

Dorsal rays VII + I,18-20; anal rays II + I,15-17; gill rakers 19-22 + 27-30; adults without teeth (young with a few feeble teeth in lower jaw); lips noticeably thick and fleshy; breast completely scaled; juveniles and small adults bright yellow to silvery with 7-11 black bars, usually alternating broad and narrow; all fins yellow, the caudal tips black; adults with a few black blotches or spots on sides; narrow dark bars, if present, very faint. Tropical Indo-Pacific eastward to the Americas; a bottom feeder that uses its highly protractile mouth to root for crustaceans, molluscs, and small fishes. Young display "piloting" behaviour with sharks and other large fishes such as groupers. Attains 110 cm.

FINNY SCAD
Megalaspis cordyla (Linnaeus, 1758)
(Plate IV-15)

Dorsal rays VIII + I,18-20, posterior 7-9 rays consisting of semi-detatched finlets; anal rays II + I,16-17, posterior 8-10 rays semi-detached; gill rakers 8-11 + 18-22; adipose eyelid completely covering eye except for vertical slit centered on pupil; straight part of lateral line with 51-59 very large scutes; bluish grey to green above, shading to silvery below; a large black opercular spot; fins dark. Indo-Pacific to Japan and Australia. Grows to 80 cm.

PILOTFISH
Naucrates ductor (Linnaeus, 1758)
(Plate V-16)

Dorsal rays IV-V (some spines often minute or embedded in adults) + I,25-29; anal rays II + I,15-17; gill rakers 6-7 + 15-20; end of upper jaw relatively narrow, terminating below front margin of eye; anal-fin base 1.6-1.9 times second dorsal-fin base; no scutes; caudal peduncle grooves present dorsally and ventrally; blue dorsally, white below, with 6 broad black bars (the first on head). Circumtropical; usually in company with sharks, rays, turtles, or large fishes; juveniles occur in floating weed or with jellyfishes. To 70 cm.

BLACK POMFRET
Parastromateus niger (Bloch, 1795)
(Plate IV-18)

Dorsal rays IV-V (embedded and not apparent in all but young) + I,41-44; anal rays II + I,35-39; profile of soft dorsal and anal fins nearly identical, with elevated, broadly rounded anterior lobes; minute pelvic fins present in young, absent in adults; straight part of lateral line with 8-19 weak scutes, forming a slight keel on caudal peduncle; silvery grey to bluish brown, fins with dark edges; a dark blotch on rear margin of opercle; young with dark bars and black pelvic fins. East Africa to southern Japan and Australia; frequently swims on its side near the surface. Reaches 55 cm.

SILVER TREVALLY
Pseudocaranx dentex (Bloch & Schneider, 1801)
(Plate IV-19)

Dorsal rays VIII + I,25-26; anal rays II + I,21-22; gill rakers 11-13 + 24-27; both jaws with a single series of blunt conical teeth; lips thick and fleshy in adults; spinous dorsal slightly higher than second dorsal lobe; breast completely scaled; straight part of lateral line with 7-16 scales + 25-31 scutes; greenish blue above, silvery white below; yellow stripe usually present (more distinct in young) along midside of body; a distinct black opercular spot. An antitropical species occurring on both sides of the Atlantic, Mediterranean and Indo-Pacific eastward to Hawaiian Islands; an opportunistic bottom feeder found mainly on banks and shelf slope habitats in 80-200 m; found in shallower water in cooler seas. Attains 94 cm.

Gnathanodon speciosus ▲   *Megalaspis cordyla* ▼

Pseudocaranx dentex

TALANG QUEENFISH
Scomberoides commersonianus Lacepède, 1801
(Plate V-5)

Dorsal rays VI-VII + I,19-21; anal rays II + I,16-19; gill rakers 0-3 + 7-12; no scutes; scales on midbody oval-shaped; posterior soft dorsal and anal fins with semi-detached finlets; maxilla extending well beyond eye in adults; adults with 5-8 large dusky blotches above or touching lateral line, first 2 may intersect lateral line; dorsal lobe dusky to dark and uniformly pigmented. East Africa to Taiwan and Australia; swims in small groups; usually frequents reefs and offshore islands. To 120 cm. Also known as Leatherskin.

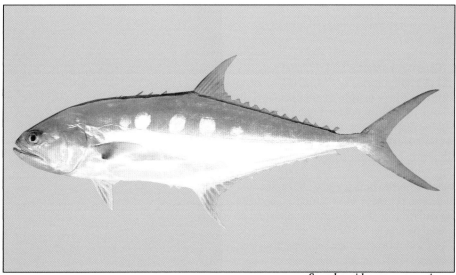

Scomberoides commersonianus

DOUBLE-SPOTTED QUEENFISH
Scomberoides lysan (Forsskål, 1775)
(Plate V-6)

Dorsal VI-VII + I,19-21; anal rays II + I,17-19; gill rakers 3-8 + 15-20; no scutes; scales on midbody lanceolate; posterior soft dorsal and anal fins with semi-detached finlets; maxilla extending to or slightly beyond rear margin of eye in adults; adults with double series of 6-8 dusky roundish blotches, one above and the other below lateral line; distal half of dorsal lobe abruptly and heavily pigmented. Indo-Pacific eastward to Hawaiian Islands; found in shallow lagoons to offshore areas from surface to 100 m. Grows to 70 cm.

Scomberoides lysan ▲

Scomberoides tol ▼

BARRED QUEENFISH
Scomberoides tala (Cuvier, 1832)
(Plate V-4)

Dorsal rays VI or VII + I,16-19; anal rays II + I,16-19; gill rakers (excluding rudiments) 1-3 + 7-11; upper jaw extending slightly beyond margin of eye in adults; scales on midbody below lateral line partially embedded and lanceolate; posterior soft dorsal and anal fin rays with semi-detached finlets; greenish grey dorsally, grey to silvery below; sides of adults with 4 to 8 vertically elongate dusky blotches, most of which intersect lateral line; dorsal and anal fins dusky to dark and uniformly pigmented; pectoral fins yellow, and pelvic fins white in adults. Sri Lanka and east coast of India to Australia and the Solomon Islands. Reaches 75 cm.

NEEDLESKIN QUEENFISH
Scomberoides tol (Cuvier, 1832)
(Plate V-3)

Dorsal rays VI-VII + I,19-21; anal rays II + I,18-20; gill rakers 4-7 + 17-20; no scutes; scales on midbody narrowly spindle-shaped; posterior soft dorsal and anal fins with semi-detached finlets; maxilla extending to rear margin of pupil in adults; adults with 5 to 8 oval or vertically oblong black blotches, the first 4 or 5 of which intersect lateral line; distal half of soft dorsal-fin lobe abruptly and heavily pigmented. Indian Ocean to Japan and Australia, eastward to Fiji; usually found in small schools near surface in coastal waters. Attains 60 cm.

OXEYE SCAD
Selar boops (Cuvier, 1833)
(Plate V-7)

Dorsal rays VII + I,24-25; anal rays II + I,20-21; gill rakers 9-12 + 27-31; eye very large and covered with a well-developed adipose eyelid, except for a vertical slit centred on pupil; a deep furrow in lower margin of gill opening; no naked area on breast; curved part of lateral line short and strongly arched posteriorly; scutes large and strong, 43-46; blue-green above, silver to silver-gold below; a distinct broad golden band from eye along upper part of body to caudal-fin base; a black spot on operculum. Tropical Indo-Pacific and eastern Atlantic. To 30 cm.

165

PURSE-EYED SCAD
Selar crumenophthalmus (Bloch, 1793)
(Plate V-8)

Dorsal rays VIII + I,24-27; anal rays II + I,21-23; gill rakers 9-12 + 27-31; a deep furrow in lower margin of gill opening with a large papilla immediately above it and a smaller papilla near upper edge; adipose eyelid covering eye except for broad oval slit centred on pupil; straight part of lateral line with 0-11 scales and 29-42 scutes; metallic blue to bluish green above, shading to white below; yellow stripe sometimes present from opercle margin to upper part of caudal peduncle; a blackish opercular spot. Worldwide in tropical and subtropical waters; forms small to large schools in inshore waters and shallow reefs to 170 m. Grows to 30 cm.

SMOOTH-TAILED TREVALLY
Selaroides leptolepis (Cuvier, 1833)
(Plate V-9)

Dorsal rays VIII + I,24-26; anal rays II + I,21-23; gill rakers 10-14 + 27-32; eye with moderately developed adipose eyelid covering posterior part of eye; upper jaw strongly protractile; breast completely scaled; lateral line gently arched, the curved part longer than posterior straight part; scutes relatively small, 24-29; metallic blue above, silvery white below, with a broad yellow stripe from upper margin of eye to caudal peduncle; a prominent black spot on upper edge of operculum. Persian Gulf eastward to Australia and Japan; occurs in schools. To 20 cm.

AMBERJACK
Seriola dumerili (Risso, 1810)
(Plate V-16)

Dorsal rays VII (first spine minute or embedded in large adults) + I,29-35; anal rays II + I,18-22; gill rakers 5-7 + 14-16 = 20-24 in juveniles, and 11-19 total in adults; maxilla reaching below rear margin of eye; height of soft dorsal-fin lobe of adults equal to or slightly longer than pectoral fin; anal-fin base 1.4-1.7 times in soft dorsal-fin base; bluish grey or olivaceous above, shading to silvery white below; often with an amber stripe along midside of body; an oblique olive band from eye to upper nape; fins mostly dusky, except pelvics pale ventrally; fins of juveniles may be yellow or olive. Tropical Indo-Pacific and Atlantic; occurs in small schools or solitary. Maximum size, 188 cm.

YELLOWTAIL KINGFISH
Seriola lalandi Valenciennes, 1833
(Plate V-15)

Dorsal rays VII (first spine minute or embedded in large adults) + I,30-35; anal rays II + I,19-22; gill rakers 7-10 + 15-20 = 22-29; maxilla reaching below front margin of pupil; in adults, height of soft dorsal-fin lobe subequal or slightly shorter than pectoral fin; anal-fin base 1.6-1.8 times in soft dorsal-fin base; blue to olivaceous above, shading to silvery white below; sometimes with narrow bronze stripe along midside of body; caudal fin olivaceous yellow. A circumglobal species restricted to subtropical and temperate waters; a highly esteemed gamefish usually found in large shoals to depths of 50 m. To 190 cm and 58 kg, common to 100 cm.

ALMACO JACK
Seriola rivoliana Valenciennes, 1833
(Plate V-14)

Dorsal rays VII (1st spine minute or embedded in large adults) + I,27-33; anal rays II + I,18-22; gill rakers 6-9 + 17-20 = 24-29 in juveniles, and 22-26 total in adults; maxilla reaching below mid-point of pupil; in adults, height of soft dorsal-fin lobe 1.3-1.6 times longer than pectoral fin; anal-fin base 1.5-1.6 times in soft dorsal-fin base; olivaceous to bluish green above; sides and belly lighter, sometimes with brassy or lavender reflections; dark nuchal band often persisting in adults; faint amber stripe frequently present along midside of body; fins mostly dark except pelvics white ventrally. Circumtropical, entering temperate waters in some areas; adults pelagic and epibenthic; rarely caught in inshore waters. Grows to 70 cm.

BLACK-BANDED KINGFISH
Seriolina nigrofasciata (Rüppell, 1829)
(Plate V-13)

Dorsal rays VII-VIII (posterior spines minute or embedded in large adults) + I,30-37; anal rays I (usually embedded) + I,15-18; gill rakers 1-2 + 5-8, mostly rudiments; maxilla reaching below rear margin of eye; height of soft dorsal-fin lobe of adults slightly longer than pectoral fin; anal-fin base 2.1-2.3 times in soft dorsal-fin base; no scutes; caudal peduncle grooves present dorsally and ventrally; bluish grey to black above, white to dusky below; spinous dorsal black, soft dorsal and anal dusky brown, the lobe tips white; caudal and pelvic fins yellowish brown to black; young with 5-7 dark oblique bands or blotches on upper body that fade with age. East Africa to Japan and Australia; solitary species preferring offshore reefs. Reaches 70 cm.

BLACK-SPOTTED DART
Trachinotus bailloni (Lacepède, 1801)
(Plate V-10)

Dorsal rays VI + I,20-24; anal rays II + I,20-24; gill rakers 7-13 + 15-19; caudal fin deeply forked; lobes of soft dorsal and anal fins greatly elevated; adults silvery blue to grey above, silvery white below; sides with 1-5 small black spots in a longitudinal row on or near lateral line, these spots equal to or smaller than eye (spots absent in fish smaller than 15 cm, the number of spots generally increasing with age); caudal, second dorsal and anal fins grey to black, the lobes usually darkest. Widespread in Indo-West Pacific from East Africa to the Marshall and Line islands; usually found in surge zone along sandy beaches. Attains 54 cm.

SNUB-NOSED DART
Trachinotus blochii (Lacepéde, 1801)
(Plate V-11)

Dorsal rays VI + I,18-20; anal rays II + I,16-18; gill rakers 5-8 + 8-10; tongue toothless; dorsal profile of snout very steep; lobes of soft dorsal and anal fins greatly elevated; generally silvery, paler below; large adults sometimes mostly golden orange, especially lower half of body; anal fin dusky to dirty orange, the lobe with brownish anterior margin; caudal and pectoral fins dark or dirty orange; pelvic fins white to dirty orange. Widespread in Indo-Pacific from East Africa to Marshall Islands. Feeds mainly on hard-shelled invertebrates, especially molluscs. Maximum size, 65 cm.

COMMON DART
Trachinotus botla (Shaw, 1803)
(Plate V-12)

Dorsal rays VI + I,22-24; anal rays II + I,19-22; gill rakers 6-9 + 11-15; lobes of soft dorsal and anal fins greatly elevated; adults bluish black above, silvery below; sides with 1-5 large dusky spots in a longitudinal row on or near lateral line, the anterior two spots larger than eye (spots absent on fish smaller than 15 cm, the number of spots generally increasing with age); caudal, second dorsal and anal fins dusky to blue-black, the lobes usually darker. East Africa to Australia; inhabits coastal waters, often preferring the rough surge zone along sandy beaches. Reaches 61 cm.

DOLPHINFISHES
FAMILY CORYPHAENIDAE

Dolphinfishes are oceanic dwellers of moderately large size characterised

by an elongate compressed body, small cycloid scales, a long dorsal fin extending nearly the entire distance between the nape and caudal fin; no finlets or scutes, and a deeply forked caudal fin. Adult males develop a bony crest on the forehead, and the anterior snout profile becomes vertical. The family contains only two species, both of which have a worldwide distribution in tropical and subtropical seas. They are pelagic in habit, generally living near the surface, often congregating around floating objects or sometimes following ships. Dolphinfishes are swift predators that feed on fishes (especially flyingfishes) and squid. They are much sought after by anglers who catch them by trolling a lure near the surface. The flesh is very tasty and in some places is

marketed under the Hawaiian name Mahimahi.

COMMON DOLPHINFISH
Coryphaena hippurus Linnaeus, 1758
(Plate V-1)

Dorsal rays 58-67; anal rays 25-30; greatest body depth in adults less than 25 per cent of standard length; an oval patch of teeth on tongue; pectoral fin more than one-half head length; back brilliant metallic blue-green, shading to golden yellow ventrally, with scattered iridescent blue-green spots; dorsal fin deep blue-green; caudal, anal, and pelvic fins mainly yellow. Brilliant colours fade to silvery grey with black spots and dark fins soon after death. Circumtropical. Attains 200 cm and 39.5 kg. The similar *C. equiselis* is distinguished by a broad square tooth patch on the tongue, body depth more than 25 per cent of standard length, and pectoral fin equal to about one-half head length.

Selaroides leptolepis

PLATE III

1 **PENNANTFISH** (*Alectes ciliaris*)

2 **DIAMOND TREVALLY** (*Alectes indicus*)

3 **FRINGE-FINNED TREVALLY** (*Absalom radiatus*)

4 **SMALL MOUTH SCAD** (*Alepes* sp.)

5 **YELLOWTAIL SCAD** (*Atule mate*)

6 **CLUB-NOSED TREVALLY** (*Carangoides chrysophrys*)

7 **ONION TREVALLY** (*Carangoides caeruleopinnatus*)

8 **BARRED TREVALLY** (*Carangoides ferdau*)

9 **GOLD-SPOTTED TREVALLY** (*Carangoides fulvoguttatus*)

10 **WHITEFIN TREVALLY** (*Carangoides equula*)

11 **EPAULET TREVALLY** (*Carangoides humerosus*)

12 **BUMP-NOSED TREVALLY** (*Carangoides hedlandensis*)

13 **WHITE-TONGUED TREVALLY** (*Carangoides talamparoides*)

14 **THICKLIP TREVALLY** (*Carangoides orthogrammus*)

15 **BLUDGER TREVALLY** (*Carangoides gymnostethus*)

16 **MALABAR TREVALLY** (*Carangoides malabaricus*)

17 **JAPANESE TREVALLY** (*Carangoides uii*)

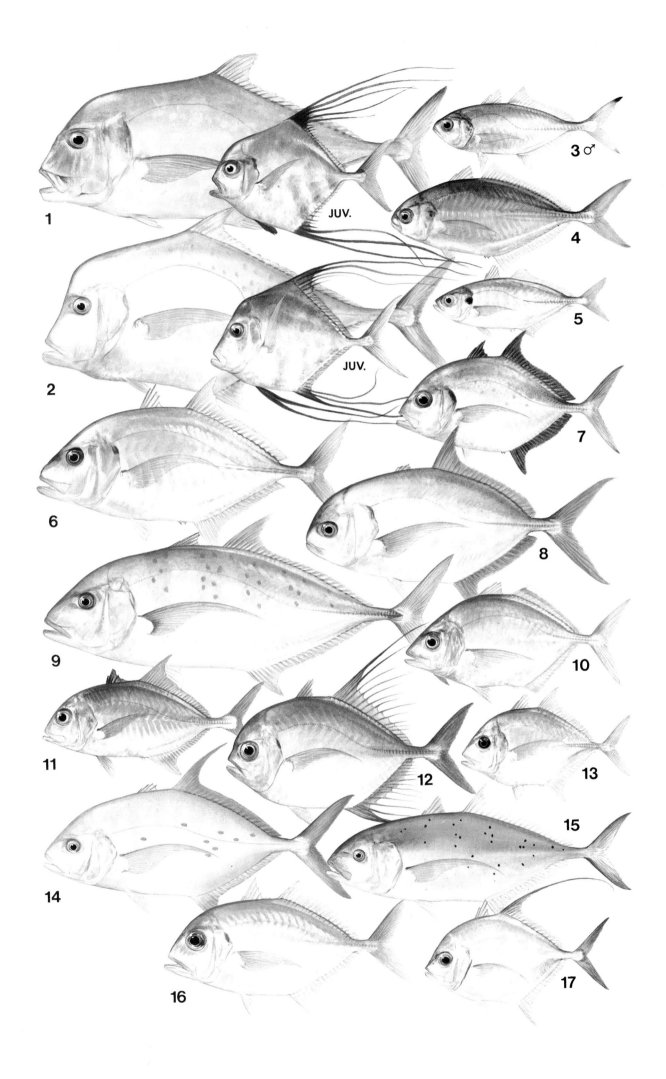

1

2

3 ♂

4

5

6

7

8

9

10

11

12

13

14

15

16

17

JUV.

JUV.

PLATE IV

1 **GIANT TREVALLY** (*Caranx ignobilis*)

2 **BLACK TREVALLY** (*Caranx lugubris*)

3 **BLUEFIN TREVALLY** (*Caranx melampygus*)

4 **BRASSY TREVALLY** (*Caranx papuensis*)

5 **TILLE TREVALLY** (*Caranx tille*)

6 **BANDED SCAD** (*Caranx para*)

7 **BLUE-SPOTTED TREVALLY** (*Caranx bucculentus*)

8 **BIGEYE TREVALLY** (*Caranx sexfasciatus*)

9 **ROUGHEAR SCAD** (*Decapterus tabl*)

10 **REDTAIL SCAD** (*Decapterus kurroides*)

11 **MACKEREL SCAD** (*Decapterus macarellus*)

12 **RUSSELL'S MACKEREL SCAD** (*Decapterus russelli*)

13 **LONG-BODIED SCAD** (*Decapterus macrosoma*

14 **GOLDEN TREVALLY** (*Gnathanodon speciosus*)

15 **FINNY SCAD** (*Megalaspis cordyla*)

16 **PILOT FISH** (*Naucrates ductor*)

17 **FRINGE-FINNED TREVALLY** (*Absalom radiosus*)

18 **BLACK POMFRET** (*Parastromateus niger*)

19 **SILVER TREVALLY** (*Pseudocaranx dentex*)

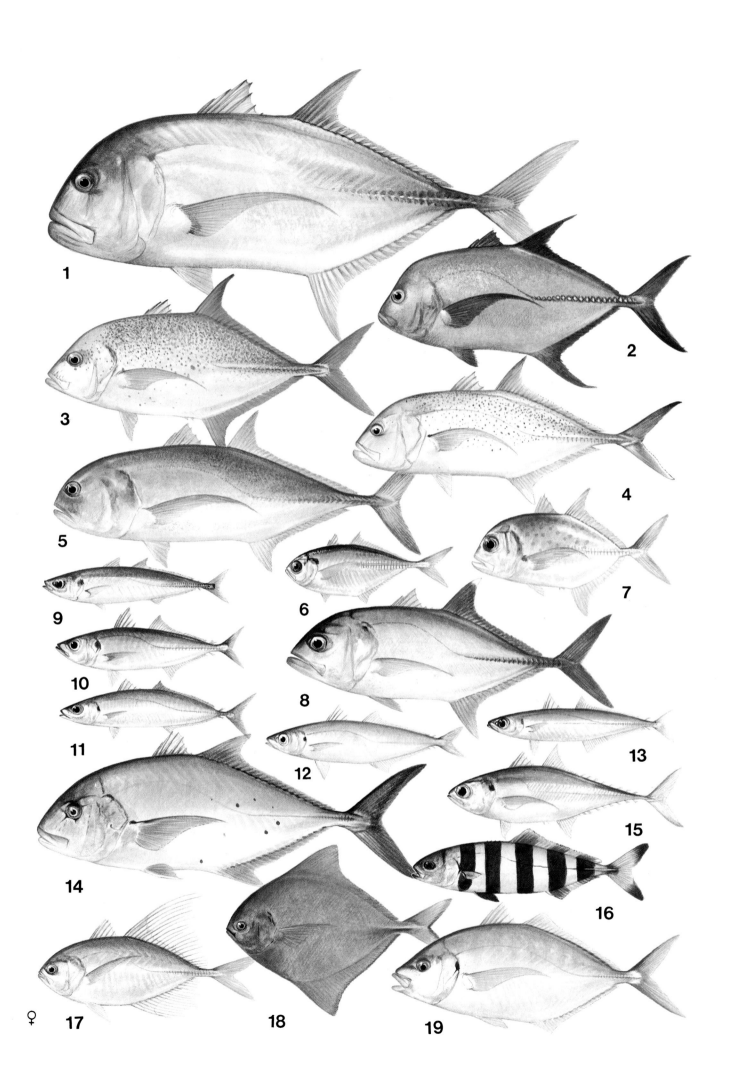

1

2

3

4

5

6

7

8

9

10

11

12

13

14

15

16

17

♀

18

19

PLATE V

1 **COMMON DOLPHINFISH** (*Crayphaena hippurus*)

2 **RAINBOW RUNNER** (*Elegatis bipunnulata*)

3 **NEEDLESKIN QUEENFISH** (*Scomberoides tol*)

4 **BARRED QUEENFISH** (*Scomberoides tala*)

5 **TALANG QUEENFISH** (*Scomberoides commersonnianus*)

6 **DOUBLE-SPOTTED QUEENFISH** (*Scomberoides lysan*)

7 **OXEYE SCAD** (*Selar boops*)

8 **PURSE-EYED SCAD** (*Selar crumenophthalmus*)

9 **SMOOTH-TAILED TREVALLY** (*Selaroides leptolepis*)

10 **BLACK-SPOTTED DART** (*Trachinotus bailloni*)

11 **SNUB-NOSED DART** (*Trachinotus blochii*)

12 **COMMON DART** (*Trachinotus botla*)

13 **BLACK-BANDED KINGFISH** (*Seriolina nigrofasciata*)

14 **ALMACO JACK** (*Seriola rivoliana*)

15 **YELLOWTAIL KINGFISH** (*Seriola lalandi*)

16 **AMBERJACK** (*Seriola dumerili*)

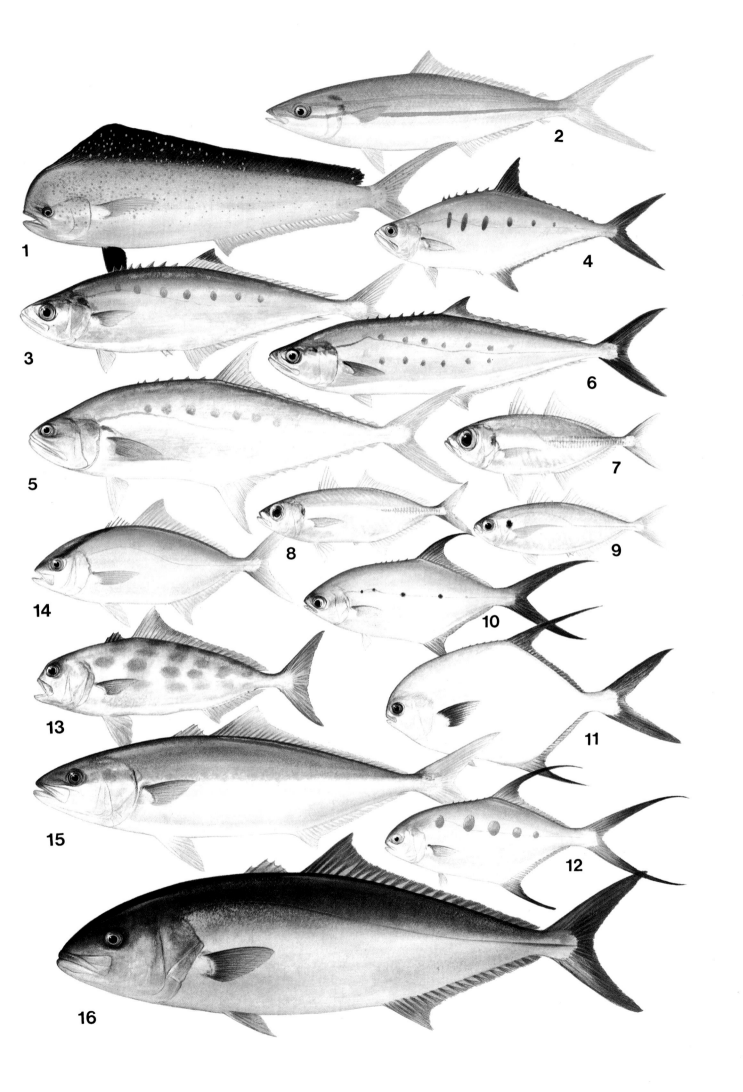

SNAPPERS
FAMILY LUTJANIDAE

Snappers are small to medium-sized fishes with an ovate to elongate, moderately compressed body. Other features include a single dorsal fin that may be notched in the middle or is sometimes deeply incised between the spines; dorsal spines usually X, the soft rays 8-18; anal fin with III spines and 7-11 soft rays; caudal fin truncate to deeply forked; pelvic axillary scale process usually well-developed; jaws usually with more or less distinct canines (absent in *Aphareus*); vomer and palatines usually with small conical teeth (absent in *Aphareus*); scales ctenoid; cheek and operculum scaly; snout, preorbital and lower jaw scaleless. The approximately 100 members of the family are distributed in all tropical seas, but the majority inhabit the Indo-Pacific region. The genus *Lutjanus* is the largest containing 64 species of which 39 occur in the Indo-Pacific (nine others in the eastern Pacific). Most snappers dwell in shallow to intermediate depths (to 100 m) in the vicinity of reefs, although there are some species largely confined to depths between 100 and 500 m. Snappers are active predators feeding mainly at night on a variety of items, but fishes are dominant in the diet of most species. Other common foods include crabs, shrimps, various other crustaceans, gastropods, cephalopods, and planktonic organisms, particularly urochordates. Plankton is especially important in the diets of *Paracaesio* and *Macolor*. The maximum lifespan of snappers has been estimated between four and 21 years based on studies of growth rings on bony structures such as otoliths and vertebrae. In general the larger snappers have longer lifespans, perhaps in the range of 15-20 years. Snappers are considered good eating and are frequently offered at

Black-Spot Seaperch (*Lutjanus fulviflamma*)

markets and restaurants. Although esteemed as food, several species of snappers have been serious offenders in causing ciguatera. A fish harbouring ciguatera toxin in its flesh can make a person eating it very severely ill, even though the fish is fresh and well-cooked. Victims with light cases may experience only weakness and diarrhoea (and hence may not realise that the fish is responsible). More severe cases suffer a variety of symptoms of which the most diagnostic is unpleasant tingling sensations of the palms of the hands and soles of the feet accentuated by contact with cold objects. Nausea, complete malaise, extreme weakness, joint pain, severe itching, and confusion of the sensations of heat and cold are common symptoms. In extreme cases there is progressive paralysis of body muscles, coma, and respiratory or cardiac failure. The organism initially producing the toxin is a dinoflagellate, *Gambierdiscus toxicus*, which lives

on benthic algae or dead coral rock. Outbreaks of ciguatera have been correlated with extensive disturbance to a coral reef which creates large areas of new surface for colonization by algae, etc. Between 1965 and 1984, up to 2,100 cases of ciguatera were reported for northern Queensland, and many of these were the result of eating snappers. The following snappers cannot be sold in Australia: Red Snapper (*Lutjanus bohar*), Paddletail (*L. gibbus*), and Chinamanfish (*Symphorus nematophorus*). In Tahiti *Lutjanus monostigma* is forbidden to be sold. These fishes all prey heavily on reef fishes. They probably obtain the toxin by eating herbivorous fishes such as surgeonfishes and parrotfishes. With each meal they get a life-time accumulation of toxin in the prey, thus it builds up rapidly in the predators, and of course, the larger the predator, the more apt it is to cause ciguatera. Often called Seaperches in Australia.

SMALL-TOOTHED JOBFISH
Aphareus furca (Lacepède, 1802)

Dorsal rays X,10-11; anal rays III,8; pectoral rays 15-16; lateral-line scales 65-75; gill rakers 5-6 + 16-18; teeth in jaws minute, no canines; vomerine teeth absent; interorbital space flattened; caudal fin deeply forked; back and upper sides purplish brown, blue-grey on sides; a silvery sheen on head and lower sides; edges of preopercle and opercle outlined with black. East Africa to Polynesia; usually seen on outer slopes between 6-70 m; a roving fish-eating predator. Maximum size, 40 cm, but usually less than 30 cm. *Aphareus furcatus* is an incorrect spelling used by most previous authors.

GREEN JOBFISH
Aprion virescens Valenciennes,1830

Dorsal rays X,11; anal rays III,8; pectoral rays 17; total gill rakers on first arch (including rudiments) 14 or 15; caudal fin deeply forked with pointed tips; colour varies from dark green to bluish or blue-grey. East Africa and Red Sea to Polynesia; usually on outer reefs to at least 100 m depth; moves freely in open water about reef and preys mainly on reef fishes, occasionally on crustaceans and octopus; an excellent table fish, but has caused ciguatera. To 100 cm.

HUSSAR
Lutjanus adetii (Castelnau, 1873)

Dorsal rays X,14; anal rays III,8; pectoral rays 17; total gill rakers on first arch 27-29; caudal fin emarginate or slightly forked; scales on back rising obliquely above lateral line; distinguished by yellowish eye and yellow to gold-brown mid-lateral stripe. Eastern Australia and Coral Sea; sometimes forms large aggregations around coral or rock outcrops during daylight hours. Reaches 50 cm. Also known as Yellow-banded Seaperch. *Lutjanus amabilis* De Vis is a synonym.

MANGROVE JACK
Lutjanus argentimaculatus (Forsskål, 1775)

Dorsal rays X,13 or 14; anal rays III,8; pectoral rays 16 or 17; total gill rakers on first arch 16-20; caudal fin emarginate; scale rows on back more-or-less parallel to lateral line or rising obliquely above posterior part; colour greenish brown to reddish; juveniles with about eight pale bars on sides and 1-2 blue lines across cheek. East Africa and Red Sea to Samoa; introduced to the eastern Mediterranean; juveniles and subadults occur in coastal estuaries and freshwater streams; adults migrate to offshore reefs and may occur to depths of at least 100 m. Attains 120 cm.

RED BASS
Lutjanus bohar (Forsskål, 1775)

Dorsal rays X,13; anal rays III,8; pectoral rays 16 or 17; total gill rakers on first arch 22 or 23; caudal fin slightly emarginate; a deep groove or pit from nostrils to front of eye; scale rows on back rising obliquely above lateral line; dark reddish brown on back, shading to reddish tan ventrally, with a faint linear pattern from dark edges on the scales; median and pelvic fins blackish orange-red; uppermost rays of pectoral fin blackish red; juveniles have two white spots below the dorsal fin. East Africa and Red Sea to the Marquesas and Line islands; common in our area, often approaching divers at close range; frequently implicated in ciguatera fish poisoning. To 75 cm. Also known as Red Bass in Australia.

Lutjanus bohar   Adult ▲ Juv. ▼

SPANISH FLAG
Lutjanus carponotatus (Richardson, 1842)

Dorsal rays X,14-16; anal rays III,8; pectoral rays 15-17; total gill rakers on first arch 15-18; caudal fin emarginate; scale rows on back rising obliquely above lateral line; white to bluish with eight or nine yellowish to brown stripes on side; black spot on upper pectoral fin base and upper part of pectoral axil. Andaman Sea to northern Australia; occurs either solitarily or in groups, usually between 15-50 m. Reaches 40 cm. Also known as the Stripey.

CHECKERED SEAPERCH
Lutjanus decussatus (Cuvier, 1828)

Dorsal rays X,13 or 14; anal rays III,8 or 9; pectoral rays 16 or 17; total gill rakers on first arch 14-16; caudal fin emarginate; scale rows on back rising obliquely above lateral line; generally whitish with a "checkerboard" pattern on upper half of side consisting of dark brown bars and stripes enclosing rectangular, whitish "windows"; lower half of side with two dark brown stripes, the upper extending from dorsal part of pectoral-fin axil to middle of caudal peduncle and the lower from the maxilla to base of posteriormost anal-fin rays or lower edge of caudal peduncle; a large black spot covering most of caudal-fin base. Andaman Sea to northern Australia; relatively rare on the Great Barrier Reef and in the Coral Sea. Attains 30 cm.

BLACK-SPOT SNAPPER
Lutjanus fulviflamma (Forsskål, 1775)

Dorsal rays X,12-14; anal rays III,8; pectoral rays 15-17; total gill rakers on first arch 16-19; caudal fin truncate or slightly emarginate; scale rows on back rising obliquely above lateral line; generally whitish or light brown on side, darker brown on upper part of head and back; a series of six or seven yellow stripes on side, mainly below lateral line; ventral portion of head, belly, most of caudal peduncle, and fins yellowish; a prominent black spot at level of lateral line below base of anterior portion of soft dorsal fin; sometimes confused with *L. russelli*, but has yellow longitudinal stripes and black spot is mostly below lateral line or bisected by it (mostly above lateral line in *L. russelli*). East Africa and Red Sea to Samoa; common in our area between 3-35 m. To 35 cm.

YELLOW-MARGINED SEAPERCH
Lutjanus fulvus (Bloch & Schneider, 1801)

Dorsal rays X,14; anal rays III,8; pectoral rays 16; total gill rakers on first arch 16-20; caudal fin slightly emarginate; a deep notch in vertical limb of preopercular margin; scales on back rising obliquely above lateral line; generally tan or brownish to pale yellow-white, with fine brownish to yellow scale margins; sometimes with a series of narrow yellow or golden brown horizontal lines (one per scale row) on side, mainly below lateral line; anterior part of head largely grey brown; belly and ventral portion of side whitish; spinous dorsal fin brown to reddish with a narrow blackish band near margin, its width increasing to cover most of soft dorsal fin; caudal fin blackish; both caudal and dorsal fins with a narrow white margin; pectoral, pelvic and anal fins yellowish. East Africa and Red Sea to south-eastern Oceania, introduced in the Hawaiian Islands; common in our area to 40 m depth. Reaches 40 cm. *L. vaigiensis* (Quoy & Gaimard) and *L. marginata* (Cuvier) are synonyms.

PADDLETAIL
Lutjanus gibbus (Forsskål, 1775)

Dorsal rays X,13 or 14; anal rays III,8; pectoral rays 16 or 17; total gill rakers on first arch 25-30; caudal fin distinctly forked with rounded lobes; a deep notch in vertical limb of preopercular margin; scale rows obliquely oriented, both above and below lateral line; generally red or grey, darker on back and upper portion of head; orange hue on lower part of opercle and in pectoral axil; fins red, or frequently dark brown to blackish; soft dorsal, caudal and anal fins with a narrow white margin; iris red; small juveniles (under about 10 cm) have the soft dorsal, anal, and caudal fin largely black. East Africa and Red Sea to southeastern Oceania; sometimes in large schools; frequently implicated in ciguatera fish poisoning. Attains 50 cm.

BLUESTRIPE SEAPERCH
Lutjanus kasmira (Forsskål, 1775)

Dorsal rays X,14 or 15; anal rays III,7 or 8; pectoral rays 15 or 16; total gill rakers on first arch 20 or 22; caudal fin slightly emarginate; a deep notch in vertical limb of pre-opercular margin; scale rows on back rising obliquely above lateral line; generally bright yellow on upper two-thirds of side and mainly white ventrally except several wavy, grey, horizontal lines sometimes evident; a series of four bright blue stripes on side; a blackish spot sometimes present on back below base of anterior soft dorsal rays; fins yellow except uppermost pectoral rays dusky brown and with brownish spot at base of these rays;. similar to *L. quinquelineatus*, but has four instead of five blue stripes. East Africa to Polynesia; introduced in Hawaiian Islands; common to reefs in our area, often forming essentially stationary schools by day. To 35 cm.

DARK-TAILED SEAPERCH
Lutjanus lemniscatus (Valenciennes, 1828)

Dorsal rays X,13 or 14; anal rays III,8; pectoral rays 16; total gill rakers on first arch 18-21; caudal fin truncate or slightly emarginate; scale rows on back rising obliquely above lateral line; generally grey-brown or olive on back and top part of head, grading to whitish ventrally (specimens from deep water frequently reddish or pink); dorsal and caudal fins dusky brown or black, frequently with a narrow white posterior margin; anal, pelvic, and pectoral fins whitish with some dusky brown; juveniles with broad black stripe along middle of sides. Sri Lanka to northern Australia; infrequently seen on deeper reefs. Reaches 65 cm.

BIGEYE SEAPERCH
Lutjanus lutjanus Bloch, 1790

Dorsal rays X-XII,12; anal rays III,8; pectoral rays 16 or 17; total gill rakers on first arch 24-26; caudal fin truncate or slightly emarginate; eye very large, its diameter much wider than distance between eye and upper jaw; scale rows on back rising obliquely above lateral line; generally silvery white; a broad yellow stripe along middle of side from eye to caudal fin base; a series of yellow horizontal lines (one per scale row) on lower half of body, and similar lines running obliquely above lateral line; fins pale yellow to whitish. East Africa to Australia, Melanesia and Mariana Islands; frequently seen in large schools to depths of at least 90 m. Attains 30 cm. Often referred to as *L. lineolatus* by previous authors.

ONESPOT SEAPERCH
Lutjanus monostigma (Cuvier, 1828)

Dorsal rays X,13 or 14; anal rays III,8 or 9; pectoral rays 15-17; total gill rakers on first arch 18 or 19; caudal fin truncate or slightly emarginate; scale rows on back rising obliquely above lateral line; silvery-white with yellow fins; usually a black spot below the middle of the dorsal fin that is intersected by the lateral line; somewhat similar to *L. fulviflamma* and *L. russelli*, but lacks a medial posterior extension of the vomerine tooth patch. East Africa and Red Sea to the Marquesas and Line islands; occasionally encountered in our area, usually close to shelter in 5-30 m. To 50 cm.

FIVE-LINED SEAPERCH
Lutjanus quinquelineatus (Bloch, 1790)

Dorsal rays X,13-15; anal rays III,8; pectoral rays 16 or 17; total gill rakers on first arch 20-23; caudal fin truncate or slightly emarginate; scale rows on back rising obliquely above lateral line; a deep notch in vertical limb of preopercular margin; generally bright yellow, including fins; a series of five blue stripes on side; a round black spot, eye-size or larger, below anteriormost soft dorsal rays and contacting lateral line, but mostly above it; similar in colour to *L. kasmira* (above), but has five instead of four blue stripes. Persian Gulf to Fiji; common on reefs, occurs solitarily or in small groups. Reaches 38 cm.

MAORI SEAPERCH
Lutjanus rivulatus (Cuvier, 1828)

Dorsal rays X,15 or 16; anal rays III,8; pectoral rays 17; total gill rakers on first arch 17 or 18; caudal fin truncate or slightly emarginate; scale rows on back rising obliquely above lateral line; lips swollen, particularly in large adults; generally brown with reddish tinge; each scale on side with a pale brown border and 2-3 small bluish white spots in central portion; head with numerous undulating blue lines; median fins yellowish although caudal and anal with some brown pigment; pelvic fins largely yellowish, but dusky brown anteriorly; pectoral fins light dusky brown with a suffusion of yellow; juveniles have 3-8 brown bars on side and a white spot with a broad black margin below the middle of the dorsal fin at the level of the lateral line. East Africa and Red Sea to Society Islands, north to Japan; occasionally seen adjacent to outer reef slopes. Attains 65 cm.

Lutjanus rivulatus Adult ▼ Juv. ▲

MOSES PERCH
Lutjanus russelli (Bleeker, 1849)

Dorsal rays X,14; anal rays III,8; pectoral rays 16 or 17; total gill rakers on first arch 13-18; caudal fin truncate or slightly emarginate; scale rows on back rising obliquely above lateral line; generally whitish or pink with silvery sheen, frequently brownish on upper part of head and back; a black spot mainly above lateral line, below anterior part of soft dorsal fin (sometimes faint);a black spot at base of upper pectoral rays; pelvic and anal fins yellowish; juveniles with 4-5 brown stripes and ocellated spot on side below rear half of dorsal fin; similar to *L. fulviflamma* (see above). East Africa to Fiji; common on the Great Barrier Reef; juveniles usually found in coastal shallows, sometimes in brackish estuaries. To 45 cm.

RED EMPEROR
Lutjanus sebae (Cuvier, 1828)

Dorsal rays XI,15 or 16; anal rays III,10; pectoral rays 17; total gill rakers on first arch 16-19; caudal fin emarginate; scale rows on back rising obliquely above lateral line; generally red or pink, darker on back; fins red except pectorals which are pinkish; small juveniles are white with three broad dark purple bars, these bars gradually becoming narrower with increased size and changing from dark purple to bright red; faint bars may be evident in adults. East Africa to western Pacific; occurs in the vicinity of lagoon coral reefs, often over adjacent sand flats; juveniles sometimes commensal with sea urchins. Reaches 60 cm.

BLACK-BANDED SEAPERCH
Lutjanus semicinctus Quoy & Gaimard, 1824

Dorsal rays X,13; anal rays III,8 or 9; pectoral rays 16; total gill rakers on first arch 14-19; caudal fin truncate or slightly emarginate; scale rows on back rising obliquely above lateral line; generally pink, grading to white on lower half of body; a series of seven narrow brown bars on upper back extending about half way down side; posterior half of caudal peduncle and adjacent caudal-fin base black; dorsal fin pale brown to whitish; caudal fin pale brown, sometimes with reddish hue; anal fin light brown; pelvic fins white; pectoral fins clear with small brown or blackish spot at base of uppermost rays. Indonesia to Fiji; seen infrequently in our area. Attains 35 cm.

BROWNSTRIPE SEAPERCH
Lutjanus vitta (Quoy & Gaimard, 1824)

Dorsal rays X,12 or 13; anal rays III,8 or 9; pectoral rays 15 or 16; total gill rakers on first arch 15-19; caudal fin truncate or slightly emarginate; scale rows on back rising obliquely above lateral line; generally whitish or pink with longitudinal brown lines (one per scale row) on side, those above lateral line slanted posteriorly toward dorsal fin base; a yellowish brown to black stripe on middle of side from eye to upper half of caudal peduncle; sometimes confused with *L. lineolatus* (above), but has broader space between eye and upper jaw (about equal to eye diameter). Seychelles to western Pacific; inhabits rubble slopes, also in areas of flat bottom with occasional low coral outcrops, sponges and sea whips at depths between 10-40 m. To 40 cm.

MIDNIGHT SEAPERCH
Macolor macularis Fowler, 1931

Dorsal rays X.13 (rarely 14); anal rays III,10; pectoral rays 17 or 18; gill rakers very numerous, total of about 110-122 on first arch; similar to *M. niger* (below), but juveniles have a very deep notch between the spinous and soft portions of dorsal fin and extremely long, narrow pelvic fins, they also lack a solid white area just behind the black hear bar; adults are mainly blackish, but are readily identified by the yellowish-brown hue on the head which has numerous short blue lines, spots, and vermiculations compared with the plain appearance of the head of *M. niger* (a pale reticulation of blue lines may be present); in addition the iris of *M. macularis* is generally bright yellow. East Indies and northern Australia to Ryukyu Islands; commonly seen on steep outer slopes. Reaches 55 cm.

Macolor macularis Adult ▼ Juv. ▲

BLACK AND WHITE SEAPERCH
Macolor niger (Forsskål, 1775)

Dorsal rays X,13 or 14 (about 65% with 14); anal rays III,11; pectoral rays 16-18; gill rakers very numerous, a total of about 85-108 on first arch; similar to *M. macularis* (see comparison above). Both species are plankton-feeders. East Africa to Samoa; often forms large mid-water schools on the edge of reefs, particularly on the upper section of steep outer slopes. To 55 cm.

Macolor niger   Adult ▼ Juv. ▲

SAILFIN SNAPPER
Symphorichthys spilurus (Günther, 1874)

Dorsal rays X,14-18; anal rays III,8-11; pectoral rays 16; total gill rakers on first arch 14 or 15; soft portions of dorsal and anal fins strongly elevated with leading edges forming a filamentous extension (or several filaments in dorsal fin of juveniles); adults developing a very steep snout profile; overall yellowish with a series of bright blue stripes on sides and head; a prominent black spot with a pale margin on upper edge of caudal peduncle; fins yellow; juveniles yellow with a striking, broad, mid-lateral black stripe. Western Pacific from northern Australia to Ryukyu Islands; seen in sand and rubble areas. Attains 60 cm. Sometimes called Blue-lined Seabream in Australia.

CHINAMANFISH
Symphorus nematophorus (Bleeker, 1860)

Dorsal rays X.15 or 16; anal rays III,9; pectoral rays 16; total gill rakers on first arch 16-19; soft portions of dorsal and anal fins moderately elevated, the anterior soft rays of juveniles forming several thread-like filaments; a deep groove between eye and nostrils; adults mainly reddish, frequently with lighter blotching or bars; young brownish on back and upper sides, yellowish below with bright blue stripes on side. Western Pacific from northern Australia to Ryukyu Islands; frequently implicated in ciguatera fish poisoning and therefore considered unsafe to eat. Up to 80 cm.

FUSILIERS
FAMILY CAESIONIDAE

The fusiliers are usually included in the snapper family (Lutjanidae), but recent investigations indicate they are deserving of their own family classification. These fishes are characterised by a slender, streamlined body, the depth 2.4-5.5 in the standard length; the mouth is small; the upper jaw is very protrusible; the upper edge of the side of the premaxilla has one or two bony processes; the teeth are small and conical (absent in the genus *Dipterygonatus*); there is a single dorsal fin with IX-XV slender spines and 9-21 soft rays; anal fin with III spines and 9-13 rays; caudal fin deeply forked; there is a band of scales across the forehead separated by a narrow scaleless area. The fusiliers are midwater zooplankton feeders that usually occur in schools. They sometimes swarm around divers in such large numbers that they virtually obliterate the surrounding seascape. These schools are most commonly encountered on the edge of outer reef dropoffs. At night the fish retire to the reef to sleep, and their colours generally fade with the white ventral portions becoming reddish or pink. The family is confined to the Indo-Pacific region; 20 species in four genera are recognized. Fusiliers are considered good eating.

GOLD-BANDED FUSILIER
Caesio caerulaurea Lacepède, 1801

Dorsal rays X,14-16 (usually 15); anal rays III,12 or 13; pectoral rays 19-22 (modally 21); lateral-line scales 57-65 (modally 61); generally blue with a single yellow stripe directly above lateral line for most of its length; ventral part of head and body whitish; each caudal lobe with a blackish streak. East Africa to Samoa. To 25 cm.

RED-BELLIED FUSILIER
Caesio cuning (Bloch, 1791)

Dorsal rays X,14-16 (usually 15); anal rays 10-12 (usually 11); pectoral rays 17-20 (usually 18 or 19); lateral-line scales 45-51 (modally 49); supratemporal band of scales continuous across top of head; body deep for the genus, the depth averaging 2.5 in standard length; mainly blue to blue-green except caudal fin, upper caudal peduncle, and posterior portion of back yellow without dark markings. Sri Lanka to New Caledonia, north to Ryukyu Islands. Reaches 25 cm. The common name refers to the red ventral colouration of freshly dead individuals, which is also typical of other members of the family.

LUNAR FUSILIER
Caesio lunaris Cuvier, 1830

Dorsal rays X,13-15 (usually 14); anal rays III,10 or 11 (usually 11); pectoral rays 18-21 (usually 19 or 20); lateral-line scales 45-53 (modally 49); supratemporal band of scales interrupted by narrow scaleless area on top of head; mainly blue with tips of caudal lobes black; juveniles have a yellow caudal fin with black tips. East Africa to Melanesia. Attains 30 cm.

BLUE AND GOLD FUSILIER
Caesio teres Seale, 1906

Dorsal rays X,14-16 (usually 15); anal rays III,12 or 13 (usually 12); pectoral rays 18-23 (usually 20-22); lateral-line scales 51-61 (modally 55); body blue, shading to white ventrally, the upper part of caudal peduncle, caudal fin and dorsal fin yellow; yellow of caudal peduncle extending variably forward onto upper back. East Africa to Line Islands, north to Japan. Reaches 30 cm.

MARR'S FUSILIER
Pterocaesio marri Schultz, 1953

Dorsal rays X,14-16 (usually 15); anal rays III,11-13 (usually 12); pectoral rays 22-24 (modally 23); lateral-line scales 68-76 (usually 70-75); generally light blue with a pair of thin yellow stripes on sides, one covering lateral line for most of its length and other one or two scales below dorsal profile of body; tips of caudal fin black. East Africa to the Marquesas, north to Japan. To 30 cm.

NEON FUSILIER
Pterocaesio tile (Cuvier, 1830)

Dorsal rays X to XII,19-22 (usually XI or XII,20 or 21); anal rays III,13; pectoral rays 22-24 (modally 23); lateral-line scales 69-76 (modally 71); scales above lateral line with bluish green centres and black margins; lateral line covered for most of its length by a black stripe with a broad neon blue zone below it; a blackish streak in each caudal lobe. East Africa to southeastern Oceania, north to Japan. Grows to 25 cm.

THREE-LINED FUSILIER
Pterocaesio trilineata Carpenter, 1987

Dorsal rays X or XI,14-16 (usually X,15); anal rays III,11 or 12 (usually 12); pectoral rays 19-22 (modally 20); lateral-line scales 62-75 (usually 63-69); back with three dark brown to yellow and three light bluish-white longitudinal stripes; body white or light blue ventrally; caudal fin lobes with black tips. Western and Central Pacific. To 15 cm.

TRIPLETAILS
FAMILY LOBOTIDAE

See discussion of the single species of the family below.

TRIPLETAIL
Lobotes surinamensis (Bloch, 1790)

Dorsal rays XI-XII,15-16; anal rays III,11-12; pectoral rays 17; lateral-line scales 43-45; gill rakers on first arch 6-7 + 13-15; body oval to oblong, its depth 2.0-2.5 in standard length; a single dorsal fin with stout spines and elevated posterior section; the common name is derived from the rounded lobes of the dorsal, anal, and caudal fins; scales ctenoid, covering body and head except preorbital region and jaws; jaws with outer row of short, close-set canines and an inner band of smaller teeth; no teeth on roof of mouth; preopercle serrate, the serrae decreasing in size and increasing in number with age; dark brown or greenish yellow on back, silvery-grey on sides; pectoral fins pale yellow; other fins dusky; juveniles generally dark brownish, but may be mottled. Tropical and subtropical seas around the world; occurs in bays and brackish estuaries or sometimes well out to sea around floating objects; juveniles sometimes in floating *Sargassum* weed; they may lay on their side at the surface and mimic a drifting dark leaf. Grows to 100 cm and at least 15 kg.

Lobotes surinamensis Juvenile

SILVER BIDDIES
FAMILY GERREIDAE

These are silvery fishes with moderately deep, compressed bodies and a distinctive concave ventral profile to the head; the mouth is very protractile, extending downward when protruded; the teeth of the jaws are tiny and brush-like and none exists on the roof of the mouth; there is a single dorsal fin, elevated anteriorly, and the dorsal and anal fins fold into a scaly sheath at their base; the scales are large and finely ctenoid. These fishes occur on sand or mud bottoms, frequently in brackish environments. A few species are regularly seen on the sandy margin of coral reefs. Gerreids are predators of buried organisms which they capture by plunging their protrusible mouth into the sediment, afterwards ejecting the sand through the gill openings. Food items include polychaete worms and small crustaceans.

OCEANIC SILVER BIDDY
Gerres oyena (Forsskål, 1775)

Dorsal rays IX,10; anal rays III,7; pectoral rays 15 or 16; lateral-line scales 39-42; depth of body 2.4-2.8 in standard length; overall silvery with a series of faint paired pink spots in rows on side of body. East Africa and Red Sea to Samoa. Maximum size, 35 cm

SWEETLIPS OR GRUNTS
FAMILY HAEMULIDAE

The sweetlips are a family of small to medium-sized fishes that occur worldwide in tropical and temperate seas. The group contains about 17 or 18 genera and approximately 120 species. A total of 10 species in two genera are known from the Great Barrier Reef and Coral Sea. They generally resemble snappers (Lutjanidae), but differ in having a smaller mouth, thicker lips (especially in *Plectorhinchus*), and the teeth in the jaws are conical and small with none developed as ca-

nines. These fishes are also known as grunts because of the sounds they make by grinding their pharyngeal teeth; the sound is amplified by the gas bladder. Many of the species in our area undergo dramatic changes in colour pattern with increasing growth. The smallest juveniles are particularly colourful and swim in a peculiar undulating fashion. They are eagerly sought by aquarium fish collectors. Sweetlips are primarily nocturnal. During the day they shelter in the reef, then disperse for feed-

ing at dusk. Their diet consists of a wide variety of benthic invertebrates. The flesh of the larger sweetlips is good eating, therefore they are a target of anglers and spearfishermen. The names Gaterinidae and Plectorhynchidae have sometimes been used for this family. Queenslanders frequently refer to these fishes as Morwongs, but this name should be reserved for the family Cheilodactylidae of southern Australia and other temperate seas.

Diagonal-banded Sweetlips
(*Plectorhinchus goldmanni*)

PAINTED SWEETLIPS
Diagramma pictum (Thunberg, 1792)

Dorsal rays IX or X,22-25; anal rays III,7; pectoral rays 16-17; lateral-line scales about 65; adults mainly light silver grey, white on belly; juveniles with conspicuous alternating black and white stripes, and yellowish head and belly; stripes eventually break up into spots that disappear in adults. East Africa and Red Sea to New Caledonia, north to Japan; more common in silty areas of inner and middle reefs of the Great Barrier Reef complex. Grows to 90 cm.

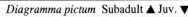
Diagramma pictum Subadult ▲ Juv. ▼

Diagramma pictum Adult

CELEBES SWEETLIPS
Plectorhinchus celebicus Bleeker, 1873

Dorsal rays XIII,19; anal rays III,7; pectoral rays 17; lateral-line scales about 75; overall blue-grey with series of narrow yellow stripes (sometime broken into spots) on side of head and body; belly and chin white; fins bright yellow. Indonesia to New Caledonia, north to Ryukyu Islands; frequently forms aggregations during daylight hours. Attains 40 cm.

MANY-SPOTTED SWEETLIPS

Plectorhinchus chaetodonoides Lacepède, 1800

Dorsal rays XII,18; anal rays III,8; pectoral rays 17; lateral-line scales about 60; adults overall white covered with numerous brown spots that extend onto most fins; belly sometimes dusky brownish; juveniles under 7-8 cm brown with large dark-edged white spots, this pattern gradually fades and is replaced by dark brown spots that become smaller and more numerous with increasing size. Cocos-Keeling Islands to Samoa, also recorded from Mauritius over 100 years ago; juveniles appear to mimic a toxic nudibranch or polyclad flatworms. Reaches 60 cm.

P. chaetodonoides Small Juv. ▲ Juv. ▼

Plectorhinchus chaetodonoides Adult

STRIPED SWEETLIPS

Plectorhinchus diagrammus (Linnaeus, 1758)

Dorsal rays XII or XIII,19-20; anal rays III,7-8; pectoral rays 16-18; lateral-line scales 53-56; adults white with four dark brown stripes on upper side; dorsal, caudal, and anal fins yellow with large black spots; a large black spot on upper portion of pectoral fin base; juveniles with three broad black stripes and narrower yellow-white band between them. Malaysia to Melanesia, north to Japan. Reported to 40 cm.

Plectorhinchus diagrammus Adult ▼ Juv. ▲

NETTED SWEETLIPS
Plectorhinchus flavomaculatus (Cuvier, 1830)

Dorsal rays XIII or XIV,20-22; anal rays III,7; pectoral rays 17; lateral-line scales about 60; dusky grey with small orange spots on body and on dorsal and caudal fins, those on body of adults tending to be aligned in rows that are mainly oblique; conspicuous narrow orange and grey-blue stripes covering head. East Africa and Red Sea to western Pacific. Maximum size, 50 cm. Also known as Gold-spotted Sweetlips.

BROWN SWEETLIPS
Plectorhinchus gibbosus (Lacepède, 1802)

Dorsal rays XIV,15-16; anal rays III,7; pectoral rays 17; lateral-line scales about 60; body deep, the depth about 2.3 in standard length; lips of adults greatly enlarged; mostly dark grey or brownish with darker scale margins; rear margins of cheek and gill cover black; similar to the Somber Sweetlips (*P. schotaf*), but has XIV rather than XI or XII dorsal spines. East Africa and Red Sea to Samoa, north to Ryukyu Islands. Grows to 60 cm. Also known as Blubber-lip Bream.

DIAGONAL-BANDED SWEETLIPS
Plectorhinchus goldmanni (Bleeker, 1853)

Dorsal rays XII or XIII,19-20; anal rays III,7; pectoral rays 17; lateral-line scales 55-58; ground colour silvery white with numerous diagonal black bands on upper two-thirds of head and body; fins and lips bright yellow; conspicuous black spots on dorsal, anal, and caudal fins. Western Pacific from Australia to Ryukyu Islands. Up to 50 cm.

GIANT SWEETLIPS
Plectorhinchus obscurum (Günther, 1871)

Dorsal rays XIII,18-19; anal rays III,7; pectoral rays 17; lateral-line scales 55-60; caudal fin slightly emarginate; lips greatly enlarged; adults dark grey with numerous small pale spots and short irregular lines; usually a broad diffuse pale bar just behind pectoral fins, extending onto abdomen; soft portion of dorsal fin and lobes of caudal fin with large black areas; anal, pelvic, and pectoral fins black or partially black. Red Sea to Fiji. The largest species of the family; to at least 100 cm. *Plectorhinchus harrawayi* Smith is a synonym.

DOTTED SWEETLIPS
Plectorhinchus picus (Cuvier, 1830)

Dorsal rays XII-XIV,17-20; anal rays III,7-8; pectoral rays 17; lateral-line scales 70-75; adults light grey or whitish with numerous small black spots on upper half of head and body; juveniles black on dorsal half and white ventrally, with white snout and large white saddles on forehead and middle of back. Seychelles to Society Islands, north to Japan. Attains maximum size of 50 cm.

Plectorhinchus picus Adult ▼ Juv. ▲

SOMBER SWEETLIPS
Plectorhinchus schotaf (Forsskål, 1775)

Dorsal rays XII,18-21; anal rays III,7; pectoral rays 16-17; lateral-line scales about 55; dusky brown to silvery grey, becoming darker with increased age; outer edges of median fins blackish; opercular membrane and sometimes hind edge of preopercle either blackish or orange-red. East Africa to the western Pacific. Attains 80 cm.

SEA BREAMS
FAMILY SPARIDAE

The sea breams are snapper-like fishes with an oblong to ovate compressed body; dorsal fin with X-XIII spines and 8-15 soft rays; anal fin with III spines and 8-14 soft rays; margin of preopercle smooth; scales usually weakly ctenoid; cheeks and opercles usually scaly; teeth conical or incisiform, molars present in some species; no teeth on roof of mouth; and caudal fin forked to emarginate. They occur in all temperate and tropical seas; approximately 100 species are known. Southern Africa has a particularly rich sparid fauna with over one-third of the world's species found there. Sea breams frequent a variety of habitats including brackish estuaries, bays, coastal reefs, and deeper waters of the continental shelf. However, only a few species are seen around coral reefs in the tropical Indo-Pacific. Australians are most familiar with a species known simply as Snapper (*Chrysophrys auratus*) that is widespread in cool southern waters of the island continent. Some sea breams are hermaphroditic, undergoing sex reversal from male to female. They feed on a variety of plants and animals, although benthic invertebrates such as molluscs, crabs, and urchins form most of the diet of many species.

SNAPPER
Chrysophrys auratus (Bloch & Schneider, 1801)

Dorsal rays XII,9-10; anal rays III,8; pectoral rays 15; lateral-line scales about 53-55; body ovate and compressed, becoming more elongate with growth; dorsal profile of head of adults very steep, the ventral profile of head and body nearly straight; with increasing age a prominent hump on the forehead develops; ground colour varying from pale pinkish silver to nearly brick red; characteristic light iridescent blue spots scattered on upper parts of the body, becoming less distinct in larger individuals. New Zealand and southern Australia, ranging north to the Capricorns; a popular eating fish known by a number of regional names that include Red Bream, Cockney Bream, Squire, Old Man Snapper, and Pink Snapper. Reaches 130 cm.

EMPERORS
FAMILY LETHRINIDAE

Emperors are conspicuous inhabitants of coral reefs in our area. They are medium to large-sized perciform fishes related to sweetlips (Haemulidae) and snappers (Lutjanidae). Diagnostic features include a terminal mouth with relatively thick lips, stout canine teeth at the front of the jaws and either conical or molariform teeth at the side of the jaws; there are no teeth on the roof of the mouth; the cheek is scaleless; the dorsal fin is continuous without a notch and contains X spines and 9 or 10 soft rays; the anal fin has III spines and 8-10 soft rays; the caudal fin is emarginate to forked. Most species occur on the sandy fringe of reefs where they actively forage on sand-dwelling invertebrates such as gastropods, polychaetes, crabs, prawns, and chitons. The larger species are also fish predators. Many emperors are nocturnal and spend daylight hours sheltering among coral or in shady crevices. Most species of *Lethrinus*, the largest genus, are capable of rapidly adopting a dark mottled or reticular colour pattern and can switch it off with equal rapidity. The flesh of emperors is good-eating and they are a favourite target of anglers. Several species are regularly caught by commercial trawlers. The family contains about 40 species (about 30 in *Lethrinus*) and is restricted to the Indo-Pacific except for one species in the eastern Atlantic.

Gold-lined Sea Bream (*Gnathodentex aurolineatus*)

GOLD-LINED SEA BREAM
Gnathodentex aurolineatus (Lacepède, 1802)

Dorsal rays X,10; anal rays III,8 or 9 (usually 9); pectoral rays 15; greatest body depth 2.3-2.8 in standard length; several scale rows on cheek; no molars in jaws; maxilla with a longitudinal denticulated ridge; inner base of pectoral fin scaleless; back finely striped with bluish silver and yellowish brown on side and below with 4-5 yellow or copper stripes; a large yellow blotch below rear end of dorsal fin; distal margins of median fins red.. East Africa to Tuamotus; common on shallow reefs down to about 20 m; sometimes seen in large aggregations. Grows to 30 cm.

COLLARED SEA BREAM
Gymnocranius audleyi Ogilby, 1916

Dorsal rays X,10; anal rays III,10; pectoral rays 14; greatest body depth 2.2-2.4 in standard length; several scale rows on cheek; no molars in jaws; head with a large blackish patch above and behind each eye; overall colour silvery. Southern Queensland, including southern portion of the Great Barrier Reef. To 40 cm. *G. bitorquatus* Cockerell is a synonym.

JAPANESE SEA BREAM
Gymnocranius euanus Günther, 1879

Dorsal rays X,10; anal rays III,10; pectoral rays 14; greatest body depth 2.4-2.5 in standard length; several scale rows on cheek; molars present on side of jaw; 4 1/2 longitudinal scale rows above lateral line (other *Gymnocranius* have 5 1/2); silvery with scattered irregular dark spots and blotches. Queensland to Tonga, north to Japan. Reaches 45 cm.

ROBINSON'S SEA BREAM
Gymnocranius grandoculis (Valenciennes, 1830)

Dorsal rays X,10; anal rays III,10; pectoral rays 14; greatest body depth 2.4-2.5 in standard length; several scale rows on cheek; no molars in jaws; adults over about 25 cm with wavy blue lines below eye, juveniles and subadults usually with 5-6 irregular dark bars on sides, otherwise colour is silvery, darker on back. East Africa and Red Sea to southeastern Oceania. Maximum size, 80 cm. *G. robinsoni* (Gilchrist & Thompson) is a synonym.

SPOTTED SEA BREAM
Gymnocranius sp.

Dorsal rays X,10; anal rays III,10; pectoral rays 14; greatest body depth 2.4-2.5 in standard length; several scale rows on cheek; no molars in jaws; silvery white with longitudinal rows of black spots on back and diffuse blackish area above eye, sometimes a blackish bar below eye. Known only from the Great Barrier Reef, Coral Sea, New Caledonia, New Guinea, and southern Japan. Attains 45 cm. This species is apparently undescribed. It has sometimes been referred to as *G. lethrinoides* (a synonym of *G. grandoculis*).

YELLOW-TAILED EMPEROR
Lethrinus atkinsoni Seale, 1909

Dorsal rays X,9; anal rays III,8; pectoral rays 13; greatest body depth 2.7-2.9 in standard length; cheek scaleless; inner base of pectoral fin scaled; molars present on lateral part of jaws; silvery to olive-brown with yellow around eye and broad diffuse yellow area often present along middle of side; caudal fin yellow. Indonesia to Tuamotus, north to Japan; outer reef slopes, sandy areas in lagoons and sea grass beds to depths of 30 m. To 43 cm. Usually referred to as *L. mahsena* (Forsskål) by previous authors, but *mahsena* is restricted to the western Indian Ocean and Red Sea.

YELLOW-SPOTTED EMPEROR
Lethrinus erythracanthus Cuvier, 1830

Dorsal rays X,9; anal rays III,8; pectoral rays 13; greatest body depth 2.5-2.7 in standard length; cheek scaleless; inner base of pectoral fin scaled; lateral teeth of jaws rounded and broad, but no distinct molars; charcoal grey, often a pale area behind head, head blue-grey, median fins yellowish; juveniles yellow with pearly stripes and spots. East Africa to Tuamotus; often sighted on outer reef dropoffs; reported to depths of 120 m. Reaches 60 cm. The name *L. kallopterus* Bleeker has been used by nearly all previous authors for this species.

Lethrinus erythracanthus Adult ▼ Juv. ▲

LANCER
Lethrinus genivittatus Valenciennes, 1830

Dorsal rays X,9; anal rays III,8; pectoral rays 13; greatest body depth 2.9-3.5 in standard length; cheek scaleless; inner base of pectoral fin scaleless; no molars in jaws, only conical teeth; 4 1/2 scale rows between lateral line and base of middle dorsal spines; second dorsal spine the longest, often much longer than other dorsal spines; tan or brown on upper sides, lower sides white with three brown or tan stripes; sides usually with scattered irregular, black oblique bars and a square black blotch above pectoral fin. Malay Peninsula to Australia, north to Japan; sandy areas and in seagrass; generally not seen on Great Barrier Reef or in Coral Sea, more common in coastal areas, including estuaries and trawling grounds. Grows to 25 cm. *L. nematacanthus* Bleeker is a synonym.

THUMBPRINT EMPEROR
Lethrinus harak (Forsskål, 1775)

Dorsal rays X,9; anal rays III,8; pectoral rays 13; greatest body depth 2.6-2.8 in standard length; cheek scaleless; inner base of pectoral fin scaled; molars present on lateral part of jaws; a large, oval, blackish spot on middle of side; overall olive or greyish, white on ventral parts. East Africa and Red Sea to Samoa; a shallow-water species usually seen in sandy areas or among weed. To 60 cm.

GRASS EMPEROR
Lethrinus laticaudis Alleyne & Macleay, 1877

Dorsal rays X,9; anal rays III,8; pectoral rays 13; greatest body depth 2.2-2.4 in standard length; cheek scaleless; inner base of pectoral fin densely covered with scales; no molars in jaws, only conical teeth; olive or bronzy with scattered irregular dark brown blotches; sometimes with dark bars on side and a dark blotch above pectoral fin; head brown or yellow with blue dots on cheeks and short blue stripes radiating in front and behind eye; often a broad dark bar between eye and jaw and blue bars sometimes present between eyes; vertical fins mottled. Southern Indonesia, northern Australia, New Guinea, and Solomon Islands; juveniles found in seagrass beds and estuaries, adults found on coral reefs. Grows to at least 56 cm. *L. fletus* and *L. anarhynchus* are synonyms. This species has also been referred to as *L. choerorynchus* and *L. fraenatus* by previous authors. Also known as Blue-spotted Emperor.

PINK-EARED EMPEROR
Lethrinus lentjan (Lacepède, 1802)

Dorsal rays X,9; anal rays III,8; pectoral rays 13; greatest body depth 2.6-2.8 in standard length; cheek scaleless; inner base of pectoral fin scaleless; no molars in jaws; 5 1/2 -6 scale rows between lateral line and base of middle dorsal spines; rear edge of gill cover and inside of mouth bright red; overall olive or light grey, longitudinal rows of white spots on back. East Africa and Red Sea to Tonga, north to Ryukyu Islands; sometimes forming large schools adjacent to coral or rocky outcrops. Grows to 40 cm. Also called Purple-headed Emperor.

SWEETLIP EMPEROR
Lethrinus miniatus (Bloch & Schneider, 1801)

Dorsal rays X,9; anal rays III,8; pectoral rays 13; greatest body depth 2.5-2.8 in standard length; cheek scaleless; inner base of pectoral fin usually with patch of scales; no molars in jaws; greyish with black scale centres, sometimes assumes dark bars; usually with red-orange area around eyes, red dorsal fin, and red bar on inner and outer pectoral fin base. Northern Australia, Coral Sea, New Caledonia, and Ryukyu Islands; inhabits coral reefs during the day where it feeds periodically in sand or rubble between bommies; at night it forages widely over open sand; depth range 5-30 m. Maximum size, 90 cm. Formerly known as *L. chrysostomus* (Richardson).

SPANGLED EMPEROR
Lethrinus nebulosus (Forsskål, 1775)

Dorsal rays X,9; anal rays III,8; pectoral rays 13; greatest body depth 2.5-2.8 in standard length; cheek scaleless; inner base of pectoral fin scaled; molars present in jaws of adults; 5 1/2 to 6 scale rows above lateral line; narrow blue bars on cheek; overall olive to yellow with numerous blue spots on sides. East Africa and Red Sea to Samoa; often forms schools in sand or rubble areas; a favourite angling fish that is good-eating. Grows to 86 cm.

ORANGE-STRIPED EMPEROR
Lethrinus obsoletus (Forsskål, 1775)

Dorsal rays X,9; anal rays III,8; pectoral rays 13; greatest body depth 2.6-2.9 in standard length; cheek scaleless; inner base of pectoral fin scaled; no molars in jaws; 5 1/2-6 scale rows above lateral line; pale olive with broad yellow stripe between pectoral fin and base of caudal fin. East Africa and Red Sea to Tonga and Samoa; common on coral reefs to 30 m; often seen sheltering among branching corals during the day while assuming a strongly mottled pattern. Reaches 40 cm. Formerly known as *L. ramak* (Forsskål).

LONG-NOSED EMPEROR
Lethrinus olivaceus Valenciennes, 1830

Dorsal rays X,9; anal rays III,8; pectoral rays 13; greatest body depth 3.0-3.3 in standard length; cheek scaleless; inner base of pectoral fin scaleless; no molars in jaws; snout very elongate and pointed; dull greenish or olive without distinctive markings. East Africa and Red Sea to Samoa; a highly active, fast-swimming emperor, easily recognised by its relatively slender body and long snout. Attains 100 cm. Formerly known as *L. miniatus* (Bloch & Schneider).

YELLOW-STRIPED EMPEROR
Lethrinus ornatus Valenciennes, 1830

Dorsal rays X,9; anal rays III,9; pectoral rays 13; greatest body depth 2.6-2.9 in standard length; cheek scaleless; inner base of pectoral fin scaled; molars present on side of jaws; olive with 5-6 yellow stripes on side; red on vertical margins of preopercle and opercle; outer edges of median fins red. Sri Lanka to Queensland, north to Ryukyu Islands; uncommon in our area. To 45 cm.

RED-EARED EMPEROR
Lethrinus rubrioperculatus Sato, 1978

Dorsal rays X,9; anal rays III,8; pectoral rays 13; greatest body depth 3.0-3.4 in standard length; cheek scaleless; no molars in jaws, only conical teeth; 4 1/2 scale rows above lateral line; olive grey to brown with scattered irregular small black blotches; lips and a spot on upper edge of operculum usually red. East Africa to Marquesas, north to Japan; mainly found in rubble areas of outer reef slopes to depths of 160 m. Attains 50 cm, common to 30 cm. Also known as Red-edged Emperor. A similar species, *L. semicinctus* Valenciennes (not shown here), also occurs in the area, but lacks the red lips and opercular spot. Its main diagnostic feature is a large dark oblong spot on the back below the soft dorsal fin.

VARIEGATED EMPEROR
Lethrinus variegatus Valenciennes, 1830

Dorsal rays X,9; anal rays III,8; pectoral rays 13; greatest body depth 3.4-3.9 in standard length; cheek scaleless; inner base of pectoral fin scaleless; no molars in jaws, only conical teeth; brown and grey, lighter on ventral part; scattered irregular dark spots and mottling on sides; often a pair of dark bands below eye, one to corner of mouth and other to lower edge of cheek; fins generally translucent except caudal with faint light and dark vertical lines. East Africa and Red Sea to New Caledonia; inhabits mainly weedy areas near coral reefs. Up to 20 cm.

YELLOWLIP EMPEROR
Lethrinus xanthochilus Klunzinger, 1870

Dorsal rays X,9; anal rays III,8; pectoral rays 13; greatest body depth 2.6-2.9 in standard length; cheek scaleless; inner base of pectoral fin scaleless; no molars in jaws; 4 1/2 to 5 scale rows above lateral line; a distinct angularity in dorsal profile of head above front of eye; olive or greyish with yellow or orange upper lip, sometimes indistinct dark spots scattered on sides; a red spot often present at upper base of pectoral fin. East Africa and Red Sea to Marquesas and Caroline islands; large solitary individuals frequently sighted on reefs. Maximum size, 60 cm.

BIG-EYE BREAM
Monotaxis grandoculis (Forsskål, 1775)

Dorsal rays X,10; anal rays III,9; pectoral rays 14; greatest body depth 2.1-2.7 in standard length; eye large; cheek with several rows of scales; inner base of pectoral fin scaled; molars present on side of jaws; maxilla with a longitudinal denticulated ridge; green or brown dorsally, silvery on sides, can rapidly assume a pattern of four broad blackish bars; two distinct colour forms are seen which has lead to speculation that two species may be involved: a dark variety with broad black saddles on the back separated by narrow white interspaces and a paler variety having the saddles more widely separated; observations on the Great Barrier Reef revealed that the darker fish are usually associated with the higher-contrasted environment of the coral reef, whereas the lighter fish are generally seen over sand or light-coloured rubble; moreover, the lighter fish were seen to quickly assume the dark pattern when harrassed by a spearfisherman; juveniles have four permanent dark bars and a more slender body. East Africa and Red Sea to southeastern Oceania and Hawaiian Islands. To 60 cm.

Monotaxis grandoculis Adult

Monotaxis grandoculis Subadult ▲ Juv. ▼

CORAL BREAMS
FAMILY NEMIPTERIDAE

The family Nemipteridae contains about four genera and 40 species that are widely distributed in the tropical Indo-Pacific region. They are brightly coloured fishes that are characterised by a slender to ovate body, a single dorsal fin with X spines and 9 or 10 soft rays, mainly small villiform jaw teeth (except enlarged anterior canines present in some species), and an emarginate to forked caudal fin. *Nemipterus* and *Parascolopsis* (neither included in our coverage) are mainly restricted to offshore areas to at least 100 m depth and often form a significant portion of trawler catches. *Pentapodus* and *Scolopsis* are commonly seen in the vicinity of coral reefs, often in adjacent sand or rubble areas. Most occur solitarily or in small groups, although the Bridled Monocle Bream and Threelined Monocle Bream are sometimes found in larger groups. Locomotion typically consists of quick darting movements interspersed with brief periods of stationary hovering. They are diurnally active fishes that feed mainly on benthic invertebrates, particularly polychaete worms, prawns, and crabs. Other food items include isopods, amphipods, ostracods, and copepods. Most species are considered good-eating, although their small size precludes keen interest by anglers.

JAPANESE BUTTERFISH
Pentapodus nagasakiensis (Tanaka, 1915)

Dorsal rays X,9; anal rays III,7; pectoral rays 16; caudal lobes not filamentous; overall tan, grading to white on belly; frequently with a pair of yellowish stripes separated by a white band along middle of side; iris yellow with blue stripes. Western Pacific from Japan to northern Australia; found below 15-20 m, sightings from Lizard Island and Lihou Reef have been reported. Attains 20 cm.

PARADISE BUTTERFISH
Pentapodus paradiseus (Günther, 1859)

Dorsal rays X,9; anal rays III,7; pectoral rays 16 or 17; upper caudal lobe filamentous in adults; tan on back, whitish ventrally; brown stripe from snout to eye, continuing behind eye to pectoral region, then widening into a diffuse bluish midlateral band; thin iridescent blue stripe along dorsal-fin base and V-shaped marking of similar colour directed posteriorly on caudal peduncle, with a small black spot in apex of V; young with a prominent yellow and black stripe on middle of side. Northeastern Australia to Arafura Sea; usually seen solitarily; juveniles occur in rubble areas. Reaches 30 cm.

Pentapodus paradiseus Juv.

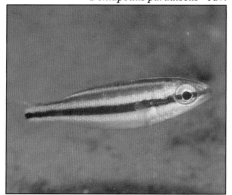

BLUE BUTTERFISH
Pentapodus sp.

Dorsal rays X,9; anal rays III,7; pectoral rays 16 or 17; caudal lobes not filamentous; blue on back, lighter below; a thin yellow stripe on upper side just above lateral line, and similar, but wider stripe along middle of side; juveniles darker blue with bright yellow stripes of equal width. Northeastern Australia to Fiji. Maximum size, 20 cm.

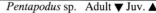

Pentapodus sp.   Adult ▼ Juv. ▲

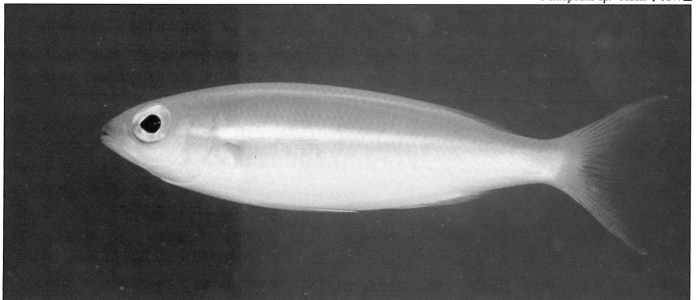

PALE MONOCLE BREAM
Scolopsis affinis Peters, 1877

Dorsal rays X,9; anal rays III,7; pectoral rays 17 or 18; 3 1/2 scale rows between lateral line and dorsal-fin base; olive to yellowish green on back, silvery white below, usually with faint, oblique dark lines on sides. Indonesia and Philippines to northern Australia and Melanesia. To 30 cm.

BRIDLED MONOCLE BREAM
Scolopsis bilineatus (Bloch, 1793)

Dorsal rays X,9; anal rays III,7; pectoral rays 17; 3 1/2 scale rows between lateral line and dorsal-fin base; a prominent curved white band with a black margin from mouth to middle of dorsal-fin base, and a pair of shorter white stripes above and behind eye; spiny part of dorsal fin bright yellow, and a prominent white mark on soft part of dorsal fin extending onto back; juveniles with conspicuous yellow and black stripes on upper half of body. Andaman Sea to Fiji, north to Japan; common on shallow reefs, sometimes in groups; juveniles usually shelter near live coral patches. Grows to 23 cm.

Scolopsis bilineatus Adult ▼ Juv. ▲

LINED MONOCLE BREAM
Scolopsis lineatus Quoy & Gaimard, 1824

Dorsal rays X,9 or 10; anal III,7 or 8; pectoral rays 15-17; 3 1/2-4 scale rows between lateral line and dorsal-fin base; upper side with a combination of two creamy white stripes and several broad blackish bars with pale spaces between them; lower sides white with silvery sheen. Cocos-Keeling Islands to Polynesia; commonly encountered over sand or rubble in the vicinity of shallow reefs. Reaches 22 cm. *Scolopsis cancellatus* Quoy & Gaimard is a commonly used synonym.

PEARLY MONOCLE BREAM
Scolopsis margaritifer (Cuvier, 1830)

Dorsal rays X,9; anal rays III,7; pectoral rays 16; 3 1/2 scale rows between lateral line and dorsal-fin base; greyish brown on back, whitish below; scales on upper side with white vertical streaks, those on middle of side frequently with yellow centres; juveniles mainly white with a black midlateral stripe. Malay Peninsula to the islands of Melanesia and northern Australia. Maximum size, 28 cm.

Scolopsis margaritifer Juv.

MONOCLE BREAM
Scolopsis monogramma (Cuvier, 1830)

Dorsal rays X,9; anal rays III,7; pectoral rays 18; 4 1/2 to 5 scale rows between lateral line and dorsal-fin base; prolonged filament on upper caudal fin lobe of adults; colour variable, often mainly pale tan except for series of slanting dotted lines on middle of side that sometimes form a solid broad stripe, or as pictured here; caudal fin with blue border and yellow submarginal band. Andaman Sea to New Caledonia, north to Taiwan; usually seen in sandy areas near reefs. Attains 30 cm. Often misidentified as *S. temporalis* (Valenciennes).

THREELINED MONOCLE BREAM
Scolopsis trilineatus Kner, 1868

Dorsal rays X,9; anal rays III,7; pectoral rays 16; 2 1/2 scale rows between lateral line and dorsal fin base; a trio of dark grey stripes on back with a brilliant white area separating them; lower sides pearly. Western Pacific eastward to Samoa. Reaches a maximum length of 25 cm.

GOATFISHES
FAMILY MULLIDAE

Goatfishes are readily distinguished by the pair of barbels on the chin, moderately elongate body, and two well-separated dorsal fins. The first dorsal fin of all of the species discussed below consists of VIII spines (the initial spine may be minute) and the second dorsal of 9 soft rays; the anal fin rays of all are I,7; the caudal fin is forked. The three genera are best distinguished by dentition: the species of *Mulloides* and *Parupeneus* lack teeth on the roof of the mouth whereas those of *Upeneus* have small teeth on the vomer and palatines. The species of *Mulloides* and *Upeneus* have bands of villiform teeth in the jaws; those of *Parupeneus* have a single row of moderate conical teeth. All of these fishes are carnivorous; they feed mainly on worms, crustaceans, brittle stars, and small mollusks and heart urchins that live in sediment; some species feed in part on small fishes. Goatfishes use their barbels, which possess chemosensory organs, to probe into the bottom in search of food; when prey animals are found, they root into the sand or mud with their snouts. Males wriggle their barbels rapidly during courtship.

YELLOWSTRIPE GOATFISH
Mulloides flavolineatus (Lacepède, 1801)

Pectoral rays 16 or 17; lateral-line scales 33-36; gill rakers 25-30; body depth 3.6-4.7 in standard length; snout 1.9-2.4 in head length; barbel length 1.4-1.8 in head; silvery white with a yellow stripe on body at level of eye, often containing a blackish spot above posterior part of pectoral fin. Indo-Pacific; frequently seen in aggregations. Reaches 40 cm. *M. samoensis* (Günther) is a synonym.

YELLOWFIN GOATFISH
Mulloides vanicolensis (Valenciennes, 1831)

Pectoral rays 16 or 17; lateral-line scales 35-38; gill rakers 32-36; body depth 3.3-3.9 in standard length; snout 2.1-2.6 in head length; barbel length 1.2-1.6 in head; white to pale pink with a yellow stripe edged in pale blue from eye to caudal-fin base; median and pelvic fins yellow. Indo-Pacific, but subspecifically different in the Indian Ocean. Closely related to *M. martinicus* of the Caribbean and *M. dentatus* of the eastern Pacific. Usually encountered by day in aggregations on reefs; feeds individually on sand-dwelling animals at night. Attains 38 cm. The invalid name *M. auriflamma* (Forsskål) is sometimes applied to this species.

BICOLOUR GOATFISH
Parupeneus barberinoides (Lacepède, 1801)

Pectoral rays 15-16 (usually 16); lateral-line scales 27-28 (true of other *Parupeneus*); gill rakers 27-33; body depth 3.2-3.5 in standard length; snout 1.8-2.0 in head; barbels 1.3-1.5 in head; head and anterior half of body dark reddish brown with two diagonal whitish bands, the posterior half of body abruptly white and yellow with a black spot nearly as large as eye on upper side below rear base of second dorsal fin; barbels red. Western Pacific, east to Micronesia and Samoa; usually encountered in the vicinity of coral reefs in protected waters such as bays or lagoons. Largest examined, 25 cm.

DASH-DOT GOATFISH
Parupeneus barberinus (Lacepède, 1801)

Pectoral rays 16-18; lateral-line scales 27-28; gill rakers 26-31; body depth 3.3-3.7 in standard length; snout 1.45-2.1 in head (snout relatively longer in larger fish); barbels 1.4-1.6 in head; spinous dorsal fin elevated in adults, the second and third spines nearly as long as head; whitish with a dark brown to red stripe from front of snout through eye to upper caudal peduncle, and a dark brown to red spot as large or larger than eye at caudal-fin base. Indo-Pacific; usually seen over sand or sand-rubble bottoms near reefs. The largest of the goatfishes; reaches at least 50 cm.

DOUBLEBAR GOATFISH
Parupeneus bifasciatus (Lacepède, 1801)

Pectoral rays 15-16 (usually 16); gill rakers 35-40; body depth 2.8-3.3 in standard length; snout 1.7-2.05 in head length; dorsal profile of snout slightly concave; barbels 1.6-1.9 in head; last dorsal ray only slightly longer than penultimate ray; yellowish grey to reddish with two broad dark bars dorsally on body, one beneath each dorsal fin (a third faint bar may be present dorsally on caudal peduncle); a dark patch on head enclosing eye (dark markings more evident on juveniles than adults). Indo-Pacific. Reaches 35 cm. *P. trifasciatus* (Lacepède) is a synonym.

CARDINAL GOATFISH
Parupeneus ciliatus (Lacepède, 1801)

Pectoral rays l5 (rarely l4); gill rakers 30-34; body depth 2.95-3.5 in standard length; snout 1.85-2.1 in head; barbels 1.55-1.9 in head; last dorsal ray only slightly longer than penultimate ray; whitish to pale pink, the scales edged in brownish red; alternating diagonal bands of reddish brown and whitish on head which continue anterodorsally on body; a pale saddle-like spot anteriorly on caudal peduncle, followed by a dark spot. Indo-Pacific. Largest specimen, 38 cm. *P. fraterculus* (Valenciennes) and *P. pleurotaenia* (Playfair & Günther) are synonyms.

GOLDSADDLE GOATFISH
Parupeneus cyclostomus (Lacepède, 1801)

Pectoral rays 15-17 (usually 16); gill rakers 29-33; body depth 3.3-3.9 in standard length; snout 1.6-1.9 in head length; barbels long, extending to or beyond end of head; two colour phases, one yellowish grey with blue markings on scales and a yellow saddle-like spot on caudal peduncle, the other entirely yellow (the yellow peduncular spot brighter yellow). To 50 cm. Indo-Pacific. Unusual for a goatfish in feeding heavily on fishes (about 70% of its diet). Has been observed to use its barbels to frighten its prey from holes in the reef. *P. chryserydros* (Lacepède) and *P. luteus* (Valenciennes) are synonyms.

Parupeneus cyclostomus Yellow phase ▲ Dark phase ▼

CINNABAR GOATFISH
Parupeneus heptacanthus (Lacepède, 1801)

Pectoral rays 15-17 (usually 16); gill rakers 26-30; body depth 3.15-3.4 in standard length; snout 1.75-2.1 in head; barbels 1.15-1.4 in head; dorsal profile of head strongly and evenly convex; rear of maxilla symmetrically convex (other species of the genus herein with a dorsoposterior lobe); yellowish to pink on back, the scales with a pale blue spot, shading to silvery white on sides and ventrally; a small reddish brown spot usually present just below lateral line beneath seventh to eighth dorsal spines. East Africa to Marshall Islands; usually seen over silty sand bottoms or seagrass beds. *P. cinnabarinus* (Cuvier) and *P. pleurospilos* (Bleeker) are synonyms.

INDIAN GOATFISH
Parupeneus indicus (Shaw, 1803)

Pectoral rays 15-17 (usually 16); gill rakers 24-27; body depth 3.3-3.75 in standard length; snout length 1.65-2.0 in head; barbels 1.3-1.55 in head; a large horizontally elongate yellow spot on middle of back centered on lateral line; a black spot larger than eye posteriorly on caudal peduncle centered slightly above midlateral line. East Africa to Samoa; usually found in silty sand or seagrass areas. Largest examined, 35 cm.

MANYBAR GOATFISH
Parupeneus multifasciatus (Quoy & Gaimard, 1825)

Pectoral rays 15-17 (usually 16); gill rakers 36-42; body depth 3.1-3.7 in standard length; snout 1.7-1.9 in head; barbels moderately long, 1.0-1.35 in head; last dorsal soft ray distinctly longer than penultimate ray; light gray to brownish red with four blackish bars dorsally on body (three in middle of body, the central one narrow) and one on caudal peduncle); a diffuse dark bar on nape, and a horizontally elongate dark spot behind eye; posterior basal part of second dorsal fin blackish. Central and western Pacific. Reaches 30 cm. Often misidentified as *P. trifasciatus.*

SIDESPOT GOATFISH
Parupeneus pleurostigma (Bennett, 1830)

Pectoral rays l5-l7 (usually l6); gill rakers 29-32; body depth 3.5-3.9 in standard length; snout 1.75-2.1 in head; barbels 1.3-1.55 in head; last dorsal soft ray noticeably longer than penultimate ray; whitish to pink with a black spot about four scales in width on lateral line beneath rear of first dorsal fin; behind this a large oval white spot, followed by a dark area; base of second dorsal fin blackish. Indo-Pacific. Reported to 33 cm.

BLACKSPOT GOATFISH
Parupeneus spilurus (Bleeker, 1854)

Pectoral rays 15-17 (usually 16); gill rakers 28-32; body depth 3.1-3.7 in standard length; snout 1.85-2.25 in head length; barbels 1.35-1.65 in head; a dark brown band, broadly bordered on each side by a white to pale red band, passing from front of snout through eye to rear base of second dorsal fin; a second dark band paralleling the first, beginning at corner of mouth (brown bands often brownish yellow posteriorly); a large saddle-like black spot on caudal peduncle reaching lateral line, preceded by a white to pale red spot of about the same size. Northern New Zealand and New Caledonia to Western Australia. Reaches at least 32 cm. *P. signatus* (Günther) is a synonym.

FRECKLED GOATFISH
Upeneus tragula Richardson, 1846

Pectoral rays 13-14 (usually l3); lateral-line scales 28-29; gill rakers 21-24; body elongate, the depth 3.9-4.5 in standard length; snout 2.25-2.65 in head; barbels 1.45-1.85 in head; a narrow dark yellowish to reddish brown stripe from front of snout through eye to upper caudal-fin base; back above stripe light greenish grey to pale orangish brown, white below, everywhere finely flecked with dark reddish brown; ventral part of body with or without large reddish blotches; barbels yellow; lobes of caudal fin with transverse black bands (the number increasing with growth); a large mottled dark reddish to black area on outer part of first dorsal fin. Western Pacific to East Africa; usually in calm silty sand areas. To 30 cm.

SWEEPERS
FAMILY PEMPHERIDAE

This family of fishes, often known as bulls-eyes in Australia, consists of only two genera, *Parapriacanthus*, with about three Indo-Pacific species, and *Pempheris*, with perhaps 20 species, two of which occur in the Atlantic. The family is in need of revision. These fishes have moderately deep compressed bodies with a strongly tapering tail, slender caudal peduncle, very large eyes, and a highly oblique mouth with projecting lower jaw; the maxilla is exposed on the cheek and does not reach beyond the pupil of the eye; the teeth are small with incurved tips, in bands in the jaws; there are small teeth on the palatines and a V-shaped patch on the vomer; the scales are small, either ctenoid and adherent or cycloid and deciduous; the lateral line in *Pempheris* extends to the end of the caudal fin but not in *Parapriacanthus*; the dorsal fin is short and unnotched, entirely anterior to middle of body, with IV-VII spines and 7-12 soft rays; the anal fin has a very long base and consists of III spines and 17-45 soft rays; the caudal fin is truncate to slightly forked with 15 branched rays. The species of *Parapriacanthus* and some of *Pempheris* have bioluminescent organs; these are associated with the digestive tract. Sweepers are nocturnal; they tend to form aggregations in caves by day and disperse at night to feed on zooplankton.

GOLDEN SWEEPER
Parapriacanthus ransonneti Steindachner, 1870

Dorsal rays V-VI (usually V),7-10; anal rays III,18-24; scales ctenoid; lateral-line scales 52-70 (55-64 in Australian waters), the lateral line extending to middle of caudal fin; no scales on anal fin (anal fin scaled basally in *Pempheris*); lower-limb gill rakers 15-20 (25-28 in *Parapriacanthus elongatus* from southern Australia); body depth 2.4-3.3 in standard length; caudal fin forked; golden anteriorly in life, transluscent reddish posteriorly; a vertical blackish line at caudal-fin base. Western Pacific east to New Caledonia and Marshall Islands and west to Western Australia; forms dense schools in caves. Reaches 10 cm. *P. unwini* Ogilby is a synonym.

BRONZE SWEEPER
Pempheris analis Waite, 1910

Dorsal rays V-VI,10-12; anal rays III,30-35; scales ctenoid and adherent; lateral-line scales 63-79; scales above lateral line 10-12; no pelvic axillary scale; gill rakers 9-11 + 23-25; body depth 2.15-2.4 in standard length; caudal fin slightly forked; bronze with a large blackish spot distally on dorsal fin and often on elevated anterior part of anal fins and tip of each caudal-fin lobe; a large dark spot at base of pectoral fins; lateral line conspicuous. Kermadec Islands (type locality), Lord Howe Island, southern Great Barrier Reef, and Western Australia; known from the depth range of 5-40 m. Attains 20 cm.

COPPER SWEEPER
Pempheris oualensis Cuvier, 1831

Dorsal rays VI,8-10; anal rays III,38-43; scales ctenoid dorsally on body posterior to rear of dorsal fin, posteriorly on side of body, and ventrally on thorax and head; scales elsewhere cycloid; lateral-line scales 60-73; scales above lateral line 6-9; small axillary scale at pelvic angle; gill rakers 8-10 + 20-24; body depth 1.85-2.4 in standard length; caudal fin slightly forked; dark brown on back, soon shading to coppery on sides and ventrally; tip and leading edge of dorsal fin broadly black; caudal fin blackish posteriorly, broadest at tips of lobes; a dark bar at pectoral-fin base. Islands of Oceania and western Pacific to Western Australia and Christmas Island in the eastern Indian Ocean; forms aggregations in caves by day. Reaches 22 cm. *P. otaitensis* Cuvier is a synonym.

SILVER SWEEPER
Pempheris schwenkii Bleeker, 1855

Dorsal rays VI,8-9; anal rays III,36-41; scales on side of body cycloid and deciduous; lateral-line scales 44-50; scales above lateral line 3-4; small axillary scale at pelvic angle; gill rakers 7-8 + 18-23; body depth 2.0-2.35 in standard length; thorax keeled ventrally (rounded on above two *Pempheris*); caudal fin slightly forked; deep purplish dorsally, soon shading to silvery on sides and ventrally with lavender iridescence; tip and leading edge of dorsal fin dusky; posterior margin of caudal fin sometimes dusky; scaled basal part of anal fin dusky. Fiji and Vanuatu through Australia and Indonesia to East Africa. To 15 cm.

DRUMMERS OR SEA CHUBS
FAMILY KYPHOSIDAE

The drummers, sometimes called rudderfishes or sea chubs, are moderately deep-bodied, compressed fishes with a small head and a small terminal mouth; the teeth are incisiform, and the maxilla slips partially under the preorbital bone when the mouth is closed. The scales are small and ctenoid, covering most of the head and soft portions of the median fins. The dorsal fin is continuous, and the caudal fin is emarginate to forked; the paired fins are relatively short, the origin of the pelvics posterior to the pectoral base. These fishes are omnivorous, but feed mainly on benthic algae; their digestive tract is very long, as would be expected from their plant-feeding habits. They sometimes occur in small aggregations. The family is divisible into two subfamilies, the Kyphosinae and the Girellinae (often regarded as a separate family). The latter group is mainly subtropical or temperate in distribution.

TOPSAIL DRUMMER
Kyphosus cinerascens (Forsskål, 1775)

Dorsal rays XI,12; anal rays III,11; pectoral rays 17-19; lateral-line scales 65-72; gill rakers 8-10 + 18-20; soft portion of dorsal fin distinctly elevated, higher than tallest dorsal spines; silvery grey with thin longitudinal dark lines on sides; fins mainly dark brown. East Africa and Red Sea to Polynesia; often seen high above the bottom in small groups. Reaches 45 cm.

LONG-FINNED DRUMMER
Kyphosus vaigiensis (Quoy & Gaimard, 1825)

Dorsal rays XI,14 (rarely 13); anal rays III,13; pectoral rays 18-20; lateral-line scales 77-80; gill rakers 9-10 + 20-24; soft portion of dorsal fin not elevated, about the same height or lower than dorsal spines; silvery grey with narrow bronzy stripes on side. East Africa and Red Sea to Polynesia. Attains 60 cm.

STRIPEY
Microcanthus strigatus (Cuvier, 1831)

Dorsal rays X or XI,17 or 18; anal rays III,14-16; lateral-line scales 56-60; gill rakers 5-7 + 12-14; distinctive pattern of oblique black stripes with yellow or whitish spaces between them. Antiequatorial distribution; isolated populations in western and eastern Australia in the Southern Hemisphere and northern populations in Hawaiian Islands and Taiwan to Japan; mainly found on southern part of the Great Barrier Reef. To 16 cm.

BATFISHES
FAMILY EPHIPPIDAE

These are distinctive fishes with deep, nearly circular, compressed bodies. The mouth is small and terminally located; the teeth in the jaws are brush-like and often have tricuspid tips; dorsal fin continuous with V to IX spines and 19-40 rays; anal fin with III spines and 17-28 rays. The colour pattern is often silvery with dark bars. Worldwide the family (also known as spadefishes) contains five genera and about 17 species; only the genus *Platax* is associated with Indo-Pacific coral reefs. *Platax* are among the most graceful of coral reef inhabitants, characterised by long flowing fins, particularly in their juvenile stages. These fishes are extremely tame and curious, especially *Platax teira*. It is not unusual for them to swarm around divers, and they can sometimes be hand fed. Batfishes occur on both sheltered and more offshore reefs. Their diet consists largely of benthic invertebrates and zooplankton. Young specimens make excellent aquarium pets and are much in demand. In nature the young of *Platax orbicularis* mimic drifting dead leaves, and those of *P. pinnatus* mimic toxic polyclad flatworms which are black with an orange border.

HUMP-HEADED BATFISH
Platax batavianus Cuvier, 1831

Dorsal rays VII,29-32; anal rays III,21-23; adults relatively elongate compared to other *Platax*, developing a hump in front of eye with growth; differs from other *Platax* in having VII rather than V dorsal spines; silvery with black bar through eye and another on body at level of pectoral fin; juveniles with greatly elevated dorsal and anal fins and elongate pelvic fins, all these fins with ragged margins; juveniles with a dark brown bar through eye, another between dorsal fin origin and pelvic fins, and a third on posterior part of body extending onto dorsal and anal fins; areas between dark bars light brown with narrow white vertical lines; pelvic fins dark brown. Malay Peninsula to northern Australia. Grows to 50 cm.

Round-faced Batfish (*Platax tiera*) Juveniles

ORBICULAR BATFISH
Platax orbicularis (Forsskål, 1775)

Dorsal rays V,34-38; anal rays III,26-38; juveniles with elevated, but relatively broad, dorsal and anal fins; adults orbiculate; silvery grey with a black bar through eye and another on body at level of pectoral fin; dorsal and anal fins with a black margin; often small black spots scattered on side; small juveniles light reddish brown to brownish yellow with a narrow brown bar through eye. East Africa and Red Sea to the Tuamotus; juveniles seen inshore off sandy beaches and around boat moorings; larger fish are solitary or occur in small groups. Reaches 50 cm.

Platax orbicularis Juv.

PINNATE BATFISH
Platax pinnatus (Linnaeus, 1758)

Dorsal rays V,30-37; anal rays III,23-27; adults orbiculate, but distinguished by protruding snout; silvery grey or brownish with a black bar through eye and another at level of pectoral fin extending onto pelvic fin; juveniles nearly black with greatly elevated dorsal and anal fins, the body and fins outlined in orange. Western Pacific from the Ryukyu Islands to Australia; reported occurrence of this species in the western Indian Ocean is doubtful. Reaches 30 cm.

Platax pinnatus Juv.

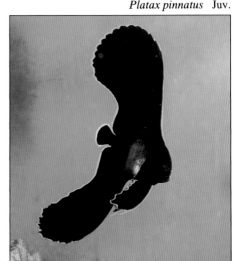

TEIRA BATFISH
Platax teira (Forsskål, 1775)

Dorsal rays V,30-37; anal rays III,23-27; young with extremely tall and narrow dorsal and anal fins; adults orbiculate except for an obtuse angularity in the dorsal contour of the nape; distinguished by a black blotch below pectoral fin and a second, vertically elongate blotch above front of anal fin; silvery grey to brownish with black bar through eye and another at level of pectoral fin. East Africa and Red Sea to Melanesia; adults may form schools. Reaches 60 cm.

SHORT-FINNED BATFISH
Zabidius novemaculeatus (McCulloch, 1916)

Dorsal rays IX,29; anal rays III,22; similar in appearance to *Platax*, but has IX instead of V-VII dorsal spines; silvery grey with a black bar through eye and another at level of pectoral fin. Northern Australia and southern New Guinea; usually not seen on reefs, but rather in more inshore areas, sometimes caught by trawlers Attains 45 cm.

BUTTERFLYFISHES
FAMILY CHAETODONTIDAE

Butterflyfishes are renowned for their striking colour patterns, delicate shapes, and graceful swimming movements. They have deep, compressed bodies and small protractile mouths with brush-like teeth in the jaws. The scales are ctenoid and cover the head, body, and median fins. There is a single dorsal fin with VI to XVI stout spines and no notch between the spinous and soft portions; the membranes of the anterior spines are deeply incised; the anal fin has III-V stout spines; there is a scaly axillary process at the upper base of the pelvic fins; the caudal fin varies in shape from rounded to slightly emarginate. These fishes have a distinctive late postlarval stage called the tholichthys larva which has large bony plates on the head and anterior body. The family contains 116 species which occur mainly in tropical seas around coral reefs. Most of the species dwell in depths of less than 20 m, but some are restricted to deeper sections of the reef, to at least 200 m. Butterflyfishes are active during daylight hours and seek shelter close to the reef's surface during the night. They often assume a drab nocturnal colour pattern. Most species are restricted to a relatively small area of the reef, perhaps an isolated patch reef or part of a more extensive reef system. They travel extensively throughout their home range foraging for food. Many species feed on live coral polyps, others consume a mixed diet consisting of small benthic invertebrates and algae. A few species, for example members of the genus *Hemitaurichthys*, feed in midwater on zooplankton. Young butterflyfishes are highly prized as aquarium fishes. The maximum length of most species is under 30 cm.

Pennant Bannerfish (*Henochus chrysostomus*)

GOLDEN-STRIPED BUTTERFLY-FISH
Chaetodon aureofasciatus Macleay, 1878

Dorsal rays X,20-22; anal rays III,17 or 18; pectoral rays 14 or 15; lateral-line scales 38-42; greatest body depth 1.2-1.5 in standard length; mainly golden yellow with dusky area covering most of sides, sometimes a pair of diffuse crossbars across body; a dark-edged orange bar through eye. Great Barrier Reef to Western Australia and New Guinea; common on inner reef complexes and coastal reefs. Attains 12.5 cm.

THREADFIN BUTTERFLYFISH
Chaetodon auriga Forsskål, 1775

Dorsal rays XIII,22-25; anal rays III,19-21; pectoral rays 14 or 15; lateral-line scales 33-43 (usually 34-40); greatest body depth 1.5-1.8 in standard length; adults with a filament trailing posteriorly from upper soft portion of dorsal fin; pattern of "chevron" markings on sides; yellow posteriorly with a large black spot on soft portion of dorsal fin; a prominent black band through eye. East Africa and Red Sea to Polynesia; common on shallow, protected reefs, also on outer reefs to 30 m; feeds on algae, polychaetes, prawns, and coral polyps. To 20 cm.

TRIANGULAR BUTTERFLYFISH
Chaetodon baronessa Cuvier, 1831

Dorsal rays XI or XII,23-26 (usually XI,25); anal rays III,20-22; pectoral rays 13 or 14; lateral-line scales 24-30 (usually 26-28); greatest body depth 1.2-1.4 in standard length; pattern of alternating cream-coloured and grey-brown to purplish chevron-shaped narrow bars on sides; a dark purplish bar with pale edges across caudal fin; three dark bars on head, including one through eye. Cocos-Keeling Islands to Fiji, north to Japan; a territorial species that feeds on *Acropora* corals. Reaches 15 cm. Sometimes classified in the genus *Gonochaetodon*. Closely related to the Indian Ocean *C. triangulum* Cuvier.

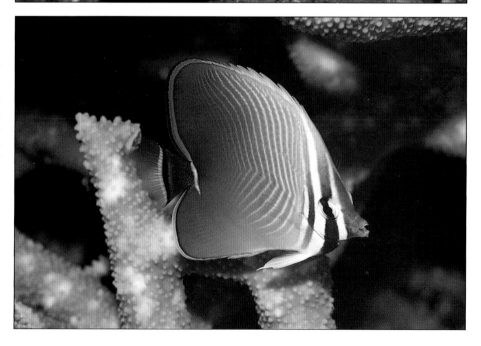

BENNETT'S BUTTERFLYFISH
Chaetodon bennetti Cuvier, 1831

Dorsal rays XIII or XIV,15-17 (usually XIV,16 or 17); anal rays III,14-16; pectoral rays 14-16 (usually 15); lateral-line scales 36-40; greatest body depth 1.4-1.8 in standard length; mainly yellow with a large black ocellus on upper sides; a pair of long narrow blue bands, one above pectoral fin and the other curving from in front of the fin to below it; a blue-edged black bar through eye. East Africa to the Pitcairn Group, north to Japan; often seen in pairs, usually on outer reefs between 5 and 25 m. To 18 cm.

SPECKLED BUTTERFLYFISH
Chaetodon citrinellus Cuvier, 1831

Dorsal rays XIV,20-22; anal rays III,16 or 17; pectoral rays 13 or 14; lateral-line scales 36-42 (usually 39-41); greatest body depth 1.7-1.9 in standard length; pale yellow with oblique to horizontal rows of small dark spots; a prominent black band through eye. East Africa to the Hawaiian Islands and Tuamotu Archipelago; common on shallow exposed reef flats and seaward reefs where coral growth is sparse; feeds on algae, benthic invertebrates, and coral polyps. Attains 11 cm. Also known as the Citron Butterflyfish.

SADDLED BUTTERFLYFISH
Chaetodon ephippium Cuvier, 1831

Dorsal rays XII to XIV,21-24 (usually XIII,23 or 24); anal rays III,20-22 (usually 21); pectoral rays 15 or 16; lateral-line scales 33-40 (usually 36-39); greatest body depth 1.6-1.8 in standard length; adults with a filament extending posteriorly from upper part of soft portion of dorsal fin; overall yellowish grey with a large black area posteriorly on back and adjacent dorsal fin, broadly bordered below by white; wavy blue lines on lower sides; a short narrow black bar through eye. Cocos-Keeling Islands to the Hawaiian Islands and Tuamotu Archipelago; often seen in pairs to 20 m depth; feeds on algae, sponges, corals and small benthic invertebrates. Reaches 23 cm.

DUSKY BUTTERFLYFISH
Chaetodon flavirostris Günther, 1873

Dorsal rays XII or XIII,24-27 (usually XII,25 or 26); anal rays III,20 or 21; pectoral rays 15 or 16; lateral-line scales 40-46 (usually 41-44); greatest body depth 1.4-1.6 in standard length; a black bump on forehead; overall blackish with broad rim of yellow on dorsal, caudal, and anal fins; snout yellow. Great Barrier Reef to Pitcairn Group in southeastern Oceania; often seen in pairs; feeds on algae, coral, and small benthic invertebrates. To 20 cm.

GÜNTHER'S BUTTERFLYFISH
Chaetodon guentheri Ahl, 1913

Dorsal rays XIII,21 or 22; anal rays III,18; pectoral rays 14; lateral-line scales 39 or 40; greatest body depth 1.5-1.7 in standard length; white with oblique to horizontal rows of small brown spots; a broad yellow zone covering posterior part of body and dorsal and anal fins; a black bar through eye. Apparently has an antiequatorial distribution; common in subtropical waters of Lord Howe Island and New South Wales, also occurs in Japan; the only sighting in our area was in 40 m depth near Lizard Island. To 14 cm.

KLEIN'S BUTTERFLYFISH
Chaetodon kleinii Bloch, 1790

Dorsal rays XIII or XIV,20-23 (usually XIII,21 or 22); anal rays III,17-20 (usually III,18 or 19); pectoral rays 13-15 (usually 14); lateral-line scales 33-41 (usually 36-40); greatest body depth 1.4-1.7 in standard length; two broad whitish bars, one behind eye and the other across middle of body, separated by brown bar; yellowish brown on posterior half of body; a black bar through eye, The upper part becoming blue in adults. East Africa and Red Sea to Hawaiian Islands and Samoa; most common on outer reef slopes below 10 cm; feeds mainly on soft corals. Attains 13 cm.

223

LINED BUTTERFLYFISH
Chaetodon lineolatus Cuvier, 1831

Dorsal rays XII,24-27; anal rays III,20-22; pectoral rays 15-17 (usually 16); lateral-line scales 26-33; greatest body depth 1.5-1.8 in standard length; overall white with black elliptical marking along base of soft portion of dorsal fin and extending across caudal peduncle to base of posterior anal rays; a series of vertical, black lines across sides; dorsal, anal and caudal fins bright yellow; a prominent black band through eye. East Africa and Red Sea to Polynesia; often seen in pairs; feeds mainly on coral polyps and anemones; the largest species in the family. Reaches 30 cm.

RACOON BUTTERFLYFISH
Chaetodon lunula (Lacepède, 1803)

Dorsal rays XI to XIII,22-25 (usually XII,24); anal rays III,17-19 (usually III,18); pectoral rays 15 or 16; lateral-line scales 35-44 (usually 41-43); greatest body depth 1.4-1.8 in standard length; golden yellow becoming brown on upper half of sides; a series of oblique reddish brown bands, most evident on lower half of body; a curved, broad, yellow-edged black band from rear edge of upper part of head to base of middle dorsal spines; a large black spot across caudal peduncle; a prominent black bar through eye with a white bar just behind it. East Africa to Polynesia; often in pairs or small groups from shallow reef flats to at least 25 m; feeds largely on nudibranchs, tubeworm tentacles, and other small benthic invertebrates; also consumes algae and coral polyps. To 20 cm.

BLACKBACK BUTTERFLYFISH
Chaetodon melannotus Bloch & Schneider, 1801

Dorsal rays XII,18-20; anal rays III,16-18 (usually III,17); pectoral rays 14 or 15; lateral-line scales 33-39; greatest body depth 1.6-1.8 in standard length; overall white with bright yellow fins; numerous, narrow, oblique black lines on sides; upper back blackish; a black blotch above anal spines; a yellow-edged, black bar through eye. East Africa and Red Sea to Samoa, north to Japan; usually seen in rich coral areas to 20 m depth; feeds mainly on coral polyps. Reaches 15 cm.

MERTEN'S BUTTERFLYFISH
Chaetodon mertensii Cuvier, 1831

Dorsal rays XII to XIV,21-23 (usually XII,22); anal rays III,16 or 17 (usually III,17); pectoral rays 14; lateral-line scales 35-43; greatest body depth 1.7-1.8 in standard length; overall whitish with narrow chevron-shaped blackish bands across sides; bright yellow on posterior part of body and adjacent dorsal and anal fins; outer two-thirds of caudal fin yellow; a white-edged black bar through eye. Lord Howe Island and Great Barrier Reef to Ryukyu Islands, eastward to the Tuamotus; usually found below 15 m on outer reef slopes; feeds on algae and small benthic invertebrates. Attains 12.5 cm.

MEYER'S BUTTERFLYFISH
Chaetodon meyeri Bloch & Schneider, 1801

Dorsal rays XII,23 or 24; anal rays III,18-20; pectoral rays 16; lateral-line scales 47-55; greatest body depth 1.3-1.6 in standard length; whitish or blue-white with curved to oblique black bands on sides; yellow-edged black bars on snout, through eye and across operculum; median fins yellowish with black submarginal bands. East Africa to the Line Islands; usually seen in pairs; found in rich coral areas between about 5-25 m; feeds on coral polyps. To 18 cm.

SPOT-TAIL BUTTERFLYFISH
Chaetodon ocellicaudus Cuvier, 1831

Dorsal rays XII,19 or 20; anal rays III, 17 or 18 (usually 17); pectoral rays 13 or 14 (usually 13); lateral-line scales 29-34; greatest body depth 1.7-1.9 in standard length; white with narrow oblique black bands, abruptly yellow on periphery of head and body and on median fins (except on outer part of caudal which is hyaline); a black bar on head through eye and a round black spot edged in pale yellow posteriorly on side of caudal peduncle. East Indies, Philippines, and northern Great Barrier Reef. Reaches 14 cm. Often confused with *C. melannotus* which it closely resembles; *melanottus* has an irregular black bar on the caudal peduncle instead of a round spot, and it usually has 14 pectoral rays.

ORNATE BUTTERFLYFISH
Chaetodon ornatissimus Cuvier, 1831

Dorsal rays XII,24-28 (usually XII,26-28); anal rays III,20-23; pectoral rays 15 or 16; lateral-line scales 47-52; greatest body depth 1.3-1.6 in standard length; similar pattern to *C. meyeri* (above), but oblique bands on sides are orange to orangish brown and generally wider; in addition they are more horizontal. Sri Lanka to Polynesia; usually seen in pairs; found in rich coral areas from the shallows to at least 30 m; feeds on coral polyps. Reaches 19 cm.

SPOTNAPE BUTTERFLYFISH
Chaetodon oxycephalus Bleeker, 1853

Dorsal rays XII,22-24; anal rays III,18-20 (usually III,19); pectoral rays 14-16 (usually 15); lateral-line scales 26-34; greatest body depth 1.7-2.0 in standard length; very similar pattern to C. *lineolatus* (above), but has a large isolated black spot on forehead. Sri Lanka to Queensland, north to the Philippines; usually seen in pairs; feeds on coral polyps and anemones. To 25 cm.

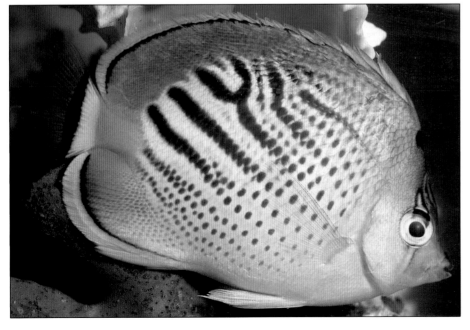

DOT-AND-DASH BUTTERFLYFISH
Chaetodon pelewensis Kner, 1868

Dorsal rays XIII,22-25 (usually XIII,24 or 25); anal rays III,17 or 18; pectoral rays 14 or 15; lateral-line scales 39-47 (usually 39-44); greatest body depth 1.6-1.7 in standard length; pale tan with oblique rows of black spots, becoming solid bands on upper half of body; a dark-edged orange bar through eye. Southern Oceania from Queensland to the Tuamotus; usually seen in pairs on outer reefs to 30 m depth; feeds on coral polyps and small benthic invertebrates. Attains 12.5 cm.

BLUESPOT BUTTERFLYFISH
Chaetodon plebeius Cuvier, 1831

Dorsal rays XIII or XIV,16-18 (usually XIV,17); anal rays IV,14-16 (usually IV,15); pectoral rays 15; lateral-line scales 36-41; greatest body depth 1.5-1.6 in standard length; overall yellow with narrow dark stripes on sides; an elongate blue patch on upper sides and large black spot on tail base; a blue-edged black bar through eye. Andaman Sea to Fiji, north to Japan; feeds mainly on coral polyps. To 13 cm.

SPOT-BANDED BUTTERFLYFISH
Chaetodon punctatofasciatus Cuvier, 1831

Dorsal rays XIII,22-25 (usually XIII,23 or 24); anal rays III,17 or 18; pectoral rays 13 or 14; lateral-line scales 37-44 (usually 39-42); greatest body depth 1.6-1.8 in standard length; yellow dorsally, shading to white ventrally, with rows of purplish grey spots on lower half of body and 7-8 purplish grey bars on upper half; a dark-edged yellow bar through eye, and a black spot on forehead. Christmas Island (Indian Ocean) to Line Islands; common on outer reef slopes, often in pairs; feeds on algae, coral polyps, and small benthic invertebrates. Attains 11 cm.

LATTICED BUTTERFLYFISH
Chaetodon rafflesi Bennett, 1830

Dorsal rays XII or XIII,21-23; anal rays III,18-20; pectoral rays 14 or 15; lateral-line scales 30-37 (usually 33-35); greatest body depth 1.4-1.8 in standard length; overall yellow with darker scale edges forming a lattice-pattern; a spindle-shaped dark bar through middle of caudal fin, and a broad submarginal dark band on rear part of dorsal fin; a prominent black bar through eye, the upper part often edged and preceded by blue. Sri Lanka to Tuamotus, north to Japan; not common on the Great Barrier Reef; feeds on coral polyps, anemones, and polychaetes. Reaches 15 cm.

RAINFORD'S BUTTERFLYFISH
Chaetodon rainfordi McCulloch, 1923

Dorsal rays XI,20-22; anal rays III,17-19; pectoral rays 14 or 15 (usually 14); lateral-line scales 37-43; greatest body depth 1.2-1.5 in standard length; light yellow to white with dusky bars edged in deep yellow, orange or orangish brown; a black spot on caudal peduncle; a black or black-edged orange bar through eye; fins yellow. Great Barrier Reef and inshore areas of the Queensland coast; usually seen in pairs in areas of sparse coral growth; feeds on algae and small benthic invertebrates. To 15 cm.

RETICULATED BUTTERFLYFISH
Chaetodon reticulatus Cuvier, 1831

Dorsal rays XII,26-29 (usually XII,27 or 28); anal rays III,20-21 (usually 21); pectoral rays 16; lateral-line scales 45-48; greatest body depth 1.3-1.6 in standard length; overall black with white to yellowish scale centres forming horizontal to oblique rows of spots; frosty white on upper back and dorsal fin; a pale-edged black bar through eye and a broad band of white just behind it. Great Barrier Reef to Taiwan, east to Polynesia; usually seen in pairs on outer reefs to 30 m depth; feeds mainly on corals. Reaches 16 cm.

DOTTED BUTTERFLYFISH
Chaetodon semeion Bleeker, 1855

Dorsal rays XIII or XIV,23-26 (usually XIV,24-25); anal rays III,19-22 (usually III,21); pectoral rays 14 or 15; lateral-line scales 33-39; greatest body depth 1.6-1.9 in standard length; a filament trailing from soft portion of dorsal fin; overall orange yellow with horizontal rows of very small black spots on sides; a broad submarginal dark brown band on anal fin and rear part of dorsal fin; a black bar, the upper part blue and black, through eye; a large blackish area often present on back above tip of pectoral fin. Maldive Islands to Tuamotus, north to Ryukyu Islands; uncommon, found on outer reef slopes, usually in pairs; more wary than most butterflyfishes. Attains 23 cm.

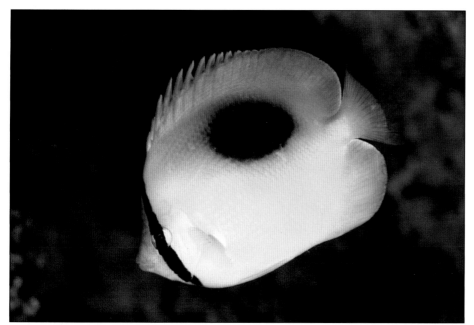

OVALSPOT BUTTERFLYFISH
Chaetodon speculum Cuvier, 1831

Dorsal rays XIV,17 or 18; anal rays III,15 or 16; pectoral rays 13-15 (usually 14); lateral-line scales 37-42; greatest body depth 1.4-1.6 in standard length; overall yellow with large round to oval black spot on middle of upper sides; a black bar through eye. Christmas Island (Indian Ocean) to Tonga, north to Japan; feeds on coral polyps and small benthic invertebrates. To 15 cm.

CHEVRONED BUTTERFLYFISH
Chaetodon trifascialis Quoy & Gaimard, 1824

Dorsal rays XIII to XV,14-16; anal rays IV or V,13-15; pectoral rays 14; lateral-line scales 22-29 (usually 24-26); greatest body depth 1.7-2.2 in standard length; overall white with narrow chevron markings on sides; basal two-thirds of caudal fin blackish in adults, yellow in juveniles; a black bar through eye. East Africa and Red Sea to Hawaiian and Society Islands; usually associated with tabular *Acropora* corals; has a small territory which it defends with great vigor; feeds exclusively on coral polyps and mucus. Reaches 18 cm. Sometimes classified in the genus *Megaprotodon*.

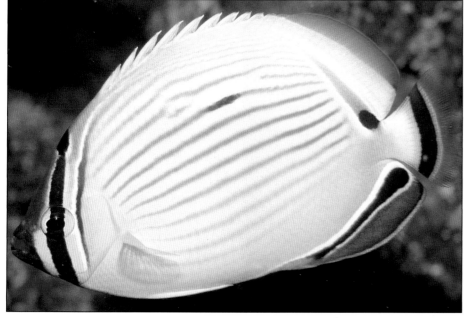

REDFIN BUTTERFLYFISH
Chaetodon trifasciatus Park, 1797

Dorsal rays XIII or XIV,20-22 (usually 21); anal rays III,18-21 (usually III,19); pectoral rays 13-15 (usually 14); lateral-line scales 30-39 (usually 34-39); greatest body depth 1.5-1.8 in standard length; golden orange with narrow slightly oblique purplish stripes on body; broad yellow-edged black bands at base of dorsal and anal fins and across middle of caudal fin; a yellow-edged black bar through eye; a broad red zone in soft part of dorsal and anal fins. East Africa to Hawaiian Islands and Tuamotu Archipelago; adults usually in pairs in protected coral habitats; feeds on coral polyps. Attains 15 cm. Also known as the Oval Buttereflyfish.

PACIFIC DOUBLE-SADDLE BUT-TERFLYFISH
Chaetodon ulietensis Cuvier, 1831

Dorsal rays XII,23-24; anal rays III,19-21 (usually III,19); pectoral rays 14 or 15; lateral-line scales 32-37; greatest body depth 1.6-1.9 in standard length; overall white, bright yellow on posterior part of body and caudal fin; a series of blackish vertical lines on sides overlaid by two broad, blackish bars; a black bar through eye and a large black spot at base of caudal fin. Cocos-Keeling Islands to Tuamotus, north to Japan; common in rich coral areas; often seen in pairs. To 15 cm.

TEARDROP BUTTERFLYFISH
Chaetodon unimaculatus Bloch, 1787

Dorsal rays XIII,21-23; anal rays III,18-20; pectoral rays 14 or 15; lateral-line scales 38-47 (usually 41-45); greatest body depth 1.4-1.6 in standard length; overall white with yellow median fins (except caudal fin is clear); a large black spot on back; a black bar through eye and narrower submarginal black bar posteriorly on dorsal and anal fins, also crossing caudal peduncle. East Africa to Polynesia; common on outer reefs to 20 m depth; feeds on coral polyps, soft corals, sponges, polychaetes, and algae. Attains 20 cm. Ground colour yellow in Indian Ocean.

MÜLLER'S CORALFISH
Chelmon muelleri (Klunzinger, 1879)

Dorsal rays IX or X,26-30; anal rays III,18-20; pectoral rays 14 or 15; lateral-line scales 49-50; greatest body depth 1.5-1.7 in standard length; snout strongly pointed and projecting; overall white to yellowish with three dark brown bars on sides; a black spot or ocellus at base of anterior soft dorsal rays; a brown-edged orange bar through eye and narrow dark brown bar across base of caudal fin. Northern Australia; coastal reefs only; feeds on small benthic invertebrates. Reaches 18 cm.

BEAKED CORALFISH
Chelmon rostratus (Linnaeus, 1758)

Dorsal rays IX,28-30; anal rays III,19-21; pectoral rays 14 or 15; lateral-line scales 48-55 (usually 50 or 51); greatest body depth 1.5-2.0 in standard length; snout extremely long and pointed; overall white with three orange bars and an ocellated black spot at base of soft portion of dorsal fin; soft portion of dorsal and anal fins yellow orange; a dark-edged orange bar through eye and narrow blue-edged brown and orange bar across base of caudal fin. Andaman Sea to Australia, north to Ryukyu Islands; common on shallow reefs of the inner portion of the Great Barrier Reef and coastal reefs. To 20 cm.

HIGHFIN CORALFISH
Coradion altivelis McCulloch, 1916

Dorsal rays VIII,31-33 (usually VIII,32); anal rays III,20-22; pectoral rays 14; lateral-line scales 49 or 50; greatest body depth 1.4 or 1.5 in standard length; snout somewhat pointed; overall whitish with two close-set dark brown bars at level of pelvic fins; a third broader dark brown bar posteriorly on juveniles which becomes orange yellow in adults; juveniles and subadults with an ocellus on dorsal fin; a dark brown bar through eye and another across base of caudal fin; pelvic fins dark brown to black. Western Pacific from Australia north to Japan; infrequently seen in our area, usually on northern sections of the inner Great Barrier Reef. Attains 15 cm.

ORANGE-BANDED CORALFISH
Coradion chrysozonus (Cuvier, 1831)

Dorsal rays IX,28-30; anal rays III,19-21 (usually III,20); pectoral rays 15 or 16; lateral-line scales 48-52; greatest body depth 1.3-1.5 in standard length; very similar to *C. altivelis* (above), but the double bars at the level of the pelvic fins are wider and mostly yellow-orange rather than dark brown; also the ocellus on the soft portion of the dorsal fin persists in adults. Western Pacific from Australia north to the Ogasawara (Bonin) Islands. Reaches 15 cm.

FORCEPSFISH

Forcipiger flavissimus Jordan & McGregor, 1898

Dorsal rays XII,22-24; anal rays III,17 or 18; pectoral rays 15; lateral-line scales 74-80; greatest body depth 1.9-2.4 in standard length; snout extremely long and attenuate, its length 1.6-2.1 in body depth; mouth with a distinct gape (hence forceps-like); overall bright yellow; upper half of head and nape black, white below; a black spot on anal fin just below base of caudal fin. East Africa to Central America and Mexico; common on outer reef slopes; feeds on hydroids, small crustaceans, tubed feet of echinoderms, pedicillaria of sea urchins, and tentacles of tube polychaete worms. To 22 cm.

LONGNOSE BUTTERFLYFISH

Forcipiger longirostris (Broussonet, 1782)

Dorsal rays XI,24-27; anal rays III,17-20; pectoral rays 14 or 15; lateral-line scales 66-75; greatest body depth 1.9-2.5 in standard length; snout even longer than that of *F. flavissimus*, 1.1-1.5 in body depth; mouth with almost no gape; very similar in colour to *F. flavissimus*; differs in rows of blackish dots on chest; occasional individuals entirely dark brown (very rare in our area). East Africa to Polynesia; generally less common than *F. flavissimus*. To 22 cm.

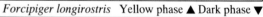

Forcipiger longirostris   Yellow phase ▲ Dark phase ▼

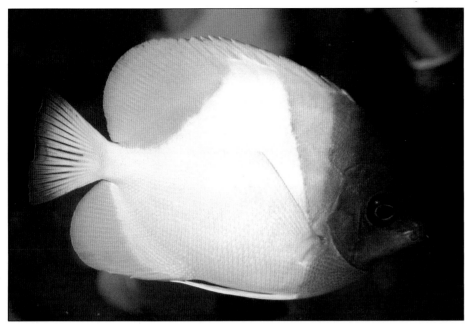

PYRAMID BUTTERFLYFISH
Hemitaurichthys polylepis (Bleeker, 1857)

Dorsal rays XII,23-26; anal rays III,20-21; pectoral rays 16-18 (usually 17); lateral-line scales 68-74; greatest body depth 1.4-1.6 in standard length; white with a triangular yellow area behind head (broader at top); dorsal fin and an area below soft portion of fin yellow (thus causing the broad white area of middle of body to be narrower at the top); caudal peduncle and fin white; anal fin yellow; head usually dark brown. Cocos-Keeling Islands to Hawaiian Islands and Pitcairn Group; forms large plankton-feeding schools on outer reef slopes. To 18 cm.

LONGFIN BANNERFISH
Heniochus acuminatus (Linnaeus, 1758)

Dorsal rays XI (rarely XII),24-27; anal rays III,17-19; pectoral rays 15-18; lateral-line scales 47-54; greatest body depth 1.2-1.4 in standard length; front of dorsal fin expanded to a very long tapering white filament; overall white with two broad, oblique, black bands on sides, the first continuous with black pelvic fins and the second ending on posterior half of anal fin; soft dorsal and caudal fins yellow; a blackish bar above eye. East Africa and Persian Gulf to Society Islands; found solitary or in small groups near the bottom; feeds on zooplankton and benthic invertebrates. To 25 cm.

PENNANT BANNERFISH
Heniochus chrysostomus Cuvier, 1831

Dorsal rays XI or XII,21 or 22; anal rays III,17 or 18; pectoral rays 16; lateral-line scales 57-61; greatest body depth 1.4-1.6 in standard length; fourth dorsal spine prolonged, the membrane broadly expanded (longer in juveniles than adults); white with three broad oblique dark brown bands, one from top of head through eye to abdomen, one from longest dorsal spine to rear of anal fin, and the last on back at base of rear part of dorsal fin; snout tip yellow. Cocos-Keeling Islands to Pitcairn Group; found solitary, in pairs or small groups; feeds mainly on coral polyps. Reaches 16 cm. *Heniochus permutatus* Cuvier is a synonym.

SCHOOLING BANNERFISH
Heniochus diphreutes Jordan, 1903

Dorsal rays XII (rarely XIII),23-25; anal rays III,17-19; pectoral rays 16-18; lateral-line scales 46-54; greatest body depth 1.2-1.5 in standard length; front of dorsal fin extended as a long, pennant-like filament; similar to *H. acuminatus* (above), but has more rounded profile on underside of head, the second dark band is placed farther forward on anal fin, and it has one more dorsal spine. East Africa to Hawaiian Islands, but reported from only a few mainly subtropical localities; a schooling species that usually swims well off the bottom; feeds mainly on zooplankton; occasionally observed cleaning other fishes. To 20 cm.

MASKED BANNERFISH
Heniochus monoceros Cuvier, 1831

Dorsal rays XII,24-27 (usually XII,25); anal rays III,18 or 19; pectoral rays 16 or 17; lateral-line scales 58-64; greatest body depth 1.5-1.7 in standard length; fourth dorsal spine prolonged as a tapering white filament; white with three broad black bands, the first from nape encompassing most of front part of head, the second across front of body and continuous with black pelvic fins, and the oblique third from middle of back to rear of anal fin; a pair of bony black knobs on forehead; dorsal and caudal fins yellow (except for white and dark brown at front of dorsal). East Africa to Tuamotus; adults usually found in pairs that shelter in coral crevices; most commonly seen on outer reef slopes. To 23 cm.

SINGULAR BANNERFISH
Heniochus singularius Smith & Radcliffe, 1911

Dorsal rays XI or XII,25-27; anal rays III,17 or 18; pectoral rays 16 or 17 (usually 17); lateral-line scales 53-64; greatest body depth 1.5-1.6 in standard length; fourth dorsal spine prolonged as a tapering white filament; similar in colour to *H. monoceros*, but dark bars on body more diffuse due to pale scale centres, also the broad white zone between the two dark bands has small blackish spots, one in each scale centre; also has isolated band encircling snout which *monoceros* lacks. Andaman Sea to Samoa, north to Japan; usually solitary or in pairs; occasionally seen on seaward reef slopes. Attains 23 cm.

HUMPHEAD BANNERFISH
Heniochus varius (Cuvier, 1829)

Dorsal rays XI,22-24; anal rays III,17-18; pectoral rays 14-15; lateral-line scales 55-65; body depth 1.3-1.5 in standard length; fourth dorsal spine prolonged, the membrane broad; a notch on forehead with a bony protruberance just above in adults; also a curved sharp horn developing above each eye with increasing age; overall dark brown to nearly black with a narrow white bar from upper nape across gill cover and expanding onto thorax and a second oblique white band from rear spinous portion of dorsal fin to caudal peduncle; pelvic and anal fins dark brown. Malay Peninsula to Samoa. Grows to 18 cm.

OCELLATED CORALFISH
Parachaetodon ocellatus (Cuvier, 1831)

Dorsal rays VI or VII,28-30 (usually VI,28 or 29); anal rays III,18-20 (usually III,19); pectoral rays 14 or 15; lateral-line scales 39-46; greatest body depth 1.3-1.4 in standard length; dorsal fin triangular in shape, the tip of first soft ray at apex; overall white with four orange to brown bars including a narrow dark-edged bar through eye; a white-edged dark brown bar (broader in middle), on caudal peduncle; a black spot about as large as eye on back near top of fourth body bar; a dark brown bar with rounded edges across base of caudal fin. Australia north to Ogasawara (Bonin) Islands; often seen in pairs; found on flat sand or silty bottoms usually on inner parts of the northern Great Barrier Reef and on coastal reefs. Reaches 18 cm.

ANGELFISHES
FAMILY POMACANTHIDAE

Angelfishes are close relatives of the butterflyfishes and until recently were considered to belong in the same family. They share a number of characteristics such as deep compressed bodies, ctenoid scales which extend out onto the median fins, a single unnotched dorsal fin and a small mouth with brush-like teeth. They differ from butterflyfishes, however, in having a long spine at the corner of the preopercle (also smaller spines on the preopercle, opercle, and preorbital); they lack a scaly axillary process at the base of the pelvic fins; the scales are more strongly ctenoid and have distinct ridges on the exposed part, and adults may have auxiliary scales; the postlarvae lack bony plates on the head and anterior body. Worldwide there are 76 known species. Most are inhabitants of tropical Indo-Pacific seas, being found mainly in the vicinity of coral reefs. They occur both solitarily or in aggregations. Many species inhabit shallow water, from only a few metres to 10-15 m depth. Others are restricted to deep water, for example some *Centropyge* and *Genicanthus* are seldom seen in less than 20 m and may range to at least 75 m depth. Angelfishes are favourite aquarium pets, well known for their brilliant array of colour patterns. Species of *Pomacanthus* exhibit dramatic changes from the juvenile to adult stage. Most angelfishes are dependent on the presence of shelter in the form of boulders, caves, and coral crevices. Typically, they are somewhat territorial and spend daylight hours near the bottom in search of food. The diet varies according to species; some such as the species of *Centropyge* feed almost exclusively on algae and detritus, others such as the species of *Pomacanthus* prefer mainly sponges supplemented by a variety of benthic invertebrates, and a few such as the species of *Genicanthus* are midwater zooplankton-feeders. Divers are sometimes startled by the powerful drumming or thumping sound which is produced by large adult angels of the genus *Pomacanthus*.

Emperor Angelfish (*Pomacanthus imperator*) Adult ▼

Juvenile ▲

THREE-SPOT ANGELFISH

Apolemichthys trimaculatus (Lacepède, 1831)

Dorsal rays XIV,16-18; anal rays III,17-19; scales in longitudinal series from upper edge of gill opening to base of caudal fin 45-50; greatest body depth 1.6-1.8 in standard length; overall bright yellow with a broad, black band on edge of anal fin and a broad white zone above it; a black spot on forehead and an ocellated dark spot just behind head; lips blue. East Africa to Samoa, north to Japan; frequently seen on outer reef slopes below 15 m depth. To 25 cm.

GOLDEN ANGELFISH

Centropyge aurantius Randall & Wass, 1974

Dorsal rays XIV,16 or 17; anal rays III,17 or 18; scales in longitudinal series from upper edge of gill opening to base of caudal fin 42-46; greatest body depth 1.6-1.8 in standard length; overall red-orange with numerous narrow, vertical, irregular golden lines on sides; several dark olive submarginal lines on dorsal, caudal and anal fins; a thin dark ring around eye. Northern Great Barrier Reef to Samoa; rare in our area. Attains 8 cm.

BICOLOR ANGELFISH

Centropyge bicolor (Bloch, 1787)

Dorsal rays XIV or XV,15 or 16; anal rays III,17 or 18; scales in longitudinal series from upper edge of gill opening to base of caudal fin 45-48; greatest body depth 1.8-2.2 in standard length; head and anterior body bright yellow, rest of body brilliant deep blue; caudal fin yellow; a deep blue bar above eye. Christmas Island (Indian Ocean) to Samoa, north to Japan; common in 10-25 m depth. Grows to 15 cm.

TWO-SPINED ANGELFISH
Centropyge bispinosus (Günther, 1860)

Dorsal rays XIV,16-18; anal rays III,17-19; scales in longitudinal series from upper edge of gill opening to caudal fin base 42-45; colour variable, usually purplish-blue on head, median fins and adjacent body; broad middle part of body red-orange with numerous dark purplish blue lines; median fins with a bright blue margin. East Africa to Tuamotus, north to Izu Islands; common on outer reef dropoffs below 10 m. To 10 cm.

WHITE-TAIL ANGELFISH
Centropyge flavicauda Fraser-Brunner, 1933

Dorsal rays XIV,15; anal rays III,17; scales in longitudinal series from upper edge of gill opening to caudal fin base 40-45 overall bluish black with white or yellowish caudal fin. Queensland and East Indies, north to Japan, east to Tuamoto Archipelago; usually found on rubble bottoms in 20-50 m. A small species, the maximum size 7 cm.

LEMONPEEL ANGELFISH
Centropyge flavissimus (Cuvier, 1831)

Dorsal rays XIV,15 or 16; anal rays III,16; scales in longitudinal series from upper edge of gill opening to caudal-fin base 44-50; bright yellow with blue opercular edge, blue cheek spine, and blue ring around eye; caudal and soft portions of dorsal and anal fins with a narrow blue outer margin and black sub-marginal line; a small orange-red area behind gill opening above pectoral-fin base; juveniles with a blue-edged black spot on middle of sides. Cocos-Keeling Islands to southeastern Oceania, north to the Ryukyu Islands; common in island groups of the tropical central and western Pacific but rare in our area. To 14 cm.

HERALD'S ANGELFISH
Centropyge heraldi Woods & Schultz, 1953

Dorsal rays XV,15; anal rays III,17; scales in longitudinal series from upper edge of gill opening to base of caudal fin 46-48; bright yellow with dusky olive patch containing yellow markings immediately behind eye. Queensland north to Taiwan, east to Tuamotus; common on some reefs in about 8-20 m. Reaches 11 cm.

FLAME ANGELFISH
Centropyge loriculus (Günther, 1874)

Dorsal rays XIV,16 or 17; anal rays III,16-18 (usually 17); scales in longitudinal series from upper edge of gill opening to base of caudal fin 44-47; brilliant orange-red with a vertically elongate black blotch above pectoral-fin base and 4-5 black bars behind on sides; posterior dorsal and anal fins with alternating short purple-blue and black bands. Oceanic coral reefs from Queensland to Samoa and the Hawaiian Islands; rarely seen in our area. Grows to 10 cm. *C. flammeus* Schultz is a synonym.

MULTI-BARRED ANGELFISH
Centropyge multifasciatus (Smith & Radcliffe, 1911)

Dorsal rays XIII,17 or 18; anal rays III,17 or 18; scales in longitudinal series from upper edge of gill opening to base of caudal fin 35-45; white with 8 dark brown bars (becoming orange-yellow ventrally), the first through eye and the last across base of caudal fin; bars extending into dorsal and anal fins; a yellow bar in middle of each white interspace on body; a black spot on outer part of soft portion of dorsal fin. Cocos-Keeling Islands to Society Islands; inhabits caves on steep dropoffs usually below 20 m. Attains 10 cm.

MIDNIGHT ANGELFISH
Centropyge nox (Bleeker, 1853)

Dorsal rays XIV or XV,15-17; anal rays III,16-18; scales in longitudinal series from upper edge of gill opening to base of caudal fin 42-48; dark brown to black, caudal fin with narrow white margin. Queensland and Melanesia north to the Ryukyu Islands; but relatively rare in our area; found on well-protected reefs. To 9 cm.

KEYHOLE ANGELFISH
Centropyge tibicen (Cuvier, 1831)

Dorsal rays XIV,15 or 16; anal rays III,16 or 17; scales in longitudinal series from upper edge of gill opening to base of caudal fin 45-48; overall black with a vertically elongate white blotch on middle of sides; most of pelvic fins and anterior outer part of anal fin yellow, the latter with a submarginal blue line; posterior edge of caudal fin narrowly blue. Christmas Island (Indian Ocean) to Melanesia, north to Japan. Maximum size, 18 cm.

PEARL-SCALED ANGELFISH
Centropyge vroliki (Bleeker, 1853)

Dorsal rays XIV or XV,15 or 16; anal rays III,16 or 17; scales in longitudinal series from upper edge of gill opening to base of caudal fin 42-49; overall pale tan or light brown with whitish scale centres, becoming blackish on posterior third of body and adjacent fins; edge of gill opening and pectoral-fin base orange; rear edge of caudal fin narrowly blue. Christmas Island (Indian Ocean) to Melanesia and Micronesia; common to depths of about 25 m; hybridizes with *C. flavissimus* in the Marshall Islands. Reaches 10 cm.

CONSPICUOUS ANGELFISH
Chaetodontoplus conspicillatus (Waite, 1900)

Dorsal rays XIII,18; anal rays III,18; more than 85 scales in longitudinal series from upper edge of gill opening to base of caudal fin; blue-grey on upper half of body, brown to blackish on ventral half; operculum and basal part of pectoral and caudal fins yellow; snout and outer part of pectoral and caudal fins black; lips and pelvic fins whitish or light blue; blue ring around eye and blue margin on cheek and gill opening. Southern part of Great Barrier Reef and Coral Sea. Attains 25 cm.

SCRIBBLED ANGELFISH
Chaetodontoplus duboulayi (Günther, 1867)

Dorsal rays XI,22; anal rays III,21; more than 85 scales in longitudinal series from upper edge of gill opening to base of caudal fin; overall black to dark brown with numerous narrow horizontal blue lines (males) or yellow speckling (females) on sides; a broad yellow bar behind head and a diagonal one on back continuing onto caudal fin; a broad bluish bar through eye with a white bar immediately behind; dorsal and anal fins with narrow brilliant blue stripes and blue margin. Northern Australia and southern New Guinea, also reported from Taiwan; mainly coastal reefs. To 25 cm.

QUEENSLAND YELLOWTAIL ANGELFISH
Chaetodontoplus meredithi Kuiter 1990

Dorsal rays XIII,17-19; anal rays III,17-19; more than 85 scales in longitudinal series from upper edge if gill opening to base of caudal fin; black , the forehead, snout, breast and caudal fin yellow; side of head largely blue with yellow spots. Queensland; coastal and inner reefs. Attains 25 cm.

LAMARCK'S ANGELFISH
Genicanthus lamarck (Lacepède, 1802)

Dorsal rays XV,15 or 16; anal rays III,16 or 17 (usually 17); scales in longitudinal series from upper edge of gill opening to base of caudal fin 45-47; overall white with three black stripes on side; a broad black submarginal band in dorsal fin; caudal fin with black dots; male with black pelvic fins; female with white pelvic fins and submarginal black band in each caudal-fin lobe. East Africa and Indonesia to Queensland and Solomon Islands, north to Japan; known from Escape Reef on the northern Great Barrier Reef. Maximum size, 20 cm.

Genicanthus lamarck Male ▲ Female ▼

Genicanthus melanospilos Male ▲ Female ▼

BLACK-SPOT ANGELFISH
Genicanthus melanospilos (Bleeker, 1857)

Dorsal rays XV,15-17 (usually 16); anal rays III,18; scales in longitudinal series from upper edge of gill opening to base of caudal fin 46-48; males light bluish with about 15 narrow black bars on sides and similar markings on dorsal part of head; females without bars, yellow on dorsal half and light blue below, and with a broad black submarginal band in each caudal lobe. Queensland to Fiji, north to Ryukyu Islands; usually seen on steep outer reef slopes and dropoffs below 20-30 m depth. To 18 cm.

WATANABE'S ANGELFISH
Genicanthus watanabei (Yasuda & Tominaga, 1970)

Dorsal rays XV,15 or 16; anal rays III,14; scales in longitudinal series from upper edge of gill opening to base of caudal fin 45-48; males light blue with eight black stripes on lower two-thirds of body (the posterior end of uppermost yellow) and adjacent anal fin; females overall light blue with a black bar above eye and black spots on forehead; both sexes with a broad black submarginal band on dorsal and anal fins; female with a black submarginal band on caudal lobes. Queensland to Tuamotus, north to Taiwan; occurs below about 20 m on outer reef slopes and dropoffs. Reaches 18 cm.

Genicanthus watanabei Male ▲ Female ▼

EMPEROR ANGELFISH
Pomacanthus imperator (Bloch, 1787)

Dorsal rays XIV,19-21; anal rays III,18-21; scales in longitudinal series from upper edge of gill opening to base of caudal fin about 90; body with alternating diagonal narrow yellow and broader purplish blue stripes; snout and cheek bluish white; a curved blue-edged black bar through eye with a greenish yellow bar just behind that confluent with same colour on forehead; a broad black bar at level of pectoral fin; juveniles black with a white ring posteriorly on side surrounded by partial circles of blue and white; head with blue and white lines. East Africa and Red Sea to Tuamotus, north to Japan; adults found near ledges and caves in rich coral areas to 60 m. Reaches 38 cm.

Pomacanthus imperator   Adult ▼ Juv. ▲

BLUE-GIRDLED ANGELFISH
Pomacanthus navarchus (Cuvier, 1831)

Dorsal rays XIII or XIV,17 or 18; anal rays III,16-18; scales in longitudinal series from upper edge of gill opening to base of caudal fin 45-50; yellow-orange with a blue spot on each scale; a broad blue-edged deep blue bar from forehead, narrowing to belly, and another posteriorly on body, joined ventrally to anterior bar by deep blue; dorsal and caudal fins yellow-orange; pelvic and anal fins deep blue; all fins except pectorals with bright blue margins; juveniles blackish with 10-12 narrow blue bars on head and body. Indonesia and Philippines to northern Queensland; rare in our area. Attains 30 cm.

SEMICIRCLE ANGELFISH
Pomacanthus semicirculatus (Cuvier, 1831)

Dorsal rays XIII,20-23; anal rays III,18-21; scales in longitudinal series from upper edge of gill opening to base of caudal fin 65-75; outer posterior part of dorsal and anal fins prolonged as a filament; anterior and posterior third of body brownish, middle portion greenish or yellowish; blue margin on edges of preoperculum, operculum, and all fins except pectorals; numerous small blue spots on body and median fins and blue lines posteriorly on body and caudal fin; juveniles blackish with about 12 alternating narrow blue and white bars on head and body which are progressively more curved posteriorly. East Africa to Samoa. To 38 cm.

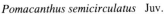

Pomacanthus semicirculatus Juv.

SIX-BANDED ANGELFISH
Pomacanthus sexstriatus (Cuvier, 1831)

Dorsal rays XIII,18-20; anal rays III,18 or 19; scales in longitudinal series from upper edge of gill opening to base of caudal fin 50-63; dorsal and anal fins elevated posteriorly; body yellowish tan with blue spot on each scale and five black bars; head blackish with a white bar behind eye; blue spots on caudal, and posteriorly on dorsal and anal fins; juveniles blackish with about 15 slightly curved, narrow, blue and white bars. Malaysia to Solomon Islands, north to Ryukyu Islands; usually seen in silty reef areas. Maximum size, 46 cm.

Pomacanthus sexstriatus   Adult ▼ Juv. ▲

YELLOWMASK ANGELFISH
Pomacanthus xanthometopon (Bleeker, 1853)

Dorsal rays XIII or XIV,16 or 17; anal rays III,16-18; scales in longitudinal series from upper edge of gill opening to base of caudal fin 46-52; scales on sides bluish with yellow edges; upper back and most of dorsal fin whitish; breast, pectoral fins, caudal fin, and rear part of dorsal and anal fins yellow; a black spot at rear base of dorsal fin; a yellow "mask" encompassing eyes; head below eye blue with small yellow spots; juveniles blackish with about 18-20 narrow blue and white bars on side. Maldive Islands to Vanuatu, north to Yaeyama Islands. Attains 38 cm.

REGAL ANGELFISH
Pygoplites diacanthus (Boddaert, 1772)

Dorsal rays XIII or XIV,17-22; anal rays III,17-19; scales in longitudinal series from upper edge of gill opening to base of caudal fin 45-57; brilliant pattern of alternating dark-edged bluish white and orange stripes on sides which narrow and angle backward in dorsal fin; posterior part of dorsal fin black with blue dots; anal fin orange with blue stripes; caudal and paired fins yellow; juveniles with a large ocellated dark spot on basal part of soft dorsal fin. East Africa and Red Sea to Tuamotus, north to Ryukyu Islands; found in rich coral areas near caves and ledges; feeds on sponges and tunicates. To 26 cm

DAMSELFISHES
FAMILY POMACENTRIDAE

The damselfishes are one of the most abundant groups of coral reef fishes. Approximately 320 species occur worldwide, including about 120 from Australian seas. They are elongate to orbicular, compressed fishes with a single continuous dorsal fin of VIII-XVII spines and 10-21 soft rays; the base of the spinous portion is longer than the soft; the anal fin has II spines and 10 to 16 rays; the caudal fin varies from slightly emarginate to forked or lunate. The scales are moderately large and ctenoid; the head is largely scaled, as are the basal parts of median fins. Most inhabit the tropics, but a number of species live in cooler temperate waters. They display remarkable diversity with regards to habitat preference, feeding habits, and behaviour. Coloration is highly variable ranging from drab hues of brown, grey and black to brilliant combinations of orange, yellow, and neon blue. A number of species have juvenile stages characterised by a yellow body with bright blue stripes crossing the upper head and back. Most damselfishes are territorial, particularly algal-feeding species such as *Stegastes lividus* and *S. nigricans*. They zealously defend their small plot against all intruders regardless of size. Damsels exhibit a highly stereotyped mode of reproduction in which one or both partners clear a nest site on the bottom and engage in courtship displays of rapid swimming and fin extension. Males generally guard the eggs which are attached to the bottom by adhesive strands. The eggs hatch within about 2-7 days and the fragile larvae rise to the surface. They are transported by ocean currents for periods which vary between about 10-50 days, depending on the species. Eventually the young fish settle to the bottom and their largely trans-

parent bodies quickly assume the juvenile coloration. The growth rate of juveniles generally ranges from about 5-15 mm per month and gradually tapers off as maturity approaches. There is very little reliable data concerning their longevity, but it appears they are capable of living to at least an age of 10 years. Damselfishes feed on a wide variety of plant and animal material. Generally, the drab-coloured species feed mainly on algae, whereas many of the brightly patterned species and also members of the genus *Chromis* obtain their nourishment from current-borne plankton. *Amphiprion* and *Premnas* occur exclusively with large tropical sea anemones. They are protected from the normally harmful stinging cells by a special mucous coat which prevents the toxic nema-

tocysts from firing. Another unusual aspect of anemonefish biology is male to female sex reversal. Typically each large anemone harbours a "family" group consisting of a large pair of adults and several smaller individuals. There is a rigid heirarchy or "pecking-order" based on size. The largest and socially dominant fish is the female. If the female disappears, each fish advances one place in the heirarchy. The former adult male reverses sex, and the next largest fish grows rapidly, and upon reaching maturity, becomes the functioning adult male. The pomacentrid generic names *Glyphidodontops*, *Eupomacentrus* and *Paraglyphidodon* are now replaced by *Chrysiptera*, *Stegastes* and *Neoglyphiphidodon*, respectively.

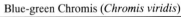
Blue-green Chromis (*Chromis viridis*)

BENGAL SERGEANT
Abudefduf bengalensis (Bloch, 1787)

Dorsal rays XIII,13-15; anal rays II,13-14; pectoral rays 16-20; lateral-line scales 19-23; body depth 1.6-2.0 in standard length; caudal lobes rounded; whitish to light grey with 6-7 black bars on side; similar to to *A. vaigiensis* and *A. sexfasciatus* but has more black bars (6-7 versus 5); prefers inshore, protected areas and is less common in the area than the other two species. Northern Indian Ocean and western Pacific on reefs of continental margins; depth range 0.5-6 m. Attains 18 cm.

BANDED SERGEANT
Abudefduf septemfasciatus (Cuvier, 1830)

Dorsal rays XIII,12-14; anal rays II,11-13; pectoral rays 17-19; lateral-line scales 20-22; gill rakers 20-26; body depth 1.7-1.9 in standard length; whitish with 6-7 dark grey bars on side; similar to *A. sordidus* but lacks the black spot on top of caudal fin base; both species inhabit boulder zone on shallow wave-swept reefs. East Africa to Tuamotu Archipelago and Line Islands; depth range 0.2-3 m. To 19 cm.

SCISSOR-TAIL SERGEANT
Abudefduf sexfasciatus (Lacepède, 1802)

Dorsal rays XIII,11-14; anal rays II,11-13; pectoral rays 17-20; lateral-line scales 18-22; gill rakers 23-30; body depth 1.8-2.0 in standard length; white with five black bars; distinguished by black streak on each lobe of caudal fin. East Africa and Red Sea to Tuamotus; common in our area; depth range 5-20 m. Reaches 17 cm.

BLACKSPOT SERGEANT
Abudefduf sordidus (Forsskål, 1775)

Dorsal rays XIII,14-16; anal rays II,13-15; pectoral rays 18-20; lateral-line scales 21-23; gill rakers 20-28; body depth 1.5-1.8 in standard length; whitish with 6-7 dark grey bars on side; distinguished by black spot at top of caudal fin base. East Africa and Red Sea to Polynesia; inhabits rocky areas exposed to waves; depth range 0.2-3 m. Attains 20 cm.

INDO-PACIFIC SERGEANT
Abudefduf vaigiensis (Quoy & Gaimard, 1825)

Dorsal rays XIII,12-14; anal rays II,11-13; pectoral rays 16-20; lateral-line scales 19-23; gill rakers 23-33; body depth 1.5-1.8 in standard length; white with five black bars; similar to A. se*xfasciatus* but frequently has yellow on back and lacks black streaks on the caudal fin. East Africa and Red Sea to Marquesas; depth range 1-12 m. Reaches 20 cm. Very closely related to the Sergeant Major, *Abudefduf saxatilis* (Linnaeus), of the Western Atlantic.

WHITLEY'S SERGEANT
Abudefduf whitleyi Allen & Robertson, 1974

Dorsal rays XIII,13; anal rays II,12-13; pectoral rays 19-20; lateral-line scales 20-22; gill rakers 22-25; body depth 1.7-1.9 in standard length; overall greenish or blue-green (sometimes with a yellow suffusion) with 4-5 narrow blackish bars; distinguished from other *Abudefduf* by the narrow dark bars and dark caudal fin. Great Barrier Reef, Coral Sea, and New Caledonia; depth range 1-5 m. Attains 17 cm.

SPINY CHROMIS
Acanthochromis polyacanthus (Bleeker, 1855)

Dorsal rays XVII,14-16; anal rays II,14-16; pectoral rays 17-18; lateral-line scales 20-22; gill rakers 21-23; body depth 1.7-2.0 in standard length; colour varies greatly according to locality; on the southern Great Barrier Reef (top) it is bluish grey with the caudal fin mainly black; on the Great Barrier Reef off Cairns (centre) the fish is mainly brown with posteriormost part of body and caudal fin abruptly white; at Chilcott Island in the Coral Sea (bottom) it is entirely whitish; best distinguished by 17 dorsal spines, highest number in the family. Indonesia and Philippines to northeastern Australia and Melanesia; depth range 1-65 m. This is the only species of pomacentrid that lacks a pelagic larval stage; the young remain with the parents after hatching and appear to feed on their surface mucus. Reaches 14 cm.

GOLDEN DAMSEL
Amblyglyphidodon aureus (Cuvier, 1830)

Dorsal rays XIII,12-16; anal rays II,14-15; pectoral rays 16-18; lateral-line scales 16-17; gill rakers 25-29; body depth 1.5-1.7 in standard length; overall yellow, sometimes grading to white on lower side; distinguished by bright yellow colour. Eastern Indian Ocean and western Pacific; found on drop-offs; depth range 12-35 m. Reaches a length of 12 cm.

STAGHORN DAMSEL
Amblyglyphidodon curacao (Bloch, 1787)

Dorsal rays XIII,12-13; anal rays II,13-15; pectoral rays 17-18; lateral-line scales 16-17; gill rakers 24-27; body depth 1.6-1.7 in standard length; distinguished by 3-4 diffuse dark bars and overall silvery-green hue. Eastern Indian Ocean and western Pacific; usually in rich coral areas; depth range 1-15 m. To 11 cm.

WHITE-BELLY DAMSEL
Amblyglyphidodon leucogaster (Bleeker, 1847)

Dorsal rays XIII,12-13; anal rays II,12-14; pectoral rays 16-18; lateral-line scales 14-17; gill rakers 24-30; body depth 1.6-1.7 in standard length; generally silver grey with dark scale outlines and dark margins on dorsal, anal, and caudal fins; the Pacific variety that occurs at Great Barrier Reef-Coral Sea is distinguished by a yellow belly and broad blackish areas on the dorsal and anal fins; several geographic varieties are represented. Red Sea to Samoa; depth range 5-45 m. Reaches 13 cm.

BLACK-BANDED DEMOISELLE
Amblypomacentrus breviceps (Schlegel & Müller, 1839-44)

Dorsal rays XIII,10-12; anal rays II,11-13; pectoral rays 16-17; lateral-line scales 16-17; gill rakers 20-23; body depth 2.1-2.3 in standard length; white with three black bars; white colour is sometimes partially replaced by yellow-brown; often longitudinal rows of blue spots on side; similar to *Chrysiptera tricincta*, but dark bars do not completely encircle body, nor do they extend onto the pelvic and anal fins. Malay Peninsula to northern Australia and Melanesia; found on sand or silty bottoms; depth range 2-35 m. Attains 7 cm.

BARRIER REEF ANEMONEFISH
Amphiprion akindynos Allen, 1972

Dorsal rays X or XI,14-17; anal rays II,13-14; pectoral rays 18-20 lateral-line scales 31-40; gill rakers 19-22; body depth 1.8-2.0 in standard length; brown with two white bars across head and body; caudal fin white; similar to, but far more common than *A. chrysopterus* (see below). Southwestern Pacific, including Great Barrier Reef and Coral Sea, northern New South Wales, New Caledonia and Loyalty Islands; associated with at least four species of anemones; depth range 1-20 m. To 12 cm.

ORANGE-FIN ANEMONEFISH
Amphiprion chrysopterus Cuvier, 1830

Dorsal rays X or XI,15 to 18; anal rays II,13-14; pectoral rays 18-21; lateral-line scales 35-42; gill rakers 18-21; body depth 1.8-1.9 in standard length; dark brown to blackish with two pale bars; similar to *A. akindynos* (see above), but has black anal fin and pale bars more bluish. Queensland and New Guinea to Tuamotus and Marshall Islands; rare in our area; associated with three species of anemones; depth range 1-20 m. Attains 16 cm.

CLARK'S ANEMONEFISH
Amphiprion clarkii (Bennett, 1830)

Dorsal rays X or XI,14 to 17; anal rays II,12-15; pectoral rays 18-21; lateral-line scales 34-35; gill rakers 18-30; body depth 1.7 -2.0 in standard length; generally brown to blackish with three white bars on head and body; there is considerable variation in the ratio of black to orange or yellow on the fins and ventral part of the head and body; somewhat similar to *A. akindynos* and *A. chrysop-* *terus*, but middle bar is wider and pale bar at base of tail is better defined. Persian Gulf to Vanuatu and Marshall Islands; rare in our area; associated with seven species of anemones; found to 50-60 m depth, but also in shallow water. To 13 cm.

RED-AND-BLACK ANEMONEFISH
Amphiprion melanopus Bleeker, 1852

Dorsal rays IX-XI,15-18; anal rays II,13-15; pectoral rays 17-20; lateral-line scales 32-42; gill rakers 16-20; body depth 1.7-1.9 in standard length; largely blackish on sides with variable amount of red-orange and reddish fins; usually has a single white bar on the head, but specimens from the Coral Sea often lack this feature. Indonesia to Society and Marshall islands; usually associated with the anemone *Entacmaea quadricolor*; common in our area, to 10 m depth. To 12 cm.

253

CLOWN ANEMONEFISH
Amphiprion percula (Lacepède, 1802)

Dorsal rays IX or X,14-17; anal rays II,11-13; pectoral rays 15-18; lateral-line scales 31-40; gill rakers 15-17; body depth 2.1-2.4 in standard length; orange with three white bars that are narrowly edged with black; also black margins on fins; usually has distinct forward projection on the midbody bar. Queensland and Melanesia; associated with two species of anemones, *Stichodactyla gigantae* and *Heteractis magnifica*; depth range 1-12 m. A very similar species, *A. ocellaris*, occurs in the Indo-Malaysian region. Attains 8 cm.

PINK ANEMONEFISH
Amphiprion perideraion Bleeker, 1855

Dorsal rays IX or X,16-17; anal rays II,12-13; pectoral rays 16-18; lateral-line scales 32-43; gill rakers 17-20; body depth 2.1-2.7 in standard length; orange-pink with a distinctive narrow white bar on postorbital head and one middorsally on head. Western Pacific, including Melanesia and Micronesia, ranging north to Japan; associated with the anemone *Heteractis magnifica*; depth range 3-20 m. Reaches 10 cm.

BIG-LIP DAMSEL
Cheiloprion labiatus (Day, 1877)

Dorsal rays XIII,13-14; anal rays II,13-14; pectoral rays 17; lateral-line scales 17-18; gill rakers 16-20; body depth 1.7-1.9 in standard length; brown, becoming darker posteriorly, with narrow blackish scale margins; juveniles black with a neon blue stripe on back; distinguished by swollen appearance of lips. Andaman Sea to northern Australia and Melanesia; feeds on coral polyps; most common on inner part of northern Great Barrier Reef or around inshore islands and coastal reefs; depth 0.5-3 m. Attains 10 cm, but usually under 8 cm.

MIDGET CHROMIS
Chromis acares Randall and Swerdloff, 1973

Dorsal rays XII,11; anal rays II,10 or 11; pectoral rays 16-18; lateral-line scales 15-17; gill rakers 21-25; body depth 2.4-2.6 in standard length; generally blue-grey; head yellowish; anterior half of anal fin black; caudal fin with broad yellow margins; a small yellow spot at rear base of dorsal fin; similar to the more common *C. vanderbilti* but lacks blue stripes and has both lobes of caudal fin yellow. Coral Sea to Society Islands and Johnston Island; one sight rercord from Oahu; depth range 2-37 m. Reaches 5.5 cm.

AGILE CHROMIS
Chromis agilis Smith, 1960

Dorsal rays XII,12-14; anal rays II,12-14; pectoral rays 17-18; lateral-line scales 15-17; gill rakers 27-30; body depth 1.7-1.9 in standard length; rich golden brown, shading to pink on lower head and chest; distinguished from other similar brown *Chromis* by the large dark spot at the pectoral fin base. East Africa to Hawaiian Islands and Pitcairn Group; depth range 3-56 m. Attains 10 cm.

YELLOW-SPECKLED CHROMIS
Chromis alpha Randall, 1988

Dorsal rays XIII,12-13; anal rays II,11-13; pectoral rays 16-18; lateral-line scales 14-16; gill rakers 27-31; body depth 1.8-2.0 in standard length; greenish to brown, the scale edges darker, shading to blue ventrally; scale centres on back often with small yellow spots; edge of opercle and preopercle dark brown; anal fin blue. Christmas Island (Indian Ocean) to Society Islands; inhabits outer reef slopes in 12-95 m (rarely less than 20 m). To 12 cm.

AMBON CHROMIS
Chromis amboinensis (Bleeker, 1873)

Dorsal rays XII,12-13; anal rays II,12-13; pectoral rays 16-17; lateral-line scales 13-14; gill rakers 26-29; body depth 1.5-1.7 in standard length; tips of caudal fin-lobes ending in two filaments; overall tan; upper and lower edges of caudal fin dark brown, broad at base and tapering to lobe tips; a yellow bar at base of pectoral fins; deeper-bodied than *C. atripes* and lacks dark spot on pectoral-fin base found in *C. agilis*. Cocos-Keeling Islands to Samoa and Marshall Islands; depth range 5-65 m. Attains 8 cm.

YELLOW CHROMIS
Chromis analis (Cuvier, 1830)

Dorsal rays XIII,11-13; anal rays II,12-13; pectoral rays 17-18; lateral-line scales 16-19; gill rakers 23-28; body depth 1.7-2.0 in standard length; similar body shape to *C. alpha*, but entirely yellow. Indonesia to Fiji and Mariana Islands; very rare in our area, usually near caves or ledges; depth range 18-70 m. To 15 cm.

BLACK-AXIL CHROMIS
Chromis atripectoralis Welander & Schultz, 1951

Dorsal rays XII,9-10; anal rays II,9-10; pectoral rays 18-20; lateral-line scales 15-16; gill rakers 28-33; body depth 2.0-2.1 in standard length; pale green to light blue; similar to *C. viridis* but pectoral fin axil black and attains larger size. Seychelles to Tuamotus; depth range 2-15 m. Attains 11 cm. Occurs in aggregations; feeds above the bottom on zooplankton but hides among branches of coral with the approach of danger.

DARK-FIN CHROMIS
Chromis atripes Fowler & Bean, 1928

Dorsal rays XII,12-14; anal rays II,12-13; pectoral rays 15-17; lateral-line scales 14-16; gill rakers 24-29; body depth 1.7-2.0 in standard length; caudal fin lobes ending in filaments; yellowish brown; anal, pelvic, and outer dorsal fins blackish (except posterior part of dorsal and anal); base of caudal fin yellow, the upper and lower edges blackish basally; a black spot at upper pectoral-fin base with an orange-yellow spot below it.. Cocos-Keeling Islands to Kiribati; abundant on most outer reefs; stays close to the bottom; depth range 2-35 m. To 7 cm.

STOUT-BODY CHROMIS
Chromis chrysura (Bliss, 1883)

Dorsal rays XIII,14-15; anal rays II,13-14; pectoral rays 18-19; lateral-line scales 17-19; gill rakers 29-33; body depth 1.6-1.8 in standard length; overall dark brown or grey, the centres of scales darker, the caudal peduncle and fin abruptly white; often forms large aggregations feeding well above the bottom on zooplankton. Three isolated antitropical populations: Southwestern Pacific; Japan to Taiwan; and Mauritius-Réunion; depth range 6-45 m. Attains 15 cm.

DEEP REEF CHROMIS
Chromis delta Randall, 1988

Dorsal rays XII,12-14; anal rays II,12-14; pectoral rays 15-17; lateral-line scales 12-14; caudal-fin lobes ending in two filaments; gill rakers 24-28; body depth 1.8-2.1 in standard length; dark brown, bluish grey ventrally, with a broad white bar on caudal peduncle, often edged anteriorly with black; a black spot covering pectoral-fin base and axil; similar to *C. margaritifer*, but has less white colour at rear of body. Cocos-Keeling Islands to Fiji; found on dropoffs to 80 m. Reaches 7 cm.

TWIN-SPOT CHROMIS
Chromis elerae Fowler & Bean, 1928

Dorsal rays XII,11 or 12; anal rays II,10 or 11; pectoral rays 17-18; lateral-line scales 15-17; gill rakers 26-31; body depth 1.8-1.9 in standard length; posterior edge of preopercle serrate; generally grey-brown; distinguished by white spot at bases of posterior dorsal and anal fin rays. Maldive Islands to Fiji and Marshall Islands; found in caves, relatively uncommon; depth range 12-70 m. Attains 6.5 cm.

YELLOW-SPOTTED CHROMIS
Chromis flavomaculata Kamohara, 1960

Dorsal rays XIII or XIV,11-13; anal rays II,10 or 11; pectoral rays 18-20; lateral-line scales 17-19; gill rakers 29-34; body depth 2.0-2.3 in standard length; overall brown with darker scale outlines; pectoral-fin base black, and a small yellow spot at base of posteriormost dorsal rays. Antiequatorial distribution with two isolated populations: (1) Lord Howe Island, Coral Sea, New Caledonia, and Loyalty Islands and (2) Japan to Taiwan; depth range 6-35 m. To 16 cm. *C. kennensis* Whitley is a synonym.

HALF-AND-HALF CHROMIS
Chromis iomelas Jordan & Seale, 1906

Dorsal rays XII,13-14; anal rays II,13-14; pectoral rays 17; lateral-line scales 15; auxiliary scales present; gill rakers 26 or 27; body depth 1.8-1.9 in standard length; tips of caudal fin lobes with two filaments; dark brown on anterior half, abruptly white posteriorly; similar to *C. margaritifer*, but has a much larger posterior white zone. Great Barrier Reef and northern New Guinea to Samoa and Society Islands; depth range 3-35 m. Reaches 7 cm.

SCALY CHROMIS
Chromis lepidolepis Bleeker, 1877

Dorsal rays XII,11-13; anal rays II,11 or 12; pectoral rays 17-19; lateral-line scales 15-18; gill rakers 27-30; body depth 1.9-2.2 in standard length; posterior margin of preopercle serrate; olivaceous brown, the upper and lower edges of caudal fin dusky, the lobe tips black. East Africa and Red Sea to Fiji and Line Islands; depth range 2-20 m. To 8 cm.

BICOLOR CHROMIS
Chromis margaritifer Fowler, 1946

Dorsal rays XII,12-13; anal rays II,11-12; pectoral rays 16-18; lateral-line scales 16-18; gill rakers 25-29; body depth 1.9-2.0 in standard length; caudal-fin lobes ending in two filaments; dark brown, nearly black, with caudal peduncle and caudal fin abruptly white; a black spot at pectoral fin base; similar to *C. delta* (see above). Cocos-Keeling Islands to Tuamotus; depth range 2-15 m. Reaches 8.5 cm.

BARRIER REEF CHROMIS
Chromis nitida (Whitley, 1928)

Dorsal rays XIII,11-13; anal rays II,10-11; pectoral rays 19; lateral-line scales 17-18; gill rakers 28-31; body depth 2.2-2.3 in standard length; white with an oblique blackish band from snout to middle of dorsal fin (and extending onto posterior margin of dorsal), the head and back above stripe yellowish brown; a narrow black streak in each caudal-fin lobe. Common on southern and central Great Barrier Reef, but rare or absent in the northern part of reefs and Coral Sea; depth range 5-25 m. Attains 8 cm.

BLACK-BAR CHROMIS
Chromis retrofasciatus Weber, 1913

Dorsal rays XII,12-13; anal rays II,12-13; pectoral rays 15-16; lateral-line scales 12; gill rakers 24-26; body depth 1.8-2.0 in standard length; caudal-fin lobes ending in two filaments; light tan to yellowish brown with a prominent black bar posteriorly on body, the caudal fin and posterior peduncle white. Indonesia and Philippines to Fiji; common on outer reef slopes; depth range 5-65 m. To 6 cm.

TERNATE CHROMIS
Chromis ternatensis (Bleeker, 1856)

Dorsal rays XII or XIII,10-12; anal rays II,10-12; pectoral rays 16-18; lateral-line scales 14-17; gill rakers 27-30; body depth 1.8-1.9 in standard length; membranes of spinous portion of dorsal fin not incised; olivaceous to dark yellowish grey, the centres of scales often with light blue iridescence; a wash of yellow dorsally on head; a dark brown streak along margin of each caudal lobe. East Africa to Fiji and Marshall Islands; forms large feeding aggregations above bottoms of rich coral; depth range 2-15 m. Attains 9 cm.

VANDERBILT'S CHROMIS
Chromis vanderbilti (Fowler, 1941)

Dorsal rays XII,10-12; anal rays II,10-12; pectoral rays 16-18; lateral-line scales 16-18; gill rakers 23-27; body depth 2.3-2.7 in standard length; alternating blue and yellow stripes on body; broad black margin on lower lobe of caudal fin; margin of spinous portion of dorsal fin broadly yellow; anal fin largely black; similar to the less abundant *C. acares*. Scattered localities in western and central Pacific; often in areas exposed to swells; depth range 2-20 m. Reaches 6 cm.

BLUE-GREEN CHROMIS
Chromis viridis (Cuvier, 1830)

Dorsal rays XII,9-10; anal rays II,10-11; pectoral rays 17-18; lateral-line scales 15-16; gill rakers 28-33; body depth 2.0-2.1 in standard length; pale green to light blue; nesting male yellow, becoming blackish posteriorly; similar to *C. atripectoralis*, but generally smaller and lacks the black area on inside of pectoral-fin base. East Africa and Red Sea to Tuamotu Archipelago and Line Islands; large aggregations characteristically feed above coral bommies into which they suddenly retreat at the approach of danger; depth range 1.5-12 m. To 9 cm. Formerly known as *C. caerulea*, a name now invalidated by the International Commission on Zoological Nomenclature.

WEBER'S CHROMIS
Chromis weberi Fowler & Bean, 1928

Dorsal rays XIII,11-12; anal rays II,11-12; pectoral rays 18-20; lateral-line scales 17-19; gill rakers 27-32; body moderately elongate, the depth 2.1-2.3 in standard length; olivaceous to bluish grey, the scale edges dark brown; edges of opercle and preopercle dark brown; a broad black band at edge of each caudal-fin lobe, the tip black; a black spot at upper base and axil of pectoral fins. East Africa and Red Sea to Line Islands and Pitcairn Group; depth range 3-12 m. Attains 12 cm.

YELLOW-AXIL CHROMIS
Chromis xanthochira (Bleeker, 1851)

Dorsal rays XIII,11; anal rays II,11-12; pectoral rays 19; lateral-line scales 16-17; gill rakers 30-32; body depth 2.0-2.2 in standard length; blue to bluish brown, the edges of scales dark; a large yellow area at base of pectoral fins; posterior margins of opercle and preopercle dark brown; a broad blackish band in each caudal-fin lobe; somewhat similar to *C. weberi*, which differs in having a black spot at upper base of pectoral fin. Indonesia and Philippines to northeastern Australia and Melanesia; depth range 10-48 cm. Reaches 14 cm.

PALE-TAIL CHROMIS
Chromis xanthura (Bleeker, 1854)

Dorsal rays XIII,10-11; anal rays II,9-10; pectoral rays 18-20; lateral-line scales 16-19; gill rakers 26-30; body depth 2.1-2.3 in standard length; bluish grey, the scale edges broadly blackish; caudal peduncle and fin abruptly white; posterior edge of preopercle and opercle blackish; a black spot at pectoral-fin base; juveniles with broad yellow margins on median fins and a large yellow area on pelvic fins. Cocos-Keeling Islands to southeastern Oceania; a distinctive *Chromis* often seen in loose aggregations adjacent to outer-reef dropoffs; depth range 3-35 m. To 15 cm.

TWOSPOT DEMOISELLE
Chrysiptera biocellata (Quoy & Gaimard, 1824)

Dorsal rays XIII,12-14; anal rays II,13-14; pectoral rays 17-19; lateral-line scales 16-18; gill rakers 23-25; body depth 2.2-2.5 in standard length; brown with white bar on middle of side; juveniles with an ocellus at base of middle dorsal rays and a small white-edged black spot behind last dorsal ray; sometimes confused with *C. unimaculatus*, but usually found in a different habitat, protected lagoon areas with sandy bottoms and scattered coral or rock outcrops (wave-exposed reef flat for *C. unimaculatus*). East Africa to Samoa and Marshall Islands; depth range 0.5-5 m. To 10 cm.

BLUELINE DEMOISELLE
Chrysiptera caeruleolineatus (Allen, 1973)

Dorsal rays XIII,12-13; anal rays II,13-14; pectoral rays 16-17; lateral-line scales 16-17; gill rakers 17-19; body depth 2.2-2.4 in standard length; mainly yellow, including fins, except a broad blue stripe from snout through upper edge of eye and continuing along back to below soft part of dorsal fin. Coral Sea to Samoa and Marshall Islands; outer reef slopes below 20 m depth. Attains 6.5 cm.

BLUE DEVIL
Chrysiptera cyanea (Quoy & Gaimard, 1824)

Dorsal rays XIII,12-13; anal rays II,13-14; pectoral rays 16-17; lateral-line scales 16-17; gill rakers 17-19; body depth 2.2-2.4 in standard length; overall bright blue with small scattered white spots; a broad dark band on snout; females lack the yellow-orange caudal fin which is typical of males; similar to *C. taupou*, but lacks yellow colour on belly; *cyanea* is far more common on the Great Barrier Reef (northern portion) than *taupou*, but is absent from the Coral Sea. Indonesia to Solomon and Mariana Islands, north to Ryukyu Islands; depth range of 0.3-10 m. To 8.5 cm.

Chrysiptera cyanea Male ▲ Female ▼

263

YELLOWFIN DAMSEL

Chrysiptera flavipinnis (Allen & Robertson, 1974)

Dorsal rays XIII,14-15; anal rays II,13-14; pectoral rays 17-18; lateral-line scales 15-18; gill rakers 20-22; body depth 2.2-2.6 in standard length; blue except yellow on upper back and dorsal fin, and whitish ventrally; somewhat similar in colour to *C. taupou*, but lacks light spots in blue area and dark spot at base of posterior dorsal rays. Southwestern Pacific, including New Guinea, eastern Australia, and Coral Sea; depth range 3-38 m. Attains 8.5 cm.

GREY DAMSEL

Chrysiptera glauca (Cuvier, 1830)

Dorsal rays XIII,12-13; anal rays II,12-13; pectoral rays 17-18; lateral-line scales 17-19; gill rakers 21-24; body depth 2.2-2.3 in standard length; a distinctive light grey damselfish found in shallow wave-swept areas; anus black; an ocellus in dorsal fin of fish less than about 4.5 cm; juveniles are light blue with a brilliant blue stripe above the eye. East Africa to Pitcairn Group and Line Islands; depth range 0.5-2 m. Reaches 11 cm.

SURGE DEMOISELLE

Chrysiptera leucopoma (Lesson, 1830)

Dorsal rays XIII,12-13; anal rays II,12-13; pectoral rays 18-19; lateral-line scales 18-19; gill rakers 19-21; body depth 2.3-2.5 in standard length; two colour varieties: dark brown with two white bars on body and a yellow bar on gill cover; and yellow with a blue band from above eye to upper caudal peduncle (may be interrupted below rear part of dorsal fin). Both forms occur in outer reef flat areas, the brown form on the wave-swept algal ridge and the yellow to areas exposed to slightly less wave action on either side of the outer reef crest; the two forms are sometimes seen together; juveniles are usually in the yellow phase. East Africa to Marquesas and Marshall islands; depth range 0.2-2 m. Attains 8.5 cm. *C. amabilis* (De Vis) is a synonym based on the dark brown form.

Chrysiptera leucopoma Dark phase ▲ Pale phase ▼

KING DEMOISELLE
Chrysiptera rex (Snyder, 1909)

Dorsal rays XIII,13-14; anal rays II,13-14; pectoral rays 16-17; lateral-line scales 16-17; gill rakers 17-19; body depth 2.4-2.7 in standard length; distinguished by its pale yellowish body and fins, dusky or bluish head, silvery iris, and small black spot on opercle at upper end of gill opening. Indonesia and Philippines to northeastern Australia and Melanesia; depth range 1-6 m. Attains 7 cm.

ROLLAND'S DEMOISELLE
Chrysiptera rollandi (Whitley, 1961)

Dorsal rays XIII,10-11; anal rays II,12-13; pectoral rays 15; lateral-line scales 14-16; gill rakers 21-22; body depth 2.1-2.2 in standard length; whitish except head and anterior-dorsal part of body blue grey; individuals from New Caledonia (and possibly eastern Coral Sea) differ from the illustrated fish in having a yellow area on the snout and forehead. Malay Peninsula to northeastern Australia and Melanesia; depth range 2-35 m. Attains 6 cm.

STARCK'S DEMOISELLE
Chrysiptera starcki (Allen, 1973)

Dorsal rays XIII,14-15; anal rays II,15-17; pectoral rays 15-17; lateral-line scales 15-17; gill rakers 21-22; body depth 2.2-2.5 in standard length; rich royal blue except yellow area dorsally and ventrally on head that extends along back and onto dorsal fin; caudal fin yellowish; similar to *C. flavipinna*, but has blue instead of yellow pelvic and anal fins. Antiequatorial distribution in western Pacific: New Caledonia to Queensland and Taiwan to Ryukyu Islands; usually found in deeper sections of the outer reef (20-60 m). Reaches 10 cm.

TALBOT'S DEMOISELLE
Chrysiptera talboti (Allen, 1975)

Dorsal rays XIII,11-12; anal rays II,11-13; pectoral rays 15-16; lateral-line scales 14-16; gill rakers 18-20; body depth 2.2-2.3 in standard length; body mauve-grey; head and pelvic fins yellowish; a large black spot at middle of dorsal fin and adjacent back. Malay Peninsula to northeastern Australia and Melanesia; depth range 6-35 m. Attains 6.5 cm.

SOUTH SEAS DEMOISELLE
Chrysiptera taupou (Jordan & Seale, 1906)

Dorsal rays XIII,12-13; anal rays II,13-14; pectoral rays 16-17; lateral-line scales 16-17; gill rakers 17-19; body depth 2.1-2.2 in standard length; bright blue with scattered small white spots on side; a black stripe often present on snout; belly bright yellow; a black spot usually present at base of posterior soft dorsal rays; males have yellow dorsal and caudal fins (bluish to translucent in females); similar to *C. cyanea* (see above). Southwestern Pacific, including Australia, to Fiji and Samoa; depth range 2-10 m. Reaches 8.5 cm.

THREEBAND DEMOISELLE
Chrysiptera tricincta (Allen & Randall, 1974)

Dorsal rays XIII,11-13; anal rays II,12-14; pectoral rays 18-19; lateral-line scales 15-17; gill rakers 23-26; body depth 2.1-2.4 in standard length; white with three black bars; similar in colour to *Dascyllus aruanus*, but has white at front of pelvic fin and a broader white area on anal fin; occurs in sandy areas around rocks versus live coral heads for *D. aruanus*. Antiequatorial distribution in western Pacific: Coral Sea to Samoa, also Ryukyu Islands; depth range 10-38 m. Attains 6.5 cm.

ONESPOT DEMOISELLE
Chrysiptera unimaculata (Cuvier, 1830)

Dorsal rays XIII,13-14; anal rays II,12-14; pectoral rays 18-19; lateral-line scales 16-18; gill rakers 22-23; body depth 2.1-2.4 in standard length; generally brown with yellowish pectoral fins; a small black spot at base of posterior dorsal rays; small juveniles mainly yellow with a blue stripe along back and an ocellus at middle of dorsal fin; sometimes confused with *C. biocellata*, but generally lacks white bar on middle of body and is usually found on wave-exposed reef flats compared with sandy lagoon habitats for *C. biocellata*. East Africa and Red Sea to Fiji; depth range 0.2-2 m. To 8.5 cm.

HUMBUG DASCYLLUS
Dascyllus aruanus (Linnaeus, 1758)

Dorsal rays XII,11-13; anal rays II,11-13; pectoral rays 17-19; lateral-line scales 15-19; gill rakers 21-26; body depth 1.5-1.7 in standard length; white with three black bars. East Africa and Red Sea to Line Islands and southeastern Polynesia; a distinctive species that forms aggregations around small coral bommies; depth range 1-12 m. To 8.5 cm.

BLACK-TAILED DASCYLLUS
Dascyllus melanurus Bleeker, 1854

Dorsal rays XII,12-13; anal rays II,12-13; pectoral rays 18-19; lateral-line scales 15-19; gill rakers 23-27; body depth 1.5-1.7 in standard length; white with three black bars and black area covering posterior half of caudal fin; the similar *D. aruanus* lacks black on caudal fin. Malay Peninsula to northeastern Australia and Melanesia; depth range 1-10 m. Attains 8.5 cm.

RETICULATED DASCYLLUS
Dascyllus reticulatus (Richardson, 1846)

Dorsal rays XII,14-16; anal rays II,12-14; pectoral rays 19-21; lateral-line scales 20; gill rakers 24-29; body depth 1.4-1.6 in standard length; whitish or very pale tan with a black bar at level of pectoral-fin base and second more diffuse dark bar across posterior part of body. Cocos-Keeling Islands to Samoa; a distinctive, very common damselfish usually associated with coral bommies; depth range 1-50 m. To 9 cm.

THREE-SPOT DASCYLLUS
Dascyllus trimaculatus (Rüppell, 1828)

Dorsal rays XII,14-16; anal rays II,14-15; pectoral rays 19-21; lateral-line scales 17-19; gill rakers 22-26; body depth 1.4-1.6 in standard length; charcoal-coloured with black scale margins; juveniles are distinguished by a white spot on the forehead as well as a prominent white spot on the upper side; the latter mark may persist as a faint remnant in adults. East Africa and Red Sea to Line Islands and Pitcairn Group; juveniles sometimes found with sea anemones; depth range 1-55 m. To 13 cm.

BLACK-VENT DAMSEL
Dischistodus melanotus (Bleeker, 1853)

Dorsal rays XIII,13-15; anal rays II,13-14; pectoral rays 17; lateral-line scales 15-17; gill rakers 21-23; body depth 2.0-2.1 in standard length; white with a large dark brown area covering anterodorsal region of body and upper part of head; a large black patch covering region above anus; pale pink blotches and streaks on ventral half of head; juveniles brown on anterior half and white behind; white bar behind head and an ocellated black spot at middle of dorsal fin. Indonesia and Philippines to northern Australia and Solomon Islands; depth range 1-10 m. Reaches 16 cm. *D. notophthalmus* (Bleeker) is a synonym.

WHITE DAMSEL
Dischistodus perspicillatus (Cuvier, 1830)

Dorsal rays XIII,14-15; anal rays II,14-15; pectoral rays 17-18; lateral-line scales 17-18; gill rakers 33-35; body depth 2.1-2.3 in standard length; white with two black saddles below dorsal fin and a third across nape; juveniles white with a black saddle on top of the head and another (with ocellated spot) at middle of body extending onto dorsal fin. Eastern Indian Ocean and western Pacific; inhabits sandy areas; depth range 1-10 m. Attains 20 cm.

HONEY-HEAD DAMSEL
Dischistodus prosopotaenia (Bleeker, 1852)

Dorsal rays XIII,14-16; anal rays II,14-15; pectoral rays 17; lateral-line scales 16-17; gill rakers 29-32; body depth 2.1-2.2 in standard length; golden brown anteriorly and white posteriorly except for a diffuse brown saddle or bar below soft part of dorsal fin; axil of pectoral fin black; light blue dots and vertical lines on scales; juveniles white, the head, thorax, a broad bar in middle of body, and dorsal fin brown; a large ocellated black spot on dorsal fin. Andaman Sea to northern Australia and Melanesia; depth range 0.5-12 m. To 19 cm.

Dischistodus prosopotaenia   Juv.

MONARCH DAMSEL
Dischistodus pseudochrysopoecilus (Allen & Robertson, 1974)

Dorsal rays XIII,13-14; anal rays II,13-14; pectoral rays 16-17; lateral-line scales 16 or 18; gill rakers 20-22; body depth 2.0-2.3 in standard length; dark brown with vertical blue lines on scales and blue markings on head; a large white blotch between lateral line and base of posterior dorsal spines; juveniles mainly brown with a white bar behind head and another below rear part of dorsal fin; a yellow-edged black spot at middle of dorsal fin. Philippines to northeastern Australia and Melanesia; depth range 1-5 m. Reaches 18 cm.

LAGOON DAMSEL

Hemiglyphidodon plagiometopon (Bleeker, 1852)

Dorsal rays XIII,14-15; anal rays II,14-15; pectoral rays 16-17; lateral-line scales 14-16; gill rakers 65-85 (the highest count of any damselfish); body depth 1.8-2.0 in standard length; brown, the median fins and base of pectoral fins generally darker; juveniles yellow, the head and anterodorsal body bluish grey; bright blue markings on head; subadults sometimes reddish brown. Andaman Sea to Queensland and Solomon Islands, north to China; northern Great Barrier Reef in lagoons, apparently absent from Coral Sea; depth range 1.5-20 m. Attains 20 cm.

FUSILIER DAMSEL

Lepidozygus tapeinosoma (Bleeker, 1856)

Dorsal rays XII,14-15; anal rays II,15-16; pectoral rays 21-22; lateral-line scales 19-20; gill rakers 25-29; body elongate, the depth 2.8-3.1 in standard length; brown on dorsal half, often with a yellowish wash; ventral half white to bluish or pink; usually a yellow streak at rear of dorsal fin. Forms large aggregations that feed high above the bottom. East Africa to Tuamotus, Marquesas, and Line Islands; depth range 5-30 m. Reaches 10 cm. *L. anthioides* Smith is a synonym.

YELLOWTAIL DEMOISELLE

Neopomacentrus azysron (Bleeker, 1877)

Dorsal rays XIII,11 or 12; anal rays II,11 or 12; pectoral rays 17-19; lateral-line scales 17-19; gill rakers 20-23; body depth 2.5-2.8 in standard length; margins of preopercle and suborbital smooth; suborbital margin hidden by scales; teeth biserial; brown with blue vertical streaks on scales; caudal and rear portion of dorsal and anal fins yellow; similar to *N. bankieri*, but yellow areas on caudal and soft dorsal fins are interconnected, and has "ear" spot and blackish pectoral-fin base; occurs in clear water, well away from the coast, whereas *bankieri* inhabits turbid coastal reefs. East Africa to New Caledonia; depth range 1-12 m. Grows to 8 cm.

CHINESE DEMOISELLE
Neopomacentrus bankieri (Richardson, 1846)

Dorsal rays XIII,11; anal rays II,11 or 12; pectoral rays 17 or 18; lateral-line scales 16-18; gill rakers 21 or 22; body depth 2.2-2.6 in standard length; brown, often with longitudinal rows of blue spots on caudal peduncle; bluish on belly; caudal and rear portions of dorsal and anal fins yellow; similar to *N. azysron* (see above); South China Sea and Java Sea to north-eastern Australia; inner and coastal reefs, depth range 1-12 m. To 7 cm.

REGAL DEMOISELLE
Neopomacentrus cyanomos (Bleeker, 1856)

Dorsal rays XIII,11-12; anal rays II,11-12; pectoral rays 17; lateral-line scales 17-18; gill rakers 22-24; body depth 2.2-2.6 in standard length; edge of suborbital hidden by scales; dark brown with large black spot on upper edge of opercle near origin of lateral line; posteriormost part of dorsal and anal fins yellow (sometimes white), more intense at base of last dorsal rays; base of caudal fin dark brown, grading to yellow on outer half. Occurs in protected waters such as lagoons and harbours. East Africa to northern Australia and Melanesia. Grows to 10 cm.

BLACK DAMSEL
Neoglyphidodon melas (Cuvier, 1830)

Dorsal rays XIII,14 or 15; anal rays II,13-15; pectoral rays 18 or 19; lateral-line scales 16 or 17; gill rakers 19-22; body depth 1.7-2.0 in standard length; margins of preopercle and suborbital smooth; suborbital scaled; teeth biserial; a distinctive jet-black fish; juveniles white to light grey with yellow on upper part of head and body, dorsal fin, and upper and lower margins of caudal fin; juveniles formerly thought to be a separate species, *N. melanopus* (Bleeker). East Africa and Red Sea to Vanuatu, north to Ryukyu Islands; depth range 1-5 m. Attains 15 cm. Has been observed to feed on soft coral.

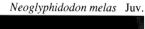

Neoglyphidodon melas Juv.

YELLOWFIN DAMSEL
Neoglyphidodon nigroris (Cuvier, 1830)

Dorsal rays XIII,13 or 14; anal rays II,13-15; pectoral rays 17; lateral-line scales 15-17; gill rakers 22-26; body depth 1.7 to 2.0 in standard length; margins of preopercle and suborbital smooth; suborbital scaled; teeth biserial; brown except caudal peduncle and fin and posterior dorsal and anal fins which are yellow; a dark bar below eye, and edges of preopercle and opercle dark brown; juveniles yellow with a pair of conspicuous black stripes on side; Andaman Sea to Vanuatu, north to Ryukyu Islands; depth range 2-25 m. Grows to 13 cm. Formerly known as *N. behni* (Bleeker).

Neoglyphidodon nigroris Juv.

MULTISPINE DAMSELFISH
Neoglyphidodon polyacanthus (Ogilby, 1889)

Dorsal rays XIV,13 or 14; anal rays II,13 or 14; pectoral rays 18; lateral-line scales 18 or 19; gill rakers 22 or 23; body depth 1.9-2.1 in standard length; margins of preopercle and suborbital smooth; suborbital scaleless; teeth biserial; adults brown with darker scale margins; juveniles yellow-orange with a narrow blue band from snout to and surrounding a black spot below middle of dorsal fin. Southernmost Great Barrier Reef, Lord Howe Island, Norfolk Island, and New Caledonia; depth range 2-30 m. To 15 cm.

BIGSCALED SCALYFIN
Parma oligolepis Whitley, 1929

Dorsal rays XIII,17-20; anal rays II,13-15; pectoral rays 20-22; lateral-line scales 22-24; gill rakers 21-24; body depth 1.6-1.9 in standard length; margins of preopercle and suborbital smooth; suborbital scaled; teeth uniserial; adults charcoal-coloured with black scale outlines; juveniles yellow with a blue-rimmed black spot on the rear part of the spinous dorsal fin, and blue lines dorsally on head and body. Common on coastal reefs of northern New South Wales and southern Queensland; generally rare on the Great Barrier Reef, but occurs as far north as Cape Tribulation, Cape York Peninsula; depth range 3-20 m. Attains 20 cm.

BANDED SCALYFIN
Parma polylepis Günther, 1862

Dorsal rays XIII,16-19; anal rays II,13 or 14; pectoral rays 20-22; lateral-line scales 26-33; gill rakers 17-23; body depth 1.6-1.7 in standard length; forehead of adults with bony knobs; adults dusky brown, often with yellowish head; a pair of dark bars usually present on side, although sometimes diffuse; juveniles with 2-3 alternating light and dark bars, and a blue-edged black spot on dorsal fin. Southernmost Great Barrier Reef, New South Wales, Lord Howe Island , Norfolk Island, and New Caledonia; depth range 1-30 m. To 22 cm.

DICK'S DAMSEL
Plectroglyphidodon dickii (Liénard, 1839)

Dorsal rays XII,17 or 18; anal rays II,14-16; pectoral rays 19; lateral-line scales 21 or 22; gill rakers 16 or 17; body depth 1.8-1.9 in standard length; margins of preopercle and suborbital smooth; suborbital scaled; teeth uniserial; mainly tan with narrow brown scale outlines; a conspicuous black bar across posterior part of body; caudal peduncle and fin white; pectoral fins yellow; similar to *P. johnstonianus*, but has narrower black bar at rear of body and white caudal fin. East Africa to Tuamotus and Line Islands; depth range 1-12 m. Reaches 11 cm.

BRIGHTEYE DAMSEL
Plectroglyphidodon imparipennis (Vaillant & Sauvage, 1875)

Dorsal rays XII,14 or 15; anal rays II,11 or 12; pectoral rays 20; lateral-line scales 19; gill rakers 10-12; body depth 2.1-2.4 in standard length; margins of preopercle and suborbital smooth; suborbital scaled; teeth uniserial; overall light grey; caudal peduncle and fin often yellow; a black vertical streak across middle of eye; iris silvery. East Africa to Pitcairn Group and Hawaiian Islands; inhabits shallow reefs exposed to wave action; depth range 0.5-3 m. Attains 6.5 cm.

JOHNSTON DAMSEL

Plectroglyphidodon johnstonianus Fowler & Ball, 1924

Dorsal rays XII,18 or 19; anal rays II,16-18; pectoral rays 19; lateral-line scales 21 or 22; gill rakers 12-14; body depth 1.7-1.9 in standard length; margins of preopercle and suborbital smooth; suborbital scaled; teeth uniserial; pale tan to pale yellowish with a broad black bar across posterior part of body (occasionally this black marking absent); similar to *P. dickii* (see above). East Africa to Pitcairn Group and Hawaiian Islands; frequently associated with *Acropora* or *Pocillopora* corals in 2-12 m depth. To 10 cm. Feeds at least in part on coral polyps.

Plectroglyphidodon johnstonianus Normal colouration ▲ Pale phase ▼

JEWEL DAMSEL

Plectroglyphidodon lacrymatus (Quoy & Gaimard, 1824)

Dorsal rays XII,18 or 19; anal rays II,13 or 14; pectoral rays 18-20; lateral-line scales 17 or 18; gill rakers 21-25; body depth 1.8-1.9 in standard length; margins of preopercle and suborbital smooth; suborbital scaled; teeth uniserial; brown with scattered blue spots; lavender or blue spots or markings on head; caudal fin tan. East Africa and Red Sea to Society Islands and Marshall Islands; depth range 2-12 m. Reaches 11 cm.

WHITEBAND DAMSEL
Plectroglyphidodon leucozonus (Bleeker, 1859)

Dorsal rays XII,15 or 16; anal rays II,12 or 13; pectoral rays 19 or 20; lateral-line scales 19 or 20; gill rakers 15-24; body depth 1.8-1.9 in standard length; margins of preopercle and suborbital smooth; suborbital scaled; teeth uniserial; brown with darker scale margins and a small pale spot on base of each scale; a white bar on side below middle of spinous dorsal fin (may be lost in large adults). East Africa to Pitcairn Group and Marshall Islands; inhabits shallow reefs exposed to wave action; depth range of 0.3-2 m. To 11 cm.

PHOENIX DAMSEL
Plectroglyphidodon phoenixensis (Schultz, 1943)

Dorsal rays XII,16 or 17; anal rays II,13 or 14; pectoral rays 20 or 21; lateral-line scales 21 or 22; gill rakers 14-16; body depth 1.9-2-1 in standard length; margins of preopercle and suborbital smooth; suborbital scaled; teeth uniserial; dark brown with three narrow pink bars and a black bar (with pink anterior edge) across caudal peduncle. East Africa to Tuamotus and Marshall Islands; inhabits shallow reefs exposed to wave action; depth range 0.1-8 m. To 10 cm.

AMBON DAMSEL
Pomacentrus amboinensis Bleeker, 1868

Dorsal rays XIII,14-16; anal rays II,14-16; pectoral rays 17; lateral-line scales 16 or 17; gill rakers 22-24; body depth 2.0-2.1 in standard length; margins of preopercle and suborbital serrate; suborbital scaleless; teeth biserial; yellow to pale mauve, the scale edges dark; a small dark spot on opercle at upper end of gill opening and one at base of uppermost pectoral rays (these two spots often found on other *Pomacentrus*); pale pink to blue blotches scattered on head; juveniles and subadults with an ocellus on middle of soft part of dorsal fin. Andaman Sea to northeastern Australia and Melanesia; depth range 2-40 m. Attains 11 cm.

AUSTRALIAN DAMSEL

Pomacentrus australis Allen & Robertson, 1973

Dorsal rays XIV (rarely XV),12-14; anal rays II,14 or 15; pectoral rays 17-19; lateral-line scales 16-19; gill rakers 19-21; body depth 2.2-2.6 in standard length; margins of preopercle and suborbital serrate; suborbital scaleless; teeth biserial; overall blue, lighter ventrally. Great Barrier Reef, but more common on southern half; also ranges south to Sydney; depth range 12-35 m. Grows to 9 cm.

SPECKLED DAMSEL

Pomacentrus bankanensis Bleeker, 1853

Dorsal rays XIII,15 or 16; anal rays II,15 or 16; pectoral rays 18; lateral-line scales 17-19; gill rakers 20-22; body depth 2.0-2.1 in standard length; margins of preopercle and suborbital serrate; suborbital scaleless; teeth biserial; brown, somewhat yellowish on breast and belly; a small blue spot on scale centres; blue lines dorsally on head; an ocellus on rear part of dorsal fin; caudal fin white; juvenile similar to *P. vaiuli*, but has a blue line down middle of forehead, which is lacking in *vaiuli*. Christmas Island (Indian Ocean) to Fiji, north to Japan; depth range 1-12 m. To 10 cm.

CHARCOAL DAMSEL

Pomacentrus brachialis Cuvier, 1830

Dorsal rays XIII,13-15; anal rays II,14 or 15; pectoral rays 16 or 17; lateral-line scales 16 or 17; gill rakers 19-21; body depth 1.8-2.0 in standard length; margins of preopercle and suborbital serrate; suborbital scaleless; teeth biserial; charcoal-coloured with black spot covering base of pectoral fin. Western Pacific to Fiji and Samoa Islands; depth range 6-40 m. Attains 11 cm. *P. melanopterus* Bleeker is a synonym.

WHITETAIL DAMSEL
Pomacentrus chrysurus Cuvier, 1830

Dorsal rays XIII,14-16; anal rays II,15 or 16; pectoral rays 18; lateral-line scales 18 or 19; gill rakers 18 or 19; body depth 1.9-2.2 in standard length; margins of preopercle and suborbital serrate; suborbital scaleless; teeth biserial; overall brown with white caudal fin; similar to *P. bankanensis*, but lacks blue stripes on forehead in all sizes. Maldive Islands to Coral Sea, Melanesia, and Micronesia; inhabits rocky outcrops in sandy areas; depth range 0.5-3 m. Reaches 10 cm. *P. rhodonotus* Bleeker and *P. flavicauda* Whitley are synonyms..

NEON DAMSEL
Pomacentrus coelestis Jordan & Starks, 1901

Dorsal rays XIII,13-15; anal rays II,14 or 15; pectoral rays 17 or 18; lateral-line scales 17 or 18; gill rakers 20-22; body depth 2.5-2.6 in standard length; margin of suborbital smooth; margin of preopercle serrate; suborbital scaleless; teeth biserial; blue, often with iridescent glow; variable amount of yellow often on ventral part of body, and on caudal and anal fins. Cocos-Keeling Islands to Tuamotus; forms large aggregations in rubble areas; depth range 1-12 m. To 10 cm.

BLUESPOT DAMSEL
Pomacentrus grammorhynchus Fowler, 1918

Dorsal rays XIII,14 or 15; anal rays II,14 or 15; pectoral rays 17 or 18; lateral-line scales 16 or 17; gill rakers 26-30; body depth 1.8-2.0 in standard length; margins of preopercle and suborbital serrate; suborbital scaleless; teeth biserial; light brown to tan with a blue spot on upper edge of caudal peduncle. Indonesia and Philippines to northeastern Australia and Melanesia; depth range 2-12 m. Attains 13 cm.

IMITATOR DAMSEL
Pomacentrus imitator (Whitley, 1964)

Dorsal rays XIII,13 or 14; anal rays II,13 or 14; pectoral rays 17 or 18; lateral-line scales 15-18; gill rakers 22-24; body depth 1.8-1.9 in standard length; margins of preopercle and suborbital serrate; suborbital scaleless; teeth biserial; grey to charcoal-coloured with pale caudal fin; a large black spot covering base of pectoral fin. Rare on the Great Barrier Reef, but commonly encountered in the Coral Sea; also found at New Caledonia, Rotuma, and Fiji; depth range 2-12 m. To 11 cm.

SCALY DAMSEL
Pomacentrus lepidogenys Fowler & Ball, 1928

Dorsal rays XIII,14 or 15; anal rays II,14 or 15; pectoral rays 18; lateral-line scales 17 or 18; gill rakers 20-22; body depth 2.0-2.4 in standard length; margin of preopercle weakly serrate; margin of suborbital smooth; suborbital scaled; teeth biserial; generally light grey to pale greenish, darker on back; fins sometimes with yellow hue. Malay Peninsula to Fiji; depth range 1-12 m. Reaches 9 cm.

LEMON DAMSEL
Pomacentrus moluccensis Bleeker, 1853

Dorsal rays XIII,14 or 15; anal rays II,14 or 15; pectoral rays 17; lateral-line scales 17 or 18; gill rakers 23 or 24; body depth 1.8-1.9 in standard length; margins of preopercle and suborbital serrate; suborbital scaleless; teeth biserial; bright yellow with a very small spot at base of uppermost pectoral rays; sometimes confused with *P. amboinensis*, but brighter yellow, has smaller spot at upper pectoral-fin base, and lacks an ocellus on the dorsal fin at all sizes. Andaman Sea to Fiji, north to Ryukyu Islands; depth range 1-12 m. To 7.5 cm. *P. popei* Jordan & Seale is a synonym.

SANDY DAMSEL
Pomacentrus nagasakiensis Tanaka, 1917

Dorsal rays XIII,15; anal rays II,15-17; pectoral rays 17-19; lateral-line scales 17-19; gill rakers 19-23; body depth 1.9-2.1 in standard length; margins of preopercle and suborbital serrate; suborbital scaleless; teeth biserial; generally light to dark grey or charcoal-coloured, often with vertical blue streaks on scales; numerous blue streaks and spots on head; base of pectoral fin with a black spot; caudal fin whitish; usually diffuse spots or mottling evident on caudal fin and rear part of dorsal and anal fins; juveniles and subadults with an ocellus basally on rear part of dorsal fin; juveniles bluish. Indonesia to Coral Sea and Vanuatu, north to Japan; inhabits rocky outcrops in sandy areas; depth range 3-35 m. Grows to 12 cm. *P. arenarius* Allen is a synonym.

BLACKMARGINED DAMSEL
Pomacentrus nigromarginatus Allen, 1973

Dorsal rays XIII,14 or 15; anal rays II,14 or 15; pectoral rays 16 or 17; lateral-line scales 13-15; gill rakers 20 or 21; body depth 2.0-2.1 in standard length; margins of preopercle and suborbital serrate; suborbital scaleless; teeth biserial; grey with darker scale edges; margins of dorsal, anal, and caudal fins narrowly black; a large black spot covering base of pectoral fin. Indonesia to Coral Sea and Solomon Islands, north to Ryukyu Islands; depth range 20-46 m. Attains 9.5 cm.

BLUE DAMSEL
Pomacentrus pavo (Bloch, 1787)

Dorsal rays XIII,12-14; anal rays II,12-14; pectoral rays 17; lateral-line scales 16 or 17; gill rakers 23 or 24; body depth 2.4-2.6 in standard length; pale blue-green to light blue, larger individuals often with ornate streaks, spots, and lines as shown in photo. East Africa to Tuamotus and Marshall Islands; generally found around coral outcrops, frequently in sandy lagoons; depth range 1-16 m. To 11 cm.

PHILIPPINE DAMSEL

Pomacentrus philippinus Evermann & Seale, 1907

Dorsal rays XIII,14 or 15; anal rays II,14-16; pectoral rays 18 or 19; lateral-line scales 17 or 18; gill rakers 23 or 24; body depth 1.9-2.0 in standard length; margins of preopercle and suborbital serrate; suborbital with a few scales; teeth biserial; charcoal with black scale outlines; caudal fin and posterior part of dorsal and anal fins often orange-yellow; a large black spot covering base of pectoral fin. Maldive Islands to Fiji; depth range 1.5-12 m. Grows to 11 cm.

REID'S DAMSEL

Pomacentrus reidi Fowler & Bean, 1928

Dorsal rays XIV,13-15; anal rays II,15 or 16; pectoral rays 17 or 18; lateral-line scales 16 or 17; gill rakers 19-21; body depth 1.8-2.0 in standard length; margins of preopercle and suborbital serrate; suborbital scaleless; teeth biserial; pale grey with blue edges on scales of body and blue spots and short lines on head. Indonesia and Philippines to northeastern Australia and Melanesia; generally found in deeper water (about 12-70 m). To 12 cm.

THREESPOT DAMSEL

Pomacentrus tripunctatus Cuvier, 1830

Dorsal rays XIII,14 or 15; anal rays II,14 or 15; pectoral rays 18; lateral-line scales 17 or 18; gill rakers 20-22; body depth 1.8-2.0 in standard length; margins of preopercle and suborbital serrate; suborbital scaleless; teeth biserial; brown with darker scale edges; distinguished by a large black spot on the upper caudal peduncle; juveniles with a blue-edged black spot in soft portion of dorsal fin. Sri Lanka to northeastern Australia and Melanesia; a shallow water species, usually found on coastal reefs. To 10 cm.

PRINCESS DAMSEL
Pomacentrus vaiuli Jordan & Seale, 1906

Dorsal rays XIII,15 or 16; anal rays II,15 or 16; pectoral rays 17 or 18; lateral-line scales 17 or 18; gill rakers 20 or 21; body depth 1.9-2.1 in standard length; margins of preopercle and suborbital serrate; suborbital scaleless; teeth biserial; bluish to purplish except orange on upper part of head, back, and dorsal fin; blue lines on orange part of head and longitudinal rows of blue spots on body; ocellus present at rear of dorsal fin; juveniles similar to *P. bankanensis*. Molucca Islands to Samoa, north to Japan; depth range 3-40 m. Reaches 10 cm.

WARD'S DAMSEL
Pomacentrus wardi Whitley, 1927

Dorsal rays XIII,15 or 16; anal rays II,15 or 16; pectoral rays 18 or 19; lateral-line scales 18 or 19; gill rakers 19-21; body depth 1.9-2.0 in standard length; margins of preopercle and suborbital serrate; suborbital scaleless; teeth biserial; overall dark brown; juveniles bright yellow with blue lines on the forehead and an ocellus on the dorsal fin. Great Barrier Reef and eastern Australian coast as far south as Sydney; common in lagoons and outer reef slopes in 1-20 m. Attains 11 cm.

RICHARDSON'S REEF-DAMSEL
Pomachromis richardsoni (Snyder, 1909)

Dorsal rays XIV,13 or 14; anal rays II,13; pectoral rays 18 or 19; lateral-line scales 18 or 19; gill rakers 24 or 25; body depth 2.5-2.7 in standard length; margins of preopercle and suborbital smooth or weakly serrate; teeth uniserial; yellowish grey dorsally, shading to bluish white ventrally, with blackish scale margins; a broad black band on upper edge of caudal peduncle, continuous with broad upper black margin of caudal fin and preceded by a small white spot (behind base of last dorsal ray); lower edge of caudal fin also broadly black; a black spot at base of upper pectoral rays. Mauritius to Fiji; usually in schools; often in areas exposed to ocean swells; depth range 5-20 m. To 8 cm.

SPINE-CHEEK ANEMONEFISH
Premnas biaculeatus (Bloch, 1790)

Dorsal rays IX or X,16-19; anal rays II,13-15; pectoral rays 16-18; lateral-line scales 36-59; gill rakers 17-21; body depth 1.9-2.3 in standard length; suborbital usually with two long spines; bright scarlet to dull red-brown; 2-3 narrow white bars across head and body; males usually much smaller and more brightly coloured than females; similar in habits to species of *Amphiprion*; associated with the anemone *Entacmaea quadricolor*. Malay Peninsula to northeastern Australia and Melanesia; depth range 1-16 m. Grows to 16 cm.

GULF DAMSEL
Pristotis jerdoni (Day, 1873)

Dorsal rays XIII,12 or 13; anal rays II,12-14; pectoral rays 17 or 18; lateral-line scales 19 or 20; gill rakers 26-28; body depth 2.5-2.8 in standard length; margins of preopercle and subopercle serrate; teeth uniserial; pale grey to bluish with a small black spot at base of upper pectoral rays. Persian Gulf and Red Sea to Australia, north to Ryukyu Islands; inhabits silty or sandy lagoons of inshore areas and coastal reefs; has depth range of 15-40 m. To 13 cm.

WHITEBAR GREGORY
Stegastes albifasciatus (Schlegel & Müller, 1839-44)

Dorsal rays XII,15 or 16; anal rays II,12 or 13; pectoral rays 19 or 20; lateral-line scales 18-20; gill rakers 19-26; body depth 1.8-2.1 in standard length; margins of preopercle and subopercle serrate; suborbital scaled; teeth uniserial; generally dark brown, but variable in markings (with or without white bar across posterior half of body), but always with black spot (with white anterior margin) at base of last dorsal rays. East Africa to Tuamotus and Line Islands; inhabits rubble and boulder bottoms exposed to wave action; depth range 0.2-2 m. Attains 12 cm. *S. eclipticus* (Jordan & Seale) is a synonym.

AUSTRALIAN GREGORY
Stegastes apicalis (De Vis, 1885)

Dorsal rays XIII,15 or 16; anal rays II,13; pectoral rays 19-21; lateral-line scales 19-21; gill rakers 18-24; body depth 1.8-2.2 in standard length; margins of preopercle and suborbital serrate; suborbital scaled; teeth uniserial; dark brown with an orange margin on dorsal fin and tip of upper lobe of caudal fin. Great Barrier Reef and eastern Australian coast to Sydney; inhabits inshore reefs and inner parts of the Great Barrier Reef; depth range 1.5-5 m. Reaches 14 cm.

PACIFIC GREGORY
Stegastes fasciolatus (Ogilby, 1889)

Dorsal rays XIII,15-17; anal rays II,12-14; pectoral rays 19-21; lateral-line scales 19-21; gill rakers 15-19; body depth 1.6-2.1 in standard length; margins of preopercle and suborbital serrate; suborbital scaled; teeth uniserial; dark brown with black scale outlines, a dark border below lower lip often present; juveniles with a yellow margin on anterior part of dorsal fin.. East Africa to Hawaiian Islands and Easter Island; inhabits rock and coral reefs exposed to moderate wave action; depth range 1-5 m. To 16 cm. *S. jenkinsi* (Jordan & Evermann) is a synonym.

CORAL SEA GREGORY
Stegastes gascoynei (Whitley, 1964)

Dorsal rays XIV,14-16; anal rays II,13 or 14; pectoral rays 19-21; lateral-line scales 19-21; gill rakers 17-22; body depth 1.9-2.0 in standard length; margins of preopercle and suborbital serrate; suborbital scaled; teeth uniserial; generally brown with darker scale margins forming series of vertical lines on side, mainly distinguished by orange-yellow hue on belly and orange-yellow anal fin. Coral Sea and northern Tasman Sea; generally rare in our area; depth range of 1-30 m. Attains 15 cm.

BLUNTSNOUT GREGORY
Stegastes lividus (Bloch & Schneider, 1801)

Dorsal rays XII,14-16; anal rays II,12-14; pectoral rays 18 or 19; lateral-line scales 17-19; gill rakers 23-29; body depth 1.9-2.0 in standard length; margins of preopercle and suborbital serrate; suborbital scaled; teeth uniserial; overall brown, frequently with an ill-defined blackish area (conspicuous ocellus in fish from other regions) below soft part of dorsal fin; similar to *S. nigricans*, but distance from eye to mouth is greater. East Africa and Red Sea to Society Islands and Line Islands; a very aggressive and pugnacious species that occurs in colonies; emits loud staccato sounds; often resides among dead staghorn corals; depth range 1-5 m. Reaches 17 cm.

DUSKY GREGORY
Stegastes nigricans (Lacepède, 1802)

Dorsal rays XII,14-17; anal rays II,12-14; pectoral rays 18-20; lateral-line scales 18-20; gill rakers 21-25; body depth 1.9-2.0 in standard length; margins of preopercle and suborbital serrate; suborbital scaled; teeth uniserial; overall brown, usually with black spot at base of last dorsal rays; lavendar markings often present on head and anterior region of anal fin; similar to *S. lividus*, but distance from eye to mouth much less. East Africa and Red Sea to Tuamotus, Marquesas, and Line Islands; lagoons and inshore reefs, often among dead staghorn corals; an aggressive species which will nip divers; depth range 1-12 m. Attains 15 cm.

HAWKFISHES
FAMILY CIRRHITIDAE

The Cirrhitidae is a small family of 10 genera and 35 species; three species occur in the Atlantic and the rest in the tropical Pacific and Indian Oceans. They may be distinguished by having 14 pectoral rays, the lower five to seven of which are unbranched and usually enlarged; all have a dorsal fin of X spines and 11-17 soft rays which is notched between spinous and soft portions; there are one to several cirri projecting from the membrane near the tip of the dorsal spines, and a fringe of cirri on the hind edge of the anterior nostril; anal rays III,6-7. With the exception of the presence or absence of palatine teeth, the dentition of cirrihitids is much the same from species to species; there are canine teeth in a single row in both jaws which are usually longest anteriorly in the upper jaw; the longest canines in the lower jaw are generally two to four on midside of jaw; a band of villiform teeth medial to the canines in both jaws, though restricted to the front of the lower jaw; small teeth present on vomer. No gas bladder. Hawkfishes are found on coral reefs or rocky substrata, typically at rest on the bottom; their thickened lower pectoral rays serve to wedge themselves in place when needed. All are carnivorous; with the exception of *Cyprinocirrhites polyactis* which is able to move up into the water column to feed on zooplankton, they are lie-and-wait predators, feeding mainly on unwary small fishes and crustaceans.

TWINSPOT HAWKFISH
Amblycirrhitus bimacula Jenkins, 1903

Dorsal rays X,12; anal rays III,6; lower 5 pectoral rays unbranched, the longest ray reaching a vertical through base of second anal spine; lateral-line scales 40-42; three rows of scales above lateral line; four or five rows of large scales on cheek; palatine teeth present; body depth 2.8-3.0 in standard length; a tuft of cirri near tip of each dorsal spine; body with ten brownish red bars or rows of large spots; a large black spot on opercle and a second at rear base of dorsal fin. Indo-Pacific. The largest examined, 8.5 cm.

THREADFIN HAWKFISH
Cirrhitichthys aprinus (Cuvier, 1829)

Dorsal rays X,12, the first soft ray filamentous; anal rays III,6; lower 6 pectoral rays unbranched; lateral-line scales 41-43; three rows of scales above lateral line, and four rows on cheek (true of other species of *Cirrhitichthys*); palatine teeth present (also generic); body depth 2.4-2.7 in standard length; bony interorbital space 1.7 in eye diameter of adults; a tuft of cirri near tip of each dorsal spine; body with large reddish brown spots, sometimes joined to form irregular bars; a pale-edged black spot on opercle; five narrow diagonal reddish brown bars on head below eye. Western Pacific. Reaches 12.5 cm.

DWARF HAWKFISH
Cirrhitichthys falco Randall, 1963

Dorsal rays X,12; anal rays III,6; lower 6 pectoral rays unbranched; lateral-line scales 42-45; body depth 2.9-3.4 in standard length; bony interorbital space 2.2 in orbit diameter; maxilla not reaching a vertrical at front edge of eye; fourth dorsal spine longest, 1.7-2.1 in head; a tuft of cirri near tip of each dorsal spine; whitish with small dark reddish brown spots, most grouped to form five bars on body which are broader dorsally, the darkest centred beneath front of dorsal fin and extending onto posterior part of head; two narrow reddish brown bars on lower head passing ventrally from eye. Western Pacific, east to Mariana Islands, Caroline Islands, and Samoa, and west to Maldives. Attains 7 cm.

PIXY HAWKFISH
Cirrhitichthys oxycephalus (Bleeker, 1855)

Dorsal rays X,12, the first soft ray prolonged; anal rays III,6; lower 6 pectoral rays unbranched; lateral-line scales 41-45; body depth 2.8-3.0 in standard length; bony interorbital space of adults 2.0 in eye; maxilla reaching or extending posterior to a vertical at front edge of eye; fifth dorsal spine longest, 1.8-2.0 in head; a tuft of cirri near tip of each dorsal spine; whitish with three rows of large subquadrate red-edged dark brown spots arranged in five vertical series (larger spots dorsally); lesser red spots between and below these series; four vertical rows of small dark spots on head. Indo-Pacific and tropical eastern Pacific. Reaches 8.5 cm.

STOCKY HAWKFISH
Cirrhitus pinnulatus (Schneider, 1801)

Dorsal rays X,11; anal rays III,6; lower 7 pectoral rays unbranched; lateral-line scales 39-42; four rows of scales above lateral line (in middle of body); small scales on cheek; palatine teeth present; body robust, the depth 2.6-2.9 in standard length; pectoral fins short, not reaching tips of pelvic fins; a tuft of cirri from near tip of each dorsal spine; body brown to olivaceous, shading to white ventrally, with scattered large white blotches and numerous small red or reddish brown spots; head with brownish orange spots and irregular short lines; median fins with small reddish spots. Indo-Pacific; lives in surge zone on rocky shores or reef fronts; feeds mainly on crabs but also on shrimps and other crustaceans, small fishes, sea urchins, and brittle stars. Attains 28 cm.

SWALLOWTAIL HAWKFISH
Cyprinocirrhites polyactis (Bleeker, 1875)

Dorsal rays X,16-17 (usually 16); anal rays III,6-7 (usually 6); lower 6 pectoral rays unbranched; lateral-line scales 45-49; three rows of scales above lateral line; four rows of large scales on cheek; palatine teeth present; body depth 2.6-2.8 in standard length; a tuft of cirri near tip of each dorsal spine; caudal fin lunate; brownish orange, sometimes faintly blotched with brown, the orange tending to be concentrated along longitudinal scale rows, thus giving a slight linear pattern. Indo-Pacific; known from the depth range of 10 to 132 m; usually found in more than 20 m; feeds on crustacean larvae, copepods, and other animals of the plankton. To 14 cm.

FLAME HAWKFISH
Neocirrhites armatus Castelnau, 1873

Dorsal rays X,13; anal rays III,6-7 (usually 7); lower 6 pectoral rays unbranched; lateral-line scales 42-45; four rows of large scales above lateral line (in middle of body); small scales on cheek in more than 12 irregular rows; palatine teeth absent; body depth 2.0-2.4 in standard length; a tuft of cirri from membrane near tip of each dorsal spine; caudal fin slightly rounded; bright red with a dark brown band along back and base of dorsal fin and a dark brown blotch behind and adjacent to eye. Islands of Oceania and western Pacific; usually seen hiding among branches of live coral. Reaches 9 cm.

LONGNOSE HAWKFISH
Oxycirrhites typus Bleeker, 1857

Dorsal rays X,13; anal rays III,7; lower 5 or 6 pectoral rays unbranched; lateral-line scales 51-53; four rows of large scales above lateral line (in middle of body); palatine teeth absent; body depth 4.4-4.6 in standard length; snout extremely long, its length about 2.0 in head; two to four cirri from membrane near tip of each dorsal spine; whitish with horizontal and near-vertical red bands forming a cross-hatch pattern. Indo-Pacific and tropical eastern Pacific; generally seen perched on black coral or gorgonians, usually at depths greater than 30 m; feeds mainly on small crustaceans, both benthic and planktonic. Reaches 13 cm.

ARC-EYE HAWKFISH
Paracirrhites arcatus (Cuvier, 1829)

Dorsal rays X,11; anal rays III,6; upper 2 and lower 6 or 7 (usually 7) pectoral rays unbranched; lateral-line scales 45-50; five rows of large scales above lateral line (in middle of body), and five or six rows of large scales on cheek with small basal scales (true of other *Paracirrhites*); no scales on snout anterior to nostrils; palatine teeth absent (characteristic of genus); body depth 2.4-2.6 in standard length; a single cirrus from membrane at tip of each dorsal spine (also generic); two colour forms, one light greyish to orangish brown, the centres of scales paler than edges resulting in a faint lengthwise banding, with a broad pale pink to white stripe over lateral line on posterior two-thirds of body, the other dark brown without the white stripe; both phases with a tricoloured "U"-shaped mark of orange, black and blue extending diagonally upward from posterior part of eye and three orange bands on a light blue zone on interopercle. Indo-Pacific; feeds mainly on shrimps, small fishes, crabs, and other crustaceans. To 14 cm.

BLACKSIDE HAWKFISH
Paracirrhites forsteri (Schneider, 1801)

Dorsal rays X,11; anal rays III,6; uppermost and lower 7 pectoral rays unbranched; lateral-line scales 45-49; scales on snout anterior to nostrils; body depth 2.6-2.9 in standard length; back yellowish to orangish brown in a linear pattern following scale rows, usually with a broad black band on upper side on posterior half of body, extending into base of caudal fin (sometimes band appears as a series of joined black spots); a broad pale yellowish to white stripe often present laterally on body and frequently one along base of dorsal fin; head (and often anterior body) grey with small dark red spots; a second colour phase is dark brown, shading to orange on caudal peduncle and fin, without black band but with anterior dark red spots. Indo-Pacific; feeds mainly on fishes, occasionally on shrimps. Largest recorded, 22.5 cm. *P. typee* Randall is a synonym.

HALFSPOTTED HAWKFISH
Paracirrhites hemistictus (Günther, 1874)

Dorsal rays X,11; anal rays III,6; uppermost and lower 7 pectoral rays unbranched; lateral-line scales 48-51; snout almost entirely scaled; body elongate for the genus, the depth 2.8-3.2 in standard length; two colour phases, not related to sex, the first greenish on back, densely spotted with black, pale yellow below with series of dark yellow spots following scale rows; an irregular white stripe slightly below midside of body with a few black spots below and occasionally within stripe; head greenish to pinkish grey; fins yellowish; second phase grey with numerous close-set dark brown spots on body and a white or pale pink spot slightly smaller than eye on upper side in middle of body. Known from islands of Oceania, Great Barrier Reef, and Christmas and Cocos-Keeling Islands in the eastern Indian Ocean; appears to be absent from large islands. Largest reported, 29 cm. *P. polystictus* (Günther) is a synonym based on the second colour phase.

Paracirrhites hemistictus   Pale phase ▲ Dark phase ▼

MULLETS
FAMILY MUGILIDAE

Mullets are silvery grey fishes with a small mouth, moderately elongate body, two widely spaced dorsal fins, and emarginate or weakly forked caudal fin. In most species the teeth are either very small or absent, also the lateral line is lacking. Mullets occur in all tropical and temperate seas, usually near shore, frequently in brackish estuaries and fresh water. A number of species are found along the Queensland coast, but only *Crenimugil crenilabis* is common in clear oceanic waters of offshore reefs. Mullets commonly form schools that may contain up to several hundred fish. They feed mainly on detritus and algae, but may also consume insects, fish eggs, and plankton. They are commercially important in many areas. In southeastern Asia mullets are frequently cultivated in ponds.

WARTY-LIPPED MULLET
Crenimugil crenilabis (Forsskål, 1775)

Dorsal rays IV-I,8; anal rays III,9; pectoral rays 16-17; lips thick with 1-10 rows of papillae (they appear at length of about 10 cm and increase with growth); lateral scale series 34-41; transverse scale rows 13-14; predorsal scales about 20; adipose eyelid absent; very elongate scale (axillary scale) present above pectoral fin base; silvery grey.

East Africa to Line and Tuamotu islands; in sandy lagoons and on shallow seaward reef flats; spawns in large aggregations after dark. To 40 cm.

DIAMOND-SCALE MULLET
Liza vaigiensis (Quoy & Gaimard, 1824)

Dorsal rays IV-I,8; anal rays III,8; pectoral rays 16; lateral scale series 25-29; transverse scale rows 10-12; predorsal scales 15-16; adipose eyelid rudimentary, not covering any part of eye; axillary scale absent from pectoral fin; caudal fin truncate; overall silvery grey with blackish scale outlines; juveniles have black pectoral fins. East Africa and Red Sea to Tuamotus; forms large schools, frequently in mangrove areas. To 55 cm.

Crenimugil crenilabis ▲ *Liza vaigiensis* ▼

BARRACUDAS
FAMILY SPHYRAENIDAE

Barracudas (also known as Sea-pikes in Australia) are very elongate fishes with a cylindrical body anteriorly, pointed snout and protruding lower jaw. The large mouth is equipped with an awesome array of long sharp-edged teeth of unequal size. Other features include a well-developed, straight lateral line, two widely separated dorsal fins, small pectoral, pelvic, and anal fins, and a forked caudal fin. The overall coloration is silvery, often with darker bars, saddles, or chevron markings. The family contains a single genus, *Sphyraena*, represented by about 20 species. Several are commonly seen in the vicinity of reefs in our area. They frequently occur in small to large schools, often on the edge of outer reef dropoffs. However, *Sphyraena barracuda*, the largest species, is often encountered alone. It is frequently attracted to divers and may approach at close range. Barracudas feed primarily on fishes. They are a favourite target of anglers, and many are caught by trolling artificial lures. The flesh is excellent eating, but large specimens should be avoided because of the risk of ciguatera poisoning (see Lutjanidae introduction).

GREAT BARRACUDA
Sphyraena barracuda (Walbaum, 1792)

Dorsal rays V-I,9; anal rays II,7 or 8; lateral-line scales 69-84; a single gill raker; silvery with faint dark oblique bars on upper side and usually with scattered blackish blotches on lower side (especially posteriorly); second dorsal, anal, and caudal fins blackish, the pointed caudal lobe tips white. East Africa and Red Sea to Hawaiian Islands and Tuamotu Archipelago; juveniles found inshore, sometimes in mangrove estuaries, adults in open sea and close to reefs. Attacks on humans have nearly all taken place in murky water or were the result of provocation, as by spearing. To 170 cm and 40 kg.

YELLOWTAIL BARRACUDA
Sphyraena flavicauda Rüppell, 1838

Dorsal rays V-I,9; anal rays II,9; pectoral rays 13; lateral-line scales about 80-90; a pair of gill rakers on first arch; silvery with pair of brown stripes on side, the first from tip of snout through eye and base of pectoral fin to caudal peduncle, a second fainter stripe from top of eye and continuing along lateral line to upper caudal peduncle; caudal fin and caudal peduncle yellow. Indo-Pacific; usually occurs in schools. Maximum size, 37 cm.

BIGEYE BARRACUDA
Sphyraena forsteri Cuvier, 1829

Dorsal rays V-I,9; anal rays II,9; lateral-line scales 105-125; gill rakers absent; eye large; greenish grey dorsally, silvery on sides, with a blackish blotch behind base of pectoral fin; tip of second dorsal and anal fins white; fins slightly dusky. East Africa to Society Islands; forms diurnal schools near coral bommies and on outer reef slopes; feeds at night. To 65 cm.

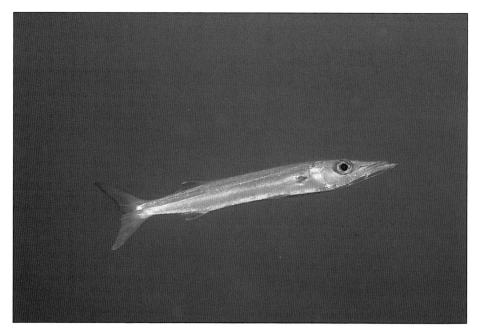

HELLER'S BARRACUDA
Sphyraena helleri Jenkins, 1901

Dorsal rays V-I,9; anal rays II,8; lateral-line scales 120-135; a single gill raker; silvery with two brassy stripes on side of body. Western Pacific, including Coral Sea to Hawaiian Islands. Forms large schools by day and feeds at night. Grows to 80 cm.

PICKHANDLE BARRACUDA
Sphyraena jello Cuvier, 1829

Dorsal rays V-I,9; anal rays II,8; lateral-line scales 123-133; gill rakers absent; silvery on sides and ventrally with about 20 wavy dark bars that extend a short distance below lateral line; caudal fin yellowish. East Africa and Red Sea to western Pacific. Attains 150 cm.

CHEVRON BARRACUDA
Sphyraena putnamiae Jordan & Seale, 1905

Dorsal rays V-I,9; anal rays II,8; lateral-line scales 129-131; gill rakers absent; lower jaw with fleshy pointed tip; silvery on sides and ventrally with about 20 chevron-shaped bars on upper two-thirds of body; caudal fin dusky with black margin. East Africa and Red Sea to western Pacific. To 90 cm.

THREADFINS
FAMILY POLYNEMIDAE

These fishes have a bluntly rounded snout and ventral mouth. There are two separate dorsal fins, and the caudal fin is deeply forked. The common name is derived from their peculiar pectoral rays. The pectoral fin is divided into an upper "normal" section with the rays attached to the fin membrane and a detatched lower section with 3-7 free, thread-like rays. The number of free pectoral rays is diagnostic for separating many of the species. Threadfins are usually encountered near the coast, often in river mouths or brackish mangrove estuaries. *Polydactylus sexfilis* occurs along sandy shores, sometimes in small schools. The diet of threadfins consists of shrimps, crabs, polychaete worms, and other benthic invertebrates.

SIX-FINGERED THREADFIN
Polydactylus sexfilis (Valenciennes, 1831)

Dorsal rays VIII-I,13; anal rays III,11; pectoral rays 15 + 6 (free rays); distinguished by the six free thread-like rays below the pectoral fin; silvery with bronze lines following scale rows; pectoral fins blackish; very small juveniles (40 mm) with three broad dark bars and black areas on all fins except pectorals. India to Hawaiian Islands and Tuamotu Archipelago. Attains 25 cm.

WRASSES
FAMILY LABRIDAE

The wrasse family is second in the number of species in the Great Barrier Reef area only to the gobies (Gobiidae). The fishes of this family vary enormously in size from the tiny *Pseudocheilinops ataenia* (not yet known from the Barrier Reef but may be expected from the northern part), a scant 5 cm long, to the giant Humphead Maori Wrasse (*Cheilinus undulatus*). They also vary greatly in form from slender to deep-bodied, short-snouted to long, etc. They usually have a terminal mouth; the maxilla is not exposed on the cheek; the teeth at the front of the jaws are generally well-developed canines that often protrude; teeth are absent from the roof of the mouth (except one or more on vomer of some *Bodianus*), but there usually are strong nodular to molariform teeth on the pharyngeal bones in the gill region; the lips are often thick. The scales are cycloid (smooth-edged), and the head is never fully scaled. There is a single continuous dorsal fin of VIII to XIV spines without a notch between spinous and soft portions (though the soft part may be slightly higher); anal spines III (reduced to II in a few species). Most wrasses are brightly and complexly coloured.

Juveniles are frequently of different colour than adults, and adult males and females are often strikingly different. Sex reversal has been demonstrated for many labrids; these fishes commence their adult life as females and are able to alter their sex to male, at which time they take on a different, often gaudier, colour pattern. For some species there are both mature males and females in the initial phase; these tend to spawn in aggregations, whereas terminal males reproduce with single females. Thus, within a single species, there may be both group spawning and pair spawning. All wrasses are carnivorous, but their food habits vary greatly. Some such as the species of *Cirrhilabrus* and certain of the *Thalassoma* feed princially on zooplankton, rising a meter or more above the bottom for this (often in aggregations). Wrasses of the genera *Cirrhilabrus*, *Paracheilinus*, *Pseudocheilinus*, *Pseudocheilinops*, and *Pteragogus* have a curious corneal double pupil that may represent a specialization to aid in the perception of small prey. The species of *Labroides* and the young of some fishes of other labrid genera such as *Labropsis* and *Bodianus* feed mainly on the crustacean ectoparasites of other fishes (and incidentally on the mucus of the host fishes). Adults of *Labropsis*, *Labrichthys*, and *Diproctacanthus* feed on coral polyps. A few wrasses such as *Cheilinus unifasciatus* and the species of *Hologymnosus* prey heavily on small fishes. Those of *Anampses* and *Stethojulis* forcefully strike the substratum with their mouths, sucking in very small animals, including crustaceans, mollusks, foraminifera, and worms, along with sand and detritus; the two *Hemigymnus* ingest mouthfuls of sand, sort out the tiny animals within, and eject the inorganic material. Most labrids feed on a variety of larger benthic invertebrate animals, especially hard-shelled ones such as molluscs, sea urchins, and crabs, which they crush with their pharyngeal teeth. Labrids are diurnal; they are among the first fishes to retire to an inactive state on the bottom with the approach of darkness and among the last to resume activity the following morning. Most of the smaller species bury themselves in sand for the night. Wrasses normally swim with their pectoral fins, bringing their caudal fin into action only when swift movement is required.

Photograph: Robert M. Pyle

Pseudocheilinus sp. (undescribed), about 50 mm, Osprey Reef, Coral Sea, 30 m

BLUESPOTTED WRASSE
Anampses caeruleopunctatus Rüppell, 1829

Dorsal rays IX,12; anal rays III,12; lateral-line scales 27 (not including one beyond base of caudal fin); head scaleless (true of other *Anampses*); gill rakers 18-21; body depth 2.3-3.0 in standard length; dentition as in the genus: a single pair of forward-projecting teeth in jaws, the uppers somewhat flattened with pointed upcurved tips, the lowers nearly conical and curved downward; no remaining teeth in jaws or only a few minute ones; caudal fin truncate to slightly rounded; pelvic fins 2.1-2.5 in head length; females olive to brown dorsally, shading to orangish ventrally, with small dark-edged blue spots on body and fins and dark-edged narrow blue bands on head (many radiating from eye); males olive with a dark-edged vertical blue line on scales of side of body; head with narrow dark-edged blue lines and a broad blue band across front of interorbital space; a broad light green bar often on body below sixth dorsal spine. Indo-Pacific; an inshore species, typically where exposed to surge, but may be seen as deep as 20 m. Largest, 42 cm. *A. diadematus* Rüppell is a synonym based on the male phase.

Anampses caeruleopunctatus   Initial phase ▲ Terminal phase ▼

Anampses femininus   Initial phase ▲ Terminal phase ▼

FEMININE WRASSE
Anampses femininus Randall, 1972

Dorsal rays IX,12; anal rays III,l2; lateral-line scales 26; gill rakers 15-17; body depth 3.0-3.4 in standard length; caudal fin rounded; pelvic fins 2.1-2.5 in head; females bright orange with narrow black-edged blue stripes on head and body, shading to blue on caudal peduncle and fin; males dusky yellow to blackish on body with a vertical blue line on each scale; head dusky orange, blue ventrally, with four diagonal blue bands, two of which extend onto thorax; a small black spot posteriorly on opercle. Southern subtropical Pacific from Easter Island to New Caledonia and the southern Great Barrier Reef. Attains 24 cm. Named *femininus* because the female is more beautiful than the male (unusual in the Animal Kingdom).

Anampses geographicus   Initial phase ▲ Terminal phase ▼

GEOGRAPHIC WRASSE

Anampses geographicus Valenciennes, 1840

Dorsal rays IX,12; anal rays III,12; lateral-line scales 48-50; gill rakers 17-20; body depth 2.7-3.1 in standard length; caudal fin rounded in juveniles, becoming truncate to slightly emarginate in females and more emarginate in males; pelvic fins 2.15 (males)-2.7 (juveniles) in head; females brown, shading to yellowish posteriorly on body and caudal fin; a large yellow-edged black spot at rear of dorsal and anal fins; males dark reddish brown with a blue line on each scale; head and thorax with very irregular dark-edged blue lines; caudal fin reddish brown with blue markings and a blue posterior margin. Western Australia and western Pacific east to the Caroline Islands and Fiji. Reaches 24 cm. *A. pterophthalmus* Bleeker is a synonym based on the female form.

SPOTTED WRASSE

Anampses meleagrides Valenciennes, 1840

Dorsal rays IX,12; anal rays III,12; lateral-line scales 26; gill rakers 18-20; body depth 3.1-3.4 in standard length; caudal fin truncate to emarginate; pelvic fins 1.5-2.0 in head; females dark brown with a small round white spot on each scale of body; head and dorsal and anal fins dark brown with small white spots; caudal fin abruptly bright yellow; males dark reddish brown with a blue line on scales of side of body, blue spots on caudal peduncle, and rows of blue dashes on abdomen; head and thorax with irregular blue lines; caudal fin orange with dark-edged blue spots and a white posterior crescent preceded by a narrow blue band. Samoa and Caroline Islands to East Africa and the Red Sea. Reaches 21 cm. *A. amboinensis* Bleeker is a synonym based on the male form.

NEW GUINEA WRASSE
Anampses neoguinaicus Bleeker, 1878

Dorsal rays IX,12; anal rays III,12; lateral-line scales 26; gill rakers 15-18; body depth 2.9-3.3 in standard length; caudal fin rounded; pelvic fins 1.5-2.25 in head; females black dorsally, becoming yellowish white below a demarcation from front of snout to rear base of dorsal fin, with small blue spots; a blue-edged black spot at end of opercle; a large black spot edged in yellow and blue posteriorly in dorsal and anal fins; males similarly bicoloured but with a vertical blue line on scales of side of body, irregular blue lines in dark upper part of head; a salmon pink instead of black spot at end of opercle, salmon pink ventrally on head and abdomen, a salmon pink submarginal band in caudal fin, and orange-red bands in anal fin. Western Pacific, east to Fiji. Maximum length about 17 cm. Photograph shows the terminal phase.

YELLOWBREASTED WRASSE
Anampses twistii Bleeker, 1856

Dorsal rays IX,12, anal rays III,l2; lateral-line scales 26; gill rakers 16-19; body depth 3.0-3.3 in standard length; caudal fin rounded; pelvic fins 1.8-2.3 in head; body, upper head, and dorsal and anal fins dark brown with black-edged blue dots; thorax and lower head bright yellow, this colour sometimes extending onto abdomen; caudal fin light red with pale blue spots and a whitish posterior margin; a large blue-edged black spot at rear of dorsal and anal fins. Indo-Pacific. Attains 18 cm.

LYRETAIL HOGFISH
Bodianus anthioides (Bennett, 1830)

Dorsal rays XII,9-10 (usually 10); anal rays III,ll-l2 (usually 12); pectoral rays 15-17; lateral-line a smooth curve, the pored scales 29-30; a scaly sheath at base of dorsal and anal fins; one or more teeth present on vomer; body depth 2.6-3.1 in standard length; snout short, 3.l-3.65 in head, the dorsal profile steep; posterior edge of preopercle serrate (usually true of other *Bodianus*); caudal fin deeply emarginate (large and lunate in juveniles); orange-brown on head and anterior third of body, white with scattered irregular dark brown spots posteriorly, the curved demarcation with an irregular dark brown band dorsally, continuing into dorsal fin; a black spot at front of dorsal fin; a dark brown band on upper and lower edges of caudal fin continuing anteriorly onto caudal peduncle. Indo-Pacific. To 21 cm.

AXILSPOT HOGFISH
Bodianus axillaris (Bennett, 183l)

Dorsal rays XII,9-10 (usually 10); anal rays III,ll-12 (usually 12); pectoral rays l5-17; lateral-line scales 30-31; a sheath of scales at base of dorsal and anal fins; body depth 2.8-3.1 in standard length; snout pointed, 2.9-3.2 in head; caudal fin varying from slightly rounded to slightly double emarginate; adults dark reddish brown, shad- ing to white posterior to a diagonal from middle of abdomen to soft portion of dorsal fin; a large black spot at base of pectoral fin and in outer anterior part of soft portion of dorsal and anal fins; a black spot at front of dorsal fin; juveniles black with two rows of large white spots, one dorsal and one ventral. Samoa and Marshall Islands to East Africa and the Red Sea; young usually found in caves; they (and occasionally adults) pick at bodies of other fishes. To 20 cm.

Bodianus axillaris Adult ▼ Juv. ▲

TWOSPOT HOGFISH
Bodianus bimaculatus Allen, 1973

Dorsal rays XII,9-10; anal rays III,12; pectoral rays 14-16; lateral-line scales 30-32; a single row of small scales at base of dorsal and anal fins; body depth 3.6-4.0 in standard length; snout 3.7-4.2 in head; caudal fin rounded; orange with six narrow red stripes, shading to yellow on lower third of head and body; a large yellow-edged black spot on opercle and a black spot about size of pupil on caudal-fin base slightly above end of lateral line. Western Pacific to Mauritius and Maldives; generally found at depths greater than 40 m. To about 10 cm.

DIANA'S HOGFISH
Bodianus diana (Lacepède, 1801)

Dorsal rays XII,9-10 (usually 10); anal rays III,10-12; pectoral rays 15-17; lateral-line scales 30-31; a broad sheath of scales basally on dorsal and anal fins; body depth 3.0-3.2 in standard length; snout pointed, 2.6-2.9 in head; caudal fin slightly rounded in juveniles to truncate or slightly double emarginate in adults; head reddish to purplish brown, shading to dull yellow on body, the scales rimmed with brown; scales dor-soposteriorly on body with a black spot; four small pale yellow spots dorsally on back; fins orange-red with a small black spot at base of caudal fin and rear base of anal fin, and a large black or red spot anteriorly on soft portion of anal fin and on pelvic fins; juveniles reddish brown with rows of white blotches and small white spots and large black spots in fins. Samoa and Marshall Islands to East Africa and Red Sea. Reaches 25 cm. *Lepidapolois aldabrensis* Smith is a synonym based on juvenile stage.

Bodianus diana Adult ▼ Juv. ▲

BLACKFIN HOGFISH
Bodianus loxozonus (Snyder, 1908)

Dorsal rays XII,10-11; anal rays III,11-12; pectoral rays 17; lateral-line scales 28-36; a broad sheath of scales at base of dorsal and anal fins; body depth 2.6-3.0 in standard length; snout length 2.8-3.2 in head; caudal fin truncate with prolonged lobes at corners (the upper longer than lower); a large black spot basally in soft portion of dorsal fin continuing as a broad diagonal black band to lower base of caudal fin, often with a white spot on back anterior and posterior to band; dorsal part of body anterior to band orange-red with rows of pale blue dashes, ventral part with narrow orange and broad white stripes (or close-set series of white spots); head orange with irregular horizontal blue lines; a black spot at front of dorsal fin, and a broad black border on anal fin (except posteriorly); pelvic fins black. French Polynesia to western Pacific. To 40 cm. Often misidentified as *B. hirsutus* (Lacepède).

SPLITLEVEL HOGFISH
Bodianus mesothorax (Bloch & Schneider, 1801)

Dorsal rays XII,9-11 (usually 10); anal rays III,11-12; pectoral rays 16; lateral-line scales 31-32; a broad sheath of scales at base of dorsal and anal fins; body depth 2.8-3.3 in standard length; snout pointed, 3.1-3.3 in head; caudal fin truncate to slightly rounded; a broad diagonal black band from spinous portion of dorsal fin to pectoral axil; body posterior to band whitish with narrow orange-yellow stripes following scale rows; head and body anterior to band purplish brown ventrally to a black streak across lower cheek; fins largely yellow except for a large black spot at pectoral base and black anterior spinous part of dorsal fin; juveniles black with two series of bright yellow spots, one dorsal and one ventral. Western Pacific east to Fiji. Attains 20 cm.

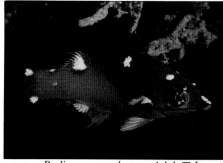

Bodianus mesothorax   Adult ▼ Juv. ▲

GOLDSPOT HOGFISH
Bodianus perditio (Quoy & Gaimard, 1834)

Dorsal rays XII,10; anal rays III,12; pectoral rays 17; lateral-line scales 30-31; a broad scaly sheath at base of dorsal and anal fins; body depth 2.7-2.9 in standard length; snout 2.7-3.0 in head; caudal fin truncate with prolonged lobes at corners; adults orange-red with small yellow spots on head and anterior body and a large elliptical black spot below posterior part of dorsal fin and extending into fin, this spot preceded by a large pale yellow spot or bar; anterior spinous portion of dorsal fin black; subadults yellow and juveniles grey with the large black and pale yellow spots on the back extending farther ventrally. Antiequatorial; islands of southern Oceania to southern Africa; Taiwan to southern Japan; may be seen in as little as 10 m, but usually occurs much deeper. Reported to 80 cm.

TWOSPOT MAORI WRASSE
Cheilinus bimaculatus Valenciennes, 1840

Dorsal rays IX,10; anal rays III,8; lateral line interrupted, the pored scales in upper anterior series 15-16 and those in midlateral series on caudal peduncle 6-7 (14-16 + 6-9 in other *Cheilinus*); head scaled except snout, chin, and anterior interorbital space (applies to other species of the genus); scaly sheath at base of dorsal and anal fins well-developed; body depth 2.6-3.1 in standard length; dorsal profile of head slightly convex; preopercular margin smooth (true of other *Cheilinus*); caudal fin rounded in females, rhomboid with a prolonged upper lobe in males; reddish brown (males may have a greenish cast), finely blotched and flecked with whitish; a dark brown blotch on side above pectoral fin, sometimes followed by three less distinct blotches; a small dark green spot behind eye and one on first dorsal fin membrane; orange lines radiating from eye. Indo-Pacific; more common on rubble or plant-dominated bottoms than well-developed coral reefs; usually found at depths greater than 15 m; recorded to 100 m. Maximum length about 15 cm

FLORAL MAORI WRASSE
Cheilinus chlorourus (Bloch, 1791)

Dorsal rays X,9 (rarely XI,8); anal rays III,8; scaly sheath at base of dorsal and anal fins well-developed; body depth 2.4-2.8 in standard length; dorsal profile of head nearly straight to nape, often with a slight concavity above eye; snout 3.0-3.6 in head; caudal fin of females rounded, that of adult males with upper and lower rays prolonged as filaments (upper usually longer); orangish to greenish brown, the head with orange-red dots and short lines, the body with pink and whitish dots and obscure small dark blotches (four midlaterally on body the most evident, especially on small fish); median and pelvic fins flecked with whitish; a blackish spot basally on first one or two membranes of dorsal fin. Indo-Pacific. To 36 cm.

CHEEKLINED MAORI WRASSE
Cheilinus digrammus (Lacepède, 1801)

Dorsal rays IX,10; anal rays III,8; scaly sheath at base of dorsal and anal fins low; body moderately elongate, the depth 2.9-3.2 in standard length; snout 2.4-2.5 in head; dorsal profile of head to nape nearly straight; lower jaw projecting; membranes of spinous portion of dorsal fin distinctly incised; caudal fin slightly rounded to truncate, the upper and lower rays slightly prolonged on large fish; pelvic fins short, not reaching anus; very changeable in coloration, the most common phase olivaceous to grey-brown on body with an indistinct orange-red bar or spot on each scale; head greyish green with irregular orange lines on upper part parallel to dorsal profile and a series of about eight diagonal maroon lines on lower cheek nearly perpendicular to upper linear series; large centroposterior part of caudal fin mainly green; may exhibit a lateral dark stripe on body. Samoa and Marshall Islands to East Africa and the Red Sea; has been observed to swim with a group of goatfish, change its color to resemble these fish, and dart out from the group to capture small fish. Rarely exceeds 30 cm. Current study of *Cheilinus* suggests that this species, *bimaculatus*, and *unifasciatus* will be shifted to the genus *Oxycheilinus*.

Cheilinus digrammus   Streaked phase ▲ Red phase ▼

REDBREASTED MAORI WRASSE
Cheilinus fasciatus (Bloch, 1791)

Dorsal rays IX,10; anal rays III,8; a well-developed scaly sheath at base of dorsal and anal fins; body depth 2.35-2.6 in standard length; dorsal profile of head convex, particularly that of large males; snout 2.2-2.6 in head; dorsal and anal fins angular posteriorly; caudal fin slightly rounded in young, truncate with elongate pointed lobes in large males; pelvic fins short, not reaching anus; body and scaled basal part of dorsal and anal fins reddish brown with six to seven narrow whitish bars, the scales with a vertical blackish streak; a light yellow-orange area in pectoral region; large males blackish with whitish bars on body and a large red-orange zone on posterior head and anterior body, including thorax. Micronesia and Samoa to East Africa and Red Sea. Maximum length, 36 cm.

SNOOTY MAORI WRASSE
Cheilinus oxycephalus Bleeker, 1853

Dorsal rays IX,10; anal rays III,8; scaly sheath at base of dorsal and anal fins well-developed; body depth 2.5-3.0 in standard length; dorsal profile of head from upper lip to above eye slightly concave, thus giving the snout an upturned appearance; snout 3.1-3.7 in head; caudal fin rounded; pelvic fins usually reaching anus; olivaceous brown to brownish red with scattered small whitish blotches and spots; three or four dark spots nearly as large as pupil often evident mid-laterally on body, the last on caudal-fin base (may be absent on large adults); a black and red spot on first two membranes of dorsal fin; often two short dark lines diverging from rear part of eye; a pair of dark spots anteriorly on each side of upper lip. Indo-Pacific; a shy secretive coral-reef species. Reaches 17 cm.

TRIPLETAIL MAORI WRASSE
Cheilinus trilobatus Lacepède, 1801

Dorsal rays IX,10 anal rays III,8; a well-developed scaly sheath basally on dorsal and anal fins; body moderately deep, the depth 2.3-2.6 in standard length; dorsal profile of head to nape straight; snout 2.7-3.2 in head; rear of dorsal and anal fins of adults angular; caudal fin rounded, the upper and lower rays prolonged as pointed lobes in large males; pelvic fins reaching anus in small fish, extending well beyond in large adults; body olivaceous to brown with a vertical orange-red line and a pale blue-green line on each scale; head and thorax with orange-red dots and irregular lines; small fish with three small dark spots in a row midlaterally on posterior part of body. Indo-Pacific; feeds mainly on small fishes, crustaceans, and mollusks. Attains at least 40 cm.

Cheilinus trilobatus   Initial phase ▼ Terminal phase ▲

303

HUMPHEAD MAORI WRASSE
Cheilinus undulatus Rüppell, 1835

Dorsal rays IX,10, anal rays III,8; scaly sheath at base of dorsal and anal fins low; body depth 2.2-2.7 in standard length (body relatively deeper in larger fish); dorsal profile of head straight to above eye, then becoming convex; adults develop a large hump on forehead that can protrude anterior to eye; snout length 2.0-2.7 in head; rear of dorsal and anal fins of adults very pointed, reaching well posterior to caudal-fin base; caudal fin rounded; pelvic fins of small fish reaching anus, extending beyond origin of anal fin in large adults; body olive to green with a vertical dark line on scales; head of adults blue-green to blue with highly irregular undulating yellowish lines; two black lines extending posteriorly from eye (more evident in juveniles which also have two more extending diagonally upward from dorsal part of eye and two diagonally downward on snout from front of eye). Indo-Pacific; feeds on a wide variety of mollusks, fishes, sea urchins, crustaceans, and other invertebrates. Reaches immense size; largest reliably recorded, 229 cm, 190.5 kg. In spite of its size, a very wary fish.

RINGTAIL MAORI WRASSE
Cheilinus unifasciatus Streets, 1877

Dorsal rays IX,10; anal rays III,8; scaly sheath at base of dorsal and anal fins low; body depth 2.6-3.2 in standard length; dorsal profile of head straight to slightly convex; snout 2.3-2.8 in head; lower jaw projecting; membranes of spinous portion of dorsal fin not incised; caudal fin rounded; pelvic fins not reaching anus; olive green, the base of each body scale with a dull orange bar; a white bar usually present at front of caudal peduncle; head with irregular orange-red lines mostly aligned with dorsal profile, and a parallel series across cheek nearly perpendicular to upper lines; caudal fin mainly green; capable of undergoing considerable change in colour. Central and western Pacific; reported from depths of 10-160 m in Hawaii; feeds mainly on fishes, but also ingests crabs, brittle stars, heart urchins, sea urchins, etc. Largest measured, 46 cm, 1.4 kg. Often misidentified as *C. rhodochrous* Playfair and Günther. If white peduncular bar not evident, easily confused with *C. digrammus*; differs in the nearly smooth margin of the dorsal fin (each interspinous membrane of *digrammus* notched). Has been implicated in ciguatera fish poisoning.

Cheilinus unifasciatus   Initial phase ▲ Terminal phase ▼

CIGAR WRASSE
Cheilio inermis (Forsskål, 1775)

Dorsal rays IX,12-13; anal rays III,11-12; pectoral rays 12-13; lateral line complete, the pored scales 45-47; head naked except for a few scales on operculum behind eye; body very elongate, the depth 5.5-7.8 in standard length; snout long, 2.2-2.4 in head; caudal fin rounded to slightly rhomboid; colour variable; may be green, brown, orange-brown, or yellow; many exhibit a narrow midlateral broken black stripe; large males lack the stripe and develop a large irregular orange to salmon pink area mixed with dark brown on upper side of body at tip of pectoral fin. Indo-Pacific; although found on coral reefs, more common on open substrata, particularly those with heavy benthic plant growth; feeds on molluscs, hermit crabs, crabs, sea urchins, and shrimps. Attains 50 cm. M. F. Gomon and B.C. Russell presented an oral paper in Sydney in 1981 pointing out that *Cheilio* should be classified with the fishes currently recognized as odacids as a tribe Odacini within the Labridae.

Cheilio inermis   Yellow initial phase ▲ Green initial phase ▼

ANCHOR TUSKFISH
Choerodon anchorago (Bloch, 1791)

Dorsal rays XIII,7; anal rays III,9; pectoral rays 15-16; lateral line a smooth continuous curve with 27 pored scales to caudal-fin base (true of other *Choerodon*); scales on preopercle small, less than one-fourth size of those on body (characteristic of the genus);two pairs of stout curved canine teeth anteriorly in each jaw (also generic), the second pair of lower jaw larger than first and flaring laterally; body deep, the depth 2.4-2.7 in standard length; dorsal profile of snout steep and nearly straight, then angling convexly to dorsal fin origin; caudal fin truncate to slightly rounded; a large blackish area on back with a pale yellowish bar at front and a broad yellowish zone on midside below; anterior body and head brown with orange-red dots except ventrally where abruptly white, the white continuing on ventral third of body and all of caudal peduncle except for a midlateral blackish streak linked to large black area of back. Western Pacific to Sri Lanka; a shallow-water species that occurs in a variety of habitats from coral reefs to seagrass beds. Attains 38 cm.

GRASS TUSKFISH
Choerodon cephalotes (Castelnau, 1875)

Dorsal rays XIII,7; anal rays III,10; pectoral rays 18-19; predorsal scales not extending anterior to a vertical at rear edge of preopercle; scales on subopercle 1-3; second lower canine tooth larger than first and strongly curving outward and backward; no posterior canine teeth; body deep, the depth of adults about 2.6 in standard length; dorsal profile of snout very steep, becoming convex on forehead; posterior dorsal and anal fins pointed; caudal fin rounded; scales of body with a vertical blue line; front of head purplish blue crossed by narrow orange bands; numerous orange dots on cheek; an orange-red area often present on body, centred below origin of dorsal fin; teeth blue. Queensland to Indonesia; often found in seagrass beds. Attains 38 cm. Also known as the Purple Tuskfish.

BLUE TUSKFISH
Choerodon cyanodus (Richardson, 1843)

Dorsal rays XIII,7; anal rays III,10; pectoral rays 15-16; predorsal scales not extending anterior to a vertical at rear edge of preopercle; second pair of lower canines about same size as first pair and angling laterally; body deep, the depth 2.4-2.8 in standard length; dorsal profile of head smoothly convex; caudal fin slightly rounded; upper side of body below dorsal fin dark brown containing a whitish spot about twice size of eye; rest of body pale yellowish, the caudal peduncle with narrow reddish stripes; head yellowish brown, becoming pale salmon pink below level of mouth; front of chin may be blue with a light red streak on lower lip; caudal fin with red vermiculations and blue outer corners; large males blue-green with five faint broad dusky bars dorsally on body; head largely grey; front of snout usually with vermiculations of pale pink and blue-green. Queensland to Western Australia; will enter very shallow water; feeds mainly on mollusks. To 70 cm. *Choerops albigena* De Vis is a synonym.

HARLEQUIN TUSKFISH
Choerodon fasciatus (Günther, 1867)

Dorsal rays XII,8; anal rays III,10; pectoral rays 14-15, the fourth or fifth rays longest; small scales on cheek extending forward nearly to corner of mouth; predorsal scales reaching a vertical at rear edge of orbit; body deep, the depth 2.2-2.5 in standard length; caudal fin truncate to slightly emarginate; white with eight to nine blue-edged orange bars, three on head and the rest on body; adults becoming blackish posteriorly and dorsally on body; teeth blue. An apparent north-south disjunct distribution: Ryukyu Islands to Taiwan in the north and New Caledonia to Queensland in the south. A valuable aquarium fish because of its striking colour. Feeds on mollusks, crustaceans, various worms, and echinoderms. Reaches 30 cm. Often classified in *Lienardella*, at best a subgenus of *Choerodon*.

GRAPHIC TUSKFISH
Choerodon graphicus (De Vis, 1885)

Dorsal rays III,7; anal rays III,10; pectoral rays 16-17; predorsal scales extending slightly anterior to a vertical at rear edge of preopercle; second lower pair of canines much smaller than first and not angling laterally; body depth; 2.6-2.8 in standard length; caudal fin rounded; brownish to greyish yellow with a vertical blue line on each body scale and large interconnected dark brown blotches; an irregular black spot larger than eye on lateral line below base of seventh dorsal spine, and a smaller black spot at rear base of dorsal fin; dark brown bands radiating from eye. New Caledonia to Queensland; easily approached underwater. Recorded to 46 cm. *Choerodon transversalis* Whitley is a synonym.

JORDAN'S TUSKFISH
Choerodon jordani (Snyder, 1908)

Dorsal rays XIII,7; anal rays III,10; pectoral rays 15; predorsal scales just reaching a vertical at rear edge of preopercle; second pair of lower canine teeth as large or larger than first, strongly curving outward and backward; body moderately elongate, the depth 2.8-3.6 in standard length; caudal fin truncate to slightly rounded, the upper rays a little prolonged on large adults; a black wedge posteriorly on upper half of body, the apex just above upper base of pectoral fin; a large pale yellow saddle-like spot within black wedge, centered at rear base of dorsal fin; head and body anterior to wedge olivaceous to light yellowish grey; body below wedge whitish. Known from Samoa, Fiji, New Caledonia, Great Barrier Reef, Western Australia, and Ryukyu Islands; usually encountered on substrata of sand, rubble, or small coral heads near reefs, generally at depths greater than 20 m. To 17 cm.

Choerodon graphicus ▲   *Choerodon jordani* ▼

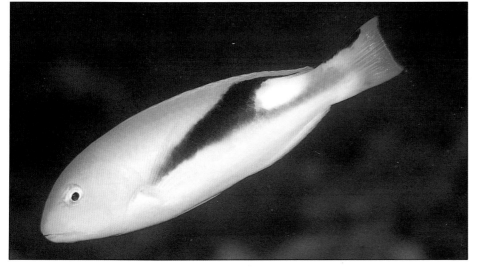

BLACKSPOT TUSKFISH
Choerodon schoenleinii (Valenciennes, 1839)

Dorsal rays XIII,7; anal rays III,10; pectoral rays 18-19; predorsal scales reaching a vertical through rear edge of eye; scales on subopercle 3-5; second pair of canines of lower jaw much shorter than first and not laterally curved; body deep, the depth 2.4-2.8 in standard length; caudal fin truncate to slightly rounded; greenish grey on back, shading to light yellowish below, with a vertical blue line on each scale, becoming spots posteriorly which coalesce to form blue stripes on caudal peduncle; a black spot smaller than eye at base of last dorsal spine; irregular blue bands extending posteriorly from eye. Western Pacific to Western Australia; occurs on outer reef slopes and around reefs in lagoons, generally at depths of 10-20 m; often observed to overturn large rocks to feed upon the invertebrate animals beneath. The largest of the tuskfishes; reported to over 90 cm, 15.5 kg.

VENUS TUSKFISH
Choerodon venustus (De Vis, 1884)

Dorsal rays XIII,7; anal rays III,10; pectoral rays 16, the third ray longest; predorsal scales 6, nearly reaching a vertical at rear edge of preopercle; scales on subopercle 6-11; two pairs of lower canines about equal in size, the second pair not outcurved; body deep, the depth 2.4-2.7 in standard length; caudal fin slightly to moderately emarginate; colour variable, but usually greenish dorsally, shading to light red on side (rosy red in pectoral region), yellowish ventrally, each scale with a blue spot; often a faint blackish blotch below first two or three dorsal spines; all fins with blue markings. Northern New South Wales to Queensland; common on or around coral reefs. Reaches at least 65 cm.

BLUESIDE WRASSE
Cirrhilabrus cyanopleura (Bleeker, 1851)

Dorsal rays XI,9; anal rays III,9-10 (rarely 10); pectoral rays 14-16; lateral-line interrupted (true of all *Cirrhilabrus*); median predorsal scales 6; scale rows on cheek 2; three pairs of canine teeth anteriorly in upper jaw, the third pair largest, recurved, and outflaring, and a single pair of canines in lower jaw (dentition comparable for all species of the genus); posterior margin of preopercle finely serrate (also generic); caudal fin rounded in females, rhomboid in males; females light red, shading to pale yellowish or white on lower head and abdomen, with a large faintly purplish quadrangular area above pectoral fin, a wedge-shaped black spot at pectoral base, and a small black spot at upper base of caudal fin; males red, the scales rimmed with purple, with a large deep blue area on upper side from beneath pectoral fin to dorsal-fin base; head greenish, the lower fourth of head and body white; black streak at pectoral base extending diagonally below fin base. Western Pacific. To 15 cm.

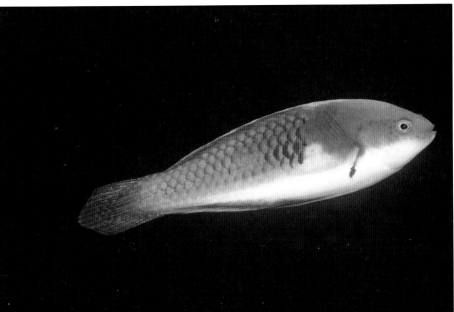

Cirrhilabrus cyanopleura   Initial phase ▼ Terminal phase ▲

EXQUISITE WRASSE
Cirrhilabrus exquisitus Smith, 1957

Dorsal rays XI,9; anal rays III,9; pectoral rays 14-15 (rarely 14); median predorsal scales 5; scale rows on cheek 2; caudal fin of young slightly rounded, of adults double emarginate with lobes prolonged; olivaceous with an oval black spot larger than eye posteriorly on caudal peduncle just above lateral line; a horizontal blue line below black spot, extending a variable distance anteriorly on body; a horizontal blue line under eye; a red or blue line from corner of mouth above eye to nape and a similar streak on head behind eye, curving onto body beneath pectoral fin (these two markings absent on small individuals); a blue-edged wedge-shaped black bar at pectoral-fin base; males more colorful, with red on median fins, particularly a broad band in outer part of soft portion of dorsal fin and a red margin on pectoral fins. Indo-Pacific, the color varying with major geographical area; known from the depth range of 2-32 m, but usually seen in less than 10 m; generally found over rubble bottoms in regions of current. Attains 12 cm.

Cirrhilabrus exquisitus   Terminal phase ▼

MAGENTA-STREAKED WRASSE
Cirrhilabrus laboutei Randall & Lubbock, 1982

Dorsal rays XI,9; anal rays III,8-9 (rarely 8); pectoral rays 15-16 (rarely 16); median predorsal scales 5; one row of scales on cheek (space for second scale occupied by two small scales, one above other); first two anal spines of males prolonged; caudal fin rounded; pelvic fins short; upper head and body of females yellowish brown with three magenta stripes, the lowermost curving downward in pectoral region, then upward to join second stripe at upper end of gill opening; lower head and body pale lavender and white; a diagonal magenta bar at pectoral base and continuing below; subadult females with red stripes and a small black spot at upper base of caudal fin; males with same linear pattern but the two main magenta stripes edged in yellow and ventral part of body deep lavender-pink. New Caledonia and Loyalty Islands to Great Barrier Reef; usually over rubble bottom near reefs; known from the depth range of 8-55 m. Reaches 12 cm.

Cirrhilabrus punctatus   Initial phase ▲ Terminal phase ▼

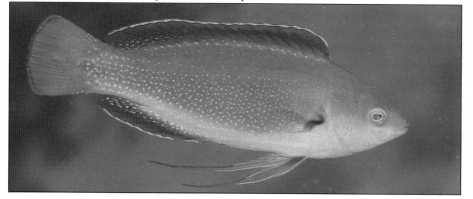

PURPLELINED WRASSE
Cirrhilabrus lineatus Randall & Lubbock, 1982

Dorsal rays XI,9; anal rays III,9; pectoral rays 15-16 (rarely 16); median predorsal scales 5; scale rows on cheek 2; caudal fin rounded; pelvic fins of males reaching origin of anal fin; lavender-pink, suffused with yellow dorsally, shading to pale yellow or white ventrally, with longitudinal rows of purple spots and dashes and a solid purple stripe along back (and in males a solid ventral stripe); median fins yellow with blue markings. New Caledonia and Loyalty Islands to Great Barrier Reef; specimens from the depth range of 20-55 m. To 12 cm.

DOTTED WRASSE
Cirrhilabrus punctatus Randall & Kuiter, 1989

Dorsal rays XI,9; anal rays III,9; pectoral rays 14-16; median predorsal scales 5-7; rows of scales on cheek 2, the lower row close to ventral margin of preopercle; caudal fin rounded; pelvic fins of males very long, often half or more standard length; upper three-fourths of body dark grey to reddish with pink to blue dots, lower fourth white; a black bar at base of pectoral fins; females and juveniles with a small black spot at upper base of caudal fin; dorsal and anal fins of adults with a broad red submarginal band; females with a black spot anteriorly in dorsal fin, males with a blackish band proximal to red zone in dorsal and anal fins. New South Wales to southern New Guinea, east to Fiji; known from the depth range of less than 2 to 32 m. Reaches 13 cm.

SCOTTS' WRASSE

Cirrhilabrus scottorum Randall & Pyle, 1989

Dorsal rays XI,9; anal rays III,9; pectoral rays 15-16 (usually 15); median predorsal scales 5; rows of scales on cheek 2; caudal fin rhomboid, large males with filament from middle of posterior margin; body green posteriorly, shading to dusky blue-green in middle, and to brighter blue-green anteriorly and on postorbital head; lower fourth of body light red; postorbital head and anterior upper half of body finely speckled with black; snout greenish yellow; dorsal fin green on basal scaled part, a middle zone of red, and a broad outer zone of deep purple flecked with blue; anal fin similar but without green at base; unscaled part of caudal fin red; presumed large males with ventral and posterior part of body white with a narrow zone of yellow and orange below dusky blue-green middle part of body. South Pacific from the Pitcairn Group to the Great Barrier Reef; known from the depth range of 3-40 m; more often seen in outer reef areas than sheltered lagoon reefs. Reaches 13 cm.

GOLDLINED CORIS

Coris aurilineata Randall & Kuiter, 1982

Dorsal rays IX,12; anal rays III,12; pectoral rays 14; lateral-line abruptly bent downward below rear part of dorsal fin (characteristic of the genus), the pored scales 49-51; head naked except for scales on nape which extend to a vertical at rear edge of preopercle; gill rakers 17-20; a canine tooth at corner of mouth (true of other *Coris*); body depth 3.15-3.5 in standard length; caudal fin rounded; females with longitudinal lines of orange-yellow and light blue-green, the lines broader ventrally; a blue-edged black spot about size of pupil at upper base of caudal fin and a large blue-edged black spot basally in soft portion of dorsal fin; males similar but the lines deeper blue-green to green, with faint narrow green bars dorsally on body, a deep green spot at upper base of pectoral fins, and without the dark spot in dorsal fin. New South Wales to southern Great Barrier Reef; a shallow-water species usually found on rubble and sand bottoms with much algal cover. Largest, 11.5 cm.

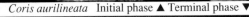
Coris aurilineata   Initial phase ▲ Terminal phase ▼

CLOWN CORIS
Coris aygula Lacepède, 1801

Dorsal rays IX,l2-13 (rarely 13), the first two spines close together and prolonged in large fish; anal rays III,12; pectoral rays 14; lateral-line scales 59-67; body depth 2.7-3.3 in standard length (body relatively deeper in larger individuals); males develop a large hump on forehead; caudal fin slightly rounded in females, truncate with filamentous rays in large males; pelvic fins of males very long; females with a whitish bar in front of anal-fin origin, the body anterior to bar light yellowish green with small maroon spots, posterior greenish, the scales dark-edged; median fins with small dark spots, the outer margins whitish; males deep blue-green, usually with one or two broad pale green bars in centre of body; juveniles whitish with small black spots anteriorly and two large semicircular orange-red spots on back with a large ocellated black spot above each in dorsal fin. Indo-Pacific; this and other large *Coris* turn over rocks to prey upon shelled molluscs, hermit crabs, crabs, sea urchins, etc. Reported to exceed 100 cm, but any over 70 cm are exceptional. *Coris angulata* Lacepède is a synonym.

Coris aygula   Juv.

Coris aygula   Initial phase ▲ Terminal phase ▼

PALE-BARRED CORIS
Coris dorsomacula Fowler, 1908

Dorsal rays IX,12; anal rays III,12; pectoral rays 13; lateral-line scales 51-53; body depth 3.4-4.0 in standard length; flexible tips of first two dorsal spines of large males slightly prolonged; caudal fin rounded; pelvic fins reaching posterior to anus; small adults usually greenish dorsally, whitish ventrally, with a dark brown to brownish orange stripe from front of snout, through eye, and continuing along upper side of body; about eight narrow pale bars dorsally on body crossing dark stripe; two pink or pinkish yellow stripes on lower side of body which break into spots posteriorly; a small black spot on opercular flap (often rimmed posteriorly with yellow), first two dorsal-fin membranes, rear base of dorsal fin, and upper base of pectoral fins; large individuals dark greenish dorsally, light green ventrally, with a dark pink stripe replacing the brown one of smaller fish, two pink stripes across cheek, two converging red bands in caudal fin which join at posterior border, and yellow above the black spots anteriorly in dorsal fin. Western Pacific; collected in the depth range of 5-32 m. Reaches 20 cm.

YELLOWTAIL CORIS
Coris gaimard (Quoy & Gaimard, 1824)

Dorsal rays IX,12; anal rays III,12; pectoral rays 13; lateral-line scales 70-79; head naked except dorsally where small scales extend forward to above rear of eye; body depth 3.3-3.7 in standard length; first two dorsal spines close together, flexible, and much longer than remaining spines (except juveniles); caudal fin rounded; body dark reddish to dark greenish with small brilliant blue spots which are more numerous pos-

teriorly; head brownish orange with green bands; unscaled part of caudal fin bright yellow; large males have more numerous and smaller blue spots posteriorly and develop a green bar on side of body above origin of anal fin; juveniles red with three large black-edged white spots dorsally on body, which extend into dorsal fin, and two similar but smaller spots on head. Central and western Pacific; closely related to *C. africana* Smith of the western Indian Ocean. Reported to 40 cm.

Coris gaimard   Adult ▼ Juv. ▲

BLACKSTRIPE CORIS
Coris pictoides Randall & Kuiter, 1982

Dorsal rays IX,12; anal rays III,12; pectoral rays 13-14 (rarely 14); lateral-line scales 48-51; head naked except for small scales on nape which extend slightly anterior to a vertical at rear margin of preopercle; body depth 3.45-3.7 in standard length; caudal fin rounded; pelvic fins short,1.8-2.3 in head; whitish with a broad black stripe from front of snout, through eye, along upper side of body into caudal fin; a second narrower dark stripe above broad stripe, separated from it by a narrow pale greenish band. Known from New South Wales, Great Barrier Reef, Western Australia, Indonesia, and the Philippines; usually found around small coral heads in silty sand-rubble areas; reported from the depth range of 9-33 m. Largest specimen,10.5 cm. Similar in colour to small individuals of the Combfish (*C. picta*) which occurs in eastern Australia south of 27° latitude; *picta* has 76-92 lateral-line scales.

SCHROEDER'S CORIS
Coris schroederi (Bleeker, 1858)

Dorsal rays IX,11; anal rays III,11; pectoral rays 13-15 (usually 14); lateral-line scales 51-53; head naked except for small scales on nape which extend forward to above rear edge of eye; body depth 2.8-3.5 in standard length; first two dorsal spines not close together and not prolonged; caudal fin slightly rounded; pelvic fins short, not reaching anus,1.6-2.0 in head; females whitish to pale greenish, mottled with brownish yellow dorsally, with short narrow pale bars and irregular narrow blackish

bars on back; centres of scales of ventral part of body white; irregular pink bands on head, and a small blue-green spot behind eye; a narrow black bar at pectoral base, a large ocellated black spot in middle of dorsal fin and a small black spot anteriorly; males are more green, the irregular blackish bars larger; often a faint pink zone on side of body, and there may be an irregular blackish area over part of abdomen (the scales still with white centers). Marshall Islands and Tonga to western Indian Ocean. To 17 cm. Usually identified as *C. variegata* (Rüppell), a closely related species endemic to the Red Sea.

KNIFEFISH

Cymolutes praetextatus (Quoy & Gaimard, 1834)

Dorsal rays IX,12, the first two spines flexible; anal rays II,12; pectoral rays 12; branched caudal rays 10 (most labrid genera with 11 or 12); pectoral rays 12; lateral-line interrupted, the scales 50-60 + 15-21; head scaleless; a pair of long slender canine teeth at front of jaws; dorsal profile of head strongly convex; caudal fin slightly rounded; females olive-grey dorsally, white ventrally, with a faint orange-yellow stripe on body passing posteriorly from upper end of gill opening and sometimes a faint narrower stripe of the same colour along back, following and extending beyond lateral line; a small black spot posteriorly on caudal peduncle near upper edge; often a faint orange border on spinous portion of dorsal fin; iris with an inner ring of yellow and outer of blue or violet; both sexes with a black line in outer part of first membrane of dorsal fin; males develop pale yellow bars on about posterior half of body and lose the small dark peduncular spot. Indo-Pacific (except Hawaii where replaced by *C. lecluse*); usually found on open sand substrata; capable of diving into sand with the approach of danger. Attains about 12 cm.

COLLARED KNIFEFISH

Cymolutes torquatus Valenciennes, 1840

Dorsal rays IX,12-13 (rarely 12), the first two spines flexible; anal rays II,11-12 (rarely 11); pectoral rays 12; lateral-line scales 56-69 + 16-20; head and dentition as in *C. praetextatus*; caudal fin slightly rounded; females light greenish dorsally, whitish ventrally, with 14-19 narrow dark brown bars (sometimes branched) on body posterior to pectoral fins, these connected dorsally by a longitudinal dark brown band; dark bars in males become orange; in addition, a diagonal black streak anteriorly on body above base of pectoral fin and three di-agonal blue lines on cheek and gill cover. Indo-Pacific; habits similar to *praetextatus*. Reaches about 12 cm.

YELLOWTAIL TUBELIP

Diproctacanthus xanthurus (Bleeker, 1856)

Dorsal rays IX,9-10 (usually 10), the soft portion of fin distinctly higher than spinous; anal rays II,9-10 (usually 9); pectoral rays 12-14; lateral-line scales 34-39; lips fleshy, forming a tube when mouth closed; two pairs of canine teeth in upper jaw and one pair in lower, followed by a few small teeth on side of jaws; a canine at corner of mouth; small scales on opercle and cheek; body depth 3.1-3.7 in standard length; caudal fin rounded in juveniles, truncate in adults; greenish white with two black stripes on upper side, one midlateral and one along back; caudal fin bright yellow; juveniles with three broad black stripes, the narrow interspaces white; caudal fin black, the upper and lower edges narrowly bluish white. Philippines, Palau, Indonesia, New Guinea, and Great Barrier Reef; typical habitat, shallow protected lagoons with rich coral growth; adults feed mainly on coral polyps; juveniles "clean" other fishes. Largest, 9.7 cm. Only one species in the genus.

SLINGJAW WRASSE
Epibulus insidiator (Pallas, 1770)

Dorsal rays IX,10; anal rays III,8-9; pectoral rays 12; lateral-line interrupted, the anterior pored scales 14-15; jaws extremely protractile; preopercular margin smooth; body deep, the depth 2.0-2.3 in standard length; caudal fin emarginate to lunate; pelvic fins of adults long, reaching to or beyond origin of anal fin; females dark brown or yellow; males brown with dark green edges on scales, a diffuse yellow bar on side behind pectoral fin,· an orange-red area beneath front part of dorsal fin, and a light grey head with black lines radiating from eye. Indo-Pacific, on coral reefs; feeds by extremely rapid extension of the jaws, the diet consisting mainly of small fishes, crabs, and shrimps. Reaches 35 cm.

Epibulus insidiator   Brown phase ▲ Yellow initial phase ▼

Epibulus insidiator   Terminal phase ▼

315

BIRD WRASSE
Gomphosus varius Lacepède, 1801

Dorsal rays VIII,13; anal rays III,11; pectoral rays 16; lateral-line scales 26-27; head naked except for a few small scales on upper operculum; snout extremely long and attenuate in adults, short in juveniles; body depth 3.5-4.0 in standard length; preopercle with no free lower margin, the vertical margin smooth; caudal fin slightly rounded in initial-phase fish, truncate to emarginate in terminal males; body of initial phase white anteriorly with a black spot on edge of each scale, soon shading to dark grey, the scales edged in black; dorsal part of snout red, shading posteriorly on upper head to reddish grey; lower part of head abruptly white; caudal fin black with a broad posterior white border; terminal males deep blue-green with a vertical red line on each scale, an irregular greenish yellow bar on body above pectoral fin, and a large light blue-green crescent in caudal fin; juveniles green dorsally, white below, with two black stripes. Occurs throughout Oceania and the western Pacific; feeds mainly on small benthic crustaceans, occasionally on small fishes, brittle stars, and molluscs. *G. tricolor* Quoy and Gaimard is a synonym based on the terminal male phase. Closely related to *G. caeruleus* Lacepède of the Indian Ocean.

Gomphosus varius Initial phase ▲ Terminal phase ▼

Gomphosus varius Juv.

BIOCELLATE WRASSE
Halichoeres biocellatus Schultz, 1960

Dorsal rays IX,12; anal rays III,12; pectoral rays 13; lateral-line scales 27, the scales with a single pore; head scaleless; scales on thorax notably smaller than those of rest of body (characteristic of the genus); preopercular margin free as much ventrally as posteriorly (also true of other *Halichoeres*); a single pair of canines anteriorly in each jaw; a canine at corner of mouth (a generic character); body depth 2.9-3.35 in standard length; females green with orange or orange-red stripes on head and anterior body which gradually break up to series of spots, one per scale, on posterior half of body; a small vertically rectangular black spot behind eye; a large blue-edged black spot in middle of dorsal fin and another posteriorly in fin; males lose the ocelli in dorsal fin, and the orange spots are altered to form three faint bars on posterior half of body and a U-shaped mark on caudal peduncle. Samoa and Marshall Islands to western Pacific. Reaches 12 cm.

PASTEL-GREEN WRASSE
Halichoeres chloropterus (Bloch, 1791)

Dorsal rays IX,10-11 (rarely 10); anal rays III,10-11 (rarely 10); pectoral rays 13-15; lateral-line scales 27, the anterior scales with 1-3 pores (usually 2); body depth 2.75-3.75 in standard length (large males deeper-bodied); females usually pale greenish on back, shading to white ventrally, with a black dot on each scale of back and side and a series of dark purplish chevron-shaped lines on abdomen; a narrow black bar at pectoral-fin base; males pastel green with a faint lavender-pink spot in center of each scale in middle and posterior part of body; anteriorly the lavender-pink spots coalesce to form irregular stripes and network, thus isolating the green as spots; head with very irregular bands of pale green and lavender-pink; males often with a large blackish area on upper side centred beneath juncture of spinous and soft parts of dorsal fin. Philippines to Great Barrier Reef; occurs on shallow protected coral reefs and adjacent silty sand and rubble bottoms. Reported to 19 cm. *H. gymnocephalus* Bloch & Schneider is a synonym based on the female form.

Halichoeres chloropterus　Initial phase ▲ Terminal phase ▼

GOLDEN WRASSE
Halichoeres chrysus Randall,1981

Dorsal rays IX,12; anal rays III,11-12 (rarely 11); pectoral rays 13-14 (rarely 14); lateral-line scales 27, the anterior scales with branched tubules (pores varying from 2-4, usually 2 or 3); body moderately elongate, the depth 3.4-3.8 in standard length; females bright yellow with a small black spot behind eye, one at upper base of caudal fin, one at front of dorsal fin, and one in middle of fin (the dorsal fin spots often rimmed with light yellow or pale blue); males similar in colour overall, but with faint orange and greenish yellow bands on head, thorax, and median fins and lacking the caudal and mid-dorsal fin spots; juveniles with a third black spot posteriorly in dorsal fin. Western Pacific, Micronesia, and Christmas Island in eastern Indian Ocean; usual habitat, small isolated coral heads on sand or sand and rubble substrata; known from the depth range of 7-60 m, but rarely seen in less than 20 m. Attains 12 cm. A popular aquarium fish.

CHECKERBOARD WRASSE
Halichoeres hortulanus (Lacepède, 1801)

Dorsal rays IX,11; anal rays III,11; pectoral rays 14; lateral-line scales 26, the scales with one pore; a patch of small scales dorsally on opercle and a near-vertical band of small scales in two or three rows just behind eye; two pairs of canine teeth at front of upper jaw, the second pair strongly recurved; one pair of canine teeth at front of lower jaw, the second pair of teeth about half as long as first; females with a longitudinal series of square black-edged white spots following scale rows; a large yellow spot on back at base of fourth and fifth dorsal spines, extending into fin, followed by a larger black spot; a second smaller yellow spot in middle of base of soft portion of fin; head greenish yellow with irregular orange-pink bands; males similar but ground colour green; juveniles white with large black areas on body and a large yellow-edged black spot in dorsal fin. Indo-Pacific. To 27 cm. *H. centiquadrus* (Lacepède) is a synonym based on the Indian Ocean form with one yellow spot in dorsal fin.

Halichoeres hortulanus　Adult ▼ Juv. ▲

PINK-BELLY WRASSE

Halichoeres margaritaceus (Valenciennes, 1839)

Dorsal rays IX,11, anal rays III,11; pectoral rays usually 13; lateral-line scales 27, the anterior scales with 1-3 pores; anterior pair of teeth of upper jaw with enlarged canines; second pair moderately enlarged and recurved; lower jaw with one pair of anterior canines; females olivaceous on back, the scale edges dark brown, pale ventrally, with whitish blotches of unequal size and a large pink area posteriorly on abdomen; a black spot on opercular flap, small one behind eye, one at front of dorsal fin, and a large one rimmed in yellow or blue in middle of fin; no black spot at upper base of pectoral fins; males green with orange-red spots, some linked to form irregular markings, the white blotches and large pink area on abdomen lost, and the black spots lost or reduced. Central and western Pacific; common on shallow reefs and rocky shores. Largest, 12.5 cm.

H. margaritaceus   Terminal phase ▼ Initial phase ▲

DUSKY WRASSE

Halichoeres marginatus Rüppell, 1835

Dorsal rays IX,13-14 (usually 13); anal rays III,12-13 (usually 12); pectoral rays 14-15 (usually 14); lateral-line scales 27-28 (usually 27), the anterior scales with 2-4 (usually 3) pores; teeth in jaws progressively longer anteriorly, the most anterior only slightly longer than the one behind; initial phase dark brown, usually with darker brown stripes following centres of scale rows; a large deep blue ocellus in middle of dorsal fin and a smaller one at front of fin; caudal fin abruptly whitish (large individuals develop a blackish crescent posteriorly in fin); anterior third of body of terminal males greenish to orangish brown with deep purplish blue lines following centres of scale rows, this pattern altering posteriorly on body to reddish with a large blue-edged greenish spot on each scale; unscaled part of caudal fin with a green crescent at base, followed by a large dark-edged reddish crescent containing small dark-edged greenish spots; outer margin of fin yellow with a blue submarginal band; juveniles with broad black and narrow pale yellow stripes. Indo-Pacific. Reaches 17 cm.

Halichoeres marginatus   Adult ▼ Juv. ▲

TAILSPOT WRASSE
Halichoeres melanurus (Bleeker, 1851)

Dorsal rays IX,12; anal rays III,12; pectoral rays 14; lateral-line scales 27, the anterior scales with 1-4 (usually 2) pores; females with alternating narrow orange-yellow and blue stripes, a blue-edged black spot about as large as pupil at upper base of caudal fin, a large one in middle of dorsal fin, and a small one at front of fin; body of males with blue-green and orange stripes and three to six narrow blue-green bars on upper side, the head with salmon pink and blue-green bands; caudal fin blue with curved orange-red bands and a large vertically elongate dusky to black spot submarginally in middle of fin; a large yellow spot at pectoral-fin base with a small black spot at upper base. Western Pacific east to Micronesia and Samoa. Largest, 10.5 cm. *Halichoeres hoevenii* (Bleeker) is a synonym based on the female phase.

Halichoeres melanurus   Initial phase ▲ Terminal phase ▼

OCELLATED WRASSE
Halichoeres melasmapomus Randall, 1980

Dorsal rays IX,12; anal rays III,12; pectoral rays 13; lateral-line scales 27, the anterior scales with 2-7 pores (larger fish, in general, with more); a pair of large projecting canine teeth anteriorly in jaws, the following pair of canines about two-thirds as long; bluish to yellowish grey with a large reddish to orange spot on each scale; head with irregular yellow and blue-green stripes and a large blue-edged black spot dorsally on opercle; females with a small black spot behind eye, an ocellus on upper base of caudal fin, and three in dorsal fin; males lose all these except the caudal spot. Known from the islands of Oceania except Hawaii and Easter and the western Pacific islands from the Philippines to the Coral Sea; also recorded from Christmas Island and Cocos-Keeling Islands in the eastern Indian Ocean; reported from depths of 20-55 m, but rarely seen in less than 30 m; often found on dropoffs or the base of such steep slopes. Largest, 14 cm.

CIRCLE-CHEEK WRASSE
Halichoeres miniatus (Valenciennes, 1839)

Dorsal rays IX,11, anal rays III,11; pectoral rays usually 13; lateral-line scales 27, the anterior scales with two to three (usually two) pores; dentition as in *H. margaritaceus;* females brownish yellow to olive with irregular longitudinal blackish lines along upper and lower edges of scales; some scale centres white or pale yellow, thus appearing as series of pale spots; abdomen reddish, the scales with vertical white lines or inverted V-shaped marks; a sickle-shaped pale pink band on cheek; dorsal fin with diagonal reddish lines; anal fin with dark reddish dots; males green, the upper half of body with irregular longitudinal reddish bands, the scale centres in bands green; five or six dark reddish bars often present ventrally on body; a circular or near-circular salmon pink band on cheek; an irregular black spot in middle of dorsal fin. Western Pacific. Reaches 10 cm.

Halichoeres melasmapomus

H. miniatus Initial phase ▲ Terminal phase ▼

NEBULOUS WRASSE
Halichoeres nebulosus (Valenciennes, 1839)

Dorsal rays IX,11; anal rays III,11; pectoral rays 14; lateral-line scales 27, the anterior scales with 1-3 pores; dentition and colouration very similar to that of *H. margaritaceus; nebulosus* has a boomerang-shaped salmon pink mark on cheek, the long posterior end of which angles downward as it passes posteriorly; *margaritaceus* has a pink band on the cheek which angles upward as it passes posteriorly; also helpful is *nebulosus* having one more pectoral ray. Western Pacific and throughout the tropical and subtropical Indian Ocean, including the Red Sea; although primarily an inshore species, it has been collected as deep as 40 m. Attains 12 cm.

Halichoeres nebulosus   Initial phase

ORNATE WRASSE
Halichoeres ornatissimus (Garrett, 1863)

Dorsal rays IX,12; anal rays III,12; pectoral rays 13; lateral-line scales 27, the anterior scales with 2-4 (usually 3) pores; a single pair of prominent canine teeth at front of jaws; body rose to brownish red with a green spot on each scale, often shading to white ventrally; head with irregular rose and green bands; a small black spot behind eye and one at front of dorsal fin; females less than about 10 cm with an ocellated black spot in middle of dorsal fin; still smaller fish have a small black spot on last dorsal-fin membrane. Islands of Oceania and the western Pacific; feeds mainly on small benthic crustaceans and molluscs. Attains 15 cm.

TWOTONE WRASSE
Halichoeres prosopeion (Bleeker, 1853)

Dorsal rays IX,12; anal rays III,12; pectoral rays 13-14 (rarely 13); lateral-line scales 27, the anterior scales with 1-3 pores; two pairs of large canine teeth at front of upper jaw, the second pair recurved, and one pair at front of lower jaw; caudal fin of adults truncate (slightly rounded to rounded on previous species of the genus); pelvic fins of adults extending beyond origin of anal fin; adults bluish grey on head and anterior third of body, becoming light grey with a vertical yellow line on each scale posteriorly (giving the effect of a half-grey, half-yellow fish); front of dorsal fin blue with a large black spot; caudal rays orange-yellow; juveniles pale bluish anteriorly, light yellow posteriorly, with four black stripes. Western Pacific east to Samoa; known in Micronesia only from Palau. Reported to 13 cm.

Halichoeres prosopeion   Adult ▼ Juv. ▲

ZIGZAG WRASSE

Halichoeres scapularis (Bennett, 1831)

Dorsal rays IX,11; anal rays III,11; pectoral rays 14; lateral-line scales 26, the anterior scales with one pore; a patch of small scales dorsally on opercle; two pairs of projecting canine teeth at front of upper jaw, the second pair recurved, and one pair of canines anteriorly in lower jaw; initial phase olivaceous to brownish yellow on back, white below, with a black stripe from eye along upper side to upper base of caudal fin, this stripe zigzag on body; stripe on postorbital head edged in yellow (especially ventrally), and there may be a yellow stripe on snout; terminal males green, the more strongly zigzag stripe lavender-pink except short first part overlaid by blackish; green ventral part of body with vertical lavender-pink lines on scales; head with broad irregular lavender-pink bands. Western Pacific to East Africa and the Red Sea; usually found in shallow lagoons or bays; associated more with sand, rubble, or seagrass bottoms than coral reefs. Reaches 20 cm.

Halichoeres scapularis Initial phase ▲ Terminal phase ▼

THREESPOT WRASSE

Halichoeres trimaculatus (Quoy & Gaimard, 1834)

Dorsal rays IX,11; anal rays III,11; pectoral rays 14-15 (usually 14); lateral-line scales 27, the anterior scales with one pore; two pairs of canine teeth at front of upper jaw, the second pair about half as long and recurved; one pair of canines anteriorly in lower jaw; initial phase light greenish to yellowish grey on back, white below, the scales rimmed with pink to blackish; a black spot nearly as large as eye on upper part of caudal peduncle; a small black spot at upper pectoral-fin base; terminal males light yellowish green with irregular pink bands and spots on head and anterior body, and vertical pink lines on scales; a black spot (or blue and black) centred on fifth and sixth lateral-line scales; yellow around black peduncular spot and extending onto upper base of caudal fin (or fin may be entirely yellow). Islands of Oceania, western Pacific, and Christmas Island in eastern Indian Ocean; occurs in shallow protected waters of lagoons and bays, at times in depths of only a few cm; typical habitat, sand or sand and rubble around small coral heads. To 20 cm.

Halichoeres trimaculatus Initial phase ▲ Terminal phase ▼

GOLDSTRIPE WRASSE
Halichoeres zeylonicus (Bennett, 1832)

Dorsal rays IX,11; anal rays III,11; pectoral rays 13; lateral-line scales 27, all scales with one pore; caudal fin slightly rounded, becoming slightly double emarginate in large males; females light bluish grey dorsally, white ventrally, with a narrow orange stripe from top of snout along back at base of dorsal fin, ending at upper base of caudal fin (where it may contain a blackish spot); a second broader orange to yellow stripe from side of snout through eye to midbase of caudal fin, the edges of this stripe wavy; a small black spot at upper base of pectoral fin; males blue-green on head and anterior body with irregular pink bands and spots; orange-yellow lateral stripe blue-edged, often with narrow ventral extensions; a blue-edged black spot on side beneath outer part of pectoral fin and one or two black spots posteriorly just above orange-yellow stripe. Western Pacific to western Indian Ocean, Red Sea, and Persian Gulf; usually found on open sand or sand-rubble bottoms, sometimes in the vicinity of isolated coral heads; known from the depth range of 20-85 m. Reaches 20 cm. *H. bimaculatus* Rüppell and *H. hartzfeldii* (Bleeker) are probable synonyms.

Halichoeres zeylonicus   Initial phase ▲ Terminal phase ▼

BARRED THICKLIP
Hemigymnus fasciatus (Bloch, 1792)

Dorsal rays IX,11; anal rays III,11; pectoral rays 14; lateral-line scales 27; a few rows of small scales on cheek; a pair of protruding canine teeth in jaws, and a broad canine at corner of mouth; lips very thick; gill opening restricted to side; body depth 2.3-2.6 in standard length; caudal fin slightly rounded to truncate; body whitish with five black bars much broader than pale inter- spaces; head yellowish green with irregular blue and black-edged pink to orange bands; a reversal of black and white colour of body, hence narrow black and broad white bars, may be a male pattern in courtship. Indo-Pacific; found more often on protected than exposed reefs; feeds mainly by extracting tiny animals from mouthfuls of sand, but also preys upon larger invertebrates such as sea urchins and molluscs. Reported to 75 cm, but probably does not exceed 50 cm.

Hemigymnus fasciatus   Adult ▼ Juv. ▲

BLACKEYE THICKLIP
Hemigymnus melapterus (Bloch, 1791)

Dorsal rays IX,11; anal rays III,11; pectoral rays 14; lateral-line scales 27; a few rows of small scales on cheek behind and below eye; lips very fleshy; teeth and gill opening as in *H. fasciatus*; head, anterior body, and abdomen grey, shading posteriorly to blackish as a result of black-edged scales; a curved blue line (or posteriorly a blue spot) on each scale; upper part of head with irregular blue-edged pink bands; a large dusky spot often present behind eye; juveniles with a white bar from front of dorsal fin to anterior abdomen and pelvic fins; head and body anterior to bar grey with dusky markings, posterior to bar, black, shading to yellow on caudal peduncle and fin. Micronesia and Samoa to East Africa and Red Sea; food habits as in *H. fasciatus*. Reported to 90 cm, but probably not over 60 cm.

Hemigymnus melapterus   Adult ▼ Juv. ▲

RINGWRASSE
Hologymnosus annulatus (Lacepède, 1801)

Dorsal rays IX,12, the spines thin and flexible; anal rays III,12; pectoral rays 13; lateral-line scales 100-118; head scaleless; two pairs of canine teeth anteriorly in jaws; no canine at corner of mouth; gill rakers 19-23; body depth 3.3-5.1 in standard length; caudal fin slightly rounded in juveniles, emarginate in adults, the caudal concavity of large males about 5 in head length; pectoral fins not short, 1.65-1.9 in head; initial-phase fish brown to olive-brown with 17-19 dark brown bars; a blue and blackish spot on opercular membrane; caudal fin with a large whitish crescentic area posteriorly; body of terminal males green, shading to blue-green ventrally, with purplish red bars; head purplish with broad irregular blue-green bands; caudal fin blue with a broad crescent of green posteriorly, shading to nearly hyaline on margin; a narrow pale bar sometimes present on body above origin of anal fin; juveniles light yellow with a very broad dark brown stripe on lower side of head and body and a narrow reddish stripe dorsally. Indo-Pacific; feeds mainly on small fishes; also on crustaceans. Reaches 40 cm. *H. semidiscus* (Lacepède) is a synonym.

Hologymnosus annulatus   Adult ▼ Juv. ▲

323

PASTEL RINGWRASSE
Hologymnosus doliatus (Lacepède, 1801)

Dorsal rays IX,12; anal rays III,12; pectoral rays 13; lateral-line scales 97-112; gill rakers 18-22; dentition as in *H. annulatus*; body depth 3.75-5.35 in standard length; caudal fin slightly rounded in juveniles and small initial-phase fish to double emarginate in large males, the caudal concavity about 11 in head; pectoral fins of adults short, 1.9-2.l in head; initial phase (mainly females) pale bluish, greenish, or pinkish grey with 20-23 orangish brown bars on body; a bluish black spot on opercular membrane; body of terminal males light blue-green to light red with lavender-blue bars and a pale zone in pectoral region bordered by purple bars; head blue to blue-green with irregular pink to orange bands; juveniles whitish with three narrow orange-red stripes. Line Islands and Samoa to East Africa. Reported to 50 cm; largest examined 38 cm.

Hologymnosus doliatus Initial phase ▲ Terminal phase ▼

Hologymnosus doliatus Juv.

SIDESPOT RINGWRASSE
Hologymnosus longipes (Günther, 1862)

Dorsal rays IX,12; anal rays III,12; pectoral rays 13; lateral-line scales 95-100; gill rakers 19-2l; dentition as in genus; body elongate, the depth 4.65-5.5 in standard length; caudal fin slightly rounded to truncate, the corners sometimes a little prolonged; pectoral fins short, 1.9-2.0 in head; pelvic fins relatively long, 2.15-2.4 in head; initial phase light greenish yellow to bluish grey with two series of vertically elongate orange spots on body which continue onto head as solid stripes, one at level of eye and one extending to chin; caudal fin orange to yellow; body of terminal male light greenish dorsally, white ventrally, with orange bars on side which become pale lavender-blue anteriorly on lower side; an oval black spot, rimmed in blue below and yellow above, on side of body above pectoral fin; head green with pink bands radiating from eye; caudal fin blue with a large whitish semicircular area posteriorly. New Caledonia, Loyalty Islands, Vanuatu, and southern Great Barrier Reef; usually over sand or rubble near coral heads; known from the depth range of 5-30 m. Attains about 40 cm.

Photograph: Yves Magnier

TUBELIP WRASSE
Labrichthys unilineatus (Guichenot, 1847)

Dorsal rays IX,11-12 (rarely 12); anal rays III,10-11 (rarely 11); pectoral rays 14-15 (usually 14); lateral-line scales 25-27; head scaled; lips thick and fleshy, forming a tube when mouth closed; upper jaw with two pairs of incurved canine teeth anteriorly, a large canine posteriorly, but no intervening teeth; lower jaw with a pair of canines anteriorly, followed by three to five small teeth; no free lower preopercular margin; body depth 2.6-3.2 in standard length; caudal fin strongly rounded; pelvic fins of males very long; females yellowish brown with a dull blue line following scale centres; mouth yellow; males dark olive with blue longitudinal lines on body, a broad yellow bar in pectoral region (sometimes faint), and a blue reticulum on head; juveniles dark brown with two thin bluish white stripes, one lateral, one ventral; larger juveniles lose the lower stripe, and the lateral one becomes yellow. Micronesia and Samoa to East Africa; occurs in sheltered coral-rich habitats; feeds on coral polyps. Largest, 17.5 cm. Only one species in the genus; *L. cyanotaenia* Bleeker is a synonym.

Labrichthys unilineatus   Adult ▼ Juv. ▲

BICOLOUR CLEANER WRASSE
Labroides bicolor Fowler & Bean, 1928

Dorsal rays IX,11; anal rays III,10; pectoral rays 13; lateral-line scales 26; small scales on cheek, opercle, and nape; lips thick, the lower strongly bilobed; one pair of canines anteriorly in jaws, and a canine at corner of mouth; side of jaws with several rows of small teeth; body depth 3.7-4.5 in standard length; caudal fin slightly rounded; females grey with a black lateral stripe anteriorly, becoming yellowish white posteriorly, with a blackish submarginal line in caudal fin; males with a deep blue head, the body black anteriorly, yellow posteriorly, with a subterminal black crescent in caudal fin, green before this marking and blue behind; juveniles black with a bright yellow stripe on back which continues to tip of snout. Indo-Pacific; feeds on ectoparasites (and mucus) of other fishes; moves more over the reef in search of host fishes than the two following species. Maximum length, 14 cm.

CLEANER WRASSE
Labroides dimidiatus (Valenciennes, 1839)

Dorsal rays IX,11; anal rays III,10; pectoral rays 13; lateral-line scales 50-52; small scales on cheek, opercle, and nape; lips and dentition as in *L. bicolor*; body depth 4.1-4.7 in standard length; caudal fin truncate to slightly rounded; adults light blue, shading to white or pale yellowish anteriorly, with a black stripe from front of snout through eye to end of caudal fin, this stripe broadening as it passes posteriorly; juveniles black with a bright blue stripe on back and dorsally on head. Indo-Pacific; establishes "cleaning" stations on the reef to which fishes come to have crustacean ectoparasites removed; also ingests mucus of the host fishes; will enter the mouth and gill chamber of some of the larger fishes. Reaches 11.5 cm.

Labroides bicolor

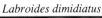

Labroides dimidiatus

BREASTSPOT CLEANER WRASSE

Labroides pectoralis Randall and Springer, 1975

Dorsal rays IX,10-12 (usually 11); anal rays III,9-10 (rarely 9); pectoral rays 13; lateral-line scales 26; cheek, opercle, and most of nape scaled; lips and dentition as in the genus; body depth 3.3-3.95 in standard length; caudal fin slightly rounded; adults with a black stripe from snout through eye to end of caudal fin, this stripe progressively broader as it passes posteriorly; a median dorsal black stripe from snout tip to dorsal fin; head and anterior body between black stripes yellow, this colour gradually changing to orange posteriorly; body below lateral stripe blue; a black spot nearly as large as eye at lower edge of pectoral-fin base; lips orange-red and blackish; upper and lower edges of caudal fin lavender-pink, the corners hyaline. Micronesia and New Caledonia to the Great Barrier Reef and Indonesia; also known from Christmas Island in the eastern Indian Ocean; same habits as *L. dimidiatus*. Attains 8 cm.

SOUTHERN TUBELIP

Labropsis australis Randall, 1981

Dorsal rays IX,12; anal rays III,11; pectoral rays 13-15 (usually 14); lateral-line scales 35-40; postorbital head and posterior suborbital region with small scales; dorsal profile of head of male strongly convex before eye; lips thick and fleshy, forming a tube when mouth closed; front of upper jaw with two pairs of large recurved canine teeth, the second pair about half as long as first, and a large canine posteriorly, with no teeth between; front of lower jaw with a pair of large recurved canines, followed by two or three lesser canines; no free lower preopercular margin; body depth 3.15-3.45 in standard length; caudal fin rounded; pelvic fins 1.4-2.25 in head, longer in males, but not reaching anal fin; females with grey head, brownish yellow body, and three brown stripes (faint on body); a dark brown spot with an orange-red spot above and below it at pectoral-fin base; males with dark bluish grey head and brown body, the scale centres golden; posterior margin of caudal fin blue (broader at corners); juveniles similar to females but brown stripes more evident. Samoa and Fiji to Great Barrier Reef, north to Solomon Islands; collected from the depth range of 2-55 m; adults feeds on coral polyps; juveniles observed to clean other fishes. To 10.5 cm.

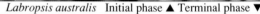
Labropsis australis   Initial phase ▲ Terminal phase ▼

YELLOWBACK TUBELIP
Labropsis xanthonota Randall, 1981

Dorsal rays IX,11; anal rays III,10; pectoral rays 14-15 (rarely 15); lateral-line scales 46-49; postorbital head and posterior suborbital with small scales (none extending anterior to centre of eye); lips and dentition as in *L. australis*; no free lower preopercular margin; body depth 3.4-3.8 in standard length; caudal fin of juveniles rounded, of females truncate with rounded corners, of males emarginate; pelvic fins short, not reaching anus; females bluish black, becoming brown on side with an orange spot in centre of each scale; head and body with longitudinal light blue lines alternating with dotted pale blue lines; dorsal fin and adjacent back yellow; a black spot at front of dorsal fin; body of males dark brown with a small golden spot in centre of each scale; head brown with a reticulum of deep blue, the operculum rimmed posteriorly with bright yellow; caudal fin with a large V-shaped white area posteriorly; juveniles similar to females but lacking brown region of upper side. Micronesia and Samoa to East Africa; depth range, 7-55 m; habits as in *L. australis*. To 13 cm.

Labropsis xanthonota   Initial phase ▲ Terminal phase ▼

SHOULDERSPOT WRASSE
Leptojulis cyanopleura (Bleeker, 1853)

Dorsal rays IX,11; anal rays III,11; pectoral rays 13; lateral-line scales 27; front of jaws with two pairs of large canine teeth, the second pair strongly recurved and outflaring; a canine tooth at corner of mouth; no well-developed molariform pharyngeal teeth; body slender, the depth 4.0-4.55 in standard length; caudal fin varying from slightly rounded in initial-phase fish to slightly double emarginate in large terminal males; pelvic fins short; initial phase whitish with an orangish brown stripe from snout through eye to midbase of caudal fin and a second narrower stripe from top of head along base of dorsal fin, ending dorsally on caudal peduncle; a longitudinal row of brownish orange spots on body above lateral stripe; terminal males bluish grey with a blue-edged yellow stripe from front of snout to middle of caudal fin, the stripe sometimes partially overlaid with blackish; a dark brown blotch in shoulder region, the scales within partly blue; caudal fin blue with two or three diagonal orange bands on upper and lower halves. Philippines to Great Barrier Reef and west to Gulf of Oman; occurs in aggregations on or near reefs, usually where the sea is somewhat turbid and rich in plankton; feeds on zooplankton a meter or more above the substratum; reported from the depth range of 6-45 m; initial-phase fish much more abundant than terminal males. Attains 13 cm.

Leptojulis cyanopleura   Initial phase ▲ Terminal phase ▼

CHOAT'S WRASSE
Macropharyngodon choati Randall, 1978

Dorsal rays IX,11; anal rays III,11; pectoral rays 13; lateral-line scales 27, the anterior scales with 1-4 (usually 2 or 3) pores; head scaleless except for a few small scales on side of nape (true of other species of the genus); lower pharyngeal plate dominated by a very large oval molariform tooth (characteristic of genus); two pairs of large canine teeth anteriorly in upper jaw, the second pair recurved; lower free edge of preopercle very short (also generic); second and third dorsal spines equal to or longer than fourth to sixth; whitish with irregular longitudinal orange bands and blotches and a large black spot on opercle edged dorsally and posteriorly by yellow. Southern Great Barrier Reef; known from depths of less than 1 to over 27 m. Reaches at least 10 cm.

M. choati ▲   *M. kuiteri* ▼

KUITER'S WRASSE
Macropharyngodon kuiteri Randall, 1978

Dorsal rays IX,12; anal rays III,12; pectoral rays 12; lateral-line scales 27, the anterior scales with 1-3 (usually 2) pores; teeth in jaws somewhat spatulate except for canine at corner of mouth; second pair of enlarged teeth at front of upper jaw subtruncate, serving to buttress front pair; caudal peduncle short, its length 2.3-2.5 in depth (1.4-1.9 for other species); dorsal spines progressively longer; females orangish with a bluish white spot in centre of each scale and a black spot as large as eye rimmed in light blue on opercle; body of males yellowish orange with a squarish white spot on each scale; dorsal half of head with six red-edged orange-yellow bands radiating from eye and a large black spot on opercle rimmed with green and blue except dorsally; lower half of head with two short orange-yellow bands. New Caledonia to New South Wales and southern Great Barrier Reef; collected from the depth range of 5-55 m. Largest reported, 10 cm.

BLACKSPOTTED WRASSE
Macropharyngodon meleagris (Valenciennes, 1839)

Dorsal rays IX,11; anal rays III,11; pectoral rays 13; lateral-line scales 27, the anterior scales with 2-4 pores; two pairs of large canines at front of upper jaw, the second pair recurved; third dorsal spine of adults equal to or slightly shorter than fifth and sixth spines; females pale greenish with numerous large irregular black spots on postorbital head and body; front of head with irregular red bands; males dull orange-red with a black and blue-edged green spot on each scale of body and green spots and short bands on head; a black spot in shoulder region with one to three small yellow spots. Islands of Oceania and western Pacific to Cocos-Keeling Islands in the eastern Indian Ocean. Reaches 15 cm. *Leptojulis pardalis* Kner is a synonym.

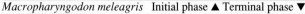

Macropharyngodon meleagris   Initial phase ▲ Terminal phase ▼

BLACK WRASSE
Macropharyngodon negrosensis Herre, 1932

Dorsal rays IX,11; anal rays III,11; pectoral rays 12; lateral-line scales 27, the anterior scales with 2-3 pores; two pairs of large canine teeth at front of upper jaw, the second pair recurved; dorsal spines progressively longer; caudal fin truncate to slightly rounded (slightly rounded in other species of the genus); females black with very small light yellow to blue-green spots or short lines on body and five light yellow blotches along back; dorsal fin light yellow with diagonal dark red to blackish lines; caudal fin abruptly whitish; pelvic and anal fins black; body of males black with blue-green edges on scales; head and thorax dark purplish with very irregular bands of lavender and pale yellow; caudal fin whitish with small light red spots on rays, the upper and lower edges broadly black. Western Pacific; known from the depth range of 8-32 m; not common. Maximum length, 12 cm.

Macropharyngodon negrosensis Adult ▼ Juv. ▲

ROCKMOVER WRASSE
Novaculichthys taeniourus (Lacepède, 1801)

Dorsal rays IX,12; anal rays III,12; pectoral rays 13; lateral-line interrupted, 19-20 pored scales on anterior upper portion and 5-6 on peduncular part; head naked except for two scales on upper opercle and a near-vertical row of small scales behind eye; a pair of large curved canine teeth at front of jaws; body depth 2.65-3.0 in standard length; body width 2.4-3.0 in depth; first two dorsal spines flexible, greatly prolonged in juveniles; adults dark brown with a vertical white line or spot on each scale; abdomen usually reddish; a blue-edged curved black band beneath pectoral-fin base; head grey with irregular black bands radiating posteriorly from eye; two black spots at front of dorsal fin; a white bar at base of caudal fin; juveniles mottled and banded green, reddish, or brown, spotted with white. Indo-Pacific; well known for its ability to overturn large rocks to prey upon invertebrate animals beneath, such as molluscs, crabs, sea urchins, worms, and brittle stars; the young mimic drifting masses of algae. Attains 30 cm.

Novaculichthys taeniourus Juv.

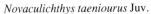

329

DISAPPEARING WRASSE

Pseudocheilinus evanidus Jordan & Evermann, 1903

Dorsal rays IX,11; anal fin III,9; pectoral rays 14; lateral-line interrupted, with 14-16 pored scales in upper anterior part and 4-6 in peduncular part; large scales on head; three pairs of canine teeth at front of upper jaw, the lateral pair curved outward and backward, and one pair anteriorly in lower jaw (true of other *Pseudocheilinus*); preopercular margin smooth; body depth 2.7-3.3 in standard length; second anal spine longer than third (also characteristic of genus); red with whitish longitudinal lines on body and a bluish white streak on cheek. Indo-Pacific; a secretive coral-reef species, like others of the genus. Further study may result in its being placed in a monotypic family. Reaches 8 cm.

SIXSTRIPE WRASSE

Pseudocheilinus hexataenia (Bleeker, 1857)

Dorsal rays IX,11; anal rays III,9; pectoral rays 15-17 (rarely 17); lateral-line 16-18 + 5-6; body depth 2.4-2.7 in standard length; about half of posterior margin of preopercle finely serrate; six dark purplish blue stripes alternating with narrow orange stripes on upper two-thirds of body and extending narrowly onto dorsal part of head; lower part of body purplish orange; lower part of head orange finely dotted with yellow; a pair of blackish dots anteriorly on lower lip (also there may be a faint pair on upper lip); caudal fin green with a small blue-edged black spot at upper base. Indo-Pacific; a common species but usually hidden in reef. Attains 7.5 cm.

EIGHTSTRIPE WRASSE

Pseudocheilinus octotaenia Jenkins, 1900

Dorsal rays IX,11; anal rays III,9; pectoral rays 14; lateral-line scales 16-18 + 5-6; body depth 2.9-3.3 in standard length; margin of preopercle smooth; body lavender-pink with eight magenta to purplish brown stripes, the pink interspaces bisected by a yellow stripe or series of yellow dashes; postorbital head with small yellow spots. Indo-Pacific; known from the depth range of 2-45 m; feeds principally on small benthic crustaceans, but also takes small mollusks and sea urchins. Largest, 13.5 cm.

REDSPOT WRASSE
Pseudocoris yamashiroi (Schmidt, 1930)

Dorsal rays IX,12; anal rays III,12; pectoral rays 13; lateral-line scales 69-73; head scaleless; a single pair of canine teeth anteriorly in jaws, the upper pair strongly curved laterally; remaining teeth in jaws small; no canine at corner of mouth; lower free margin of preopercle longer than upper margin; body moderately elongate, the depth 3.5-4.1 in standard length; first two dorsal spines close together, prolonged in males; caudal fin slightly emarginate; pelvic fins short, 2.2-2.7 in head; females lavender-grey, the centres of scales darker than edges; head behind eye partially blue-green; a large orange-red spot covering pectoral-fin base; axil of pectoral fin and region above blue; males light blue-green on dorsal three-fifths of body, densely spotted with vertically elongate small black spots; lower two-fifths of body bluish white with small yellow spots; head blackish dorsally, shading to bluish grey on side and to blue ventrally; caudal black with a large white semicircular area centrally and posteriorly in fin; juveniles with pale blue-green lines, the most evident being one from front of snout, passing over eye, and along upper part of body, and a second one from mouth, across cheek, and along lower side of body. Micronesia and Samoa to western Pacific; occurs in aggregations, the females greatly outnumbering males; feeds on zooplankton. Reaches 15 cm.

Pseudocoris yamashiroi   Initial phase ▲ Terminal phase ▼

CHISELTOOTH WRASSE
Pseudodax moluccanus (Valenciennes, 1839)

Dorsal rays XI,12; anal rays III,14; pectoral rays 15; lateral-line continuous without a sharp bend, the pored scales 30-31; head scaled except for interorbital, snout, and chin; a pair of large spatulate incisiform teeth anteriorly in jaws, those of lower jaw followed by a second pair; remaining teeth coalesced into a cutting ridge; pharyngeal dentition more like that of parrotfishes than wrasses; caudal fin rounded; grey with a reddish brown spot on each body scale; a wash of orange-red on nape; upper lip yellow with a blue streak above it which crosses lower cheek; teeth blue; caudal fin blackish with a pale yellow bar at base; juveniles dark brown with two blue stripes, one dorsal, one ventral. Indo-Pacific; juveniles have been observed "cleaning" other fishes. The only species of the genus. To 25 cm.

Pseudodax moluccanus   Juv.

SMALLTAIL WRASSE
Pseudojuloides cerasinus (Snyder, 1904)

Dorsal rays IX,11; anal rays III,12; pectoral rays 13; lateral-line scales 27; head scaleless; scales on thorax much smaller than those of body; a single pair of canine teeth at front of jaws; remaining teeth in a single row, almost incisiform; no tooth at corner of mouth; preopercular margin smooth; body slender, the depth 3.8-4.4 in standard length; caudal fin truncate to slightly rounded; females light red, shading to white or pale yellowish ventrally; snout often yellowish; males olive green dorsally, pale blue ventrally, with a double lateral stripe of blue (above) and yellow; caudal greenish yellow with a large vertically elongate blue-edged black spot posteriorly in fin. Indo-Pacific; has been collected from the depth range of 2.5-61 m; rarely seen in less than 20 m; often found over rubble bottoms, closely oriented to the substratum. Largest specimen, 12 cm.

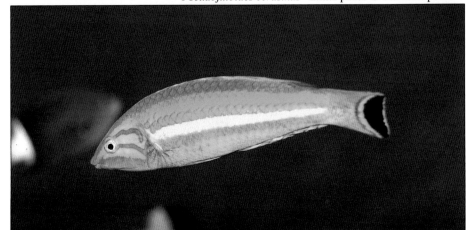

Pseudojuloides cerasinus   Initial phase ▲ Terminal phase ▼

GÜNTHER'S WRASSE
Pseudolabrus guentheri Bleeker, 1862

Dorsal rays IX,11; anal rays III,10; pectoral rays 13; lateral-line scales 25-26; rows of scales behind eye 2; cheek scale rows below eye 4-6; a single pair of enlarged canine teeth anteriorly in upper jaw and two pairs in lower; a canine at corner of mouth; dorsal and anal fins with a low scaly sheath; caudal fin rounded; initial phase reddish brown to green, often with five to seven faint dark bars on body; two longitudinal rows of small black spots along back; alternating stripes of pale orange-red and reddish brown to green on head and anterior body; a dark spot at front of dorsal fin with red on fin margin above; terminal males more brightly coloured, the dark bars more evident, and tend to lose the small black spots on back. New South Wales to southern Great Barrier Reef, from the shallows to about 20 m; feeds mainly on small benthic crustaceans. Largest specimen, 18 cm.

Pseudolabrus guentheri   Initial phase ▲ Terminal phase ▼

REDSTRIPED WRASSE
Pteragogus amboinensis (Bleeker, 1856)

Dorsal rays IX,11; anal rays III,9; pectoral rays 13; lateral-line scales 24; head with large scales except interorbital, snout, and chin; scales on thorax not much smaller than those on rest of body; two pairs of canine teeth anteriorly in jaws, the lateral pairs larger and outcurved, especially the upper pair; posterior margin of preopercle with numerous sharp serrae; body moderately deep, the depth 2.3-2.5 in standard length; males with filaments extending from first two dorsal spines (though not as long as spine length); caudal fin rounded; pelvic fins short, not reaching or just reaching anal fin origin; back above lateral line brownish red, below yellowish brown with red stripes following centres of scale rows; median fins heavily striped with red; a faint dark spot on opercle; some small dark brown spots on head behind eye and on nape. Indonesia to the Coral Sea; rarely seen underwater due to its secretive habits. Reported to 15 cm.

CRYPTIC WRASSE
Pteragogus cryptus Randall, 1981

Dorsal rays X,10; anal rays III,9; pectoral rays 13; lateral-line scales 24;scales and dentition as above; males with long filaments from membrane tips of first four dorsal spines; caudal fin rounded; pelvic fins short, not reaching or just reaching origin of anal fin; mottled red to reddish brown with a yellow-edged dark spot on opercle, a small dark spot behind eye, one enclosing anterior nostril, and one on first membrane of dorsal fin; small whitish and dark brown spots along lateral line. Red Sea and western Pacific to Micronesia and Samoa; known from the depth range of 2-60 m; very secretive; tends to hide in algae or soft corals, exposing itself only briefly as it moves from one area of cover to another. Largest specimen, 9.5 cm.

BLUELINED WRASSE
Stethojulis bandanensis (Bleeker, 1851)

Dorsal rays IX,11; anal rays III,11; pectoral rays 14-15 (rarely 15); lateral-line scales 25; head scaleless, and scales on thorax as large as those on rest of body (characteristic of *Stethojulis*); gill rakers 27-30; small incisiform teeth in jaws, none notably enlarged, and a canine at corner of mouth (true of other species of genus); body depth 2.9-3.3 in standard length; base of pectoral fins about 30° to the horizontal (also a generic character); upper half of head and body of initial phase dark grey finely dotted with white, lower half with basal half of scales dark grey, outer half white; a bright red spot above upper base of pectoral fin; one to three (usually two) small blue-edged black spots midlaterally at rear of caudal peduncle; body of terminal male bluish to greenish grey dorsally, abruptly pale bluish ventrally, the two zones separated by a light blue line; a crescentic bright red spot above pectoral-fin base; four blue lines on head, the uppermost passing along base of dorsal fin, the second stopping on nape, the third rimming upper edge of red spot and continuing onto front third of body, the fourth on lower head, then angling upward to join lateral blue line of body. Islands of the tropical eastern Pacific, Oceania (except Hawaii where re-

Stethojulis bandanensis Initial phase ▲ Terminal phase ▼

placed by *S. balteata*), and western Pacific; a shallow-water coral-reef species; like others of the genus, an active swimmer. To

12.5 cm. *S. rubromacula* Scott and *S. linearis* Schultz are synonyms based on the terminal-male form.

CUTRIBBON WRASSE
Stethojulis interrupta (Bleeker, 1851)

Dorsal rays IX,11; anal rays III,11; pectoral rays 12-13 (rarely 12); lateral-line scales 25; gill rakers 19-23; body depth 3.6-4.1 in standard length; initial phase yellowish brown to brownish grey (and occasionally pale red) with bluish white dots and short lines on back, white below with black dots, the two zones usually separated by a diffuse blackish streak that contains pale blue longitudinal lines; often a wash of red extending anteriorly from axil and upper base of pectoral fin; terminal male greenish to yellowish grey on upper half of body, abruptly white below, the two zones separated by a blue line on posterior half of body and beneath pectoral-fin base; a bright orange-red spot above base of pectoral fin; a blue line from top of head along base of dorsal fin, and two blue lines on head passing anteriorly and posteriorly from eye. Samoa and Mariana Islands to East Africa; like others of the genus, feeds mainly by sorting small animals from mouthfuls of sand and detritus taken by quick pecks at the substratum. Attains 13 cm. *S. kalosoma* (Bleeker) is a synonym based on the initial phase.

Stethojulis interrupta Initial phase ▲ Terminal phase ▼

STRIPEBELLY WRASSE
Stethojulis strigiventer (Bennett, 1832)

Dorsal rays IX,11; anal rays III,11; pectoral rays 15 (rarely 14); lateral-line scales 25; gill rakers 24-28; body depth 3.5-3.9 in standard length; initial phase greenish to brownish grey dorsally with faint whitish longitudinal lines, white ventrally with dark longitudinal lines; a small blue-edged dark spot at base of caudal fin above lateral line and another at rear base of dorsal fin; terminal male greenish to yellowish brown dorsally, white ventrally, with blue lines as follows: top of head along base of dorsal fin, snout through eye and upper end of gill opening to middle of caudal fin, upper lip to upper edge of pectoral-fin base, and edge of gill opening beneath lower pectoral base to middle of body; region of overlap of two lower blue lines at pectoral-fin base bright red; a small black spot on upper part of opercular flap, and the same black spot at caudal-fin base as initial phase, but without blue rim. Micronesia and Samoa to East Africa; usually found on algal flats, seagrass beds, or sandy areas around reefs. Reaches 15 cm. *S. renardi* (Bleeker) is a synonym based on the terminal-male phase.

THREE-RIBBON WRASSE
Stethojulis trilineata (Bloch & Schneider, 1801)

Dorsal rays IX,11; anal rays III,11; pectoral rays 12-13 (rarely 12); lateral-line scales 25; gill rakers 25-28; body depth 2.85-3.3 in standard length; upper half of head and upper two-thirds of body greenish to brownish grey with numerous whitish dots, white ventrally with a small black spot on each body scale; a salmon pink stripe on body between upper dark and lower white zones; a blackish spot on the two pored scales of lateral line on caudal-fin base; terminal male green on upper two-thirds of body, shading to orange-yellow anteriorly and on head, abruptly greenish white ventrally; four dark-edged longitudinal blue lines on head and body, three passing posteriorly and one ending above pectoral-fin base; dorsal fin bright red; caudal fin yellow. Western Pacific to Maldives; a fast-moving shallow-water fish often found on exposed reefs. Attains 15 cm. *S. phekadopleura* (Bleeker) is a synonym based on the initial phase.

Stethojulis strigiventer Initial phase ▲ Terminal phase ▼

Stethojulis trilineata Initial phase ▲ Terminal phase ▼

SLENDER WRASSE
Suezichthys gracilis (Steindachner & Döderlein)

Dorsal rays IX,11; anal rays III,10; pectoral rays 13-14; lateral-line scales 25-26; scale rows above lateral line 1.5; predorsal scales 4-5; cheek scale rows behind eye 2-3; cheek scale rows below eye 3; a pair of curved canine teeth at front of upper jaw and two pairs of smaller canines at front of lower; a canine at corner of mouth; body slender, the depth 4.0-4.8 in standard length; caudal fin slightly rounded; initial phase with a brownish orange stripe, narrowly edged in dark brown anteriorly, passing from front of snout through eye, along upper side, and ending in a blackish spot at upper caudal-fin base; a small blue and blackish spot within stripe above pectoral fin; body above stripe dull salmon, below white, some scales faintly marked with light red; terminal males similar but with a blue longitudinal band in dorsal and anal fins and a blue-edged V-shaped orange band in caudal fin. Antitropical; known from southern Japan, Korea, and Taiwan in the north, and New Caledonia to southern Great Barrier Reef and New South Wales in the south; the food has been reported from Japan as amphipods, other small crustaceans, and polychaete worms. Attains at least 10 cm.

Thalassoma amblycephalum   Initial phase ▲ Terminal phase ▼

BLUNTHEADED WRASSE
Thalassoma amblycephalum (Bleeker, 1856)

Dorsal rays VIII,13; anal rays III,11; pectoral rays 15; lateral-line scales 26-27; head scaleless; scales on thorax about half size of those on body (true of all *Thalassoma*); gill rakers 16-19; jaws with one pair of canine teeth anteriorly, followed by progressively shorter conical teeth; no canine at corner of mouth (dentition essentially the same for all *Thalassoma*); body depth 3.8-4.2 in standard length; caudal fin truncate to slightly emarginate, becoming lunate in large males; initial phase with a broad blackish stripe from snout through eye to upper caudal-fin base; body above stripe greenish to yellowish, below white; lobes of caudal fin orange, this colour broader basally; terminal males reddish with vertical green lines on body; nape and anterior body below first four or five dorsal spines yellow, this colour sometimes continuing onto thorax; head green with two golden lines; pectoral fins yellow with a large elongate black-edged blue spot on outer part of fin. Indo-Pacific; occurs in aggregations over shallow reefs; feeds on zooplankton; initial-phase fish far more numerous than terminal males. Reaches 16 cm. *T. melanochir* (Bleeker) is a synonym based on the terminal-male form.

SIXBAR WRASSE
Thalassoma hardwicke (Bennett, 1828)

Dorsal rays VIII,13; anal rays III,11; pectoral rays 16; lateral-line scales 25; head

naked except for a patch of small scales dorsally on opercle; body depth 2.9-3.2 in standard length; caudal fin truncate in young, emarginate in adults; initial phase light green with six wedge-shaped slightly diagonal

dark bars (mixed blackish and red) dorsally on body which are progressively shorter posteriorly; terminal males green dorsally, blue ventrally, the six bars solid black, the first five extending basally into dorsal fin; a midlateral pink stripe on body (more evident posteriorly); broad deep pink bands radiating from eye and two diagonal reddish black bands on nape. Indo-Pacific; a common shallow-water reef fish. Attains 18 cm. *T. schwanefeldii* (Bleeker) is a synonym.

JANSEN'S WRASSE
Thalassoma jansenii (Bleeker, 1856)

Dorsal rays VIII,13; anal rays III,11; pectoral rays 15-16 (usually 15); lateral-line scales 26-27; gill rakers 20-23; body depth 3.3-3.9 in standard length; caudal fin truncate in young, slightly emarginate in initial phase, and very lunate in large terminal males; initial phase white with three broad black bars, the first on upper half of head and anterior body, containing a yellow streak at edge of opercle, the second across spinous dorsal fin from fourth to last dorsal spines and narrowing to anus, the third covering most of soft portions of dorsal and anal fins and the body between; posterior caudal peduncle and base of caudal fin light yellow; terminal male with more yellow than white on body, the black bars on body somewhat reduced, and pectoral fins partly blue. Fiji and western Pacific to Maldives, the Indonesian and Indian Ocean form with more black bars; often found on reef flats at depths of a meter or less. Reaches 20 cm.

MOON WRASSE
Thalassoma lunare (Linnaeus, 1758)

Dorsal rays VIII,13; anal rays III,11; pectoral rays 15; lateral-line scales 25; head naked except for a small patch of scales dorsally on opercle; gill rakers 18-20; body depth 3.1-3.7 in standard length; caudal fin varying from truncate in juveniles to very lunate in larger terminal males; initial phase green with vertical red lines on scales; head green with many irregular rose pink bands; a blue-edged rose pink band in each lobe of caudal fin, the broad central and posterior part of fin yellow; pectoral fins blue with a broad pink band in upper central part; terminal males similar but more blue overall (still more blue in courtship); juveniles with a large black spot in middle of dorsal fin and a large diffuse blackish spot at caudal-fin base. Indo-Pacific; an active bold fish that feeds mainly on benthic invertebrates and small fishes. Maximum length 25 cm.

SUNSET WRASSE
Thalassoma lutescens (Lay & Bennett, 1839)

Dorsal rays VIII,13-14 (usually 13); anal rays III,11; pectoral rays 15-17 (usually 16); lateral-line scales 25; head naked except for a patch of small scales dorsally on opercle; gill rakers 20-23; body depth 3.0-3.5 in standard length; caudal fin varying from slightly rounded in juveniles to lunate with prolonged lobes in large terminal males; initial phase yellow to greenish yellow with vertical light orange-red lines on body and faint light red bands on head; head and anterior body of terminal males rose pink with narrow curved green bands, followed by a broad zone of blue, shading to greenish yellow posteriorly; caudal fin yellow with a blue-edged salmon pink band in each lobe; pectoral fins yellow, black distally, with a broad submarginal blue band; juveniles with a black lateral stripe ending in a black spot at caudal-fin base; body above stripe yellow or green (rarely red), white below with a faint orange ventral stripe. Tropical eastern Pacific, islands of Oceania (including Easter), the western Pacific, and Christmas Island, eastern Indian Ocean; feeds most heavily on benthic crabs and shrimps, but also on molluscs, polychaete worms, brittle stars, and sea urchins. Largest, 24.7 cm.

Thalassoma lutescens Initial phase ▲ Terminal phase ▼

SURGE WRASSE
Thalassoma purpureum (Forsskål, 1775)

Dorsal rays VIII,13; anal rays III,11; pectoral rays 15-17 (nearly always 16); lateral-line scales 25; head naked except for a patch of small scales dorsally on opercle; gill rakers 20-25 (modally 23); body depth 2.8-3.6 in standard length (larger fish deeper bodied, in general); caudal fin slightly rounded to truncate, the lobes prolonged in terminal males; initial phase green with two red stripes and vertical lines which divide the green on side of body to two series of vertically elongate subrectangular close-set spots; head with irregular pink to maroon spots and short lines (one diagnostic marking a vertical line on side of snout before and below eye which may branch to form a Y); a large Y-shaped pink band at and below pectoral-fin base; terminal males green dorsally, shading ventrally to blue-green or blue, with three pink to magenta stripes with irregular margins; head blue-green to blue with broad irregular deep pink bands, one extending diagonally downward toward pectoral base, branching as it crosses preopercle; caudal and paired fins blue, the caudal sometimes with lavender-pink markings basally and in lobes. Indo-Pacific; occurs on reefs and rocky shores exposed to surge; may be found in surprisingly shallow water; a very active fish, constantly on the move; feeds mainly on crabs, sea urchins, brittle stars, and small fishes. Attains 43 cm. *T. umbrostygma* Rüppell is a synonym based on the initial phase.

Thalassoma purpureum Terminal phase

FIVESTRIPE WRASSE
Thalassoma quinquevittatum (Lay & Bennett, 1839)

Dorsal rays VIII,13; anal rays III,11; pectoral rays 15-17 (usually 16); lateral-line scales 25; head naked except for a patch of small scales dorsally on opercle; gill rakers 20-25; body depth 3.2-3.6 in standard length; caudal fin varying from slightly rounded in young to emarginate in adults; upper two-thirds of body of initial phase with green and rose pink stripes, the uppermost green stripe along back and on base of dorsal fin; second green stripe a series of close-set vertically elongate spots which merge to a solid band posteriorly; thorax and anterior abdomen with two very oblique rose red bands alternating with green or blue; head with alternating bands of red and green, the ventral green one a semicircle with upper convex end touching lower edge of eye; a pink to red band in lobes of caudal fin; terminal males with the same basic pattern but head violet to purple with green bands except space between lower two green bands behind eye which is red; green of body posterior to pectoral-fin base may be altered mainly to yellow; juveniles with a row of small black spots along base of dorsal fin and two larger black spots in fin. Indo-Pacific; known from coral reefs at depths of less than a meter to 40 m; feeds mainly on crabs, shrimps, small fishes, gastropod molluscs, and sea urchins. Reaches 17 cm.

Initial phase ▲ Terminal phase ▼

LADDER WRASSE
Thalassoma trilobatum (Lacepède, 1801)

Dorsal rays VIII,13; anal rays III,11; pectoral rays 15-17 (usually 16); lateral-line scales 25; head naked except for a patch of small scales dorsally on opercle; gill rakers 17-24 (usually 19-21); body depth 2.75-3.6 in standard length; caudal fin of initial phase slightly rounded to truncate, of terminal males truncate to slightly double emarginate; initial phase coloured like that of *T. purpureum* except the pink to maroon mark on side of snout in front of eye is not a vertical line but in a C shape continuing diagonally below eye; body of terminal male salmon pink to orange with two longitudinal rows of close-set vertically elongate subrectangular green to blue-green spots on side; four green spots of upper row with dorsal extensions linking to irregular green band at base of dorsal fin; head and thorax orange-brown without markings; caudal fin greenish to brownish orange, shading distally to pink, the outer third of rays blue. Indo-Pacific; also an inshore species most often found in areas exposed to wave action, but does not penetrate water as shallow as *T. purpureum*, in general; feeds primarily on crustaceans (especially crabs), mollusks, and brittle stars. Largest specimen, 30 cm. Often identified as *T. fuscum* (Lacepède), but this name is invalid due to homonymy.

WHITEBANDED SHARPNOSE WRASSE
Wetmorella albofasciata Schultz and Marshall, 1954

Dorsal rays IX,10; anal rays III,8; pectoral rays 12; lateral-line interrupted, the pored scales 13-15 + 5-7; head with large scales; preopercular edge scaled over (true of *W. nigropinnata*); gill rakers 11-16; head pointed, the dorsal profile straight (also characteristic of *nigropinnata*); body depth 2.8-3.3 in standard length; longest dorsal spine 1.9-2.25 in head; third anal spine 2.0-2.3 in head; greyish to reddish brown with three white bars narrower than pupil on body and three radiating from eye; a large black spot on abdomen between pelvic fins and one on soft portions of dorsal, anal, and pelvic fins. Indo-Pacific; specimens from 10-42 m, but most from 30 m or more; rarely seen underwater (we have observed it only fleetingly in deep recesses in caves). Largest, 5.5 cm.

SHARPNOSE WRASSE
Wetmorella nigropinnata (Seale, 1901)

Dorsal rays IX,10; anal rays III,8; pectoral rays 12; lateral line interrupted, the pored scales 13-15 + 5-7; gill rakers 12-17; body

depth 2.55-3.15 in standard length; longest dorsal spine 1.7-2.05 in head; third anal spine 1.7-2.1 in head; a dark-edged yellow bar on head behind and adjacent to eye and a second one at front of caudal peduncle; juveniles, in addition, with two broad pale bars on body; black spots on fins and ventrally on abdomen as in *W. albofasciata*. Indo-Pacific; known from the depth range of 1-30 m; collected from caves and crevices; like the preceding species, rarely seen underwater. Attains 8 cm. *W. philippina* Fowler & Bean, *W. ocellata* Schultz & Marshall, and *W. triocellata* Schultz & Marshall are synonyms.

WHITEPATCH RAZORFISH
Xyrichtys aneitensis (Günther, 1862)

Dorsal rays IX,12; anal rays III,12; pectoral rays 12; lateral line interrupted, the pored scales 20-22 + 4-5; a band of small scales rimming lower posterior part of eye and continuing vertically downward from eye (but not reaching to or below corner of mouth); two small scales dorsally on opercle; a pair of long curved canine teeth anteriorly in jaws (true of other *Xyrichtys*); dorsal profile of snout of adults nearly vertical, the fleshy leading edge sharp (also characteristic of the genus); body depth 2.6-3.0 in standard length; origin of dorsal fin slightly anterior to upper end of preopercular margin; space between second and third dorsal spines nearly twice space between first two spines; membrane between second and third dorsal spines incised more than half length of third spine; first two dorsal spines flexible and curved, not higher than longest dorsal soft ray; light grey with three faint narrow dusky bars on body, the middle one ending dorsally in a black spot at base of second to third dorsal rays; a large circular white patch on lower side partly covered by pectoral fin (scales within white patch of females with blue on bases); a diagonal dusky area adjacent to upper anterior edge of white patch in females (yellow in males); a faint vertical blue line passing ventrally from front edge of eye. Central and western Pacific; lives on open clean sand areas at depths of about 6 to at least 35 m. To 20 cm.

W. albofasciata ▲   *W. nigropinnata* ▼

Xyrichtys aneitensis

PAVO RAZORFISH
Xyrichtys pavo Valenciennes, 1840

Dorsal rays II-VII,12; anal rays III,12; pectoral rays 12; lateral-line interrupted, the pored scales 20-22 + 4-5; one or two short rows of small scales from behind to below eye and one or two scales dorsally on opercle; body depth of adults 2.4-2.7 in standard length (of juveniles 2.8-3.3); first two dorsal spines separated from rest of fin, originating over posterior edge of eye, flexible and prolonged (greatly elongate in juveniles); caudal fin small, slightly rounded; adults grey dorsally, yellowish white ventrally, with three indistinct broad dark bars on body and one at caudal-fin base; a small black spot, partially rimmed in light blue, just above eighth lateral-line scale; juveniles with dark bars more evident than adults and may have two ocellated black spots in soft portion of dorsal fin; still smaller juveniles may be primarily dark brown. Indo-Pacific; lives on open sand areas near reefs; dives into sand with the approach of danger; juveniles hold the elongate detached front part of dorsal fin forward over head and mimic drifting dead leaves. Attains about 35 cm.

Xyrichtys pavo Juv.

FIVEFINGER RAZORFISH
Xyrichtys pentadactylus (Linnaeus, 1758)

Dorsal rays IX,12; anal rays III,12; pectoral rays 12; lateral-line scales 20 + 4-5; about eight vertical rows of small scales on cheek from below eye to below level of mouth, and a few scales dorsally on opercle; body depth of adults 2.8-3.0 in standard length; origin of dorsal fin over rear edge of eye; space between second and third spines notably greater that between any other adjacent spines; membrane between second and third spines incised about two-thirds length of spines; females light grey with a blackish spot on side between tip of pectoral fin and lateral line; most scales of body with an orange-red dot; upper abdomen with a pale pink area crossed by diagonal red lines; males with a less distinct blackish spot on upper side, no red dots, and no pink area on abdomen; a series of dark red spots (usually five or six) nearly as large as eye in a row from behind eye along anterior lateral line. Western Pacific to East Africa and Red Sea; found over open sand areas or areas with some seagrass or algae; like other razorfishes, dives head-first into sand when threatened. To 25 cm.

PARROTFISHES
FAMILY SCARIDAE

Parrotfishes are aptly named for their bright colours and the fusion of their teeth to form beak-like plates in the jaws. They are rather homogeneous in general morphology; all have an unnotched dorsal fin of IX,10 rays and an anal fin of III,9 rays; the scales are cycloid and relatively large, 22-24 in the lateral line; their dental plates have a median suture, and adults may have one or two short canine teeth posteriorly on the side of these plates; the pharyngeal dentition is unusual; each of the interlocking upper pharyngeal bones has one to three rows of molariform teeth which form a convex surface that bears against the concave molar-studded surface of the single lower pharyngeal bone. This family of fishes has clearly evolved from the wrasse family, and a few ichthyologists have considered classifying it as a subfamily of the Labridae. However, parrotfishes are very distinct in having fused teeth in the jaws, unique pharyngeal dentition, a very long intestine, no true stomach, and by being herbivorous. They feed mainly on benthic algae which they scrape from dead coral rock, at the same time often removing some of the surface layer of limestone. The algae and rock fragments are ground together in their pharyngeal mill, thus making the algae more digestible. The bits of rock are rendered to sand in the process. It is now realized that scarid fishes are a major producer of sediment in tropical and subtropical seas. A few of the larger parrotfishes feed in part on live coral. Like the wrasses, parrotfishes usually exhibit two strikingly different adult colour patterns. The first mature phase, sometimes only female but more often both male and female, is called the initial phase. Females of most species in this phase are able to alter their sex to male and undergo a change in colour to the terminal phase; this is usually gaudier than the colour of the initial phase and often dominated by green. Many of the species have two patterns of reproduction: group spawning of initial-phase fish from aggregations in which males greatly outnumber females, and pair spawning by an initial-phase female and a terminal male. In both cases eggs and sperm are released into the sea at the peak of a very rapid upward rush. Terminal males tend to establish sexual territories and maintain harems of females. Some of the species have juvenile colour patterns very different from that of adults; several have dark brown stripes. Normal swimming is achieved by the pectoral fins; the tail is brought into action only when speed is needed, as during spawning, to chase a rival male, or to escape predation. These fishes sleep at night in small caves or beneath ledges; some secrete a veil-like mass of mucus around themselves during the night.

Parrotfish in mucus envelope

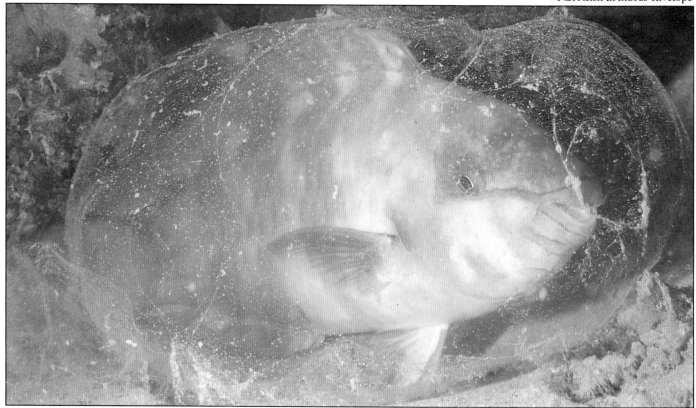

BUMPHEAD PARROTFISH
Bolbometopon muricatum (Valenciennes, 1840)

Pectoral rays usually 16; median predorsal scales 2-5 (usually 4); three rows of scales on cheek, the lower row with 1 or 2 scales; one row of scales on interopercle; dental plates largely exposed, each tooth forming a small bump on the plate surface; no canine teeth on plates; dorsal profile of head with a prominent convexity before and above eye (evident on individuals as small as 25 cm); body depth 2.05-2.5 in standard length; caudal fin rounded, the lobes slightly prolonged in adults; adults dull green, the front of the head pale yellowish to pink; juveniles greenish to brown with five vertical rows of small whitish spots. Line Islands and Samoa in the Central Pacific to East Africa and the Red Sea; usually seen in small aggregations; difficult to approach; feeds on benthic algae and live coral. The largest of the parrotfishes; reaches 120 cm; one of 117 cm weighed 46 kg.

STAREYE PARROTFISH
Calotomus carolinus (Valenciennes, 1840)

Pectoral rays 13; median predorsal scales 3-4 (usually 4); a single row of 4 or 5 scales on cheek below eye; teeth not fully fused to form plates, the individual flattened teeth readily apparent on outer surface of jaws, imbricate, the tips of outer row forming a jagged cutting edge; lips nearly covering teeth; dorsal spines flexible; body depth 2.2-2.75 in standard length; caudal fin slightly rounded in juveniles, truncate in subadults, and truncate with lobes prolonged in adults; initial phase mottled dark orangish brown, shading ventrally to pale orangish; base of pectoral fins dark; posterior margin of caudal fin narrowly white; body of terminal males a mixture of brownish red and blue-green; head blue-green with orange-pink bands radiating from eye. Indo-Pacific and tropical eastern Pacific. Reported to 50 cm. Often misidentified as *C. spinidens*; *C. sandwicensis* (Valenciennes) is a synonym.

Calotomus carolinus Initial phase ▲ Terminal phase ▼

RAGGEDTOOTH PARROTFISH
Calotomus spinidens (Quoy and Gaimard, 1824)

Pectoral rays 13; median predorsal scales 4; a single row of 4 or 5 scales on cheek below eye; dentition as in *C. carolinus*; lips nearly covering teeth; body depth 2.7-3.1 in standard length; dorsal spines flexible; caudal fin rounded; initial phase mottled reddish to greyish brown, often with three longitudinal rows of whitish spots (some-

times with faint broad stripes); upper and lower edges of caudal fin with small dusky spots; terminal males with faint orangish spots on body, small orange spots and short lines on head, a blackish bar at pectoral-fin base, and a broad dark margin on anal fin. Marshall Islands and Tonga to East Africa; occurs in seagrass beds or substrata with heavy algal growth; can alter its colour quickly to match its surroundings. A small species, the largest 19 cm.

BICOLOUR PARROTFISH
Cetoscarus bicolor (Rüppell, 1829)

'Pectoral rays 14-15 (usually 14); median predorsal scales 5-7 (usually 6); three rows of scales on cheek, the lower row with 3-7 scales; outer surface of dental plates nodular (smooth on *Hipposcarus* and *Scarus*); no canine teeth on dental plates; lips largely covering dental plates; snout long,1.8-2.2 in head; caudal fin emarginate; initial phase reddish brown, yellow on back, the scales on side rimmed and spotted with black; terminal males green, the edges of scales pink, the head and anterior body finely spotted with pink (orange in dead fish); juveniles white with a broad orange bar covering head except snout and chin, and an orange-edged black spot in dorsal fin. Indo-Pacific. Attains about 80 cm. *Scarus pulchellus* Rüppell is a synonym based on the terminal-male phase.

Cetoscarus bicolor   Initial phase ▲ Terminal phase ▼

Cetoscarus bicolor   Juv.

PACIFIC LONGNOSE PARROTFISH
Hipposcarus longiceps (Valenciennes, 1840)

Pectoral rays 15; median predorsal scales 4; cheek scales small, in a nearly isolated subtriangular patch; dental plates narrow, their height 1.5-2.0 in eye diameter; terminal male with one or two canine teeth on upper dental plate; head pointed; caudal fin rounded with slightly prolonged lobes; initial phase pale grey, the caudal peduncle and fin yellowish; terminal male light blue, the scales edged with orange; margin of upper lip orange; fins blue and orange; juveniles with an orange lateral stripe ending in a black spot at caudal-fin base. Western Pacific east to French Polynesia; often seen in aggregations; more common in lagoons than outer reef areas. Reaches 40 cm.

Hipposcarus longiceps   Terminal phase (Night) ▼ Juv. ▲

SLENDER PARROTFISH
Leptoscarus vaigiensis (Quoy & Gaimard, 1824)

Pectoral rays 13; median predorsal scales usually 4; a single row of scales on cheek below eye; oblique rows of teeth fused to form dental plates, the upper enclosed by lower when mouth closed; lips covering dental plates; body elongate, the depth 2.9-3.8 in standard length; dorsal spines flexible, the interspinous membranes distinctly incised; caudal fin rounded; mottled olive to brown, shading to dull yellow or pale greenish ventrally; fins mottled yellowish; males with small blue spots on head, body, anal, and caudal fin. Indo-Pacific, from scattered localities; occurs in seagrass beds or weedy bottoms where it is well camouflaged. Reported to 35 cm. Also called the Marbled Parrotfish.

MINIFIN PARROTFISH
Scarus altipinnis (Steindachner, 1879)

Pectoral rays 15; median predorsal scales 5-6; three rows of scales on cheek, the lower row with 1-3 scales; one or two canine teeth on side of upper dental plate; dental plates exposed, dark green in both colour phases; spinous portion of dorsal fin distinctly higher than soft, the distal part of last spine and first soft ray extended as a short filament in adults; caudal fin rounded, the lobes prolonged in adults; initial phase reddish brown with four or five vertical series of very small whitish spots; terminal male green posteriorly on body, the scales edged and finely spotted with salmon pink, salmon anteriorly, densely spotted with green; head orange, suffused with green posteriorly, with a very broad transverse blue-green band at front of snout and two on chin; region around eye and postorbital head with numerous blue-green spots and short lines; juveniles dark grey with scattered small white spots, shading to whitish on caudal peduncle and fin and to yellow on snout. Islands of Oceania and Great Barrier Reef; usually found in outer reef areas, often in shallow water; frequently seen in large aggregations. To 60 cm. *S. brevifilis* (Günther) is a synonym. Terminal male sometimes misidentified as *S. chlorodon* Jenyns, a synonym of the related western Pacific-Indian Ocean *S. prasiognathos* Valenciennes.

Scarus altipinnis Juv.

Scarus altipinnis Initial phase ▲ Terminal phase ▼

BLEEKER'S PARROTFISH
Scarus bleekeri (de Beaufort, 1940)

Pectoral rays 15; median predorsal scales 4; two rows of scales on cheek; one or two canine teeth on side of upper dental plate; lips not covering dental plates; caudal fin truncate; initial phase dark brown (sometimes showing about four narrow pale yellowish bars on body), the scale edges narrowly orange, shading to dull orange-red ventrally and to yellowish posteriorly on caudal peduncle and base of fin; upper lip with a narrow orange margin and broad submarginal dark blue-green band; chin orange with three transverse dark blue-green bands; terminal males green with a salmon pink bar on each scale; a large whitish area on cheek bordered by green, this border linked anteriorly to two narrow blue-green bands on chin. Western Pacific east to Fiji and islands of Micronesia. Reaches about 30 cm.

Scarus bleekeri   Initial phase ▲ Terminal phase ▼

CHAMELEON PARROTFISH
Scarus chameleon Choat & Randall, 1986

Pectoral rays 14; median predorsal scales 4, preceded by a pair of medially overlapping scales; three rows of scales on cheek, the lower with 1-3 scales; lips covering about three-fourths of dental plates; one or two canine teeth posteriorly on side of dental plates of large adults; caudal fin of initial phase slightly rounded to slightly emarginate, of terminal males emarginate to lunate; initial phase brown, the lower third of body often abruptly pale; dorsal fin orangish brown with a violet-grey margin; unscaled part of caudal fin brownish yellow; terminal male with a broad zone of salmon pink anteriorly on lower side of body, the scales above and posteriorly salmon pink with a green bar; head with a blue-green band crossing upper interorbital space; central part of caudal fin with a large D-shaped blue-green mark. Western Pacific east to Fiji and west to Western Australia; occurs in a variety of reef habitats from depths of 1 to at least 30 m; named for the ability of both phases to alter their colour to several different patterns. Largest, 31 cm.

Scarus chameleon   Initial phase ▲ Terminal phase ▼

346

YELLOWBARRED PARROTFISH
Scarus dimidiatus Bleeker, 1859

Pectoral rays 14; median predorsal scales 5-6 (rarely 5); three rows of scales on cheek, the lower row with 1-4 scales; no canine teeth on side of dental plates; lips usually covering or nearly covering dental plates; caudal fin slightly rounded to truncate; initial phase light greyish yellow with four alternating slightly diagonal bars of dark grey and yellow on back; upper half of head dark grey, darkest in a stripe extending posteriorly from eye; caudal fin yellow; terminal male with a dark grey stripe extending back from eye, the head above it and anterior body above pectoral fin solid blue-green; rest of body green, the scales rimmed with salmon pink; a green-edged whitish streak on cheek below dark grey stripe, the green extending forward as a band which broadens to cover chin and front of snout; unscaled part of caudal fin blue-green. Western Pacific east to Samoa and islands of Micronesia; usually found on shallow protected reefs of lagoons and bays. Attains about 30 cm.

Scarus dimidiatus Initial phase ▲ Terminal phase ▼

YELLOWFIN PARROTFISH
Scarus flavipectoralis Schultz, 1958

Pectoral rays 14; median predorsal scales 4, the second scale largest; three rows of scales on cheek, the lower row with 1-2 scales; terminal males with one or two canine teeth posteriorly on side of lower dental plate and one on upper; lips nearly covering dental plates; caudal fin truncate in initial phase, emarginate in terminal male; initial phase grey to brown, darker on head, paler ventrally with faint whitish stripes on abdomen; caudal fin dark purplish grey; pectoral fins clear yellowish, brighter yellow at base with a black spot at upper corner; terminal male with head and anterior body beneath and above pectoral fin orangish brown, becoming abruptly green elsewhere on body with a salmon pink bar on each scale; a broad blue-green band from front of snout to above pectoral base; snout and interorbital space lavender-grey. Philippines to southern Great Barrier Reef, east to Marshall Islands; occurs in sheltered areas, often deeper than other scarid fishes. To 30 cm.

Scarus flavipectoralis Initial phase ▲ Terminal phase ▼

WHITESPOT PARROTFISH
Scarus forsteni (Bleeker, 1861)

Pectoral rays 13-14 (rarely 13); median predorsal scales 6-7; three rows of scales on cheek, the lower row with 2-5 scales; large adults with one to two canine teeth posteriorly on upper dental plate; lips partially covering dental plates; caudal fin of initial phase emarginate, of terminal male lunate; initial phase reddish brown dorsally, pale reddish ventrally, with a broad bluish zone on side of body extending anteriorly to eye; a white spot on side near tip of pectoral fin in life; caudal fin orange-red; terminal male green, the scale edges of body salmon pink; dorsal part of head above eye and on to nape violet; region around mouth broadly dark blue-green, continuing as a streak to below eye; margin of upper lip narrowly salmon pink; dental plates dark blue-green; dorsal and anal fins blue-green with a basal salmon pink band which broadens posteriorly; unscaled part of caudal fin blue-green except for a salmon pink band in each lobe. Pitcairn Group and islands of Micronesia to western Pacific; usually found on exposed outer reefs. Attains 55 cm.

BRIDLED PARROTFISH
Scarus frenatus Lacepède, 1802

Pectoral rays 14-15 (usually 14); median predorsal scales 6-7, with two small scales side by side anterior to first median predorsal; three rows of scales on cheek, with 2-4 scales in lower row; lips covering most of dental plates, the mouth slightly inferior; 0-2 canine teeth posteriorly on side of upper dental plate; caudal fin truncate in small adults to double emarginate with prolonged lobes in large terminal males; initial phase brownish yellow to reddish brown, paler on caudal peduncle, with six dark brown stripes on side of body following centres of scale rows; fins red; terminal male green, the scales of anterior two-thirds of body and dorsal half of head with orange vermiculations; lower half of head green with a salmon pink band on each lip and some irregular salmon pink markings, especially ventrally; dental plates blue-green; caudal fin blue-green with a large arc of orange containing

Scarus frenatus Juv.

green markings extending into each lobe. Indo-Pacific; generally found on exposed outer reefs, sometimes in very shallow water.

Scarus forsteni Initial phase ▲ Terminal phase ▼

Largest examined, 47 cm. *S. sexvittatus* Rüppell is a synonym based on the initial phase.

Scarus frenatus Initial phase ▲ Terminal phase ▼

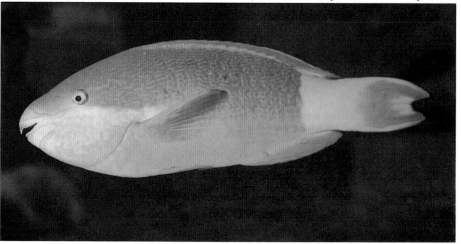

REEFCREST PARROTFISH
Scarus frontalis Valenciennes, 1840

Pectoral rays 15; median predorsal scales 4; two rows of scales on cheek; adults with two to three canines on side of upper dental plate; dental plates exposed, often with algae growing basally; dorsal profile of head steep with a break in contour in anterior interorbital space; caudal fin of adults emarginate to lunate; unusual in not showing two very different adult colour patterns; green with a salmon pink bar on each scale of body; irregular light salmon pink to lavender bands anterior and dorsal to eye and on chin. Islands of Oceania to western Pacific; rare on Great Barrier Reef; usually seen in small schools in shallow water over reefs. Reaches 50 cm.

BLUEBARRED PARROTFISH
Scarus ghobban Forsskål, 1775

Pectoral rays 15-16 (rarely 16); median predorsal scales usually 6; three rows of scales on cheek, the lowermost with 1-2 scales; large adults with 1-3 canine teeth posteriorly on side of upper dental plate; lips covering more than half of dental plates; posterior nostril oval and large; caudal fin slightly emarginate in small initial-phase fish to lunate in large terminal males; initial phase dull orange-yellow, whitish ventrally, the centres of scales bluish; five irregular blue bars often present on body (from more intense blue in centres of scales within bars); fins yellowish; terminal males green dorsally, the scales rimmed with salmon pink, shading to pale green ventrally with a pale salmon pink bar on each scale; head green dorsally, shading to pale salmon on cheek and chin, with two transverse blue bands on chin and three narrow irregular green bands extending posteriorly from eye. Indo-Pacific and tropical eastern Pacific; usually seen on shallow reefs and adjacent sandy areas of lagoons and bays; more inclined to penetrate silty environments than other parrotfishes. Reaches 75 cm. Twenty-two scientific names are synonyms.

Scarus ghobban Initial phase ▲ Terminal phase ▼

GLOBEHEAD PARROTFISH
Scarus globiceps Valenciennes, 1840

Pectoral rays 14; median predorsal scales 5-7 (rarely 7, most often 5), the third or fourth largest; usually a pair of small scales in front of anterior predorsal scale; three rows of scales on cheek, the lower row with 1-4 scales; initial phase with no canines on dental plates; large terminal males with l-2 canines on upper and lower plates; lips nearly covering dental plates; caudal fin of initial phase truncate, of terminal males emarginate to lunate; initial phase greyish brown with three whitish stripes on abdomen; terminal male green, the edges of the scales salmon pink, the green anterodorsally on body and dorsally on head breaking into numerous small spots and short lines; head with a green-bordered pink band from front of snout through eye to end of opercle; a small blackish spot at base of fourth dorsal spine; caudal fin green with a salmon pink band in each lobe. Indo-Pacific; seen more in outer reef habitats than protected waters. Maximum length about 27 cm.

Scarus globiceps   Initial phase ▲ Terminal phase ▼

HIGHFIN PARROTFISH
Scarus longipinnis Randall & Choat, 1980

Pectoral rays 14; median predorsal scales 3-4 (usually 4); three rows of scales on cheek, the lowermost with l-3 (usually 2) scales; adults with one or two canine teeth on side of upper dental plate; body deeper than most *Scarus*, 2.55-2.8 in standard length; dorsal fin elevated, the longest dorsal ray 1.7-2.1 in head; caudal fin slightly double emarginate in initial phase, very lunate in large terminal males; initial phase light brownish orange, often with dark brown bars; three blue-green stripes ventrally on body; an irregular vertical blue-green bar from in front of eye to chin and continuing ventrally on head; a blue-green band across upper interorbital and another across cheek from lower edge of eye; terminal male orange with green bars on scales; blue-green bands on head and ventrally on body similar to those of initial phase; five irregular green bars on body (by virtue of the scales within bars being more green than orange); dorsal fin salmon pink anteriorly with a blue margin and a small blackish spot at base of first membrane, becoming mainly yellowish green posteriorly with a diffuse purplish zone posterior to seventh spine at base of

fin. Southern subtropical Pacific from Pitcairn to Great Barrier Reef; may be seen in as little as 10 m in the southern Great Barrier Reef but generally in more than 20 m in the northern part; has been observed as deep as 55 m. Attains about 40 cm.

STEEPHEAD PARROTFISH
Scarus microrhinos Bleeker, 1854

Pectoral rays 15-17 (usually 16); median predorsal scales 4; three rows of scales on cheek, the lower row with 1-8 scales (usually 5 or 6); side of upper dental plate with one or two canines; dental plates broadly exposed; dorsal profile of head of adults steep, approaching the vertical in large males; caudal fin slightly rounded in juveniles, truncate with greatly prolonged lobes in adults; adults of both sexes green with a salmon pink bar on each scale of body; dental plates blue-green; a blue-green band on upper lip and a broader one on chin joining posteriorly to an irregular band across cheek; head below this band often greenish yellow; head of large adult males above this band purple; an occasional color morph is red, shading to yellow ventrally, with yellow fins; juveniles dark brown with three narrow pale yellowish stripes. Islands of Oceania and western Pacific. Closely related to *S. strongyloce-phalus* Bleeker of Indonesia and the Indian Ocean and *S. gibbus* Rüppell of the Red Sea, and often misidentified as *gibbus*. Reaches 70 cm.

Scarus microrhinos   Terminal phase ▼ Juv. ▲

SWARTHY PARROTFISH
Scarus niger Forsskål, 1775

Pectoral rays 13-15 (usually 14); median predorsal scales 6-8 (usually 7), the fourth usually largest; three rows of scales on cheek, the lower row with 2-5 scales; usually two canine teeth on upper dental plate of terminal male, usually none on initial phase; dental plates largely covered by lips; caudal fin of small initial-phase fish slightly rounded, the lobes becoming prolonged in larger individuals; adults dark reddish brown, the centres of scales of body broadly dark greenish with faint small dark spots (except over thorax and abdomen); a small black-edged yellow-green spot at upper end of gill opening; dental plates blue-green; upper lip bright salmon pink with a transverse blue-green band above; two blue-

Scarus niger   Juv.

green bands across chin, an irregular one from behind mouth to below eye, and two short ones from behind eye; a broad blue-edged orange band in each lobe of caudal fin; large males becoming darker purplish green; juveniles dark brown with pale blue dots, shading to red on caudal peduncle and to white on caudal fin with a large black spot basally at upper and lower edges of fin. Indo-Pacific; males in courtship swim rapidly with the caudal fin elevated and the posterior part of the anal fin depressed. Attains 35 cm.

Scarus niger   Initial phase ▲ Terminal phase ▼

Scarus oviceps   Initial phase ▲ Terminal phase ▼

EGGHEAD PARROTFISH
Scarus oviceps Valenciennes, 1840

Pectoral rays 14-15 (rarely 15); median predorsal scales 6; three rows of scales on cheek, the lower with 2-3 scales; no canine teeth on dental plates; lips covering dental plates; caudal fin of initial phase emarginate, becoming deeply emarginate in terminal males; upper head and body of initial phase dark brownish grey with two diagonal yellow bars, one beneath posterior spinous portion of dorsal fin and one below middle of soft portion; rest of body pale pinkish to yellowish grey; often a broad zone of yellow from corner of mouth to lower opercle; median fins reddish grey; terminal males blue-green with narrow pink margins on scales, the upper head and body to below base of eighth dorsal spine abruptly dark purple; dental plates blue-green; a broad bright blue-green band across head below eye, broadening to cover lips except for a narrow salmon pink margin on upper lip. Islands of Oceania and western Pacific; more often seen in sheltered habitats than exposed reefs. Closely related to *S. dimidiatus* (discussed above) and *S. scaber* Valenciennes of the Indian Ocean. Attains about 30 cm.

PALENOSE PARROTFISH
Scarus psittacus Forsskål, 1775

Pectoral rays 13-15 (nearly always 14); median predorsal scales 4, the first largest in juveniles, the second in adults; two rows of scales on cheek; usually one canine on upper dental plate of initial phase; usually one canine on lower and two on upper plate of terminal males; lips largely covering dental plates; caudal fin of initial phase slightly emarginate, of large terminal males deeply emarginate; initial phase reddish brown to grey; snout paler than rest of head; a diffuse dark spot at base of first membrane of dorsal fin and a small black spot at upper base of pectoral fins; a narrow white posterior margin on caudal fin; scales of body of terminal male about half green and half salmon pink, the green forming four or five longitudinal series of spots on caudal peduncle and three stripes on abdomen; head orange, suffused with green, with blue-green bands; snout lavender-grey. Indo-Pacific; initial-phase fish often form small feeding schools. Rarely exceeds 30 cm. *Scarus forsteri* Valenciennes is one of ten junior synonyms.

Scarus psittacus   Initial phase ▲ Terminal phase ▼

REDTAIL PARROTFISH
Scarus pyrrhurus (Jordan & Seale, 1906)

Pectoral rays 15; median predorsal scales 4; two rows of scales on cheek; no canines on lower dental plate, 0-2 on upper plate of initial phase and usually 2 on plate of terminal males; lips only slightly covering dental plates; front of head strongly rounded; caudal fin of initial phase slightly rounded to truncate, of terminal male slightly emarginate; initial phase dark brown, the caudal fin red with a narrow black posterior margin; terminal male yellowish with an orange bar on each scale, becoming blue-green on caudal peduncle with an orange spot on each scale; an overlying wash of dusky purplish dorsoanteriorly on body, this color continuing diagonally downward as a broad band to posterior abdomen and above base of anterior part of anal fin; top of head dark purplish grey; cheek pale pinkish yellow; three blue-green bands passing posteriorly from eye and two anteriorly, the lower extending to corner of mouth to join blue bands on upper lip and chin; lips salmon pink. Western Pacific, east to Samoa; rare on the Great Barrier Reef. Reaches 30 cm. At times misidentified as *S. japanensis* (Bloch) or its synonym, *S. capistratoides* Bleeker.

Scarus pyrrhurus   Initial phase ▲ Terminal phase ▼

Scarus rivulatus   Initial phase ▲ Terminal phase ▼

SURF PARROTFISH
Scarus rivulatus Valenciennes, 1840

Pectoral rays 13-15 (nearly always 14); median predorsal scales 5-7 (usually 6), the third or fourth largest; a pair of small scales in front of anterior predorsal scale; no canine teeth on dental plates of initial phase, usually 2 upper and 0-1 lower on terminal male; caudal fin slightly rounded to truncate in initial phase, the lobes slightly prolonged in terminal males; initial phase grey to greyish brown with two whitish stripes on abdomen; terminal male green with a salmon to lavender pink bar on scales of body; head orange with irregular blue-green lines and small spots partially forming a reticulum on snout and chin, extending to eye; posterior cheek orange to orange-red. Western Pacific east to the Caroline Islands and New Caledonia; often occurs in aggregations which may move onto reef flats at high tide to feed on algae. Largest examined, 40 cm. *S. fasciatus* Valenciennes is a synonym. Initial phase difficult to distinguish from that of *S. globiceps*.

EMBER PARROTFISH
Scarus rubroviolaceus Bleeker, 1847

Pectoral rays 14-16 (usually 15); median predorsal scales 6; three rows of scales on cheek, the lower row with 1-3 (usually 2) scales; initial phase with 0-1 canine teeth on upper dental plate, terminal males with 1-3; lips covering about half of dental plates; body moderately elongate, the depth 2.75-3.1 in standard length; dorsal profile of head rising steeply from mouth to level of eye, then curving sharply, the remaining contour to dorsal fin origin nearly straight; caudal fin of adults in the initial phase slightly emarginate, of terminal males lunate; initial phase reddish brown to grey, shading to light red ventrally, with small black spots and irregular lines on scales of body; fins red; terminal male green, the edges of the scales narrowly salmon pink, with a wash of salmon over side of body; upper lip narrowly salmon pink; above this a broad band of blue-green; lower lip and chin with a double blue-green band (separated by salmon pink) which continues as a single band to below eye; cheek yellowish; dental plates blue-green; adults in life may be strongly bicoloured, the head and body to pectoral tips abruptly darker (in terminal males overall purplish) than posteriorly. Indo-Pacific and tropical eastern Pacific. Attains 70 cm. *S. jordani* (Jenkins) is one of nine junior synonyms.

SCHLEGEL'S PARROTFISH
Scarus schlegeli (Bleeker, 1861)

Pectoral rays 13-15 (rarely 13, usually 14); median predorsal scales 4, the second scale largest; two rows of scales on cheek; initial phase without canine teeth on dental plates; large terminal males usually with one on upper plate and two on lower; dental plates nearly covered by lips; caudal fin of initial phase slightly rounded to truncate, of terminal male slightly double emarginate; initial phase reddish to olivaceous brown with an orangish to reddish bar on each scale of body; five curved pale bars 1.5-2 scales in width usually present on body; a small black spot at upper base of pectoral fin; snout and chin reddish with a transverse dull blue band on upper lip continuing to eye, and two on chin; terminal male green, the scales rimmed with lavender-pink, with a bright yellow spot at base of dorsal fin between last spine and second soft ray, and extending onto back, this spot continuing below as a pale green bar; lower part of body anterior to bar and lower head overlaid with dark purplish; bluish bands anteriorly on head of initial phase now more evident in bright blue-green on the terminal male; in addition, three short bands extending posteri-

Scarus rubroviolaceus   Initial phase ▲ Terminal phase ▼

orly from eye. Islands of Oceania (except easternmost) and western Pacific; occurs in a variety of habitats; capable of quickly changing its colour pattern. Largest, 38 cm. Often misidentified as *S. venosus* Valenciennes, a synonym of *S. psittacus*.

Scarus schlegeli   Initial phase ▲ Terminal phase ▼

BULLETHEAD PARROTFISH
Scarus sordidus Forsskål, 1775

Pectoral rays 14-15 (rarely 14); median predorsal scales 4, progressively larger anteriorly; two rows of scales on cheek; no canine teeth on lower dental plate; large adults with up to two canines on side of upper dental plate; lips covering less than half of dental plates; front of head strongly rounded, the dorsal and ventral profiles about equally convex; caudal fin usually truncate in adults (slightly emarginate in some large terminal males); initial phase dark brown, becoming red around mouth; two longitudinal rows of five or six whitish spots often present on side of body; a broad whitish bar containing a large round blackish spot sometimess present on caudal peduncle (this and the small white spots can be rapidly eliminated and just as rapidly reinstated by the living fish); terminal males green, the

Scarus sordidus Juv.

edges of scales salmon pink except caudal peduncle which is solid light green; thorax and abdomen pale salmon with indistinct green stripes; upper side of body sometimes broadly suffused with light yellow; front of snout lavender-pink, bordered by blue-green

Scarus sordidus Initial phase ▲ Terminal phase ▼

bands; dental plates blue-green; juveniles with four dark brown stripes. Indo-Pacific; occurs in a variety of coral reef habitats; the most common parrotfish at many localities. Reaches 40 cm. *Callyodon bipallidus* Smith is one of 13 junior synonyms.

Scarus spinus Initial phase ▲ Terminal phase ▼

GREENSNOUT PARROTFISH
Scarus spinus (Kner, 1868)

Pectoral rays 13-14 (rarely 13); median predorsal scales 3-5 (usually 4, the anterior scale may be small and embedded); a pair of medially overlapping small scales anterior to first median scale; three rows of scales on cheek, the lower row with 1-2 (usually 2) scales; initial phase generally with one canine on side of lower dental plate, and terminal males with one or two on each plate; dental plates covered by lips; head bluntly rounded, especially that of terminal male; caudal fin of initial phase slightly rounded to truncate, of terminal male moderately to deeply emarginate; initial phase dark brown, shading ventrally to reddish brown; body often with four or five indistinct pale bars one to two scales in width (due to whitish centres of scales within bars); terminal male green, the edges of body scales lavender-pink; front of snout yellow-green to green, shading ventrally on chin to blue-green where two bright salmon pink areas are enclosed; cheek broadly yellow. Western Pacific east to islands of Micronesia and Samoa; usually seen on ocean side of reefs; not common. Largest collected, 30 cm. Often misidentified as *S. formosus* Valenciennes, a synonym of the Hawaiian endemic *S. dubius* Bennett.

355

JAWFISHES OR SMILERS
FAMILY OPISTOGNATHIDAE

These are small to medium-sized fishes with narrow tapering bodies and a noticeably enlarged head and mouth. The group occurs in all warm seas, containing an estimated 70 species in three genera. They construct elaborate burrows by scooping sand or small stones with the mouth and can shift larger rocks by using their powerful jaws. The burrows are frequently lined and reinforced with pebbles and shell fragments. Jawfishes are relatively rare in our area and a sharp eye is required to sight one before it backs tail first down its burrow. These fishes exhibit the unusual habit of oral egg incubation. They feed chiefly on benthic and planktonic invertebrates.

CORAL SEA JAWFISH
Opistognathus sp.

Dorsal rays XI,14-15; anal rays II,14-15; gill rakers 8-9 + 16-18; scaled area of body extends from just behind pectoral fins to caudal fin base; lateral scale rows posterior to opercular flap about 45-50; overall brownish with longitudinal row of large white "windows" on lower half of side, and row of smaller white spots just above; head and sides may be punctuated with widely scattered small dark brown spots; dorsal and anal fins with submarginal brown band and brown mottling on outer portion. Known from only four specimens collected in 20-29 m at Lizard Island and Lihou Reef, Coral Sea. To 12 cm. An undescribed species. Another undescribed species in the area has a similar appearance, but is easily distinguished by its reduced scalation on the side of the body (only the posterior half of the body is scaled).

PAPUAN JAWFISH
Opistognathus papuensis (Bleeker, 1868)

Dorsal rays XII,16; anal rays II,15; pectoral rays 22; lateral scale rows posterior to opercular flap about 110-120; overall brown to light tan with small black spots and dashes covering head and body, also extending onto fins; a large blackish or brownish blotch on side hidden under pectoral fin; eye with prominent black spoke-like markings. Southern New Guinea and northeastern Queensland. Grows to 40 cm.

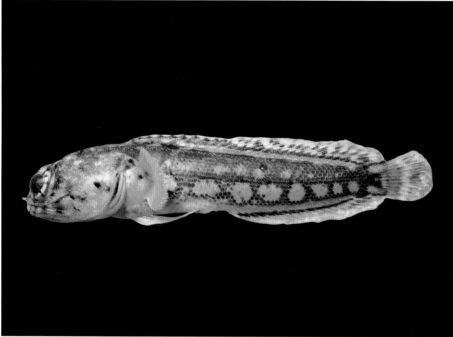

Opistognathus sp. ▲

Opistognathus papuensis ▼

STARGAZERS
FAMILY URANOSCOPIDAE

The bizarre fishes of this family are aptly named stargazers because the eyes of most species are directed dorsally (the others partly upward); the head is massive, nearly cuboidal in shape, flat on the top; the mouth is highly oblique to vertical; the lips are usually fringed with cirri; the outer bones of the head are without overlying dermis, the surface rough and highly sculptured; the pelvic fins are inserted on the isthmus; most species have small cycloid scales arranged in inconspicuous oblique rows on the body; there is a large venomous cleithral spine in the shoulder region; wounds from this spine can be serious (deaths from stargazer stings have been reported but not fully documented). Three of the seven genera of the family, including the largest, *Uranoscopus*, have a fleshy lure that has developed from tissue of the oral valve of the lower jaw. These fishes are rarely seen underwater because they spend most of their time buried in sand or mud with only the eyes showing; the cirri on the edge of the mouth serve to keep out sand during respiration. The oral lure can be wriggled enticingly above the surface of the sand to attract prey within striking range of the mouth.

WHITEMARGIN STARGAZER
Uranoscopus sulphureus Valenciennes, 1831

Dorsal rays IV+12-13, the spinous fin almost continuous with soft; anal rays 13; pectoral rays 18-19; lower edge of preopercle with five small spines; fleshy edge of operculum lined with cirri; spinous dorsal fin low, less than half height of soft dorsal; third dorsal soft ray longest, about 2.5 times longer than first and last rays; caudal fin slightly rounded; greyish brown dorsally, white ventrally, with a faint broad dark bar on side of head and two on body; a row of small dark brown spots on upper side, and some brown blotches anterodorsally on body; spinous dorsal fin largely black; pelvics whitish; outer margins of remaining fins white. Known from Tonga, Fiji, Samoa, Indonesia, and the Red Sea. *U. fuscomaculatus* Kner is a synonym. Attains about 35 cm.

Uranoscopus sulphureus Lateral view ▲ Dorsal view ▼

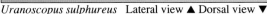

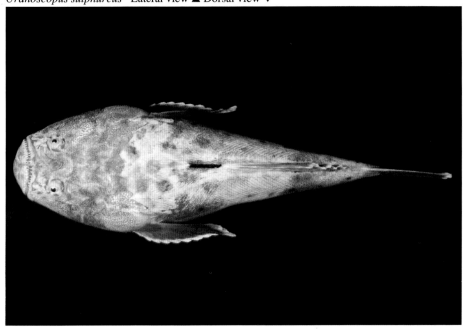

SAND-DIVERS
FAMILY TRICHONOTIDAE

Sand-divers are extremely elongate, slender fishes with a projecting lower jaw, numerous dorsal and anal fin rays; the first few dorsal rays of males usually form elongate filaments. A small family containing only six species that are confined to the Indo-Pacific region. Trichono- tids are typically found hovering above clean sandy bottoms. The long-finned males are generally greatly outnumbered by females and frequently engage in spectacular displays in which the fins are fully extended. If distrubed, these fishes quickly take cover by darting into the sand. When the danger has passed, they first expose their head and eyes before fully re-emerging. Similar in shape and habits to the Sand Burrowers (Creediidae). See next family.

Trichonotus sp.   Male ▲ Female ▼

THREADFIN SAND-DIVER
Trichonotus sp.

Dorsal rays III,43-45; anal rays I,40-42; pectoral rays 14; lateral-line scales 55-60; males generally white or tan with brilliant pearl white to blue spots on head, body, and fins; a blackish spot at base of elongate dorsal spines and an ocellated black spot above beginning of lateral line; females white or tan with 2-3 longitudinal rows of small brown spots or lines, 1-2 blackish spots at beginning of dorsal fin. Coral Sea to Mariana and Marshall islands; an apparently undescribed species that is very similar to *T. elegans* Shimada & Yoshino from the Ryukyu Islands. To 18 cm.

SPOTTED SAND-DIVER
Trichonotus setiger (Bloch & Schneider, 1801)

Dorsal rays V-VII,39-41; anal rays I,34-36; pectoral rays 12-15; lateral-line scales 52-55; no scaleless areas on side of body; males generally whitish with about 10 brown bars on side and smaller saddles or spots on back between bars; body and median fins with longitudinal rows of small blue to white spots; females whitish with a pair of longitudinal rows of blue to brown spots (may merge to form solid or broken line on upper side); a blackish spot on anterior part of dorsal fin. Persian Gulf to Queensland and Melanesia. Attains 15 cm.

SAND BURROWERS
FAMILY CREEDIIDAE

SANDPERCHES
FAMILY PINGUIPEDIDAE

Sand burrowers are small cryptic fishes that live on sandy or gravel bottoms and therefore are seldom noticed. They are characterised by an elongate body, a fleshy, projecting snout, long-based dorsal and anal fins, and a lack of spines in the fins except for the pelvics. The 14 species and seven genera are confined to the Indo-Pacific region. They occur from shallow tide pools to at least 150 m depth. The general coloration is white to semi-transparent which blends in well with the substratum. The pointed snout is used for burrowing and the eyes are directed upwards for sighting prey (small invertebrates).

BARRED SAND BURROWER
Limnichthys fasciatus Waite, 1904

Dorsal rays 29-33; anal rays 26-29; pectoral rays 12-13; lateral-line scales 38-43; overall pale with 7-9 brown dorsal saddles on head and body. Western Pacific from Japan to Australia and the Kermadec Islands. Grows to 5 cm. Two additional members of this family that occur in the region can be distinguished as follows: *Chalixodytes chameleontoculis* Smith - dorsal rays 37-40; anal rays 37-40; lateral-line scales 57-59; 13-19 brown dorsal saddles; *Limnichthys donaldsoni* Schultz - dorsal rays 21-24; anal rays 25-27; lateral-line scales 36-38; 9-11 brown dorsal saddles.

This small family of four genera is more often called the Mugiloididae or the Parapercidae in the literature. The common name for the group is also variable, grubfishes, weevers, or whitings in Australia, sandsmelts in South Africa, and sandperches in most other English-speaking areas. The largest genus and the only one represented in Indo-Pacific seas is *Parapercis*. The pinguipedid fishes are characterized by a moderately elongate, little-compressed body; terminal protractile mouth with curved canine teeth in an outer row at front of jaws; teeth on vomer; a long dorsal fin with IV-VII spines and 20-24 rays; anal fin rays I,14-22; well-separated pelvic fins which originate below or in advance of pectoral-fin base, the rays I,5, the fourth soft ray longest; a complete lateral line; and small ctenoid scales. The species of *Parapercis* live on open bottoms, often sand and rubble areas near coral reefs. They rest upon the substratum, propping themselves on their pelvic fins; their eyes are oriented as much upward as laterally. All are carnivorous, feeding mainly on benthic crustaceans, especially crabs and shrimps, and occasionally on small fishes. They are, in general, easily approached underwater. Many species of *Parapercis* show at least some colour difference with sex; no males of small size have been noted; sex reversal from female to male has been demonstrated for some species; it seems likely that all will prove to be hermaphroditic.

LATTICED SANDPERCH
Parapercis clathrata Ogilby, 1911

Dorsal rays IV-V (rarely V),20-21 (usually 21); anal rays I,17; pectoral rays usually 17; lateral-line scales 57-60; six canine teeth at front of lower jaw; no palatine teeth; second and third dorsal spines longest; membrane from last dorsal spine linked to first soft ray nearly as high as spine; light brown to greenish dorsally with rows of small dark blotches, shading to white below, with a series of nine or ten vertically elongate reddish brown spots with black centres on lower side; an ocellated black spot above gill opening of males; caudal fin with a broad yellow or white middle zone and scattered dark brown spots. Samoa and islands of Micronesia to the Persian Gulf. Largest, 17.5 cm.

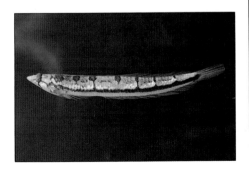

SHARPNOSE SANDPERCH
Parapercis cylindrica (Bloch, 1797)

Dorsal rays V,21; anal rays I,17; pectoral rays usually 15; lateral-line scales 48-52; ten canine teeth at front of lower jaw; palatine teeth present; interopercle serrate; middle dorsal spine longest; membrane from last dorsal spine joined to base of first soft ray; light brown dorsally, shading to whitish ventrally, with a series of vertically elongate dark brown spots covering entire ventral half of body, the two anterior spots narrow; two series of narrow dark brown blotches linked to form a double band from behind eye to upper middle part of body; spinous dorsal fin yellowish with a large dark brown spot near base; a series of double black spots basally in soft dorsal fin; caudal fin whitish to yellow with small dark spots and a narrow white margin except at corners. Western Pacific east to Fiji and the Marshall Islands; usually seen around shallow silty reefs. Reaches 15 cm.

SPECKLED SANDPERCH
Parapercis hexophtalma (Cuvier, 1829)

Dorsal rays V,21-22 (rarely 22); anal rays I,17-18 (rarely 18); pectoral rays 17-18; lateral-line scales 58-61; eight canine teeth at front of lower jaw; palatine teeth absent; fourth dorsal spine longest; membrane from tip of last dorsal spine joining first soft ray at level of spine tip; light greenish brown dorsally, speckled with brown, white ventrally; a series of large elliptical whitish spots along side of body with a small blackish spot or group of small spots in centre of each; lower side of body with a row small black spots, many rimmed with bright yellow; head of females with small dark brown spots, of males with a series of brown to yellow diagonal lines on cheek; caudal fin with a very large black blotch in centre. Fiji and western Pacific to East Africa and Red Sea; a shallow-water species found on sand and rubble around protected reefs. To 23 cm. *P. polyophtalma* (Cuvier) is a synonym based on the female form.

SPOTTED SANDPERCH

Parapercis millepunctata (Günther, 1860)

Dorsal rays IV,21; anal rays I,17; pectoral rays usually 17; lateral-line scales 55-58; six canine teeth at front of lower jaw; palatine teeth absent; second and third dorsal spines longest; membrane from last dorsal spine joined to first soft ray at level of spine tip; body whitish with four close-set longitudinal series of brown spots, those of lower row largest, vertically elongate, covering all of lower side, their centres usually black (spots of upper row small and irregular, partially joined to those of second); two large dark brown spots on cheek; caudal fin with small blackish spots and a large squarish white spot centroposteriorly (sometimes preceded by a black blotch); males with diagonal pale lines on cheek. Islands of Oceania to Maldives; the most common species of the genus at many localities. Largest, 18 cm. Usually identified as *P. cephalopunctata* (Seale), but *P. millepunctata* is the valid earlier name.

REDBARRED SANDPERCH

Parapercis multiplicata Randall, 1984

Dorsal rays V,21; anal rays I,16-17; pectoral rays 14-16; lateral-line scales 56-58; eight canine teeth at front of lower jaw; no palatine teeth; fourth dorsal spine longest; last interspinous membrane of dorsal fin incised nearly to base of first soft ray; caudal fin truncate; upper fourth of body orange-red, with or without series of small black spots; lower three-fourths white with eight narrow red bars, each with two small black or deep red spots; two indistinct irregular narrow orange stripes on side of body; a red spot, with or without a black centre, below pectoral-fin base; small black to deep red spots dorsally on head; a large black spot on first three membranes of dorsal fin and a row of red dots in soft dorsal and anal fins. Known to date from the Ryukyu Islands, Indonesia, New Caledonia, Western Australia, and the Coral Sea; collected from the depth range of 4-30 m, usually on rubble substrata. Attains 12 cm.

BARRED SANDPERCH

Parapercis nebulosa (Quoy & Gaimard, 1825)

Dorsal rays V,22; anal rays I,18; pectoral rays 16-17 (rarely 16); lateral-line scales 68-76; six canine teeth at front of lower jaw; no palatine teeth; third dorsal spine longest; membrane from last dorsal spine attaches to first soft ray at a height of about one-fourth to one-third length of spine; caudal fin emarginate (slightly rounded in previous species); light reddish, shading to white ventrally, with six dark reddish bars on body (these may be broken by an indistinct pale midlateral stripe); spinous dorsal fin largely black. New South Wales to Western Australia; inhabits sedimentary substrata, often near reefs; occurs adjacent to inner reefs of the Great Barrier Reef or on coastal reefs; usually not found in less than 15 m. Reaches 25 cm.

Parapercis nebulosa Adult ▼ Juv. ▲

REDSPOTTED SANDPERCH

Parapercis schauinslandi (Steindachner, 1900)

Dorsal rays V,21; anal rays I,17; pectoral rays usually 16; lateral-line scales 56-59; six canine teeth at front of lower jaw; no palatine teeth; middle dorsal spine longest; membrane from last dorsal spine joined to first soft ray near its base; caudal fin emarginate; white with two longitudinal series of squarish red spots on body, one along back (these spots often faint but may contain a few small dark red spots) and the other midlateral; two red lines at base of pectoral fin; spinous portion of dorsal fin red with a large black spot basally in centre of fin; caudal fin pale with two red spots at base (one above the other). Indo-Pacific; colour slightly variable with major locality; usually found on rubble substrata near reefs, generally at depths greater than 20 m. Reaches 13 cm.

U-MARK SANDPERCH
Parapercis snyderi Jordan & Starks, 1905

Dorsal rays V,21; anal rays I,16-18 (usually 17); pectoral rays 14-15 (usually 14); lateral-line scales 38-44; eight canine teeth at front of lower jaw; palatine teeth present; middle dorsal spine usually longest (second spine subequal); membrane from last dorsal spine connected to base of first soft ray; caudal fin truncate; three U-shaped dusky bars dorsally on body followed by two more posteriorly with bottom of U missing (hence as double bars); a series of nine narrow dusky bars on side of body, every other one extending ventrally from bottom of U markings (bars sometimes faint; each may contain a blackish spot at level of pectoral fin); a scattering of blackish dots on head behind eye and anteriorly on side of body; some fish with blackish dots forming three lines from behind eye onto anterodorsal part of body; a black line from eye to front of upper lip, converging anteriorly with line from other side. Western Pacific; in silty sand and rubble areas near reefs. Attains 10 cm. Specimens from Japan (type locality) more strongly coloured, red with black U-shaped bars.

YELLOWBAR SANDPERCH
Parapercis xanthozona (Bleeker, 1849)

Dorsal rays V,21; anal rays I,17; pectoral rays usually 17; lateral-line scales 56-60; six canine teeth at front of lower jaw; palatine teeth absent; third and fourth dorsal spines longest; membrane from last dorsal spine joined to first soft ray nearly at level of spine tip; caudal fin slightly rounded, the upper corner usually slightly prolonged; a midlateral whitish stripe extending nearly to end of caudal fin (where pure white), body above stripe gray, speckled with dark brown, below light brown with nine dusky bars which may penetrate or even faintly cross midlateral whitish stripe; an orange-yellow bar at pectoral-fin base; blackish spots above and below white stripe in caudal fin; males with curved diagonal dark-edged pale blue lines on cheek. Western Pacific, east to Fiji, west to East Africa; generally found in protected waters of bays or lagoons. Reaches 23 cm.

TRIPLEFINS
FAMILY TRIPTERYGIIDAE

The triplefins are small (usually 3-5 cm), relatively inconspicuous inhabitants of tropical and temperate reefs. The family occurs worldwide, but most of the estimated 150 species occur in the Indo-Pacific. The taxonomy of this group has long been neglected, consequently the identification of many species is problematical and there are a number of undescribed forms. The common name is derived from the division of the dorsal fin into three parts: the first consists of III or IV spines, the second of VIII to XVI spines, and the third of 8-12 soft, segmented rays. Many of the species are cryptically coloured or semitransparent; this in combination with their small size often makes them difficult to detect. They dwell on the reef's surface, often in weedy areas, on algal-covered rocks, or on rubble. Their food consists primarily of tiny invertebrates and algae. We thank Ronald Fricke for preparing the species descriptions for this family.

HIGHFIN TRIPLEFIN
Ennaepterygius altipinnis Clark, 1980

Dorsal rays III + XI-XII + 7-8; anal rays I,15-16; pectoral rays 13-14; 31-34 scale rows; lateral-line scales 10-11 + 21-25 scales present on nape; a short orbital tentacle present; side of head red or pink, body lime green, a white bar at rear of first and third dorsal fins. Indo-Pacific. To 3.5 cm.

SADDLED TRIPLEFIN
Enneapterygius annulatus (Ramsay & Ogilby, 1888)

Dorsal rays III + XII-III + 10-12; anal rays I,18-19; pectoral rays 14-16; lateral-line scales 16-17 + 17-19; scales present on nape; orbital tentacle present; mottled reddish to brown with lighter blotches and saddles; tip of snout white. Indo-Pacific Attains 3.5 cm.

TAILBAR TRIPLEFIN
Enneapterygius sp.

Dorsal rays III + XII-XIII + 7-9; anal rays I,16-19; pectoral rays 15-16; lateral scale rows 32-36; lateral-line scales 14-18 + 17-22; scales present on nape; a three-tipped orbital tentacle present; mottled brownish with several pale saddles on upper half of side, whitish below; a white-margined black band across base of caudal fin. Indo-Pacific. Reaches 3.5 cm.

RED-FINNED TRIPLEFIN
Helcogramma gymnauchen (Weber, 1909)

Dorsal rays III + XII-XIII + 9-11; anal rays I,15-18; pectoral rays 15-17; scale rows 34-37; lateral-line scales 16-19; mandibular pore formula 2+3+2 or 3+3+3; nape naked; no orbital tentacles; whitish with irregular red bar and circles on side, snout blackish, dorsal fins with red bands. Indo-Pacific. To 4 cm.

NEON TRIPLEFIN
Helcogramma striata Hansen, 1986

Dorsal rays III + XIII + 10-11; anal rays I,18-20; pectoral rays 16-18; scale rows 36-40; lateral-line scales 16-20; mandibular pore formula 3+2+3; nape naked; no orbital tentacles; red, becoming white to lavender below; three narrow white stripes on side. Western Pacific east to Line Islands and west to Sri Lanka. Attains 4 cm.

BIGMOUTH TRIPLEFIN
Helcogramma sp.

Dorsal rays III + XII-XIV + 9-12; anal rays I,17-20; pectoral rays 15-17; scale rows 32-40; lateral-line scales 8-10 (rarely 7-11); mandibular pore formula 2+2+2 or 3+2+3; nape naked; no orbital tentacles; semitransparent with 10-12 diffuse reddish bars. Indo-Pacific. Grows to 5 cm.

BLENNIES
FAMILY BLENNIIDAE

The Blenniidae is a large family (over 300 species) of small agile bottom-dwelling fishes. All are scaleless, and all have their pelvic fins clearly anterior to the pectoral fins, with one indistinct spine and 2-4 soft rays (hence less than the usual I,5 pelvic rays of most perciform fishes). Most blennies are blunt-headed, and many have tentacles, cirri, or a fleshy crest on the upper part of the head. There is a single dorsal fin with III-XVII flexible spines; the fin may be deeply notched between spinous and soft portions, and the last ray may be joined by membrane to the caudal peduncle; all have II spines in the anal fin, but one or both may be reduced in size or embedded in females, hence easily overlooked; in males they may be capped by fleshy tissue believed to secrete an attracting substance at spawning time; the soft rays of fins are not branched except for the caudal rays of some species. The mouth is low on the head and not protractile; the teeth are numerous, slender, and close-set, either fixed or movable; some species have formidable canine teeth. Many blennies, such as those of the genera *Istiblennius, Alticus,*and *Entomacrodus*, live inshore on rocky substrata, sometimes in the surf-swept intertidal zone; some are able to leap from one pool to another (hence the common name rockskipper). Blennies tend to take refuge in small holes in the reef into which they back tail-first. The majority of tropical blennies are herbivorous; the Shortbodied Blenny (*Exallias brevis*) feeds on coral polyps, and one species of *Ecsenius* has also been reported with the same food habit. The sabretooth blennies are unique in possessing two enormous canine teeth in the lower jaw which are used for defence. Those of the genus *Plagiotremus*

(*Runula* is a synonym) feed on the scales, dermal tissue, and mucus of other fishes. The mimic blenny (*Aspidontus taeniatus*) mimics the cleaner wrasse (*Labroides dimidiatus*), thus enabling it to get close enough to unsuspecting fishes so it can tear pieces from their fins. One genus of this group, *Meiacanthus*, has a venom gland associated with the canines, and predators learn to avoid these species. They are usually seen swimming a short distance above the bottom; no doubt their poisonous canines provide considerable protection from predation and enable them to swim in such an exposed manner. Other fishes, including species of the blenny genera *Ecsenius*, *Plagiotremus*, and *Petroscirtes*, are mimics of species of

Meiacanthus in order to deceive predators. The blenniid fishes for which the reproductive habits are known lay demersal eggs that are guarded by the male parent. No subfamilies other than the Blenniinae are currently recognized in the Blenniidae; instead there are five tribes, three of which are represented by species from the Great Barrier Reef: the Nemophini (sabretooth blennies or fangblennies); the Omobranchini, which contains such genera as *Omobranchus, Enchelyurus*, and *Parenchelyurus*, and the Salariini which includes such speciose genera as *Cirripectes, Ecsenius, Entomacrodus*, and *Istiblennius*. The species will be discussed below alphabetically by tribe, genus, and species.

Mimic Blenny
Aspidontus taeniatus Close-up of head

TRIBE NEMOPHINI

LANCE BLENNY
Aspidontus dussumieri (Valenciennes, 1836)

Dorsal rays IX-XI,29-33, the fin not notched; anal rays II,26-30; pectoral rays 13-15; segmented caudal rays 11, none branched; body elongate, the depth 6.7-8.4 in standard length; head moderately pointed, the front of snout rounded, the mouth ventral; teeth in jaws close-set and slender except for a very large recurved canine on each side of lower jaw and a small canine on each side at back of upper jaw; caudal fin slightly rounded, becoming lanceolate in adults (middle two rays elongate in large adults); whitish with a black stripe from eye to caudal fin; dorsal and anal fins dull yellow; females with an ocellated black spot anteriorly in the dorsal fin. Indo-Pacific; limited data suggest that the principal food is algae and detritus. Reaches 12 cm.

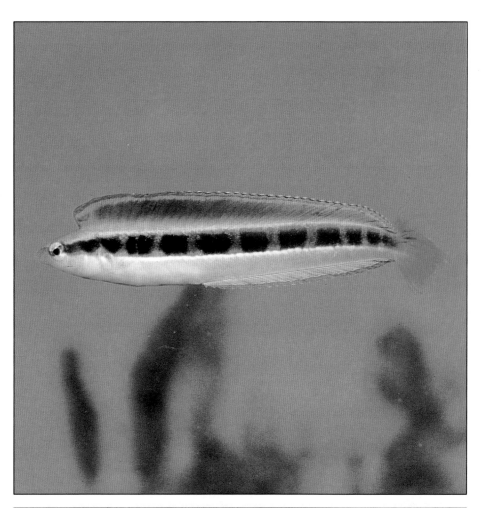

MIMIC BLENNY
Aspidontus taeniatus Quoy & Gaimard, 1834

Dorsal rays X-XII,26-29, the fin not notched; anal rays II,25-28; pectoral rays 13-15; segmented caudal rays 11; body moderately elongate, the depth 5.0-6.5 in standard length; mouth ventral, the conical snout strongly overhanging; teeth in jaws close-set and slender, except for a very large recurved canine on each side of lower jaw; four small cirri in a transverse row on chin; origin of dorsal fin posterior to rear of eye, nearly uniform in height (except for prejuveniles where it is elevated anteriorly); caudal fin truncate to slightly rounded; blue, whitish anteriorly, with a lateral black stripe from front of snout to hind edge of caudal fin, the stripe progressively broader as it passes posteriorly. Indo-Pacific; mimics the cleaner wrasse *Labroides dimidiatus* in colour (including, when it is juvenile, the deeper blue and broader black stripe of the young cleaner wrasse) and behaviour, thus gaining protection from predation and enabling it to approach fishes in order to bite pieces from their fins; also feeds in part on demersal fish eggs and the tentacles of plume worms. Largest, 11.5 cm.

YELLOWTAIL FANGBLENNY
Meiacanthus atrodorsalis (Günther, 1877)

Dorsal rays IV,26-28; anal rays II,15-18; segmented caudal rays usually 11, none branched (true of other *Meiacanthus* herein); pectoral rays usually 14; an enormous curved canine tooth on each side of lower jaw, grooved on anterior surface, with a venom gland at base (characteristic of the genus); origin of dorsal fin over posterior margin of preopercle, the fin low and unnotched (also characteristic of the genus); caudal fin lunate, the lobes prolonged in large males; head and anterior half of body grey-blue, posterior half yellow; a diagonal black band through eye, continuing dorsoposteriorly onto nape; a black stripe in dorsal fin except posteriorly; caudal fin yellow; a black spot in lower part of pectoral-fin axil. Western Australia and western Pacific east to Micronesia and Samoa; tends to be solitary; believed to be mimicked by the blue-yellow phase of *Ecsenius bicolor* and *Plagiotremus laudandus*. Feeds on both benthic and planktonic animals, especially small crustaceans and worms. To 11 cm.

DOUBLEPORE FANGBLENNY
Meiacanthus ditrema Smith-Vaniz, 1976

Dorsal rays V,23-25; anal rays II,15-18 (rarely 15 or 18); pectoral rays usually 14; lateral line absent (present on other *Meiacanthus*); mandibular pores 2 (3 in other species of the genus); supratemporal canal ending in a pair of pores on top of head; caudal fin emarginate, the third and ninth segmented rays very prolonged in large males; bluish grey with a black stripe beginning on top of snout and passing along back to upper caudal peduncle; two parallel narrow stripes crossing head (one starting on forehead and one at mouth), joining as one broader band beneath pectoral fin, and continuing along lower side to caudal fin. Western Australia and western Pacific east to Samoa and Tonga; usually seen in small aggregations a short distance above the bottom. Largest, 6.7 cm, including caudal filaments.

STRIPED FANGBLENNY
Meiacanthus grammistes (Valenciennes, 1836)

Dorsal rays IV,25-27; anal rays II,14-16; pectoral rays usually 14 or 15; males developing prolonged lobes in caudal fin; dorsal part of head and upper front part of body yellow, shading to white ventrally and posteriorly, with three dark stripes on head and body about equal in width to pale interspaces, these stripes black on head and anterior body but changing to grey posteriorly where they contain a series of black spots; a few isolated black spots posteriorly on body and in caudal fin; a black stripe in dorsal fin. Western Pacific west to Western Australia and east to Caroline Islands and Santa Cruz Islands; usually solitary; mimicked by *Petroscirtes breviceps* and *Cheilodipterus nigrotaeniatus*. To 12 cm.

LINED FANGBLENNY
Meiacanthus lineatus (De Vis, 1884)

Dorsal rays IV,25-28 (rarely 25 or 28); anal rays II,15-17 (rarely 17); pectoral rays usually 15; caudal lobes elongate in males; upper two-thirds of head and body yellow with three black stripes of equal width to yellow interspaces; head and body below lowermost stripe white; dorsal fin yellow with a submarginal black stripe edged in bluish white; caudal fin yellow. Known only from the Great Barrier Reef, but reported from its entire length; mimicked by *Petroscirtes fallax* and the young of *Scolopsis bilineatus*. Reaches 9.5 cm.

YELLOW FANGBLENNY
Meiacanthus luteus Smith-Vaniz, 1987

Dorsal rays IV,26-28 (rarely 28); anal rays II,16-18 (rarely 16); pectoral rays usually 15 or 16; pelvic fins and lobes of caudal fin prolonged in males; a midlateral dark brown to black stripe from front of snout through eye to caudal-fin base; a second dark brown stripe commencing above eye and passing dorsally on body at base of dorsal fin; head and body between two stripes bright yellow, below white. Known only from Queenland at 19°S to Western Australia at 20°S; the type locality is Darwin. Largest, 10.3 cm.

DECEIVER FANGBLENNY
Petroscirtes fallax Smith-Vaniz, 1976

Dorsal rays XI,18-20; anal rays II,18-20 (rarely 20); segmented caudal rays 11, none branched (true of all *Petroscirtes*); pectoral rays 14; an enormous curved canine tooth on each side of lower jaw, not grooved and not associated with a venom gland (characteristic of the genus); lower edge of gill opening ending above pectoral-fin base (also generic); body depth at anal-fin origin 4.65-6.8 in standard length; no flap on rim of posterior nostril; a small unbranched cirrus on chin; other cirri absent except a small posttemporal one; caudal fin slightly emarginate, the interradial membranes of males incised, and the lobes of the fin of large males prolonged; head and body with three parallel dark brown stripes, the first from top of head along back at base of dorsal fin,

the second mid-lateral, and the third on lower side; spaces between stripes dusky yellow; ventral head and body white; dorsal fin yellow; caudal and anal fins yellowish.

Great Barrier Reef south of 17°S to New South Wales; a mimic of *Meiacanthus lineatus*. Largest, 9.5 cm.

WOLF FANGBLENNY
Petroscirtes lupus (De Vis, 1886)

Dorsal rays XI,19-20; anal rays II,19-20; pectoral rays usually 14; body depth at anal-fin origin 4.5-7.0 in standard length; no flap on rim of posterior nostril; small cirrus on chin unbranched; other small cirri on head present or absent; second dorsal spine of males prolonged; interradial membranes of caudal fin incised, especially on males; grey-brown, finely mottled and spotted with white, with a series of four indistinct large dark blotches on upper side in approximate heavy H shape. Queensland, New South Wales, Lord Howe Island, and New Caledonia; like most of the genus, cryptically coloured; tends to hide in seagrasses, seaweeds, or empty mollusc shells; often lays its eggs, which are guarded by the male, on the inner surface of a dead bivalve shell. To 13 cm.

Petroscirtes lupus Male ▲ Female ▼

HIGHFIN FANGBLENNY
Petroscirtes mitratus Rüppell, 1830

Dorsal rays X-XI (rarely X),14-16, the anterior part of fin elevated (first spine longer than second and distinctly longer than fourth); anal rays II,14-16; pectoral rays 14-15; body depth at anal-fin origin 3.6-4.9 in standard length; snout short, its dorsal profile steep; a well-developed flap on anterior rim of posterior nostril; cirrus on chin broad and unbranched; other cirri present on head; caudal fin slightly rounded, the interradial membranes of males incised; pelvic fins of males prolonged (may be one-third or more of standard length); light brown, finely and densely mottled and spotted with white and dark brown; usually about six very irregular large dark blotches along upper side containing a small black-edged white spot (the black broader below); an irregular row of small orange-red spots often present on side. Samoa, Tonga, and islands of Micronesia to East Africa and the Red Sea; the most common species of the genus, judging from museum collections. Largest, 7.7 cm.

VARIABLE FANGBLENNY
Petroscirtes variabilis Cantor, 1850

Dorsal rays XI,16-18 (rarely 16); anal rays II,16-18; pectoral rays usually 14; body slender, the depth at anal-fin origin 4.65-6.75 in standard length; head moderately pointed, the snout as long or longer than eye diameter; posterior nostril usually with a short flap on anterior rim; cirrus on chin unbranched; other cirri on head variably present or absent; caudal fin slightly rounded with no prolonged rays; colour variable, but often olive to green dorsally, shading to greenish yellow ventrally, densely mottled and spotted with whitish and dark olive; six large irregular dark blotches usually evident along upper side; some small blue spots sometimes visible posteriorly; fins yellowish, the dorsal and anal with dark spots. Western Pacific to Sri Lanka; like others of the genus, prone to bite with its long lower fangs when handled. The largest of the genus; attains 15 cm.

SMOOTH FANGBLENNY
Petroscirtes xestus Jordan & Seale, 1906

Dorsal rays XI,14-16; anal rays II,14-16; pectoral rays usually 14; body slender, the depth 5.1-6.6 in standard length; snout short, its length usually less than eye diameter, its profile steep; posterior nostril usually with a short flap on anterior rim; cirrus on chin fringed; second dorsal spine prolonged in males; caudal fin slightly rounded, the second and tenth rays prolonged in adult males; light brown, finely and densely mottled and spotted with white and dark brown, with a narrow irregular dark brown stripe from upper part of eye, along upper side, to caudal fin; dorsal fin yellowish with numerous small light blue spots, a white margin, an outer row of small black spots and two larger black spots, one within the series of black spots between the ninth and last spines, and an elongate one distally on first membrane. Indo-Pacific; named from a juvenile in Samoa; usually found in flat sandy or weedy habitats, often using empty mollusc shells for refuge. Reaches 7.5 cm.

BICOLOUR FANGBLENNY
Plagiotremus laudandus (Whitley, 1961)

Dorsal rays IX,27-29; anal rays II,22-24; segmented caudal rays 11, pectoral rays usually 12, and pelvic rays I,3 (true of other *Plagiotremus*); no lateral line (also characteristic of the genus); body very elongate (generic), the depth 6.5-8.5 in standard length; snout bluntly rounded, the mouth distinctly ventral; dorsal fin originating slightly posterior to eye, nearly uniform in height; caudal fin lunate; pelvic fins small, shorter than eye diameter; greyish blue on head and anterior body, shading posteriorly to bright yellow, the dorsal fin above with the same change in colour except for a broad black anterior margin; caudal lobes bright yellow. Samoa and islands of Micronesia to western Pacific and Western Australia; the species in Fiji and Tonga is entirely yellow and has been named as a different subspecies, *P. l. flavus* Smith-Vaniz. A mimic of *Meiacanthus atrodorsalis*, in spite of its slender body (holds its dorsal and anal fins fully erect, thus making it seem deeper-bodied). Reaches 7.5 cm.

BLUESTRIPED FANGBLENNY

Plagiotremus rhinorhynchos (Bleeker, 1852)

Dorsal rays XI,32-36; anal rays II,29-33; snout conical; origin of dorsal fin slightly posterior to vertical margin of preopercle; caudal fin emarginate, the interradial membranes somewhat incised; pelvic fins small, usually slightly longer than eye diameter; colour variable: dark brown, yellowish brown, or yellow with two narrow blue stripes, one dorsal, starting above eye, and the other on lower side, commencing from tip of snout; or blue with a black stripe from snout through eye to caudal-fin base (broader as it passes posteriorly); median fins yellowish in both forms. Indo-Pacific except Hawaii where the closely related endemic *P. ewaensis* is found. Feeds by rapid attacks on other fishes, removing dermal tissue, mucus, and sometimes scales. In the blue, black-striped phase it resembles the cleaner wrasse *Labroides dimidiatus*; in this guise it may get closer to its prey fishes than otherwise; in the yellow phase with the blue stripes very narrow, it approximates the colour of the common and harmless anthiine fish *Pseudanthias squamipinnis*, again to get close enough to attack other fishes. Reported to attain 12 cm.

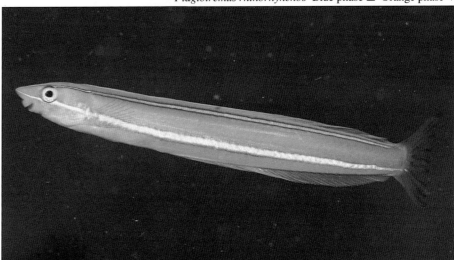

Plagiotremus rhinorhynchos Blue phase ▲ Orange phase ▼

PIANO FANGBLENNY

Plagiotremus tapeinosoma (Bleeker, 1857)

Dorsal rays VII-IX (usually VIII),34-39; anal rays II,28-33; snout conical; origin of dorsal fin slightly posterior to vertical margin of preopercle; caudal fin slightly emarginate; pelvic fins distinctly longer than eye diameter, prolonged in males (up to one-fifth or more standard length); a blackish stripe from front of snout, through upper part of eye, along upper side, and ending in a narrow streak in middle of caudal fin, this stripe on body containing a series of contiguous vertically elongate black spots; back above stripe brownish orange with a pale yellowish longitudinal line, below a broad zone of bluish white, grading to dusky purplish ventrally except lower part of head which is orange-yellow. Indo-Pacific except Hawaii where replaced by the endemic *P. goslinei*; also feeds by rapid attacks on other fishes to remove skin tissue, mucus, and occasionally scales; this species and *R. rhinorhynchos* occasionally "attack" divers, but the contact is little more that a light touch. Reaches 13 cm.

HAIRTAIL BLENNY
Xiphasia setifer Swainson, 1839

Dorsal rays XIII-XIV,107-119; anal rays II,107-119; segmented caudal rays 10; pectoral rays usually 13; a huge curved canine tooth on each side at front of lower jaw (not associated with a venom gland); body extremely elongate, the depth about 40 in standard length; origin of dorsal fin slightly anterior to a vertical at front edge of eye; caudal fin rhomboid, the two inner rays of adult males prolonged; light brownish yellow with about 28 brown bars that extend into dorsal fin, the bars of about equal width to pale interspaces. Western Pacific, including New Caledonia and Vanuatu, to East Africa and Red Sea; most specimens have come from shallow-water trawling over sand or mud bottoms; one in 2.5 m in the Red Sea was vertical in the water; with the approach of the observer it backed tail-first into a tube in the sand. Reported to 53 cm.

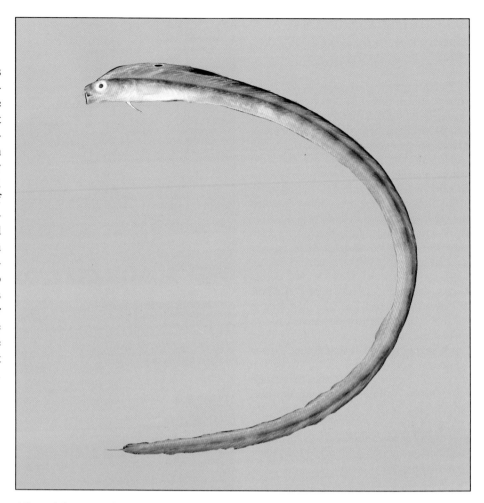

TRIBE OMOBRANCHINI

BLACK BLENNY
Enchelyurus ater (Günther, 1877)

Dorsal rays VIII-X (usually IX), 20-24; anal rays 20-23; segmented caudal rays 13, none branched; pectoral rays 14-15 (usually 15); pelvic rays I,2 (characteristic of the Omobranchini); body depth at anal-fin origin 4.7-5.0 in standard length; head bluntly rounded anteriorly, the snout overhanging mouth; enlarged canine tooth posteriorly on each side of both upper and lower jaws (also true of the tribe except one species of *Omobranchus*); no crest or cirri on head; dorsal and anal fins fully connected with caudal fin; dark brown to black, the head variably marked, often with numerous close-set small pale spots within a dark reticulum; a black spot distally at front of dorsal fin. Southern Oceania from the Tuamotu Archipelago to the Coral Sea; not known from the Great Barrier Reef. Attains 5.5 cm.

KRAUSS'S BLENNY
Enchelyurus kraussi (Klunzinger, 1871)

Dorsal rays VI-IX (usually VII or VIII),21-24; anal rays 20-22; pectoral rays 14-16; body depth at anal-fin origin 4.8-5.2 in standard length; head bluntly rounded anteriorly; no crest or cirri on head; dorsal and anal fins fully connected to caudal fin; brown on body, the head yellowish to yellow, often with diagonal dark brown lines or elongate spots on cheek; dorsal fin brown, or may be yellow anteriorly, with a black spot at front. Western Pacific east to the Mariana Islands and west to the Comoros, Seychelles, and Red Sea; the senior author collected both *E. ater* and *E. kraussi* from shallow lagoon patch reefs on the Chesterfield Bank, Coral Sea. Reaches 5.5 cm.

Enchelyurus ater ▲

Enchelyurus kraussi ▼

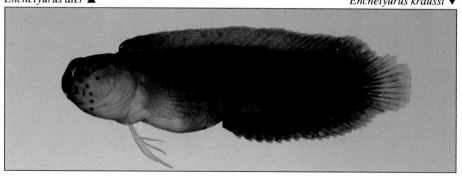

374

OYSTER BLENNY
Omobranchus anolius (Valenciennes, 1836)

Dorsal rays XI-XIII (usually XII),17-19; anal rays II,19-22 (usually 20 or 21); segmented caudal rays usually 13, none branched; pectoral rays usually 13; enlarged canine tooth posteriorly on each side of both jaws; mandibular pores 3 (true of *Omobranchus*); body depth about 5.5 in standard length; males with a prominent crest on head (poorly developed or absent on females); flap on side of lower lip; males with several posterior dorsal soft rays prolonged and free of membrane; caudal fin rounded, the interradial membranes slightly incised; yellowish brown with three rows of small black spots on side of body and numerous wavy whitish lines on head and body which are primarily vertical except posteriorly where four are horizontal. Spencer Gulf, South Australia to the Queensland coast of the Gulf of Carpenteria; usually found in shallow estuarine waters; observed to shelter in pairs in dead oyster shells. Reported to 7.5 cm. Two other blennies of the genus *Omobranchus* occur in Queensland waters, *O. germaini* (Sauvage) with dorsal rays XII-XIV,18-23, and *O. rotundiceps* (Macleay) with dorsal rays XI-XIII,11-12.

Omobranchus anolius   Adult ▼ Juv. ▲

HEPBURN'S BLENNY
Parenchelyurus hepburni (Snyder, 1908)

Dorsal rays XI-XII (rarely XII),19-20; anal rays 21-22; segmented caudal rays 13; pectoral rays usually 13; lateral-line consisting of 3-8 bipored tubes anteriorly on body; mandibular pores 2; body depth at anal fin origin about 5.3 in standard length; front of head bluntly rounded; dorsal fin not notched; dorsal and anal fins joined only basally to caudal fin; caudal fin rounded; black, the males with scattered small blue spots on body and median fins, those on body mainly in three longitudinal rows. Samoa and Marshall Islands to western Pacific; one recent record from Mauritius; found in intertidal zone beneath rocks. Attains 4.5 cm.

375

TRIBE SALARINII

BROWN CORAL BLENNY
Atrosalarias fuscus (Rüppell, 1835)

Dorsal rays IX-XI (usually X),18-22; anal rays II,18-21; pectoral rays 15-18 (usually 16 or 17); fin membrane behind last ray of dorsal and anal fins attached to caudal fin; segmented caudal rays 10-14 (usually 12 or 13); lateral line ending above pectoral fin; a short cirrus on each side of nape, above eye, and on hind rim of anterior nostril; body deep, the depth of adults at anal-fin origin about 3 in standard length; dorsal profile of head convex; dorsal and anal fins progressively longer posteriorly; caudal fin rounded; dark brown, the caudal fin yellow in Great Barrier Reef individuals; a semicircular black spot edged posteriorly with orange-red on upper half of pectoral-fin base; juveniles bright yellow. Indo-Pacific; divisible into two subspecies, *A. f. fuscus* from the Indian Ocean and *A. f. holomelas* (Günther) from the Pacific (including Western Australia); lives on sheltered shallow reefs; hides among the branches of live or dead coral. To 14.5 cm.

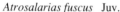
Atrosalarias fuscus Juv.

WHITE-DOTTED BLENNY
Cirripectes alboapicalis (Ogilby, 1899)

Dorsal rays XII,15-17; anal rays II,16-18; pectoral rays usually 15 (true of all *Cirripectes*); pelvic rays I,4 (the spine and inner ray difficult to detect); segmented caudal rays 13, the middle 9 branched (also applies to other *Cirripectes*); lateral-line tubes 9-17, the last posterior to twelfth dorsal soft ray; small scale-like flaps over anterior part of lateral line; a transverse fringe of cirri on nape (characteristic of the genus), with a median gap, the total cirri usually 32-39; middle of lower lip crenulate; teeth in jaws movable and very numerous, and a canine tooth posteriorly on each side of lower jaw (also generic); dorsal fin deeply incised above last spine; last dorsal fin membrane attached to caudal fin membrane in advance of base of caudal fin (attached to caudal-fin base in remaining *Cirripectes* herein); dark brown with white dots on head and at least anteriorly on body; a black spot on head behind eye. Southern subtropical Pacific from Easter Island to Lord Howe Island and the southern Great Barrier Reef. Largest, 15.5 cm. *C. patuki* De Buen is a synonym.

CHESTNUT BLENNY
Cirripectes castaneus (Valenciennes, 1836)

Dorsal rays XII,13-15; anal rays II,14-16; pelvic rays I,4; lateral-line tubes 1-13, the last below or posterior to sixth dorsal soft ray; cirri on nape in four groups, the total cirri usually 32-40; dorsal fin deeply incised above last dorsal spine; females usually dark brown with numerous close-set irregular pale spots about size of pupil (occasional females uniform dark brown); males dark brown, the head and anterior body lighter brown to almost white with slightly diagonal orange-red to reddish brown bars. Tonga and Caroline Islands to East Africa and the Red Sea; feeds on benthic algae like other species of the genus. Reaches 12.5 cm. *C. sebae* (Valenciennes) is a synonym.

LADY MUSGRAVE BLENNY
Cirripectes chelomatus Williams & Mauge, 1983

Dorsal rays XII,14-16; anal rays II,15-17; pelvic rays I,4; lateral-line tubes 0-8, the end of lateral line below space between last dorsal spine and tenth soft ray; cirri on nape in four groups, the total number usually 27-32; middle of lower lip smooth; dorsal fin with a very shallow notch above last spine; dark brown with red dots on head and body (dots pale in preservative). Tonga and Fiji to Lord Howe Island, Great Barrier Reef (type locality, Lady Musgrave Reef), and southeastern Papua New Guinea. Attains 12 cm.

FILAMENTOUS BLENNY
Cirripectes filamentosus (Alleyne & Macleay, 1877)

Dorsal rays XII,13-16 (usually 14-15); anal rays II,14-17 (usually 15-16); pelvic rays I,3-4 (usually 4); lateral-line tubes 0-8, the lateral line ending below second to sixth dorsal soft rays; cirri on nape in four groups, the total number usually 25-31; middle of lower lip smooth; dorsal fin incised over last dorsal spine more than half length of first soft ray; most dorsal spines filamentous in adults, the anterior spines longest; dark brown, the head and anterior body of males sometimes lighter brown, with orange-red dots on snout and cheek; dorsal spines reddish, especially distally; soft dorsal and caudal fins of females yellowish; only the upper part of caudal fin of males yellowish. Western Pacific to western Indian Ocean, including Persian Gulf and southern Red Sea. To 9 cm.

BARRED BLENNY
Cirripectes polyzona (Bleeker, 1868)

Dorsal rays XII,13-15; anal rays II,14-16; pelvic rays I,3; lateral-line tubes 2-9, the last posterior to seventh dorsal soft ray; cirri on nape in four groups, the total number usually 37-41; middle of lower lip smooth; dorsal fin deeply incised over last dorsal spine; juveniles and subadults with a lateral dark brown stripe on body and a white bar below eye; with growth dark stripe breaks into about 12 dark brown bars; head and anterior body of adults grey with orange-red reticulations; chin with white spots; nuchal cirri black. Line Islands and Samoa to East Africa. Largest, 8.5 cm.

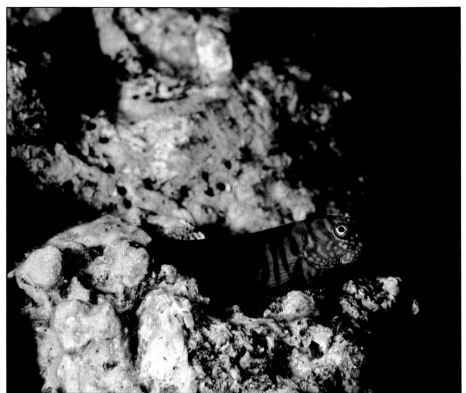

Cirripectes polyzona Juv.

ZEBRA BLENNY
Cirripectes quagga (Fowler & Ball, 1924)

Dorsal rays XII,14-16; anal rays II,15-17; pelvic rays I,4; lateral-line tubes 7-18, the last posterior to seventh dorsal soft ray; row of nuchal cirri with a distinct gap medially on nape; middle of lower lip crenulate; dorsal fin deeply incised over last spine; dorsal-fin membrane not connected to caudal fin in adults; colour highly variable, sometimes uniform brown, often with l2-14 dark bars on body separated by narrow whitish interspaces (may be reduced to a vertical row of whitish dots), sometimes with a broad red area posteriorly on body. Indo-Pacific; usually found on reefs in less than 10 m. Attains 9 cm. *C. lineopunctatus* Strasburg from Hawaii is a synonym.

RETICULATED BLENNY
Cirripectes stigmaticus Strasburg & Schultz, 1953

Dorsal rays XII,14-16; anal rays II,15-17; pelvic rays I,4; lateral-line tubes 1-10, the last posterior to seventh dorsal soft ray; cirri on nape in four groups, the total number usually 34-40; middle of lower lip smooth; dorsal fin deeply incised above last dorsal spine; females olivaceous with a rust-coloured reticulum which breaks up into irregular rust spots posteriorly on body; males dark brown with a scarlet reticulum on head which breaks into irregular bright scarlet spots and short lines on body and basally in dorsal and anal fins; a submarginal scarlet line in anal fin; dorsal and caudal rays largely scarlet. Samoa and islands of Micronesia to East Africa; usually found on exposed reefs from the shallows to 20 m, but generally less than 10 m. Reaches 12 cm.

TRIPLESPOT BLENNY
Crossosalarias macrospilus Smith-Vaniz & Springer, 1971

Dorsal rays XII,16-18, the fin deeply incised between spinous and soft portions; anal rays II,18-20, the last ray connected by membrane to base of caudal fin; segmented caudal rays 13, the middle 9 branched; pectoral rays 15; pelvic rays I,3; numerous movable teeth in jaws, with a canine posteriorly on each side of lower jaw; a short barbel at corner of lower lip; gill opening ending at or slightly below level of lowermost pectoral ray; a palmate cirrus on each side of nape; a median fleshy keel-flap at base of first dorsal spine and slightly anterior to spine; middle dorsal spines may be filamentous on large adults; head whitish, densely spotted with greenish to reddish brown above level of mouth, the body olivaceous to light reddish brown with whitish spots; a deep blue to black spot as large as eye on nape at origin of dorsal fin, enclosing flap at base of first spine, and a pair of comparable deep blue spots ventrally on throat. Western Pacific east to Tonga; on coral reefs in the depth range of less than 1 to 25 m, but usually in less than 10 m. Largest, 8.2 cm. The only species of the genus.

FOURLINE BLENNY
Ecsenius aequalis Springer, 1988

Dorsal rays XII,13-15, the fin deeply notched between spinous and soft portions; anal rays II,14-17 (usually 16); last dorsal and anal rays connected by membrane to caudal peduncle (true of all *Ecsenius*); pelvic rays I,3 (characteristic of the genus); segmented caudal rays 13; no caudal rays branched (generic character); pectoral rays usually 13; front of head strongly convex, overhanging the ventral mouth (generic); four to eight canine teeth posteriorly on each side of lower jaw; a cirrus present only on posterior rim of anterior nostril; translucent tan with four longitudinal black lines, one at base of dorsal fin and three equally spaced on side of body (lines may be broken; may be absent in Coral Sea fish). Great Barrier Reef, Coral Sea, and Trobriand Islands, Papua New Guinea; a shallow coral-reef species, as are most of the genus. Largest, 4.3 cm.

AUSTRALIAN BLENNY
Ecsenius australianus Springer, 1988

Dorsal rays XII,13-15, the fin deeply notched; anal rays II,15-17; segmented caudal rays 13; lateral line terminating below tenth to twelfth dorsal spines; usually one canine tooth posteriorly on each side of lower jaw; cirrus present only on posterior rim of anterior nostril; upper two-thirds of body red to brownish red with two longitudinal rows of about ten round to oblong white spots; lower third of body abruptly white; a white-edged dark reddish brown band across interorbital and extending posteriorly from eye. Northern Great Barrier Reef. Reaches 6 cm. Formerly identified as *E. opsifrontalis* Chapman & Schultz, this name now restricted to a species from the islands of Micronesia and Samoa.

BICOLOUR BLENNY
Ecsenius bicolor (Day, 1888)

Dorsal rays XII,16-18, the fin incised between spinous and soft portions only about half length of first dorsal ray; anal rays II,18-20; segmented caudal rays 14, the third and eleventh very prolonged in large adults (presumed males); lateral line ending below tenth to thirteenth dorsal spines; usually a single canine tooth (sometimes none) posteriorly on each side of lower jaw; a cirrus from both anterior and posterior rim of anterior nostril; three different colour phases: uniform dark brown (though the head may be yellowish to reddish brown); head and anterior half of body dark bluish to purplish grey, the posterior half of body bright orange-yellow; and a form with a broad black stripe from behind eye along upper side of body, ending within a yellow zone on upper half of posterior fourth of body; a broad white band on body below and adjacent to black stripe and posterior yellow area; head below black stripe and ventral part of body lavender-grey; common to all three phases, a curved salmon pink line posterior to lower part of eye. Islands of Micronesia and Samoa to the Maldives; known from the depth range of about 1-21 m. Attains 11 cm, including caudal filaments.

QUEENSLAND BLENNY
Ecsenius mandibularis McCulloch, 1923

Dorsal rays XII,14-16, the fin deeply incised; anal rays II,16-18; segmented caudal rays 13; lateral line terminating below ninth to eleventh dorsal spines; three to eight canine teeth posteriorly on each side of lower jaw; a cirrus only from posterior rim of anterior nostril; upper half of body grey-brown, lower half abruptly white with a grey-brown stripe from cheek through pectoral base and along lower side of body; two longitudinal rows of small white spots on body, one along back and one midlaterally along the brown-white demarcation. Queensland from Cape York Peninsula at 12°S to the Bunker Group, southern Great Barrier Reef; usually found on coastal reefs. Attains 7.5 cm.

MIDAS BLENNY
Ecsenius midas Starck, 1969

Dorsal rays XIII,18-21 (usually 19 or 20), without a notch between spinous and soft portions; anal rays II,20-23 (rarely 20); segmented caudal rays usually 14; lateral line ending below seventh to ninth dorsal spines; canine teeth posteriorly on lower jaw 0-2 (usually 1); a pair of anterior teeth at front of lower jaw about twice as large as adjacent slender teeth; total slender teeth in lower jaw 13-16 (usually 14) (more than 31 in other *Ecsenius*); body elongate, the depth 5-6 in standard length; cirrus only from posterior rim of anterior nostril; caudal fin deeply emarginate; origin of dorsal fin over middle of head length (more posterior on other species of the genus); colour variable, but usually orange-yellow or dark slate blue, in either case with a large black spot directly in front of anus. Indo-Pacific; occurs to at least 30 m; the orange-yellow phase has been observed to school with the anthiine fish *Pseudanthias squamipinnis* which it resembles in colour; it has been cited as a possible mimic of the anthiine; reported to feed on zooplankton. Reaches 13 cm.

GREAT BARRIER REEF BLENNY
Ecsenius stictus Springer, 1988

Dorsal rays XII,13-15, the fin deeply notched; anal rays II,15-17; segmented caudal rays 13; lateral line ending below ninth to eleventh dorsal spines; canine teeth posteriorly in lower jaw 0-1 (usually 1); cirrus present only on posterior rim of anterior nostril; pale grey with about four longitudinal rows of dusky to yellowish elongate spots anteriorly on body, the upper two of which continue onto head where they are darker; three to four rows of blackish dots on posterior half of body; a horizontal Y-shaped black mark on pectoral-fin base; a black line on lower edge of operculum and a transverse one on chin. Known only from the Great Barrier Reef. Largest, 5.8 cm. Formerly identified as *E. yaeyamensis* (Aoyagi), a name now restricted to a species which ranges from the Ryukyu Islands south to Vanuatu and west to Sri Lanka.

TIGER BLENNY
Ecsenius tigris Springer, 1988

Dorsal rays XII,13-14 (usually 14), the fin deeply notched; anal rays II,15-16 (usually 16); segmented caudal rays 13; lateral line ending below tenth to twelfth dorsal spines; a single canine tooth posteriorly on each side of lower jaw; a short cirrus on posterior rim of anterior nostril, none on anterior rim; body reddish to orangish brown, white ventrally, with three rows of vertically elongate black spots (many of which are joined to form narrow black bars) and two rows of white spots, one along back and the other (partly as dashes) midlateral; head peach with a narrow brown band passing posteriorly from eye. Known thus far only from Osprey, Bougainville, and Holmes Reefs in the western Coral Sea. Attains about 5 cm.

WAVYLINE ROCKSKIPPER
Entomacrodus decussatus (Bleeker, 1858)

Dorsal rays XIII,16-18 (rarely 18, usually 17), the fin deeply incised between spinous and soft portions; anal rays II,16-19 (rarely 19); last dorsal ray linked by membrane to caudal-fin base, but anal fin not joined by membrane to caudal peduncle; segmented caudal rays 13, the middle 9 branched, pectoral rays usually 14, and pelvic rays I,4 (these counts also apply to other *Entomacrodus*); gill rakers 17-30; teeth in jaws very numerous and movable except for a canine tooth posteriorly on each side of lower jaw, and teeth present on vomer (generic); margin of upper lip of adults usually fully crenulate; one cirrus on each side of nape; supraorbital cirrus with many short branches; whitish with numerous wavy dark grey-brown longitudinal lines and small dark blotches, the blotches tending to form double bars; median and pectoral fins with blackish and whitish spots. Central and western Pacific to Western Australia. Attains 19 cm.

BLACKSPOTTED ROCKSKIPPER
Entomacrodus striatus (Quoy & Gaimard, 1836)

Dorsal rays XIII,15-16, the fin deeply incised; anal rays II,16-17; gill rakers 14-22 (usually 16-20); margin of upper lip usually fully crenulate; nape with one cirrus on each side (occasionally absent); supraorbital cirrus with many short side branches; whitish with numerous small irregular black spots on body which may group to form about four indistinct large blotches on upper side; an irregular black line behind eye; median fins faintly but densely marked with small dusky spots. Indo-Pacific; the most common and widespread species of the genus; may be found in the intertidal zone of both protected lagoons and wave-swept outer reefs. Attains 11 cm. *E. plurifilis* Schultz & Chapman is a synonym.

SHORTBODIED BLENNY
Exallias brevis (Kner, 1868)

Dorsal rays XII,12-13 (usually 13); anal rays II,13-14 (usually 14); segmented caudal rays 13, the middle 9 branched; pectoral rays 15; pelvic rays I,4; body deep, the depth at anal-fin origin 2.6-2.8 in standard length; snout slightly convex and vertical; teeth incisiform, very numerous, those in upper jaw movable, those in lower nearly fixed; a transverse band of cirri on nape; a branched tentacle over eye; a pair of tiny barbels on chin; dorsal fin deeply notched over last spine; dorsal fin connected to base of caudal fin by membrane, but anal fin not; caudal fin slightly rounded; whitish with numerous dark spots the size of pupil or smaller on head, body, and fins which tend to form clumps on body, these spots brown on females, bright red on males except head and abdomen; dorsal and caudal fins of males mainly red. Indo-Pacific; feeds on coral polyps. Largest, 14.5 cm. The only species of the genus.

GOLDSPOTTED ROCKSKIPPER
Istiblennius chrysospilos (Bleeker, 1857)

Dorsal spines XIII,19-21; anal rays II,20-22; segmented caudal rays 13, the middle 9 branched (true of all *Istiblennius*); pectoral rays 14-15 (usually 14), pelvic rays I,3; anterior lateral line with 5 or more vertical pairs of pores; teeth in jaws slender, close-set, numerous (more than 200 in upper jaw and more than 160 in lower), and movable (also characteristic of the genus); a canine tooth posteriorly on each side of lower jaw (difficult to see without prying mouth open); margin of upper lip crenulate, of lower lip smooth; no obvious crest on head; orbital cirrus slender but broader than thick, usually bifid at tip, sometimes with three or four branches; dorsal fin notched between spinous and soft portions (generic); last dorsal ray joined by membrane to caudal peduncle; last anal ray not connected by membrane to caudal peduncle (generic); pale tan with about nine dark double bars on body, smaller posteriorly; head and upper anterior body with small bright orange spots; a diagonal orange line behind eye; spinous portion of dorsal fin with numerous small orange spots and short lines, each spine tip with a small black spot; females with small dark reddish brown spots on body; males suffused with purplish, with small pale blue spots and usually a black spot as large or larger than pupil in fourth dark bar. Central and western Pacific to western Australia; generally found on outer reef flats exposed to surge but not the high intertidal zone. Reaches 13 cm. *I. coronatus* (Günther) is a synonym.

DUSSUMIER'S ROCKSKIPPER
Istiblennius dussumieri (Valenciennes, 1836)

Dorsal rays XIII,20-22; anal rays II,22-24; pectoral rays 14; pelvic rays I,3; no vertical pairs of lateral-line pores; lower canine teeth usually absent; margins of lips smooth; male with a crest on head; cirrus over eye branched, the branches more numerous with age; no cirri on nape; last dorsal ray connected to caudal fin about half length of first segmented ray; olive with dark reddish bars which bifurcate ventrally; head with small orange-red spots and irregular lines; males with broad blackish borders on median fins, three large blackish areas basally in second dorsal fin, and often with a dark spot between first two dorsal spines; females with small black spots posteriorly on body and in median fins. Western Pacific to East Africa; often found in mangrove areas. Reaches 12 cm.

RIPPLED ROCKSKIPPER
Istiblennius edentulus (Forster, 1801)

Dorsal rays XIII,19-21; anal rays II,21-23; pectoral rays 14; pelvic rays I,3; lateral line without vertical pairs of pores; no canine teeth; lips smooth; male with a crest on head (large females may have a low fleshy ridge); cirrus above eye unbranched; a small cirrus on each side of nape; last ray of dorsal fin connected by membrane to caudal fin about half length of first segmented ray; pale greenish grey with dark grey double bars on body which extend basally into dorsal fin; vertical double orangish lines in pale interspaces on body; a diagonal dark grey spot or double spot edged in pale blue behind eye; females may have small dark orange spots posteriorly on body, especially ventrally. Indo-Pacific; common along rocky shores. Largest specimen examined, 17 cm, from Pitcairn Island.

Istiblennius edentulus Male ▲ Female ▼

LINED ROCKSKIPPER
Istiblennius lineatus (Valenciennes, 1836)

Dorsal rays XIII,21-25; anal rays II,22-24; pectoral rays 14; pelvic rays I,3; lateral line without vertical pairs of pores; no canine teeth; margin of upper lip crenulate, of lower lip smooth; male with a crest on head; cirrus over eye short and triangular, at right angles to surface of eye, fringed on edges; no cirri on nape; last dorsal ray connected by membrane to caudal peduncle; pale grey with dark brown longitudinal lines, some interconnecting, breaking into short lines and spots on caudal peduncle; some vertical to slightly diagonal dark lines on cheek and behind eye; six pairs of small dark brown spots along base of dorsal fin; dorsal fin with diagonal whitish lines. Indo-Pacific; occurs along rocky shores, often in tide-pools. Attains 14 cm.

PEACOCK ROCKSKIPPER
Istiblennius meleagris (Valenciennes, 1836)

Dorsal rays XIII,18-20; anal rays II,19-21; pectoral rays 14; pelvic rays I,3; lateral line without vertical pairs of pores; no canine teeth; margin of upper lip crenulate, of lower lip smooth; male with a crest on head; cirrus over eye large and bushy; nuchal cirri present or absent; last dorsal ray connected by membrane to caudal peduncle; body greenish with dark double bars (more evident in females than males) and small pale blue spots; median fins grey-brown, the dorsal with diagonal white lines, and the caudal and anal fins with white dots. Queensland to western Australia; found along rocky and mangrove shores. Reported to 15 cm.

BULLETHEAD ROCKSKIPPER
Istiblennius periophthalmus (Valenciennes, 1836)

Dorsal rays XIII,19-21; anal rays II,20-22; pectoral rays 14; pelvic rays I,3; lateral line with no vertical pairs of pores; a canine tooth posteriorly on each side of lower jaw; margin of upper lip crenulate; no crest on head (but males may have a fleshy hump on head); cirrus over eye a slender filament (occasionally with one or two branches); a small cirrus on each side of nape; last dorsal ray connected by membrane to caudal peduncle; pale greenish grey with eight H-shaped dark brown bars along side of body (the cross-bar of H broad), each containing one or more horizontally elongate small dark-edged pale blue spots; females, depending on locality, may have numerous small red spots on body and red dots on head. Indo-Pacific; a common species in both wave-swept shores and calm rocky shores of lagoons; may be found outer reef flats in 1 or more meter depths, always with a small hole in the reef to serve as shelter. To about 15 cm. *I. paulus* (Bryan & Herre), a form found on islands of Oceania which lacks small red spots in the female phase, is regarded as a synonym.

THROATSPOT BLENNY
Nannosalarias nativitatus (Regan, 1909)

Dorsal rays XII,15-16; anal rays II,16-18; segmented caudal rays 13, the middle 9 branched; pectoral rays 15; pelvic rays I,3; more than 75 slender close-set fairly rigid teeth in upper jaw and more than 40 in lower; a canine posteriorly on each side of lower jaw; a few small teeth on vomer; margins of lips smooth; supraorbital, nasal, and nuchal cirri small and unbranched; dorsal fin deeply incised between spinous and soft portions; basal two-thirds of last dorsal and anal rays connected by membrane to caudal peduncle; light brown on back, finely mottled with pale greenish and dark brown, whitish below, with a longitudinal row of nine dark brown spots nearly as large as eye, the third and fourth very close together (as are to a lesser extent the first and second and fifth and sixth); dusky bars extending ventrally from these spots across lower half of body; a large oval black spot on each side of throat of male; dorsal and caudal rays orange-red or dotted with this colour. Western Pacific east to Tonga and west to Christmas Island, Indian Ocean (type locality); occurs on reefs exposed to surge. Maximum length, 5 cm.

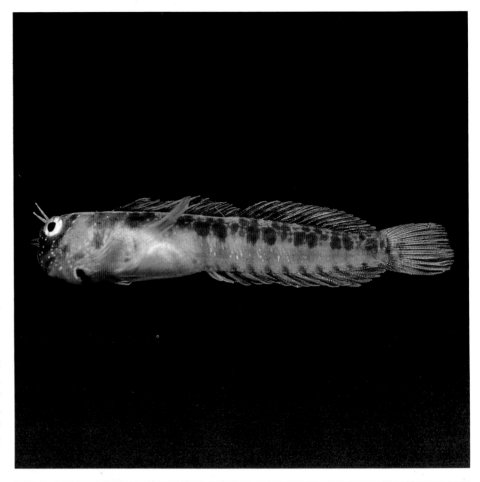

BARRED-CHIN BLENNY
Rhabdoblennius ellipes (Jordan & Starks, 1906)

Dorsal rays XII,18-21; anal rays II,20-21; segmented caudal rays 13, the middle 9 branched; pectoral rays 14; pelvic rays I,3; slender teeth in jaws not movable, 40-50 in upper jaw and 28-38 in lower jaw; a canine tooth posteriorly on each side of lower jaw; a few small conical teeth on vomer; margins of lips smooth; body slender, the depth at anal-fin origin 6.5-7.0 in standard length; no crest on head; supraorbital cirrus slender and long, without branches; no cirri on nape; dorsal fin not notched; last dorsal and anal rays connected by membrane to caudal peduncle; light yellowish brown dorsally, white below, with a series of seven large dusky spots along side of body; dusky areas in dorsal fin above these spots; a lateral row of long pale blue dashes on side of body and two rows of shorter dashes on back; ventral part of head with three transverse blackish bands that fail to meet midventrally, the first on chin and the third following lower edge of operculum; three diagonal pale blue lines on head. Islands of Oceania and the Great Barrier Reef; common on the outer reef front in surge channels and pools where exposed to heavy surf. A small species, the largest 5 cm. *R. rhabdotrachelus* (Fowler & Ball) appears to be a synonym.

JEWELLED BLENNY
Salarias fasciatus (Bloch, 1786)

Dorsal rays XII,18-20; anal rays II,19-2l; segmented caudal rays 13, the middle 9 branched (true of other *Salarias*); pectoral rays 14; pelvic rays I,3, the inner ray minute (true of genus); teeth slender, numerous, and movable, except for a canine posteriorly on each side of lower jaw (characteristic of all *Salarias*); no teeth on vomer (generic); margins of lips smooth; body depth at anal-fin origin 3.7-4.2 in standard length, the abdomen frequently distended; head small, without a crest; supraorbital and nuchal cirri branched; dorsal fin without a notch; last dorsal ray bound by membrane to base of caudal fin and last anal ray to caudal peduncle; anterior anal rays of adult males prolonged; colour variable but usually olivaceous to brown with irregular dark bars and many round to oblong white spots of various size (some on lower side may be larger than eye); usually longitudinal dark lines anteriorly on body and some small dark-edged bright blue spots on upper posterior part of body. Samoa and islands of Micronesia to East Africa and the Red Sea; usually seen on reef flats with heavy algal cover in 0.5-3 m. Reaches 14 cm.

FRINGELIP BLENNY
Salarias sinuosus Snyder, 1908

Dorsal rays XII,16-17; anal rays II,17-19; pectoral rays 14; margin of upper lip crenulate, of lower smooth; no crest on head (there may be a low fleshy ridge); cirrus over eye long, slender, and unbranched; a small cirrus on either side of nape; body depth at anal-fin origin 5.0-5.8 in standard length; dorsal fin notched between spinous and soft portions; last dorsal ray connected by membrane to base of caudal fin and last anal ray to caudal peduncle; anterior anal rays of males elongate; upper two-thirds of body brown with eight dark brown bars and small dark-edged blue spots, lower third reddish with close-set oblong whitish spots in four rows, the spots progressively smaller ventrally; dorsal and caudal rays with small dark reddish spots. Western Pacific; generally found in tidepools in coral reefs. Reaches 6 cm.

Salarias sinuosus Male ▲ Female ▼

TALBOT'S BLENNY
Stanulus talboti Springer, 1968

Dorsal rays XII,11-12; anal rays II,12-13; segmented caudal rays 13, the middle 9 branched; pectoral rays 15; pelvic rays I,4; close-set slender teeth in jaws numerous and movable; lips smooth; no crest on head; supraorbital, nasal, and nuchal cirri small and unbranched; dorsal fin deeply notched between spinous and soft portions; last dorsal ray bound to caudal peduncle by a membrane, but last anal ray free of peduncle; a lateral row of dark brown spots forming a stripe on side of body; back above stripe brown with whitish spots, body below whitish; white dots on ventral half of head; a small dark brown spot at midbase of pectoral fin. Known from the southern Great Barrier Reef, Lord Howe Island, Ryukyu Islands, and Ogasawara Islands; occurs in the surge channel zone of exposed outer reefs at depths of 3-15 m. Largest, 4.8 cm.

DRAGONETS
FAMILY CALLIONYMIDAE

Dragonets are generally small, scaleless fishes with a broad and somewhat flattened head. The dorsal fin consists of separate spinous and soft parts, and the single anal fin contains only soft rays. The upper jaw is strongly protrusible, and there is a stout, often multi-barbed, spine on the lower rear corner of the cheek. Dragonets are bottom-living fishes that prefer sand, mud, or dead coral rubble. They usually rest on their outstretched pelvic fins and move about the reef in slow, short bursts. The diet consists mainly of small benthic invertebrates. Over 125 species are known from the Indo-Pacific region. Although there are a number of species close to shore along the Queensland coast, relatively few are encountered on the Great Barrier Reef and offshore Coral Sea reefs.

GORAM DRAGONET
Diplogrammus goramensis (Bleeker, 1858)

Dorsal rays IV-8; anal rays 7; pectoral rays 17-20; body with a ventrolateral fold of skin below the lateral line; operculum with a free flap of skin; first dorsal spine of males forming an elongate filament; head with brown bars and vertical blue lines; upper sides brown with irregular white mottling and brown bars that extend ventrally; first dorsal fin with oblique banding, other fins mottled with brown and white spots; females generally less ornate. Western Pacific from China to Fiji. Attains 6 cm.

MORRISON'S DRAGONET
Synchiropus morrisoni Schultz, 1960

Dorsal rays IV-8; anal rays 7; pectoral rays 18-23; preopercular spine with 2 spinules on dorsal surface; soft dorsal fin rays branched; anal fin rays unbranched except last; first dorsal fin of males much taller than second dorsal fin, that of females shorter than second dorsal fin; mottled red with white spots of variable size; a prominent dark brown blotch covering one-half to entire pectoral-fin base; first dorsal fin of males with zebra-like bars edged in pale blue; lower head and thorax of males with blue dots; females generally less ornate than males. Japan to Australia and eastward to the Marshall Islands and Fiji. Maximum size, 7 cm.

Diplogrammus goramensis ▲   *Synchiropus morrisoni* ▼

OCELLATED DRAGONET
Synchiropus ocellatus (Pallas, 1770)

Dorsal rays IV-8-9; anal rays 7-9; pectoral rays 18-23; soft dorsal and anal fin rays branched; preopercular spine with a single spinule on dorsal surface; first dorsal fin of males much taller than second dorsal fin, that of females shorter than second dorsal fin; brown with irregular whitish saddles and blotches; red or brown spots on caudal rays forming irregular bars; blue dots on thorax and lower head of males; first dorsal fin of males highly ornate with wavy bands and ocelli. Japan to Australia and eastward to Pitcairn Island. Grows to 7 cm.

MANDARINFISH
Synchiropus splendidus (Herre, 1927)

Dorsal rays IV-8; anal rays 6-8 (usually 7); pectoral rays 28-35; preopercular spine with 2-5 spinules on dorsal surface; most soft dorsal and anal fin rays branched; orange or orangish brown with broad curved bands, elongate spots, and dashes of green; blue markings on head and blue margins on fins; an unmistabable species that is prized by aquarium fish collectors; often occurs among living corals. Western Pacific from the Ryukyu Islands to Australia. Reported to 6 cm.

STARRY DRAGONET
Synchiropus stellatus Smith, 1963

Dorsal rays IV-8 or 9; anal rays 8 or 9; pectoral rays 19-24; preopercular spine with a single spinule on dorsal surface; most soft dorsal and anal rays branched; first dorsal fin of males much taller than second dorsal fin, that of females shorter than second dorsal fin; males reddish with irregular white blotches, first dorsal fin with zebra-like bars and ocellus; females overall white with irregular red blotches, some of them roughly star-shaped, first dorsal fin mostly black with pale outer edge. East Africa to western Pacific. To 6 cm. The population from the western Pacific may represent an undescribed species.

GUDGEONS OR SLEEPERS
FAMILY ELEOTRIDAE

Gudgeons are primarily fresh and brackish water fishes that occur mainly in the tropics. Worldwide there are about 300 species, of which 250 are found in the Indo-Pacific region. Only a few species inhabit coral reef environments. Gudgeons are close relatives of gobies (Gobiidae), and the two groups share a number of morphological features including a generally elongate body, similar head shape, two separate dorsal fins, and absence of a lateral line. Most gobies however, have the pelvic fins completely or partially fused to form a disc-shaped structure, whereas the pelvics are completely separated in gudgeons. They are mainly bottom-living fishes, although a few species are free-swimming. The diet consists primarily of benthic invertebrates, particularly crustaceans.

TAILFACE SLEEPER
Calumia godeffroyi (Günther, 1877)

Dorsal rays VI-I,6-7; anal rays I,6-7; pectoral rays 16-17; lateral scales 21-23; predorsal scales 7-9; lower gill rakers 6, short and stubby; five broad dark brown bars with narrow white spaces on side; fins mostly dark brown, but caudal fin with pair of white-edged black spots at base of uppermost and lowermost rays. East Africa to Society Islands; found in shallow sandy habitats. Attains 3.6 cm.

WRIGGLERS
FAMILY XENISTHMIDAE

These are very small fishes that live on the sandy fringe of coral reefs. They were formerly included in the Family Eleotridae. Wrigglers are characterised by an elongate body, a small depressed head, projecting lower jaw, oblique mouth, relatively low dorsal and anal fins, and a rounded caudal fin. There are VI spines in the first dorsal fin, a single spine and 10-12 soft rays in the second dorsal and anal fins, and 17 segmented caudal rays. The body is covered with numerous small scales; sometimes much of the head is scaleless.

BULLSEYE WRIGGLER
Xenisthmus polyzonatus (Klunzinger, 1871)

Dorsal rays VI-I,11; anal rays I,10; pectoral rays 15-17; lateral scales 57-60; predorsal scales 15-20; lower gill rakers 12; mottled brown, sometimes with hint of darker crossbars; a brown bar below eye; the most distinctive mark is an ocellated black spot at the base of the caudal fin. Red Sea to Samoa, north to Ryukyu Islands. Grows to 3 cm.

GOBIES
FAMILY GOBIIDAE

The gobies are the largest family in the region with more than 200 species represented. Indeed it is the largest family of marine fishes in the world with about 220 genera and 1,600 species, of which about 160 genera and 1,200 species inhabit the Indo-Pacific region. However, our coverage in this section is limited to relatively common genera and species that divers and reef walkers are likely to encounter. As might be expected in such a huge assemblage, there is considerable variation in size, colouration, and body shape. Generally, gobies are elongate fishes with two dorsal fins, and the pelvic fins of most species are either partly connected or completely fused to form a cup-shaped disc. Most reef species have VI flexible spines in the first dorsal fin and I flexible soft spine and 6-15 soft segmented rays in the second dorsal. They are usually under 10 cm in length, and many are considerably smaller. In fact some of the world's smallest known vertebrates are included. Members of the genus *Trimmaton* seldom exceed 12-15 mm. Most gobies live in marine or estuarine habitats, but there are a number of purely freshwater species as well. They are either bottom-dwellers or hover a short distance above the bottom. They are associated with a variety of substrata. Members of the genera *Gobiodon* and *Paragobiodon* live among branches of living coral (usually *Acropora* and pocilloporid corals, respectively), those in *Eviota* on both branching and encrusting corals, and members of *Bryaninops* commonly dwell on the surface of sea whips. The tiny species of the genus *Trimma* are common in caves and crevices of outer reef slopes; several occur in aggregations that hover in midwater. Most of the other reef species are associated with sand or rubble habitats, often sheltering in burrows. The shrimp gobies are particularly noteworthy because of their habit of sharing their burrow with alpheid shrimps. The shrimps build and maintain the burrows, while the gobies serve as sentinels. This group, that includes members of *Amblyeleotris*, *Cryptocentrus*, *Ctenogobiops*, *Stonogobiops*, and *Vanderhorstia*, contains some of the most brilliantly coloured gobies. Because of their small size, gobies are usually not used for human food, but due to their huge numbers they are an important part of the reef's food chain. Gobies are sometimes kept as aquarium pets, and a number of species have been successfully bred in captivity. Gobies exhibit a wide range of feeding habits, but most species are carnivorous. Much of the diet is composed of crabs, prawns, smaller crustaceans (such as copepods, amphipods, and ostracods), molluscs, annelids, polychaetes, formaninferans, sponges, and eggs of various invertebrates and fishes. The graceful members of the genera *Nemateleotris* and *Ptereleotris* were formerly included in the goby family, but recent studies indicate they belong in the Microdesmidae. Some gobies are among the most difficult fishes to identify. Taxonomic problems are compounded by their small size, the presence of many closely related species with similar appearance, and a lack of goby researchers.

Redeye Goby (*Bryanops natans*)

SPOTTED SHRIMP GOBY
Amblyeleotris guttata (Fowler, 1938)

Dorsal rays VI-I,12; anal rays I,12; pectoral rays 19-20; lateral scales 65-70; predorsal scales present; white to light grey with conspicuous small orange-yellow spots on head, body, and median fins (only basally on anal fin which is mainly blackish); diffuse dark bars on lower side to below pectoral fin; pelvic fins, thorax, and belly blackish. East Indies to Samoa, north to Ryukyu Islands; lives in burrow with alpheid shrimps. To 8 cm.

BLOTCHY SHRIMP GOBY
Amblyeleotris periophthalma (Bleeker, 1853)

Dorsal rays VI-I,12; anal rays I,12; pectoral rays 19; lateral scales about 80-85; predorsal scales absent; whitish with six reddish-brown bars and small orange spots on head and dorsal fins; also brown blotches dorsally in pale areas between bars. Western Pacific eastward to Samoa; lives in burrows with alpheid shrimps. To 8 cm. *A. maculata* Yanagisawa is a synonym.

STEINITZ' SHRIMP GOBY
Amblyeleotris steinitzi (Klausewitz, 1974)

Dorsal rays V-I,12; anal rays I,12; pectoral rays 18-19; lateral scales 62-66; predorsal scales absent; whitish with five reddish-brown bars across side; faint yellowish lines in pale spaces between bars; orange dots on dorsal fins; snout and area around eyes often dusky brown. Red Sea to Samoa; lives in burrow with alpheid shrimps. Maximum size, 8 cm.

WHEELER'S SHRIMP GOBY

Amblyeleotris wheeleri Polunin & Lubbock, 1977

Dorsal rays VI-I,12; anal rays I,12; pectoral rays 18-20; lateral scales 50-58; area immediately in front of dorsal fin scaled; pale yellowish to white with small pale blue spots and seven brown to red bars on head and body (first bar on head faint, with small orange spots). East Africa to Australia and Marshall Islands; lives in burrow with alpheid shrimps. Attains 8 cm.

ORANGE-STRIPED GOBY

Amblygobius decussatus (Bleeker, 1855)

Dorsal rays VI-I,14; anal rays I,14; pectoral rays 17; lateral scales about 57-58; bluish white with four narrow orange stripes (two extending prominently onto head) and faint narrow orange bars on sides; an orange spot edged in pale bluish at base of caudal fin. Western Pacific; usually found on silty sand at edge of protected reefs. Maximum size to 8 cm.

BANDED GOBY

Amblygobius phalaena (Valenciennes, 1837)

Dorsal rays VI-I,14; first dorsal fin pointed; anal rays I,14; pectoral rays 19-20; lateral scales about 55-58; cheek scales absent; mottled greenish brown on dorsal half of body and whitish below with five narrow blackish bars edged with pale blue on body; characteristic markings include a prominent ocellated spot on middle of first dorsal fin and a black spot on upper caudal fin near base. Indo-Pacific; inhabits sandy or sparse seagrass substrata in the vicinity of protected reefs; hovers just above the bottom; takes refuge in a burrow. To 15 cm.

OLD GLORY
Amblygobius rainfordi (Whitley, 1940)

Dorsal rays VI-I,15-16; anal rays I,15-16; pectoral rays 16-18; lateral scales 55-60; snout pointed; first dorsal fin pointed; yellowish to brown on head and anterior part of body, purplish to grey posteriorly, with five blue-edged orange-red stripes on head and body, about five white spots along base of dorsal fin, an ocellated black spot on middle of second dorsal fin, and one at base of upper caudal fin rays. Queensland and Coral Sea to Philippines. To 6.5 cm.

SPHINX GOBY
Amblygobius sphynx (Valenciennes, 1837)

Dorsal rays VI-I,13-15; first dorsal fin low and rounded; anal rays I,13-15; pectoral rays 17-19; lateral scales 46-52; cheek with only a few scales; greenish brown with numerous pale blue dots and 5-6 dark browm bars extending onto lower sides; head yellowish brown with blue spots and lines and some blackish blotches posteriorly on lower part of head; a black spot edged in pale blue at upper base of caudal fin. East Africa to western Pacific; habits similar to *A. phalaena*. Maximum size, 18 cm.

STARRY GOBY
Asterropteryx semipunctatus Rüppell, 1828

Dorsal rays VI-I,9-10; anal rays I,8-9; pectoral rays 16-18; lateral scales 23-25; preoperculum with 3-6 short spines; third dorsal spine filamentous; pelvic fins separated; brown with darker blotches; horizontal rows of brilliant blue spots on head and body. East Africa and Red Sea to Hawaiian Islands and Tuamotus; occurs on sand-rubble area near shallow reefs of lagoons and bays. Grows to 6.5 cm.

COMMON GOBY
Bathygobius fuscus (Rüppell, 1830)

Dorsal rays VI-I,9; anal rays I,8; pectoral rays 17-19 (usually 17 or 18), the three upper rays free from membranes (uppermost with 2-3 branches); lateral scales 29-36; predorsal scales 10-19, reaching nearly to eyes; cheeks bulbous; brown with blackish mottlings and numerous bluish dots; dorsal and anal fins with faint spotting; first dorsal fin dusky, sometimes with yellowish margin. East Africa and Red Sea to Tuamotus and Hawaiian Islands; occurs in shallow rocky areas, often in pools of the intertidal zone. Attains 8 cm.

COCOS GOBY
Bathygobius cocosensis (Bleeker, 1854)

Dorsal rays VI-I,9; anal rays I,8; pectoral rays 18-20, the upper three or four rays free from membranes; lateral scales 33-35; predorsal scales 6-14, reaching nearly to eyes; cheeks bulbous; overall brown with about six to eight black spots along middle of sides; males with numerous longitudinal lines; females mottled, sometimes with dark saddles on upper sides. East Africa to Marshall Islands and Tuamotus. To 8 cm.

LARGE WHIP GOBY
Bryaninops ampulus Larson, 1985

Dorsal rays VI-I,6-9; anal rays I,6-9; pectoral rays 14-17; lateral scales 37-69; mostly semi-transparent, but suffused with fawn, golden brown, or orange on lower half of body; a bright silvery-white line above vertebral column. Madagascar and Seychelles to Hawaiian Islands; associated with gorgonian sea whips to at least 30 m depth. Reaches 6 cm.

ERYTHROPS GOBY

Bryaninops erythrops (Jordan & Seale, 1906)

Dorsal rays VI-I,7-9; anal rays I,7-9; pectoral rays 13-16; lateral scales 34-49; head and body semitransparent with a white line over vertebral column; reddish-brown to violet band covering most of lower half of head and body; eye with a broad rim of pink to violet red. Chagos Archipelago to Marshall Islands and Samoa; lives on live coral (*Porites*) and stinging coral (*Millepora*). Reaches 2.3 cm.

REDEYE GOBY

Bryaninops natans Larson, 1985

Dorsal rays VI (rarely IV, V, VII, or VIII)-I,7-9; anal rays I,8-9; pectoral rays 14-17; lateral scales 19-40; mostly semitransparent; chrome yellow peritoneum; eye bright violet-red, also violet or reddish stripes and bands on head and snout. Red Sea to Micronesia and Cook Islands; associated with *Acropora* coral, usually hovering 30-60 cm above; depth range 5-30 m. Grows to 2.5 cm.

BLACK CORAL GOBY

Bryaninops tigris Larson, 1985

Dorsal rays VI-I,7-8; anal rays I,8-9; pectoral rays 12-14; lateral scales 32-59; upper half mostly semitransparent; white internal line overlies vertebral column; lower half golden brown; about 12 orange to brown spots along middorsal line and 6-9 internal orange to brown bars on upper half of sides; iris golden to reddish. Chagos Archipelago to Hawaiian Islands; associated with antipatharian corals below 15 m depth. To 5.5 cm.

WHIP GOBY
Bryaninops yongei (Davis & Cohen, 1969)

Dorsal rays VI-I,7-9; anal rays I,7-10; pectoral rays 13-17; lateral scales 26-58; mostly semi—transparent with a silvery-white line above vertebral column; about six brown to reddish bars or blotches on side. Australia to Hawaiian Islands and Rapa; associated with the antipatharian seawhip *Cirripathes anguina* in 3-45 m depth; usually in male-female pairs, one pair per seawhip. Attains 4 cm. Has been classified in the genus *Tenacigobius*, now known to be a synonym of *Bryaninops*.

OSTRICH GOBY
Callogobius maculipinnis (Fowler, 1918)

Dorsal rays VI-I,9; anal rays I,7; pectoral rays 17-19; lateral scales 22-25; some cycloid scales present on anterior part of body; predorsal scales 6-7; generally mottled brown; first dorsal fin with oblique white and brown stripes, other fins dusky brown to blackish with whitish spots. East Africa and Red Sea to Samoa and Marshall Islands. To 6.5 cm. The genus *Mucogobius* is a synonym of *Callogobius*.

TRIPLEBAND GOBY
Callogobius sclateri (Steindachner, 1880)

Dorsal rays VI-I,9; anal rays I,7; pectoral rays 16-17; lateral scales 27-28; pelvic fins united by membrane only at base; prominent transverse and longitudinal rows of flap-like papillae on head; whitish or light grey with three irregular broad dark brown bars, first at level of first dorsal fin, second at level of anterior part of second dorsal fin, and third across caudal peduncle. Indo-Pacific; dwells in crevices and caves. Reaches 3 cm.

397

YELLOW SHRIMP GOBY
Cryptocentrus cinctus (Herre, 1936)

Dorsal rays VI-I,10; anal rays I,9; pectoral rays 16-18; scales cycloid; lateral scales about 75; predorsal scales absent; two distinct colour phases, one yellow and the other with whitish ground colour; both colour forms with 4-5 dusky bars (although faint in yellow fish) and fine pale blue or white spotting on head and anterodorsal part of body and fins; a dark brown streak above maxilla. Western Pacific; lives in burrow with alpheid shrimps. Grows to 7.5 cm.

Cryptocentrus cinctus   Yellow phase ▲ White phase ▼

Y-BAR SHRIMP GOBY
Cryptocentrus fasciatus (Playfair & Günther, 1867)

Dorsal rays VI-I,10; anal rays I,9; pectoral rays 18; scales cycloid; lateral scales 81-92; predorsal scales present; whitish with five broad dark brown bars, the middle three divided dorsally to form an approximate broad Y-shape; head and body finely dotted with pale blue; second dorsal and anal fins with longitudinal blue lines. Also has a yellow phase like the related *C. cincta*. East Africa to Melanesia and the Great Barrier Reef; lives in burrow with alpheid shrimps. Maximum size, 8 cm.

SADDLED SHRIMP GOBY
Cryptocentrus leucostictus (Günther, 1871)

Dorsal rays VI-I,10 or 11; anal rays I,9 or 10; pectoral rays 16-17; lateral scales about 90; brown, finely spotted with white; a prominent white snout and large white saddles on upper half of head and body; also a pair of large white spots on base of pectoral fin; a midlateral row of dark brown spots on body. Western Pacific; lives in burrow with alpheid shrimps. Reaches 7 cm.

TARGET SHRIMP GOBY
Cryptocentrus strigilliceps (Jordan & Seale, 1906)

Dorsal rays VI-I,10; anal rays I,9; pectoral rays 17; lateral scales about 50; scales mainly ctenoid; predorsal scales present; second and third dorsal spines of adults prolonged; whitish, the body with nine brown bars, three of which are joined dorsally (two triple bars, one double bar); head and anterior part of body strongly mottled with brown and white; some small blue spots on posterior half of body (mainly ventrally). East Africa to Marshall Islands and Samoa; lives in burrow with alpheid shrimps. To 7 cm. *Obtortiophagus koumansi* Smith is a synonym.

SPOTFIN SHRIMP GOBY
Ctenogobiops pomastictus Lubbock & Polunin, 1977

Dorsal rays VI-I,11; anal rays I,11; pectoral rays 19 or 20; lateral scales 55-59; whitish with a midlateral row of six brown spots (anterior ones as large as eye) on body and small yellowish brown spots above and below and on head; a bright white spot on lower basal part of pectoral fin; similar to *C. feroculus* Lubbock & Polunin which also occurs in our area, but it lacks spots on lower side below the midlateral row. Queensland to Ryukyu Islands, east to Mariana Islands; lives in burrow with alpheid shrimps. Attains 6 cm.

MASTED SHRIMP GOBY

Ctenogobiops tangaroae Lubbock & Polunin, 1977

Dorsal rays VI-I,11; anal rays I,11; pectoral rays 19 or 20; lateral scales 47-51; first dorsal fin well forward, just behind head; first and second dorsal spines greatly elongate; whitish, nearly translucent, with orange and a few white spots on body and orange spots and lines on head; two small brown spots often present on lower cheek; prolonged anterior part of first dorsal fin brown; a white streak on pectoral fin. Australia to Samoa; lives in burrow with alpheid shrimps. To 5.5 cm.

SPIKEFIN GOBY

Discordipinna griessingeri Hoese & Fourmanoir, 1978

Dorsal rays V-I,7-8; anal rays I,8; pectoral rays 17-19; lateral scales 22-25; first dorsal fin very tall with pointed tip; ground colour white, a red to brown longitudinal band on lower side from pectoral-fin base to lower base of caudal fin; conspicuous black spots on head; fins largely pinkish to red; second dorsal and caudal fin with red-brown spots (may be ocellated); dark red margin along upper edge of pectoral fin. Red Sea to Marquesas. Maximum size, 2.5 cm.

DOUBLEBAR GOBY

Eviota bifasciata Lachner & Karanella, 1980

Dorsal rays VI-I,8-10; anal rays I,8-10; pectoral rays 14-16, unbranched; lateral scales 22; pelvic fins separate; rays of first dorsal fin with filamentous tips, third ray the longest; a pair of purplish longitudinal stripes on side separated by a white midlateral band; a pair of short blackish stripes at base of caudal fin. Philippines and Indonesia to northern Australia. Reaches 2.5 cm.

BLACKBELLY GOBY
Eviota nigriventris Giltay, 1933

Dorsal rays VI-I,9-10; anal rays I,8-9; pectoral rays 15-18, unbranched; lateral scales 21-23; pelvic fins separate; first dorsal fin rays elongate or filamentous, the second or third ray the longest; light brown or greenish on back; a broad dark brown longitudinal band covering most of side; belly and chin whitish. Philippines to Melanesia and eastern Australia. Largest, 2.3 cm.

BEAUTIFUL GOBY
Exyrias bellissimus (Smith, 1959)

Dorsal rays VI-I,10; anal rays I,9; pectoral rays 17-18; lateral scales 31-32; predorsal scales 8-9; cheek scaled; first dorsal fin with filamentous rays; caudal fin more than 30% standard length; generally brownish, but with indications of about 10 darker brown bars on sides, these bars overlaid with scattered dark brown or blackish spots, particularly on their lower half and on upper back; numerous small white spots on head and larger white spots scattered on sides; all fins except pelvics mottled or spotted; particularly conspicuous brown spotting on anal fin. East Africa to Samoa; depth range 0-20 m. Grows to 13 cm. *E. puntang* Bleeker also occurs in Queensland waters; it differs in having 10 or more predorsal scales and two narrow orange-red stripes on anal fin.

SAND GOBY
Fusigobius neophytus (Günther, 1877)

Dorsal rays VI-I,9; anal rays I,8; pectoral rays 18; lateral scales 22-24; semitransparent with scattered numerous small yellowish-brown spots; a small black spot at midbase of caudal fin and another on first dorsal fin between first two spines. East Africa to Tuamotus; common on sandy fringe around coral bommies. Maximum size, 7.5 cm.

BLOTCHED SAND GOBY
Fusigobius sp.

Dorsal rays VI-I,9; anal rays I,8; pectoral rays 18; lateral scales 23-25; overall semi-transparent with numerous small orange spots on head, body, dorsal fins, caudal fin, and anal fin; 4-5 large internal blackish blotches, mainly along middle of side, the last one at base of caudal fin; a brilliant white blotch between last pair of blackish blotches and smaller white spots along dorsal-fin base. Western Pacific. To 7.5 cm. An undescribed species.

SHOULDERSPOT GOBY
Gnatholepis scapulostigma Herre, 1953

Dorsal rays VI-I,11; anal rays I,11; pectoral rays 17; lateral scales 29; overall whitish with series of reddish-brown lines on sides and indications of 6-7 large brownish blotches on lower side between bases of pectoral and caudal fins; a thin dark bar through eye and across cheek; the most distinctive marking is a dusky-margined orange spot just above pectoral-fin base. Eastern Indian Ocean and western Pacific. Attains 5.5 cm. *G. inconsequens* Whitley is probably a synonym.

FOURBAR GOBY
Gobiodon citrinus (Rüppell, 1838)

Dorsal rays V-I,10 or 11 (usually 10); anal rays I,9; pectoral rays 18; no scales; bright yellow with pair of vertical blue lines below eye; two additional blue lines, one from forehead to edge of gill cover and the other across base of pectoral fin; small black spot just above pectoral-fin base. East Africa and Red Sea to Samoa; lives on branches of live coral (*Acropora*); produces a toxic mucus. Grows to 6.6 cm.

BROAD-BARRED GOBY

Gobiodon histrio (Valenciennes, 1837)

Dorsal rays VI-I,10; anal rays I,9; pectoral rays 21; no scales; mainly lime green with series of violet stripes (or forming broken lines or spots) on side and 4-5 violet to brownish bars on head; belly and basal part of fins may be bluish. Western Pacific; lives on branches of live coral (*Acropora*). Maximum size, 3.5 cm.

SMALL-EYED GOBY

Gobiodon micropus Günther, 1861

Dorsal rays VI-I,12-13; anal rays I,10-11; pectoral rays 19; no scales; head and body mostly dark greenish; an oblique pale blotch above and behind eye, with a narrower brown bar next to its anterior and posterior margin. Indo-Pacific; lives on branches of live coral (*Acropora*). Reaches 3.5 cm.

OKINAWA GOBY

Gobiodon okinawae Sawada, Arai & Abe, 1973

Dorsal rays VI-I,10; anal rays I,9; pectoral rays 17; no scales; head, body, and fins lemon yellow, sometimes a whitish patch on cheek. Western Pacific, Japan to Australia; lives on branches of live coral (*Acropora*); usually occurs in groups of 5-15 individuals. Grows to 3.5 cm.

DECORATED GOBY
Istigobius decoratus (Herre, 1927)

Dorsal rays VI-I,10-11; anal rays I,9-10; pectoral rays 17-19; branched caudal rays usually 14; lateral scales 29-33; cheek scaleless; head length 24-30% standard length; overall whitish with a brown "honey-comb" pattern on upper half of side; two longitudinal rows of rectangular, dark brown spots along lower side; dorsal, caudal, and anal fins with red to dark brown spots. East Africa and Red Sea to Samoa; common on sandy margins of coral reefs. To 12 cm.

ORANGE-SPOTTED GOBY
Istigobius rigilius (Herre, 1953)

Dorsal rays VI-I,10-11; anal rays I,9-10; pectoral rays 17-19; branched caudal rays usually 13; lateral scales 29-33; cheek scaleless; whitish with longitudinal rows of brownish-orange spots, the largest mid-lateral, alternating single and double spots; brown spotting on dorsal and caudal fins. Molucca and Philippine Islands to Australia, eastward to Fiji and Marshall Islands; occurs in 1-30 m depth in sandy areas near live coral and rubble patches. To 10 cm.

WHITECAP GOBY
Lotilia graciliosa Klausewitz, 1960

Dorsal rays VI-I,9-10; anal rays I,9; pectoral rays 16; longitudinal scales series 44-50; no scales on head; no predorsal scales; black with a white band from top of head to origin of dorsal fin; a white spot on back extending onto front of second dorsal fin and another dorsally on caudal peduncle; a yellow-edged black spot in first dorsal fin; caudal fin transparent; pectoral fins transparent with black spots and a broad white bar near base. Red Sea to southern Japan, Marshall Islands and Fiji; lives symbiotically with *Alpheus rubromaculatus* (this snapping shrimp rarely occurs with other shrimp gobies); very shy; usually seen hovering just above burrow entrance. Reaches 4.5 cm.

WILBUR'S GOBY
Macrodontogobius wilburi Herre, 1936

Dorsal rays VI-I,10; anal rays I,9; pectoral rays 15-17; lateral scales 27-31; cheek scaled; has large recurved canine at bend in lower jaw; overall whitish or slightly yellowish to semi-transparent; numerous small brown spots on head and body, also scattered small pearly blotches; longitudinal row of 4-5 enlarged brown spots or blotches between bases of pectoral and caudal fins; brown lines or spotting on dorsal, caudal, and anal fins. Seychelles to New Caledonia and Line Islands; in sandy or silty areas near reefs. Grows to 6.5 cm.

SPINECHEEK GOBY
Oplopomus oplopomus (Valenciennes, 1837)

Dorsal rays VI-I,10; anal rays I,10; pectoral rays 18-19; lateral scales 24-26; preopercle with 1-3 flattened spines; first spine in each dorsal fin thickened and stiff; pale grey to whitish, with a midlateral row of 4-5 brownish blotches, also a row of smaller blotches along back; head and body with numerous small pale blue and orange spots; elongate blue streaks on cheek; an orange streak covering middle rays of caudal fin. East Africa to Society Islands; in sandy areas. Attains 8 cm.

REDHEAD GOBY
Paragobiodon echinocephalus Rüppell, 1828

Dorsal rays VI-I,9; anal rays I,9; pectoral rays 20-22; lateral scales 22-24; head and nape scaleless with numerous bristles; head reddish or orange, sometimes with bluish spots, remainder of body and fins black. East Africa and Red Sea to Tuamotus and Marshall Islands; lives on branches of live coral (*Stylophora*). Maximum size, 3.5 cm.

YELLOWSKIN GOBY
Paragobiodon xanthosomus (Bleeker, 1852)

Dorsal rays VI-I,9; anal rays I,9; pectoral rays 20-22; lateral scales 22-24; head and nape scaleless with numerous bristles; overall yellowish to lime coloured, often with numerous small bluish spots on head (sometimes on body). Chagos Archipelago to Samoa; lives on branches of live coral (*Seriatopora hystrix*). Grows to 4 cm.

SILVERLINED MUDSKIPPER
Periophthalmus argentilineatus (Valenciennes, 1837)

First dorsal fin with XI-XVI rays, none elongate, the outer edge of fin straight to slightly convex; second dorsal fin with I,9-12 rays; anal fin with I,8-11 rays; longitudinal scale series 64-100 (usually more than 75); snout very steep; eyes protruding well above dorsal profile of head; pectoral fins with a muscular base; pelvic fins with little or no membrane linking the bases of their innermost rays; brown, mottled with dark brown, silvery white ventrally, with short silvery white vertical lines and small spots extending into brown zone from below; first dorsal fin red with a pale grey margin, a black stripe, and scattered white dots at base. Southern Red Sea south to Natal and east to the Marianas and Samoa; one of five mudskippers known from Queensland; occurs on mudflats in mangrove areas; amphibious and very agile. Reaches 12 cm. *P. dipus* Bleeker and *P. vulgaris* Eggert are synonyms.

CORAL GOBY
Pleurosicya sp.

Dorsal rays VI-I,8; anal rays I,8; pectoral rays 17-18; lateral scales 22-25; outer row of teeth in upper jaw enlarged, and a large pair of canines at front of lower jaw; semi-transparent or pinkish with a reddish-brown midlateral stripe and a silvery-white line overlying vertebral column; iris yellow; lives on corals. Western Pacific. To 2.5 cm. The classification of *Pleurosicya* is poorly understood, and the genus contains several new species. These fishes are found on various invertebrate hosts such as sponges, soft corals, and hard corals.

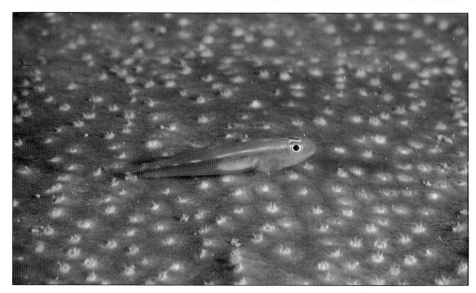

GIRDLED GOBY
Priolepis cincta (Regan, 1908)

Dorsal rays VI-I,10-11; anal rays I,9-10; pectoral rays 17-19; lateral scales 25-28; yellowish brown with conspicuous dark-edged narrow whitish bars on head and body; fins yellowish with narrow blue-white margins; brown spotting on dorsal and caudal fins. East Africa to southeastern Polynesia; lives in rocky crevices and caves; rarely observed. Reaches 6 cm. *P. naraharae* (Snyder) is a synonym.

TWINSPOT GOBY
Signigobius biocellatus Hoese & Allen, 1977

Dorsal rays VI-I,11; anal rays I,11; pectoral rays 20-22 (usually 21); a very distinctive goby with irregular brown blotches on body and dorsal fins and a thin brown bar below eye; dorsal fins fan-shaped, each with a conspicuous ocellated black spot; anal and pelvic fins mostly blackish with small blue spots. Philippines, Indonesia, and Palau Islands to Melanesia and the Great Barrier Reef; usually found in pairs that share a burrow; it has been suggested that this goby mimics a crab, the dorsal fin ocelli corresponding to eyes. To 6.5 cm.

YELLOWNOSE SHRIMP GOBY
Stonogobiops xanthorhinica Hoese & Randall, 1982

Dorsal rays VI-I,11; anal rays I,10; pectoral rays 16 or 17; lateral scales 75-92; white with four oblique black bars, first across gill cover, second between pelvic fin base and space between dorsal fins (it also extends along rear edge of first dorsal fin), third between bases of anterior anal rays and posterior dorsal rays, and fourth across base of caudal fin; chin, snout, upper half of iris, and interorbital region yellow. Western edge of Pacific from Japan to the Great Barrier Reef; lives in burrow with alpheid shrimps. Maximum size to 5.5 cm.

ORANGE-RED GOBY
Trimma okinawae (Aoyagi, 1949)

Dorsal rays VI-I,9-10; anal rays I,8-9; pectoral rays 16-18; lateral scales 26-27; no scales on head; pelvic fins separate; orange with a bright red spot on each scale of body, and red spots and narrow bars on head; fins with red dots. Western Pacific; one of the most common *Trimma* on Great Barrier Reef; usually found hovering upside-down in small caves in coral reefs. To 2.5 cm.

STRIPEHEAD GOBY
Trimma striata (Herre, 1945)

Dorsal rays VI-I,9; anal rays I,8-9; pectoral rays 16-17; lateral scales 25-28; pelvic fins separate; second ray of first dorsal fin with elongate filament; body reddish with an orange spot on most scales; head purplish with prominent red stripes. Philippines to Australia. Reaches a length of 3 cm.

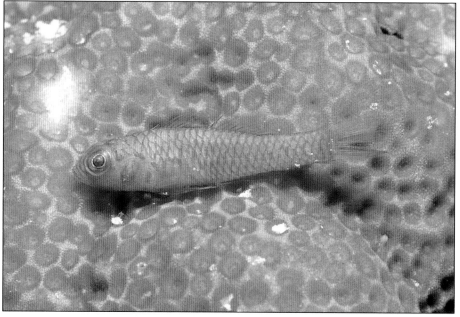

ORANGE-SPOTTED GOBY
Trimma sp. 1

Dorsal rays VI-I,8; anal rays I,8; pectoral rays 17-18; lateral scales 22-24; overall mauve with scattered orange spots on head and body; fins translucent with reddish hue. Western Pacific. To 2.5 cm. An undescribed species that gobiid specialist D. F. Hoese refers to as species DFH-9.

REDFACE GOBY
Trimma sp. 2

Dorsal rays VI-I,10; anal rays I,9; pectoral rays 19-20; lateral scales 24; overall pinkish red to orange; snout, cheeks and iris reddish; fins without conspicuous markings. Western Pacific. Attains 2.5 cm. An undesdribed species that gobiid specialist D.F. Hoese refers to as species DFH-4.

TWOSTRIPE GOBY
Valenciennea helsdingenii (Bleeker, 1858)

Dorsal rays VI-I,11; anal rays I,11; pectoral rays 21-23; lateral scales 100-120; caudal fin with pair of elongate filaments; pelvic fins separated; white with a pair of brown to orange stripes along middle of side extending onto head; a prominent black spot broadly edged with white on first dorsal fin. East Africa to western Pacific; usually seen in pairs that share a sandy burrow. Attains 16 cm. Species of *Valenciennea* are sometimes classified in the genus *Eleotriodes*, now regarded as a synonym.

LONG-FINNED GOBY
Valenciennea longipinnis (Lay & Bennett, 1839)

Dorsal rays VI-I,12; anal rays I,12-13; pectoral rays 20-22; lateral scales about 80-110; pelvic fins separated; overall whitish with narrow orange-brown stripes punctuated with small dark brown spots on upper half of side; a row of five blue-edged, flask-shaped pink bars on side of body, with a dark brown spot in lower section of each; blue and pink lines and spots on head. Eastern Indian Ocean and western Pacific. Grows to 15 cm.

STRIPED GOBY
Valenciennea muralis (Valenciennes, 1837)

Dorsal rays VI-I,12; anal rays I,12; pectoral rays 19-21; lateral scales 80-95; pelvic fins separated; bluish white with series of pink to brown stripes on head and body; a prominent black spot on rear part of first dorsal fin. Indonesia to Melanesia and northern Australia; usually found on silty substrata. Maximum size to 13 cm.

ORANGE-DASHED GOBY
Valenciennea puellaris (Tomiyama, 1956)

Dorsal rays VI-I,12; anal rays I,12; pectoral rays 20-23; lateral scales about 70-90; pelvic fins separated; tan or light grey on upper half of head and body, whitish ventrally; a blue-edged orange longitudinal stripe from mouth to base of caudal fin; a series of elongate orange spots on upper side of body; head with two series of elongate light blue spots. Red Sea to Samoa and Marshall Islands. Reaches 14 cm. This and other species of *Valenciennea* are usually seen in pairs; they construct a burrow in sand, generally under a rock, by removing mouthfuls of sand.

SIXSPOT GOBY
Valenciennea sexguttata (Valenciennes, 1837)

Dorsal rays VI-I,12; anal rays I,11-13 (usually 12); pectoral rays 19-21 (usually 20); lateral scales 70-91; pelvic fins separated; whitish, usually with two pale red stripes on side connected by narrow bars of the same colour; 6-8 small blue spots on cheek and opercle; tip of first dorsal fin with a small black spot. East Africa to Samoa and the Marshall Islands; lives in sandy burrow under rocks. To 14 cm.

BLUEBAND GOBY
Valenciennea strigata (Broussonet, 1782)

Dorsal rays VI-I,17-19; anal rays I,16-19; pectoral rays 21-23; lateral scales 103-120; pelvic fins separated; tips of second and third dorsal spines filamentous; light grey, darker on back; snout, iris, and lower half of head yellow; a black-edged blue stripe below eye between mouth and edge of gill cover; a short blue streak behind eye and 2-3 blue streaks ventrally on head. East Africa to Society Islands and Line Islands; usually seen in pairs over rubble bottoms. Grows to 18 cm.

PARVA GOBY
Valenciennea sp. 1

Dorsal rays VI-I,12; anal rays I,12; pectoral rays 18-20; lateral scales 67-85; pelvic fins separated; olive to brownish on back and top of head, whitish below; a pair of thin orange to brown stripes on side of body connected by faint brownish bars; back with light blotches and mottling; a white stripe below eye between snout and edge of gill cover; fins transparent. Western Pacific. The smallest species of the genus; attains only 7 cm. This and the following species soon to be named by Hoese and Larson (in press, *Indo-Pacific Fishes*). An undescribed species.

DECORA GOBY
Valenciennea sp. 2

Dorsal rays VI-I,11; anal rays I,11; pectoral rays 21-23; lateral scales 88-106; light grey or whitish, sometimes with a longitudinal yellow stripe on lower side with one or more yellow bars radiating upward from pectoral fin; blue or white spots on snout and upper part of head, and a prominent black margin on upper lip; outer part of first dorsal fin with a white-edged brown blotch. Great Barrier Reef to New Caledonia. Reaches 12 cm. An undescribed species.

AMBANORO GOBY
Vanderhorstia ambanoro (Fourmanoir, 1957)

Dorsal rays VI-I,13; anal rays I,13; pectoral rays 18-19; lateral scales 73-85; light grey to whitish with a longitudinal row of black or dark brown spots along middle of side and an additional row of smaller spots on upper part of head and along base of dorsal fins; faint vertical blue lines more-or-less connecting the two rows of spots. East Africa to Samoa; lives in a burrow with alpheid shrimps. Maximum size, 7 cm.

OCELLATED GOBY
Vanderhorstia ornatissima Smith, 1959

Dorsal rays VI-I,13; anal rays I,13; pectoral rays 17-19; lateral scales 57-62; third spine of first dorsal fin filamentous; white with numerous blue-edged orange spots and lines on head and body; also may have large brown blotches on sides. East Africa to Samoa; lives in a burrow with alpheid shrimps. To 8 cm.

SHADOW GOBY
Yongeichthys nebulosus (Forsskål, 1775)

Dorsal rays VI-I,9; anal rays I,9; pectoral rays 18-19; lateral scales 26-30; no scales on cheek and operculum; enlarged curved tooth on each side of lower jaw; second spine of first dorsal fin prolonged as a filament; whitish, the upper half of head and body finely mottled with brown; a mid-lateral row of three blackish spots larger than eye, the last a base of caudal fin; three or four large diffuse blackish spots on back. East Africa to western Pacific; found on mud bottoms around inner reefs; poisonous, the toxin concentrated in the skin. Grows to 18 cm.

WORMFISHES AND DARTFISHES
FAMILY MICRODESMIDAE

The Microdesmidae formerly included just the wormfishes. Recent studies have shown that the dartfishes (also known as hover gobies) are more closely related to the wormfishes than to the gobies (Gobiidae) or sleepers (Eleotrididae) where previously classified. As currently understood, the Microdesmidae is divided to two subfamilies, the Microdesminae (represented below by three species of wormfishes of the genus *Gunnellichthys*) and the Ptereleotrinae (includes the dartfish genera *Ptereleotris*, *Nemateleotris*, *Parioglossus*, *Oxymetopon*, and *Ailiops*). It is possible that the Ptereleotrinae will eventually be given full family status. The microdesmids are allied to the gobies (not to the blennies as once believed) and are classi-

fied, along with the gobies and sleepers, in the suborder Gobioidei. These fishes have elongate bodies (extremely elongate in some) with small, embedded, usually nonoverlapping, cycloid scales (may be weakly ctenoid posteriorly on body of some Ptereleotrinae), no lateral line, and usually a heavy protruding lower jaw; the gill opening is restricted to the side; the pelvic fins of one spine and 2-5 soft rays are inserted below the pectoral fins. The very slender wormfishes have a long continuous dorsal fin with X-XXVIII flexible spines and 28-66 soft rays and an anal fin with 23-61 soft rays. With the exception of one species (*Ptereleotris monoptera*), all dartfishes have a divided dorsal fin, the first part of IV-VI flexible spines. Most microdesmid fishes live over

sand or mud bottoms and take refuge in burrows. None are known to exceed 30 cm. We include below only those species most apt to be encountered in the reef environment or adjacent habitats. For identification of the highly compressed mud-dwelling species of *Oxymetopon* the reader is referred to Klausewitz and Condé (1981, *Revue Française d'Aquariologie*); for the tiny usually estuarine *Parioglossus* (three Queensland species, all less than 3.8 cm standard length) to Rennis and Hoese (1985, *Records of the Australian Museum*); and for the even smaller *Aioliops* (all with a dark stripe on back and a large black spot in caudal fin; one Queensland species, to 2 cm standard length) to Rennis and Hoese (1987, *Records of the Australian Museum*).

SUBFAMILY MICRODESMINAE

CURIOUS WORMFISH
Gunnellichthys curiosus Dawson, 1968

Dorsal rays XX-XXI,40-42; anal rays 38-40; pectoral rays 14-15; pelvic rays I,4; body elongate, the depth 10-12 in standard length, and compressed, the body width about half the depth; lower jaw massive and strongly projecting (true of other *Gunnellichthys*); dorsal fin origin above anterior third of pectoral fin; caudal fin rounded; pelvic fins about 1.5 times longer than eye diameter; whitish with an orange stripe from front of lower jaw through eye (stripe dusky on head), along lower side of body, broadening posteriorly to cover more than half of ventral part of body, this stripe extending to end of caudal fin except where interrupted by a large elliptical black spot on basal half of caudal fin; a vertically elongate black spot within orange stripe at edge of opercle; head and anterior body above orange stripe light blue. Described from the Seychelles; now known from Hawaii, Society Islands, Coral Sea, Indonesia, and Maldives. Largest specimen, 11.5 cm.

ONESPOT WORMFISH
Gunnellichthys monostigma Smith, 1958

Dorsal rays XXI,36-40; anal rays 36-41; pectoral rays 14-15; pelvic rays I,4; body elongate, the depth 10-15 in standard length, and compressed; dorsal fin origin slightly anterior to upper end of gill opening; caudal fin slightly rounded; pelvic fins about twice eye diameter; whitish with an elliptical black spot nearly as high as eye diameter posteriorly on opercle; a narrow yellow to pink stripe may begin diffusely in middle of back, descend posteriorly to slightly below midbase of caudal fin and continue to end of fin (some blackish pigment may be present in stripe posteriorly on body). Indo-Pacific; lives individually over open sand areas, sometimes with sparse plant growth. Reaches 11 cm.

BROWNSTRIPE WORMFISH
Gunnellichthys pleurotaenia Bleeker, 1858

Dorsal rays XIX-XX,36-40; anal rays 34-38; pectoral rays 12-13; pelvic rays I,4; body elongate, the depth 9.5-13.5 in standard length, and compressed· caudal fin rounded; origin of dorsal fin slightly posterior to pectoral-fin base; pelvic fins small, their length about 1.5 times eye diameter; whitish with a narrow dark brown stripe commencing on chin, passing through eye and above pectoral-fin base to midbase of caudal fin, then continuing as a yellow stripe to end of fin. Western Pacific east to Samoa and the Mariana Islands; swims by sinuous movements of the body; dives head-first into sand with the approach of danger (as do others of the genus). Attains 9 cm.

YELLOWSTRIPE WORMFISH
Gunnellichthys viridescens Dawson, 1968

Dorsal rays XX-XXI,38-41; anal rays 36-40; pectoral rays 12-13; pelvic rays I,4; body very elongate, the depth 11.5-16 in standard length, and compressed; origin of dorsal fin slightly posterior to pectoral-fin base; caudal fin rounded; pelvic fins small, about equal to eye diameter; whitish with a narrow yellow stripe commencing on chin, crossing snout to eye, emerging wider behind eye, then gradually narrowing as it passes above pectoral-fin base, and continuing in same width to middle of end of caudal fin. Described from the Seychelles and Maldives; recently discovered in the Marshall Islands and Great Barrier Reef. Largest specimen, 7.2 cm.

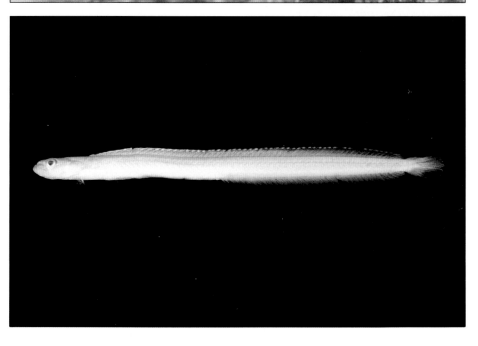

414

SUBFAMILY PTERELEOTRINAE

ELEGANT FIREFISH
Nemateleotris decora Randall & Allen, 1973

Dorsal rays VI-I,27-32; anal rays I,28-31; pectoral rays 20-21; pelvic rays I,5; body depth 4.8-5.7 in standard length; elongate anterior part of first dorsal fin 3.2-4.0 in standard length; caudal fin slightly emarginate with rounded lobes; body whitish anteriorly, shading gradually to purplish black posterior to origin of anal fin; head whitish except lips, snout, and a broad median dorsal band which are violet; prolonged anterior part of first dorsal fin orange-red, the leading edge magenta; median fins coloured like body basally, then mainly orange-red with narrow magenta bands. Western Pacific to islands of western Indian Ocean; known from the depth range of 27-67.5 m; habits similar to *N. magnifica*. To 8.5 cm.

FIRE DARTFISH
Nemateleotris magnifica Fowler, 1928

Dorsal rays VI-I,28-32; anal rays I,27-30; pectoral rays 19-20; pelvic rays I,5; body depth 4.4-4.9 in standard length; filamentous anterior part of first dorsal fin very long, l.2-2.0 in standard length; caudal fin rounded; whitish anteriorly, gradually shading to red posterior to anal fin origin; head with a median magenta band from interorbital to dorsal fin; spinous dorsal fin white, the basal half of leading edge red; dorsal and anal fins primarily red, suffused with blackish posteriorly and distally, with a narrow posterior dark olive stripe; caudal fin blackish red with two converging narrow dark olive bands. Indo-Pacific; known from the depth range of 6-6l m, but not often seen over 28 m; feeds on zooplankton, especially copepods and crustacean larvae; does not stray far from its burrow into which it quickly darts when frightened; may be seen as solitary fish or in pairs. Reaches 8 cm. A popular aquarium fish.

415

TWOTONE DARTFISH

Ptereleotris evides (Jordan & Hubbs, 1925)

Dorsal rays VI-I,23-26 (rarely 23); anal rays I,23-26 (rarely 26); pectoral rays 21-24; body depth 5.2-6.9 in standard length; anterior part of second dorsal and anal fins elevated, the longest ray (about sixth) 1.2-1.4 in head; caudal fin emarginate; light bluish grey, shading posteriorly to black; iridescent blue markings on operculum; caudal fin whitish, the lobes broadly reddish black; second dorsal and anal fins blackish, the margin black; juveniles light bluish grey with a large oval black spot on lower half of caudal-fin base. Indo-Pacific; generally found in exposed outer reef areas in 2-15 m; often seen in pairs which share the same burrow; like others of the genus, a zooplankton-feeder; juveniles usually occur in small aggregations. Largest examined, 13.8 cm. *P. tricolor* Smith is a synonym.

LINED DARTFISH

Ptereleotris grammica Randall & Lubbock, 1982

Dorsal rays VI-I,25-27; anal rays I,23-26; pectoral rays 22-23; body elongate, the depth 6.7-8.1 in standard length; first dorsal fin about twice as high as second; caudal fin truncate to very slightly emarginate, the corners rounded; body pale grey with a narrow lateral orange stripe edged in brown and bordered by blue; a second narrow brown stripe dorsally on body; head with narrow orange-yellow and blue stripes; second dorsal and anal fins with narrow longitudinal yellow and blue bands; caudal fin with a large orange area posteriorly, the rest of fin orange-yellow, blue, and white. Western Pacific; a different subspecies named from Mauritius; occurs on rubble or sand substrata, generally at depths greater than 40 m. Attains 10 cm.

THREADFIN DARTFISH

Ptereleotris hanae (Jordan & Snyder, 1901)

Dorsal rays VI-I,24-26; anal rays I,22-25; pectoral rays 21-24; body depth 6.45-8.0 in standard length; caudal fin rounded (occasionally truncate centrally), the adults with two to six long trailing filaments; pale blue to light bluish grey with a narrow pale salmon pink stripe posteriorly on lower side of body (pink stripe may be contained within a broad dark bluish stripe which extends full length of body); a light red to violet bar, usually edged in bright blue, at lower pectoral-fin base. Western Pacific, east to Samoa and the Line Islands, and west to Western Australia; usually found on rubble and sand bottoms near reefs; specimens have been collected from the depth range of 3-43 m; 2 adults may occupy the same burrow. Reaches 12 cm (not including caudal filaments).

SPOTTAIL DARTFISH
Ptereleotris heteroptera (Bleeker, 1855)

Dorsal rays VI-I,29-33; anal rays I,27-30; pectoral rays 21-24; body depth 6.2-7.8 in standard length; caudal fin emarginate, the corners rounded; light blue to pale bluish grey, the caudal fin yellowish with a large horizontally elongate dusky to black spot (faint or absent on juveniles); a faint narrow salmon pink bar edged in blue at pectoral-fin base. Indo-Pacific; collected from the depth range of 7-46 m; most often seen in 15-35 m on rubble-sand substrata near reefs; may be found in lagoons, bays, or exposed outer reef areas; sometimes forms colonies. Largest specimen, 12 cm.

PALE DARTFISH
Ptereleotris microlepis (Bleeker, 1856)

Dorsal rays VI-I,25-29; anal rays I,24-27; pectoral rays 21-24; body depth 5.5-7.0 in standard length; second dorsal fin nearly twice height of first; caudal fin slightly emarginate, the corners not rounded; pale bluish grey, usually with two faint pale orange lines posteriorly on side of body which converge slightly as they pass onto caudal fin; a narrow black bar, edged in blue, basally on lower half to two-thirds of pectoral fin (faint or absent on juveniles). Indo-Pacific; usually encountered in lagoons or bays over sand or sand-rubble bottoms in the depth range of 1-22 m; often a pair, but at times a small group, will occupy the same burrow. Reaches 13 cm.

MONOFIN DARTFISH
Ptereleotris monoptera Randall & Hoese, 1985

Dorsal rays VI-I,35-39, the fin continuous; anal rays I,33-37; pectoral rays 23-25; body moderately elongate, the depth 6.05-7.05 in standard length; dorsal and anal fins low, the spinous portion of dorsal fin distinctly lower than soft; caudal fin emarginate, the lobes filamentous in large adults; pale blue to pale yellowish with a wash of blue over upper abdomen; a broad blackish bar extending ventrally from eye; iridescent blue markings on postorbital head; outer two-thirds of anal fin reddish with a blue margin. Indo-Pacific but from scattered localities (mostly insular); usually found in the depth range of 6-15 m; tends to form large, though diffuse, colonies. Largest specimen, 15.5 cm (including caudal filaments).

BANDTAIL DARTFISH
Ptereleotris uroditaenia Randall & Hoese, 1985

Dorsal rays VI-I,26; anal rays I,24; pectoral rays 22; body depth 6.2 in standard length; first dorsal fin much higher than second, the third to fifth spines filamentous; caudal fin rounded; pale bluish with two oblique black bands in caudal fin which converge posteriorly, the central part of fin yellow; iridescent blue markings on head. Known to date only from Indonesia, Solomon Islands, and Great Barrier Reef; occurs in silty rubble-sand areas at depths of about 18-30 m; only one specimen has been collected (deposited in the Australian Museum in Sydney); it measures 8.2 cm.

ZEBRA DARTFISH
Ptereleotris zebra Fowler, 1938

Dorsal rays VI-I,27-29; anal rays I,25-28; pectoral rays 23-26; body depth 4.8-6.0 in standard length; a well-developed fleshy barbel on chin (absent from other species of the genus herein); second dorsal fin higher than first; caudal fin slightly emarginate; yellowish to greenish grey with about 20 narrow orange to pink bars edged with blue or purple on body; a blue-edged dark red to purple area enclosing lower part of eye and extending onto chin; an orange-red bar bordered by blue on pectoral-fin base; a deep blue margin on dorsal fins; juveniles lack the pink bars, but fish as small as 3 cm show the dark edging on the dorsal fins. Indo-Pacific; typical habitat, exposed coral reefs in 1.5-10 m (mostly from 2-4 m); usually encountered in aggregations over hard bottom, with many fish seeking refuge in the same hole in the reef; males in courtship lower and spread the pale pelvic fins. Attains 12 cm.

SURGEONFISHES
FAMILY ACANTHURIDAE

The surgeonfishes are named for the sharp spine or spines they possess on the caudal peduncle. The family is divisible into three subfamilies, the Acanthurinae, in which the caudal spine is single and folds into a horizontal groove on the side of the peduncle (includes the genera *Acanthurus*, *Zebrasoma*, *Paracanthurus*, and *Ctenochaetus*), the Nasinae with one or two fixed keel-like spines on each side of the peduncle (one genus, *Naso*), and the Prionurinae with three to six such spines (only *Prionurus*). The fishes of the genus *Naso* are popularly known as unicornfishes because many have a horn-like rostral projection on the forehead; those of the genus *Zebrasoma* are called tangs. The surgeonfish family consists of 72 species; the largest genus is *Acanthurus* with 36 species, of which five occur in the Atlantic. The remaining fishes of the family are found in the Pacific and Indian Oceans. All have a deep compressed body with the eye high on the head and a long preorbital bone, a single unnotched dorsal fin with IV to IX spines and 19-33 rays, an anal fin with II or III spines (only *Naso* with II) and 18-28 rays, pelvic fins with I spine and 3 or 5 rays (*Naso* and *Paracanthurus* with 3), very small ctenoid scales, a small terminal mouth with a single row of close-set teeth which may be spatulate with denticulate edges or numerous and comb-like with expanded incurved tips, and no teeth on the palate; all have a long intestine. The species of *Ctenochaetus* and several of *Acanthurus* have a thick-walled gizzard-like stomach. Most of the surgeonfishes graze on benthic algae, but four species of *Acanthurus* and many of *Naso* feed mainly on zooplankton; those of the genus *Ctenochaetus* are detritus-feeders. The species with a gizzard-like stomach tend to ingest sand as they feed which probably aids in triturating their algal food in the stomach. Surgeonfishes are able to slash other fishes (or humans who do not handle them carefully) with their sharp caudal spines by a rapid side sweep of the tail. Some species have bright hues around their spines to serve as warning colouration. Acanthurid fishes sleep at night in small caves or crevices in the reef. The postlarvae are orbicular, transparent with silvery over the abdomen, and scaleless with narrow vertical ridges on the body. This stage has venomous dorsal, anal, and pelvic spines; these are retained in the adult of *Paracanthurus hepatus* and at least some of the species of *Naso*.

White-spotted Surgeonfish
(*Acanthurus guttatus*)

WHITEFIN SURGEONFISH
Acanthurus albipectoralis Allen & Ayling, 1987

Dorsal rays IX,25; anal rays III,23; pectoral rays 16 or 17; gill rakers 14; body depth 2.3-2.4 in standard length; snout short, its length contained about 2 times in head; caudal spine small, about 5.5 in head; caudal fin deeply emarginate; blackish overall except outer third of pectoral fins which is abruptly white. Great Barrier Reef and reefs of the Coral Sea to Tonga; occurs off steep outer-reef escarpments at depths of about 5-20 m; may be solitary but usually encountered in small aggregations feeding on zooplankton well off the bottom. Largest recorded, 33 cm. Has been confused in the past with *A. mata*.

SUBFAMILY ACANTHURINAE

ORANGE-SOCKET SURGEONFISH
Acanthurus auranticavus Randall, 1956

Dorsal rays IX,25-26; anal rays III,23-24 (usually 24); pectoral rays 16-17; gill rakers 20-23; body depth 2.05-2.15 in standard length; caudal spine large, 2.2-4.4 in head; caudal fin deeply emarginate; body very finely striped with light purplish blue and dark olive brown; head brown without spots; a tilted orangish brown band about 1.3 eye diameters in length at upper end of gill opening; a narrow irregular white bar at base of caudal fin; socket of caudal spine and a narrow margin around it orange. Known from the Philippines, Indonesia, and Great Barrier Reef; recently found by the senior author in the Maldives; occurs on shallow reefs, both in lagoons and outer reef areas; usually encountered in small groups which are frequently on the move. Attains about 35 cm.

ROUNDSPOT SURGEONFISH
Acanthurus bariene Lesson, 1830

Dorsal rays IX,26-28; anal rays III,25-26; pectoral rays 17; gill rakers 19-23; body depth 1.9-2.0 in standard length; dorsal profile of head of large adults notably convex; caudal fin of adults lunate; body brown, shading to yellowish brown ventrally, with numerous irregular longitudinal grey-blue lines; a round black spot about as large as eye at upper end of gill opening; a yellow bar from behind spot to below pectoral fin; dorsal fin yellow with a narrow blue margin, some fine blue lines submarginally, and a narrow blue band at base; lobes of caudal fin yellow. Western Pacific to Maldives; usually seen on outer reeef slopes, generally at depths greater than 30 m. Maximum length about 50 cm. *A. nummifer* Valennciennes is a synonym.

RINGTAIL SURGEONFISH

Acanthurus blochii Valenciennes, 1835

Dorsal rays IX,25-27; anal rays III,24-25; pectoral rays 17; gill rakers 20-25; body depth 1.9-2.1 in standard length; caudal spine large, 3.0-4.4 in head; caudal fin lunate; a gizzard-like stomach; body bluish grey with numerous very small dark yellowish brown spots tending to form irregular longitudinal lines; a white bar at base of caudal fin; head with narrow irregular stripes of brownish yellow and blue; a yellow spot about as large as eye just behind eye; a blue to black margin around caudal spine equal in width to spine; dorsal and anal fins with eight to nine narrow blue stripes alternating with orange-yellow bands; pectoral fins uniform brown; seems nearly black underwater except for white ring around base of caudal fin. Indo-Pacific; closely tied to reefs for shelter, but frequently seen grazing on algal film on compact sand. Attains at least 42 cm. Misidentified by most recent authors as *A. mata*.

EYESTRIPE SURGEONFISH

Acanthurus dussumieri Valenciennes, 1835

Dorsal rays IX,25-27; anal rays III,24-26; pectoral rays 16-17 (usually 17); gill rakers 23-26; body depth 1.9-2.1 in standard length; large adults with a strongly convex forehead; caudal spine large, 3.0-5.0 in head; caudal fin lunate; gizzard-like stomach; yellowish brown with irregular longitudinal blue lines on body; head yellowish with blue spots and lines; a broad yellow band across interorbital space and an irregular yellow spot behind and adjacent to eye; opercular membrane blackish; caudal spine white, the socket broadly rimmed with black; dorsal and anal fins yellow with a blue band at base and a blue margin (fins of young fully striped with blue); caudal fin blue with small blackish spots, yellow at base. Hawaii and Line Islands to East Africa; generally seen in more than 10 m; submarine observations in Hawaii to 128 m. Reaches about 50 cm. Sometimes misidentified as *A. bariene*.

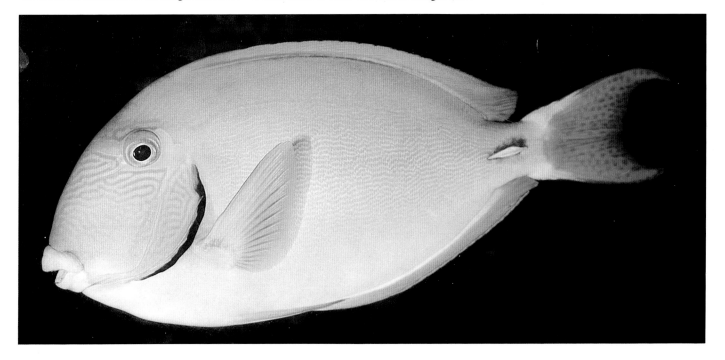

FINELINED SURGEONFISH

Acanthurus grammoptilus Richardson, 1843

Dorsal rays IX,25-26; anal rays III,23-24; pectoral rays 16-17; gill rakers 16-18; body depth 1.9-2.5 in standard length (subadults deeper-bodied); caudal fin lunate; body dark yellowish brown with irregular bluish longitudinal lines; adults with a faint dark brown band at upper end of gill opening which extends an eye diameter posterior; a black margin around caudal spine which in adults extends as a narrow band anterior to spine a distance greater than eye diameter; caudal fin with a white bar at base and a narrow white posterior margin; dorsal and anal fins with a blue margin; pectoral fins brown on basal three-fourths, yellow on outer fourth. Philippines to Australia; common on silty reefs of the inner islands of the Great Barrier Reef. Reaches at least 35 cm.

WHITESPOTTED SURGEONFISH

Acanthurus guttatus Forster, 1801

Dorsal rays IX,27-28; anal rays III,23-26; pectoral rays 15-17; gill rakers 21-24; body deep, the depth 1.5-1.6 in standard length; caudal fin slightly emarginate; brown with three white bars, the body posterior to middle bar with numerous small white spots; pelvic fins yellow. Oceania to islands of western Indian Ocean; lives in surge zone of exposed reefs, often in small schools; the white spots may simulate the swirling white bubbles from the action of surf; feeds mainly on filamentous algae but ingests some calcareous species such as *Jania*.

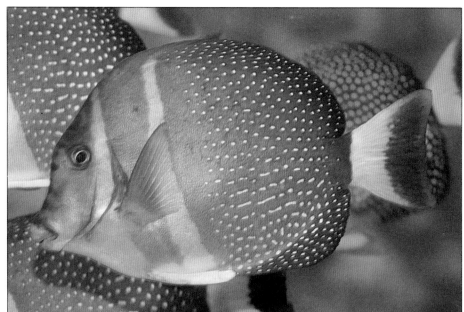

STRIPED SURGEONFISH

Acanthurus lineatus (Linnaeus, 1758)

Dorsal rays IX,27-29; anal rays III,25-28; pectoral rays 16; gill rakers 14-16; body depth about 2.2 in standard length; caudal spine very long, 1.9-2.0 in head; caudal fin lunate; upper three-fourths of head and body alternately banded with black-edged blue and yellow stripes; lower fourth lavender to pale blue. Indo-Pacific, except Red Sea where replaced by the related *A. sohal* (Forsskål); lives at the outer edge of reefs exposed to wave action; an aggressive territorial species. Reaches 38 cm. The caudal spine is venomous and can cause painful wounds.

ELONGATE SURGEONFISH
Acanthurus mata Cuvier, 1829

Dorsal rays IX,24-26; anal rays III,23-24; pectoral rays 16-17 (usually 17); gill rakers 13-15; body of adults elongate for the genus, about 2.5 in standard length; caudal peduncle slender; head sloping, the dorsal profile forming an angle of about 45°; snout short, 6.6-6.9 in standard length; mouth small; caudal fin of adults lunate; dark brown with lengthwise blue lines on head and body; a yellow area behind eye and two yellow bands extending anteriorly from eye; capable of changing color to pale bluish overall. Indo-Pacific; feeds on zooplankton; more inclined than other surgeonfishes to enter turbid water; may occur in schools. To 50 cm. *A. bleekeri* Günther is a synonym.

WHITECHEEK SURGEONFISH
Acanthurus nigricans (Linnaeus, 1758)

Dorsal rays IX,28-31; anal rays III,26-29; pectoral rays 16; body depth 1.75-1.9 in standard length; gill rakers 17-19; caudal fin slightly emarginate; black with a white spot broader than eye below and adjacent to eye; a narrow white band nearly encircling mouth; a yellow band at base of dorsal and anal fins which broadens to nearly full height of these fins posteriorly; caudal fin whitish with a yellow bar in posterior third. Islands of the tropical Pacific, including those of eastern Pacific; usually found in relatively shallow water of exposed reefs or rocky shores, but has been observed in 45 m; an aggressive species. Largest specimen, 21.3 cm. Usually identified as *A. glaucopareius* Cuvier, now known to be a synonym.

BLACKSTREAK SURGEONFISH
Acanthurus nigricauda Duncker & Mohr, 1929

Dorsal rays IX,25-28; anal rays III,23-26; pectoral rays 17; gill rakers 20-21; body depth 1.9-2.2 in standard length (smaller fish deeper-bodied); dorsal profile of head of large adults convex; caudal spine 4.5-7.5 in head; caudal fin lunate; a gizzard-like stomach; dark brown (one phase is purplish grey) without lines on body or spots on head; a horizontal black band passing posteriorly from upper end of gill opening (absent on juveniles less than 6 cm standard length); a lanceolate black line extending anteriorly from caudal spine; an elongate purple band may be present anterior to dorsal fin origin; caudal fin brown, often with a white bar across base, the posterior margin narrowly white; outer third of pectoral fin pale. Indo-Pacific; usually seen over sand near coral heads or rocky outcrops of lagoons and bays. Attains 40 cm. Has been mislabeled as *A. nigricans* and *A. gahhm* (Forsskål).

BROWN SURGEONFISH
Acanthurus nigrofuscus (Forsskål, 1775)

Dorsal rays IX,24-27; anal rays III,22-24; pectoral rays 16-17; gill rakers 20-24; body depth 2.0-2.3 in standard length; caudal fin lunate; brown to lavender-brown, with or without fine bluish grey longitudinal lines on body; head and thorax with numerous small orange spots; lips blackish; a prominent black spot at rear base of dorsal and anal fins, its diameter contained less than 2 times in eye; caudal fin with a narrow whitish posterior border. Indo-Pacific; a common shallow-water reef fish. Maximum length, 21 cm. Sometimes identified as *A. elongatus* (Lacepède), a species named from an unidentified juvenile, but clearly not *nigrofuscus*.

BLUELINED SURGEONFISH
Acanthurus nigroris Valenciennes, 1835

Dorsal rays IX,24-27; anal rays III,23-25; pectoral rays 15-16; gill rakers 21-25; body depth 1.8-2.0 in standard length; caudal fin emarginate; dark brown with irregular longitudinal lines on body about one-fourth as broad as brown interspaces (fewer lines on smaller individuals); a small black spot at rear base of dorsal and anal fins (dorsal spot contained more than 2 times in eye diameter); caudal fin with a narrow white posterior margin. Islands of Oceania; rare on Great Barrier Reef. Attains 25 cm. Has been misidentified as *A. lineolatus* Valenciennes, a probable synonym of *A. nigrofuscus*.

ORANGEBAND SURGEONFISH
Acanthurus olivaceus Forster, 1801

Dorsal rays IX,23-25; anal rays III,22-24; pectoral rays 16-17 (usually 17); gill rakers 24-28; body depth 2.0-2.4 in standard length; caudal fin lunate; stomach gizzard-like; greyish brown with a horizontal orange band, broadly edged in deep blue, passing posteriorly from upper end of gill opening; an orange line at base of dorsal fin; a large crescentic white area posteriorly in caudal fin; head and anterior half of body often abruptly paler than posterior half; juveniles yellow. Islands of Oceania to western Pacific; usually seen over sand bottoms near reefs; sometimes encountered in small groups. Reaches about 35 cm.

Acanthurus olivaceus Juv.

MIMIC SURGEONFISH
Acanthurus pyroferus Kittlitz, 1834

Dorsal rays VIII,27-28; anal rays III,24-26; pectoral rays 16; gill rakers 23-26; body depth 1.85-2.1 in standard length; snout somewhat protruding, the dorsal profile to eye concave; dorsal fin rather high, the longest ray about 4.5 in standard length; caudal fin rounded in juveniles, truncate with prolonged lobes in adults; a gizzard-like stomach; brown, shading to brownish red on thorax; a large vertically elongate orange-red spot on side of body above pectoral-fin base; a broad black band beginning at upper end of gill opening and continuing on margin of operculum to isthmus; a narrow white band encircling chin and extending above corner of mouth; median fins dark brown, the caudal with a broad yellow posterior border; juveniles exhibit three different colour patterns: yellow, yellow with blue markings (a precise mimic of the angelfish *Centropyge flavissimus*) and pale greenish grey shading posteriorly to black (an exact mimic of *C. vrolikii*). Islands of Oceania to western Pacific; juveniles mimic *Centropyge* spp. because these little angelfishes are secretive; therefore, predators learn not to hunt them. To about 25 cm.

Acanthurus pyroferus   Adult ▼ Juv. mimic of *Centropyge vrolicki* ▲

THOMPSON'S SURGEONFISH
Acanthurus thompsoni (Fowler, 1923)

Dorsal rays IX,23-26; anal rays III,23-26; pectoral rays 17; gill rakers 15-16; body moderately elongate, the depth 2.2-2.4 in standard length; dorsal profile of head smoothly convex; snout very short, 7.9-8.2 in standard length; mouth small; caudal fin lunate; olive brown with a white caudal fin; a large dark brown spot in axil of pectoral fin and extending slightly below; a small dark brown spot may be present at rear base of dorsal fin; capable of rapidly changing to light bluish grey overall. Indo-Pacific; generally from outer reef areas; feeds on zooplankton well above the substratum. Largest recorded, 27 cm. *A. philippinus* Herre is a synonym.

CONVICT SURGEONFISH

Acanthurus triostegus (Linnaeus, 1758)

Dorsal rays IX,22-26 (usually 23 or 24); anal rays III,19-22 (usually 21); pectoral rays 15-16; gill rakers 18-22; body depth 1.8-2.0 in standard length; caudal spine small, about 10 in head; caudal fin slightly emarginate; light greenish grey with six narrow black bars on head and body. Indo-Pacific and tropical eastern Pacific; an inshore species but has been observed to depths of 45 m; spawning occurs in aggregations at dusk; the duration of larval life in Hawaii is 2.5 months; postlarvae seek the shallows, often tidepools, at night to transform to the juvenile stage (takes four to five days); juveniles grow at the rate of 12 mm per month; maturity is attained at a length of about 12 cm, at which time growth has slowed to 2 mm per month; adults often feed in large aggregations, thus overwhelming territorial plant-feeding fishes. Largest specimen, 26.3 cm.

YELLOWFIN SURGEONFISH

Acanthurus xanthopterus Valenciennes, 1835

Dorsal rays IX,25-27; anal rays III,23-25; pectoral rays 16-17 (usually 17); gill rakers 16-24; body depth 1.95-2.25 in standard length; caudal spine relatively small, 4.4-5.7 in head; caudal fin lunate, a gizzard-like stomach; purplish grey to brown but able to change to a pattern of very irregular longitudinal narrow bands; some yellow behind and in front of eye but not as a distinct band; caudal fin bluish grey without spots, often with a faint whitish bar at base; dorsal and anal fins with four to five dull yellow stripes alternating with blue, the base with a pale blue band; outer third of pectoral fins yellow. Indo-Pacific and tropical eastern Pacific; occurs in habitats dominated by sand, generally at depths greater than 20 m; submarine observations to 90 m. The largest of the genus; reported to 56 cm.

TWOSPOT BRISTLETOOTH

Ctenochaetus binotatus Randall, 1955

Dorsal rays VIII,24-27; anal rays III,22-25; pectoral rays 15-16 (usually 16); gill rakers 23-29; teeth numerous, in a single row in jaws, movable, elongate with tips expanded, incurved, and denticulate on lateral margin (true of other *Ctenochaetus*); upper teeth with 6 denticulations, lowers with 3 (including tip); adults with as many as 42 upper and 45 lower teeth; body depth 1.95-2.15 in standard length; a single caudal spine fitting into a groove on each side of caudal peduncle (also generic); caudal fin lunate; stomach gizzard-like (generic); body orangish brown with longitudinal pale blue lines; blue dots on head and thorax; iris blue; a black spot nearly as large as pupil at rear base of dorsal and anal fins; juveniles dark brown with a yellow caudal fin. Indo-Pacific. Reaches 22 cm.

Ctenochaetus binotatus   Adult ▼ Juv. ▲

LINED BRISTLETOOTH

Ctenochaetus striatus (Quoy & Gaimard, 1825)

Dorsal rays VIII,27-31; anal rays III,24-28; pectoral rays l6-17 (usually 17); gill rakers 28-36; upper teeth with 5-7 denticulations and lowers with 4 (including tip); adults with as many as 45 upper and 53 lower teeth; body depth 1.9-2.3 in standard length; caudal fin lunate; body dark brown with numerous blue longitudinal lines; orange-yellow dots dorsally on head and nape; soft portions of dorsal and anal fins with about five narrow bluish stripes; a small black spot at rear base of dorsal fin. Indo-Pacific; one of the most abundant of reef fishes at most localities; like others of the genus, feeds on fine detrital and soft algal material by a combination of whisking with its movable comb-like teeth and suction. Attains 26 cm.

GOLDRING BRISTLETOOTH
Ctenochaetus strigosus (Bennett, 1828)

Dorsal rays IX,25-27; anal rays III,22-25; pectoral rays 15-16 (rarely 15); gill rakers 27-31; upper teeth with 5 denticulations, lowers with 3 (including tip); adults with as many as 47 upper and 60 lower teeth; body depth 1.7-2.0 in standard length; caudal fin emarginate; yellowish brown with bluish grey longitudinal lines on body and yellow dots on head and anterior body; eye with a narrow yellow rim; juveniles bright yellow, the eye mainly blue. Indo-Pacific, but forming distinct populations throughout its range; not common on the Great Barrier Reef. Largest specimen, 18 cm.

PALETTE SURGEONFISH
Paracanthurus hepatus (Linnaeus, 1766)

Dorsal rays IX,19-20; anal rays III,18-19; pectoral rays 16; pelvic rays I,3; scales on head modified to tuberculate plates; body depth 2.2-2.5 in standard length; a single caudal spine on side of peduncle folding into a shallow groove; spines of fins stout and venomous; caudal fin truncate with lobes slightly projecting; brilliant blue with a large black area on upper part of body containing an elliptical blue spot, the black extending as a band dorsally on head to eye and to lobes of caudal fin; a bright yellow triangle with apex anterior to caudal spine extending to end of caudal fin. Samoa, Gilbert Islands (Kiribati), and Mariana Islands to East Africa; generally found in clear outer reef areas or channels where there is substantial current; feeds on zooplankton; difficult to approach underwater; juveniles hide among branches of live coral. To 31 cm. The only species in the genus.

BRUSHTAIL TANG
Zebrasoma scopas (Cuvier, 1829)

Dorsal rays V (rarely IV),23-25; anal rays III,19-21; pectoral rays 14-16; body very deep, the depth 1.5-1.7 in standard length; snout pointed (characteristic of the genus); a single folding spine on side of caudal peduncle folding into a groove (true of other *Zebrasoma*); an oval brush-like patch of setae on side of body anterior to caudal spine (not in young less than 7 cm, and the patch larger with longer setae in males); dorsal and anal fins elevated, the longest dorsal ray 2.7-3.6 in standard length; caudal fin truncate to slightly rounded; dark yellowish brown with tiny pale blue dots on head and body, those on body tending to join to form longitudinal lines; sheath of caudal spine white; juveniles with vertical pale lines on body. Indo-Pacific; common on shallow reefs in calm areas. Reaches 20 cm. Closely related to the bright yellow *Z. flavescens* (Bennett) which ranges from Hawaii to the Ryukyu Islands.

SAILFIN TANG
Zebrasoma veliferum (Bloch, 1797)

Dorsal rays IV,29-33; anal rays III,23-26; pectoral rays 15-17; dorsal and anal fins very elevated, the longest dorsal ray 2.1-2.5 in standard length; no patch of setae posteriorly on body; caudal fin truncate to slightly rounded; body with alternating broad dark brown and narrow whitish bars, both containing vertical yellow lines except last broad bar which is solid black and covers caudal peduncle; head whitish with yellow dots and vertical lines and a black bar through eye; caudal fin yellow with a narrow bluish white margin; juveniles yellow with dark bars. Islands of Oceania and western Pacific; very closely related to Z. *desjardinii* (Bennett) of the Indian Ocean and Red Sea which has been regarded by some authors as a geographical variant of Z. *veliferum*. Reported to 40 cm.

Zebrasoma veliferum Juv.

Naso annulatus Adult ▼ Juv. ▲

SUBFAMILY NASINAE

WHITEMARGIN UNICORNFISH
Naso annulatus (Quoy & Gaimard, 1825)

Dorsal rays V,28-29; anal rays II,27-28; pectoral rays 17-19; pelvic rays I,3 (all *Naso*); body depth about 2.2 in standard length of subadults to about 2.8 in large adults; adults with a long tapering bony horn anterior to eye which can project as much as a head length in front of mouth; subadults of about 20 cm show the beginning of the horn as a bump in front of lower edge of eye; profile of snout to base of horn about 60°; two peduncular plates, each developing a knife-like keel in adults; caudal fin of subadults truncate, of adults scalloped, some (believed to be males) developing a long filament from each corner; olivaceous to brown without dark markings but capable of altering quickly to pale bluish grey; caudal fin of subadults with a white posterior border and submarginal blackish band; adults with caudal rays blackish, the narrow membranes and trailing filaments white; juveniles with a white ring around caudal peduncle. Indo-Pacific; adults generally encountered in small schools off dropoffs, usually in more than 25 m. Reported to 100 cm. *N. herrei* Smith is a synonym.

HUMPBACK UNICORNFISH

Naso brachycentron (Valenciennes, 1835)

Dorsal rays IV-V,28-30; anal rays II,27-28; pectoral rays 17; body depth 2.3 (in subadults) to 2.7 (in large adults) in standard length; a hump developing on back (at about 20 cm in length) below front of soft portion of dorsal fin, the profile beneath spinous portion concave; adult males with a long tapering horn anterior to upper edge of eye (females with only a bump at this site); dorsal profile of snout straight, forming an angle of about 45°; two peduncular plates on each side of caudal peduncle, those of adults with a sharp lateral keel ending in a forward-projecting point; caudal fin emarginate with a filament from each corner in adults; olive grey, shading to pale yellowish ventrally; rear edge of caudal fin and margins of dorsal and anal fins white. Indo-Pacific. Attains at least 60 cm (reported to 90 cm).

SPOTTED UNICORNFISH

Naso brevirostris (Valenciennes, 1835)

Dorsal rays VI,27-29; anal rays II,27-29; pectoral rays 16-17; body depth varying from 2.0 in standard length of subadults to 2.7 in adults; a broad-based tapering horn in adults extending more than half a head length in front of mouth (first appearing as a bump in juveniles of about 10 cm); profile of snout to base of horn very short and nearly vertical; two peduncular plates on each side, the keels only moderately developed; caudal fin truncate to slightly rounded, without filaments; olivaceous brown to grey; subadults with small dark spots on head and body, adults with vertical lines on side of body; caudal fin whitish with a large dusky spot at base. Indo-Pacific; feeds on benthic algae when young, shifting principally to zooplankton when adult. Reported to 60 cm, but any over 50 cm exceptional.

SLEEK UNICORNFISH

Naso hexacanthus (Bleeker, 1855)

Dorsal rays VI,27-29; anal rays II,27-30; pectoral rays 17-18 (usually 17) body depth varying from about 2.0 in standard length of subadults to 2.75 in adults; dorsal and anal profiles of head equally convex; two peduncular plates, those of adults with large knife-like spines; caudal fin emarginate in young, truncate in adults; brown to bluish grey dorsally, shading ventrally to yellowish; capable of quickly changing to pale blue; margin of operculum and preopercle often dark brown; tongue black at lengths of 25 cm or more; males in courtship rapidly exhibit a large pale blue area on upper head and dorsoanterior body and some pale blue vertical lines and spots anteriorly on side of body. Indo-Pacific; generally seen in schools on steep outer reef slopes, usually at depths greater than 15 m; submarine observations to 135 m; feeds on zooplankton. Attains about 75 cm.

ORANGESPINE UNICORNFISH
Naso lituratus (Forster, 1801)

Dorsal rays VI,27-30; anal rays II,28-30; pectoral rays 16-17; teeth of adults incisiform, smooth-edged, with rounded ends, 30-35 in jaws; body depth 2.0-2.4 in standard length (subadults deeper-bodied); dorsal profile of head nearly straight, forming an angle of about 45°; two peduncular plates, each with a large forward-curved knife-like keel; caudal fin emarginate, the fin of males with a filament from each corner; greyish brown, the peduncular plates bright orange; a narrow curved yellow band from behind mouth to below eye; snout in front of band black; a diffuse yellow area behind and above eye; lips orange-yellow; dorsal fin black basally, white outwardly, with a blue margin and narrow blue band at base; caudal fin with a submarginal yellow band posteriorly. Indo-Pacific; Indian Ocean form differs in having a largely orange-yellow dorsal fin and a black band in caudal fin; feeds mainly on leafy brown algae such as *Sargassum*. To 45 cm.

ELONGATE UNICORNFISH
Naso lopezi Herre 1927

Dorsal rays V,28-31; anal rays II,27-30; pectoral rays 17; body very elongate, the depth 3.3-3.7 in standard length; dorsal and ventral profiles of head equally convex; interorbital broad, nearly flat; two peduncular plates, the keel rounded to angular (not pointed); first dorsal spine longest and strongest; caudal fin slightly emarginate, higher than body depth; bluish grey, paler ventrally, the upper half of head and body with numerous small round dark grey spots; caudal fin also dark-spotted. Western Pacific; occurs off escarpments as solitary fish or in small groups; rarely seen in less than 30 m. Reaches at least 50 cm. Few specimens in museums.

THORPE'S UNICORNFISH
Naso thorpei Smith, 1966

Dorsal rays VI-VII (usuallyl VI),27-29; anal rays II,27-29; pectoral rays 16-18; body depth of subadults about 2.2 in standard length, of adults 2.6-2.8; two peduncular plates with knife-like keels in adults; caudal fin slightly emarginate to truncate; bluish grey to brownish grey dorsally, paler ventrally; no dark margin on operculum and preopercle; capable of rapidly assuming a pattern of indistinct roundish to vertically elliptical blotches on upper half to two-thirds of body which may be either darker or paler than ground colour; tongue not black. Known in the literature only from the type specimen from Natal, but recently found in Hawaii, Marshall Islands, New Caledonia, and the Coral Sea, hence probably widespread in the Indo-Pacific; easily confused with *N. hexacanthus* and sometimes schools with it. Reaches at least 60 cm.

HUMPNOSE UNICORNFISH
Naso tuberosus Lacepède, 1802

Dorsal rays V,27-29; anal rays II,26-27; pectoral rays 16-18; body depth of subadults about 2.0 in standard length, of adults 2.5; adults with a hump on back centred at base of first dorsal soft ray, and a large rounded protuberance on snout extending to or anterior to a vertical at mouth; two peduncular plates with knife-like keels in adults; caudal fin emarginate without filaments; grey, shading ventrally to yellowish grey, with a large area of body below hump on the back densely dotted with black (also with scattered small pale spots); pectoral and caudal fins blackish posteriorly. Samoa and islands of Micronesia to East Africa; a shallow-water reef species often seen in small groups. Reaches at least 60 cm.

BLUESPINE UNICORNFISH
Naso unicornis (Forsskål, 1775)

Dorsal spines VI,27-30; anal rays II,27-30; pectoral rays 17-18; body depth 1.8 (in subadults) to 2.6 (in adults) in standard length; a trapering bony horn in adults projecting anteriorly at level of eye but not extending in front of mouth (horn first showing as a bump on forehead at a length of about 12 cm); dorsal profile of snout to horn straight, forming an angle of about 45°; two peduncular plates with well-developed forward-curving knife-like spines; caudal fin emarginate in young, truncate with filamentous lobes in adults; olivaceous with blue peduncular plates and spines; dorsal and anal fins yellowish with narrow blue stripes. Indo-Pacific; a shallow reef species which feeds mainly on coarse leafy algae such as *Sargassum*; will enter surprisingly shallow water for such a large fish; a wary species. Attains 70 cm.

VLAMING'S UNICORNFISH
Naso vlamingii (Valenciennes, 1835)

Dorsal rays VI,26-27; anal rays II,27-29; pectoral rays 17-19; body depth varying from 2.1 in standard length of young to 2.6 in adults; adults with a prominent convexity on forehead at level of lower edge of eye; two peduncular plates with knife-like pointed keels; dorsal fin elevated, the first spine 1.5-1.7 in head; caudal fin of adults truncate to slightly rounded with a long filament from each corner; adults yellowish brown with irregular vertical blue lines on side of body and small blue spots above and below; head with a few blue spots and a broad blue band extending anteriorly from eye; lips blue; caudal fin with a yellow posterior border and blue filaments; in life can quickly change its markings from dull bluish to brilliant blue; young with scattered small dark spots.

Indo-Pacific; usually seen in outer reef areas in open water near drop-offs; appears to feed on zooplankton. Maximum length about 55 cm.

SUBFAMILY PRIONURINAE

YELLOWSPOTTED SAWTAIL
Prionurus maculatus Ogilby, 1887

Dorsal rays IX,24-26; anal rays III,23-25; pectoral rays 17-18; body depth of adults 2.2-2.3 in standard length; dorsal profile of head slightly convex, sloping at an angle of about 45°; three peduncular plates with low lateral keels; caudal fin slightly emarginate; bluish grey with numerous small yellow spots on head, body, and fins, many of those on body horizontally elongate; side of body at level of pectoral fin with broad yellow bars; peduncular plates black, the keels bluish. New South Wales and Lord Howe Island to Queensland; on the Great Barrier Reef, only Capricorn Group and Swains Reefs. Reaches about 45 cm.

SIXPLATE SAWTAIL
Prionurus microlepidotus Lacepède, 1804

Dorsal rays VIII,21-22; anal rays III,20-21; pectoral rays 16; body depth varying from about 2.0 in standard length in subadults to 2.7 in large adults; a pronounced bump on snout of large adults just above mouth; six keeled plates posteriorly on each side of body; caudal fin emarginate; dark greenish grey on back, shading to greenish silver ventrally; keeled plates dark greyish brown. New South Wales north to Townsville, Queensland; found along rocky shores; feeds on benthic algae. Largest recorded, 70 cm.

433

MOORISH IDOL
FAMILY ZANCLIDAE

See discussion of the single species of the family below.

MOORISH IDOL
Zanclus cornutus (Linnaeus, 1758)

Dorsal rays VII,40-43; anal rays III,33-35; pectoral rays 19; body very deep, 1.0-1.4 in standard length, and compressed; third dorsal spine extremely long and filamentous, normally longer than standard length; snout strongly pointed; mouth small, the teeth slender and slightly incurved; adults with a small bony projection in front of each eye (larger in males); white anteriorly, yellow posteriorly, with two broad black bars, one from nape to thorax and abdomen (enclosing eye) and the other curving across posterior body and entering dorsal and anal fins; a black-edged orange saddle on snout; caudal fin largely black. Indo-Pacific and tropical eastern Pacific; occurs over a large depth range from the shallows to at least 180 m; omnivorous but feeds more on benthic animal life, such as sponges, than algae. *Z. canescens* (Linnaeus) is a synonym based on the large postlarval stage (to 8 cm).

RABBITFISHES
FAMILY SIGANIDAE

The rabbitfishes, also known in Australia as spinefeet, are unique in having pelvic fins with a spine at each end and three soft rays between. All the species have the same dorsal and anal fin counts: dorsal rays XIII,10 (in addition, an anterior recumbent "spine" which is largely or completely embedded); anal rays VII,9. The spines are venomous; wounds from these spines are very painful, though not as serious as injuries from scorpionfishes. The body of siganid fishes is ovate and compressed with a narrow caudal peduncle. The mouth is small, somewhat ventral, and not protractile; the upper lip is broader than the lower; the teeth are small, incisiform, bicuspid, or tricuspid, and in one row. The skin is smooth, the scales minute and cycloid. The caudal fin varies in shape from truncate to deeply forked. The intestine is long. These fishes are diurnal and mainly herbivorous, feeding on benthic algae and seagrasses; some feed heavily on sessile invertebrate animals such as tunicates or sponges. Most reef-dwelling species are usually encountered in pairs; others are sometimes seen in schools which range over seagrass and algal flats. Rabbitfishes are able to change their colour to a very mottled pattern when they come to rest on the bottom and when they sleep at night. There are 28 species in the family, all from the Indo-Pacific region, and all classified in the genus *Siganus*. Five of the species have notably long attenuate snouts, some of which have been placed in the genus *Lo*, now regarded as a subgenus of *Siganus*. Rabbitfishes, in general, are regarded as good food fishes, in spite of their not attaining large size. Some species have been considered for aquaculture because of their herbivorous food habits, rapid growth, and commercial value. Descriptions of the following species of *Siganus* based on a revision of the family by David J Woodland (In press, *Indo-Pacific Fishes*)

FORKTAIL RABBITFISH
Siganus argenteus (Quoy & Gaimard, 1825)

Pectoral rays usually 18 (rarely 17 or 19); scale rows above lateral line 16-22; body elongate for the genus, 2.6-3.0 in standard length; snout short, 2.55-2.7 in head; caudal fin deeply forked; blue to bluish grey with numerous small yellow spots (often fused on lower side to form undulating stripes). Indo-Pacific; the most widespread of the genus; eggs pelagic; late postlarval stage (prejuvenile), which can attain a maximum of 8 cm, has been observed to form large compact balls offshore at the surface; small juveniles (to about 11 cm) found on reef flats; adults usually seen off seaward reefs; more than other siganids they tend to swim away in midwater rather than take refuge in the reef; feeds on a wide variety of algae; grows to a length of 22 cm and weight of 150 g in 11 months, at which time sexually mature. Maximum length, 37 cm. *S. rostratus* (Valenciennes) is a synonym.

CORAL RABBITFISH
Siganus corallinus (Valenciennes, 1835)

Pectoral rays 16-17; scale rows above lateral line 16-23; body deep, the depth 1.7-2.3 in standard length; snout length 1.9-2.0 in head, the dorsal and ventral profiles concave; caudal fin forked; orange-yellow, the head and body with numerous small dark-edged pale blue spots; a triangular dark smudge diagonally above and behind eye, sometimes continuing onto snout; may take on a pattern of large dark blotches. Western Pacific to Seychelles; juveniles (3-6 cm) tend to live in small schools in shallow seagrass beds and reefs; at a length of about 7 cm length pair bonding beings to form; adults nearly always seen in pairs on shallow coral reefs where they feed on benthic algae. Attains 28 cm.

BARRED RABBITFISH
Siganus doliatus Cuvier, 1830

Pectoral rays 16-17; scale rows above lateral line 19-26; body moderately deep, the depth 1.8-2.2 in standard length; snout 2.0-2.2 in head; dorsal profile of head slightly convex before eye; caudal fin forked; light blue dorsally and posteriorly, white ventrally, with vertical yellow lines of about equal width to blue interspaces on most of body (yellow lines horizontal on thorax and caudal peduncle, the top of peduncle mainly yellow); head blue with highly irregular yellow lines; two diagonal orangish brown bands, one from nape through eye to chin (sometimes just from eye) and the other from below base of fifth dorsal spine to upper base of pectoral fin; caudal fin yellow. Western Pacific to Western Australia, east to Caroline Islands and Fiji; habits similar to *S. corallinus*. Very closely related to the blue-spotted *S. virgatus* (Valenciennes) and apparently hybridizes at times with it in the Indo-Malayan region. Reaches a maximum length of about 25 cm.

DUSKY RABBITFISH
Siganus fuscescens (Houttuyn, 1782)

Pectoral rays 15-17; scale rows above lateral line 16-21; body depth 2.4-2.8 in standard length; snout somewhat convex, 2.2-2.4 in head; caudal fin slightly forked; greenish to yellowish brown, shading to whitish ventrally, with small pale bluish spots, the diameter of which is about equal to or slightly greater than space between adjacent spots; spots on head pinhead size, larger on body, those on side and ventrally often horizontally elongate; a dark blotch nearly as large as eye frequently present just behind upper end of gill opening; small dark brown spots and large dark blotches and irregular oblique bars may be present which partially obscure pale spots; small fish may exhibit a broad dark lateral stripe. Western Pacific; eggs negatively buoyant and adhesive; postlarvae transform to juvenile stage at a length of 2.4-2.9 cm; juveniles form schools on algal and seagrass flats, feeding mainly on filamentous algae; subadults and adults also school, move with rising tide into the shallows to feed on benthic plants; in Palau a mean length of 20 cm was attained in one year. Attains 40 cm. Often misidentified as *S. canaliculatus* (Park), a closely related species not known from Australia.

JAVA RABBITFISH
Siganus javus (Linnaeus, 1766)

Pectoral rays 17-18 (rarely 17); scale rows above lateral line 30-38; body depth 2.0-2.3 in standard length; dorsal profile of head straight; snout length 3.0-3.4 in head (3.4-3.9 in fish less than 100 mm standard length); caudal fin truncate to slightly emarginate; bluish white with narrow dark bluish grey stripes on ventral part of body, these becoming progressively more irregular until on dorsal half of body they form a reticulum, isolating spots or short irregular segments of bluish white; white spots on nape and dorsally on head very small. Persian Gulf to Philippines and northern Australia; in northern Queensland mainly in brackish areas and on coastal reefs; feeds on benthic algae; often seen in small groups. The largest of the Siganidae; attains at least 53 cm.

GOLDLINED RABBITFISH
Siganus lineatus (Valenciennes, 1835)

Pectoral rays 16-17; scale rows above lateral line 18-27; body moderately deep, the depth 1.9-2.2 in standard length; dorsal profile of head slightly convex; snout 1.8-2.2 in head; caudal fin slightly forked; pale blue with narrow wavy variously broken orange-yellow stripes on body and very irregular bands on head and nape; orange-yellow markings dorsally and ventrally on body more often as spots or short irregular bands than stripes; a bright yellow spot about as large as eye on back below rear base of dorsal fin. Western Pacific to Sri Lanka and India; young occur in small schools in mangrove areas and seagrass flats; adults are usually seen in small groups in protected waters such as lagoons and bays in the vicinity of rocky substrata or reef for shelter and benthic algal food; reported also to feed in part on sponges. Recorded to 43 cm. Very closely related to *S. guttatus* (Bloch) which differs by being entirely yellow-spotted.

BLUELINED RABBITFISH
Siganus puellus Schlegel, 1852

Pectoral rays usually 16 (rarely 15 or 17); scale rows above lateral line 18-25; body depth 2.3-2.6 in standard length; dorsal profile of head above upper lip straight; snout 1.95-2.2 in head; caudal fin moderately forked; yellow with wavy variously broken pale blue lines which are vertical anteriorly on body and horizontal posterior to pectoral region; ventrally on body the yellow as spots on a ground colour of pale blue to white; head yellow, white posteriorly, with a diagonal dark brown band from nape through eye to chin, the part above eye with black spots; fins yellow. Western Pacific east to islands of Micronesia and west to Cocos-Keeling Islands in the eastern Indian Ocean; juveniles feed on filamentous algae, adults on algae, tunicates and sponges; adults occur as pairs, generally on reefs at depths of 3-10 m. Reaches about 38 cm.

FINESPOTTED RABBITFISH
Siganus punctatissimus Fowler & Bean, 1929

Pectoral rays 16; scale rows above lateral line 17-21; body depth 2.0-2.2 in standard length; dorsal profile of head nearly straight; snout length 1.9-2.1 in head length; caudal fin deeply forked; dark purplish brown densely dotted with bluish white; a dark brown spot about as large as eye just behind upper end of gill opening; caudal fin yellowish brown, the entire edge blackish. Ryukyu Islands to northern Great Barrier Reef; usually seen in pairs on reefs to depths of about 30 m; limited data indicate that it grazes on algae. Reaches about 30 cm.

GOLDSPOTTED RABBITFISH
Siganus punctatus (Forster, 1801)

Pectoral rays 16-18 (rarely 18); scale rows above lateral line 23-27; body depth 1.9-2.3 in standard length; dorsal profile of head straight; snout 1.9- 2.1 in head; caudal fin of adults deeply forked (slightly forked on juveniles); blue, the head, body, and caudal fin with numerous small (2-3 mm) close-set dark-edged orange spots; a faint dark spot about as large eye sometimes apparent behind upper end of gill opening; more than a few meters away this fish appears uniform dark brown underwater, though it can display a pale saddle-like spot anteriorly on caudal peduncle. Western Pacific, east to islands of Micronesia and Samoa, west to Western Australia and Cocos-Keeling Islands; replaced in the western Indian Ocean by the near-relative *S. stellatus* Forsskål; adults tend to swim together as pairs, usually on reefs. Attains about 40 cm. *S. chrysospilos* Bleeker is a synonym.

SPINY RABBITFISH
Siganus spinus (Linnaeus, 1758)

Pectoral rays 17 (occasionally 16 or 18); scale rows above lateral line 14-18; body moderately elongate, the depth 2.5-2.8 in standard length; snout short, 2.5-2.7 in head, its dorsal profile very convex; caudal fin of adults truncate (emarginate in juveniles); whitish with a labyrinth of narrow brown bands over head and body; fins translucent, mottled with dark brown. French Polynesia to Andaman Sea; usually encountered in small groups in shallow outer-reef areas where they graze on algae; transforms to the juvenile stage at a length of about 4.5 cm; grew in captivity to a mean length of 14 cm in seven months. The smallest of the siganid fishes; recorded to 24 cm, though seldom exceeds 19 cm. *S. marmoratus* (Quoy& Gaimard) is a synonym.

VERMICULATE RABBITFISH
Siganus vermiculatus (Valenciennes, 1835)

Pectoral rays 16-17; scale rows above lateral line 17-26; body moderately deep, the depth 1.8-2.2 in standard length; dorsal profile of head steep and straight above mouth to in front of eye, then curving slightly to a more sloping straight section for rest of head; snout 1.9-2.1 in head; caudal fin slightly forked; bluish white with a very irregular vermiculate pattern of dark yellowish brown bands on body except ventrally where spotted with brown; head with a similar pattern but less marked, the bands narrower; caudal fin with small dark brown spots. Fiji and the Caroline Islands to India; occurs in shallow brackish areas, usually in small groups; eggs demersal and adhesive, laid on sand bottom; the young feed on algae from rock, mangrove roots or seagrass fronds; sexual maturity attained in one year. Reaches 45 cm. Highly esteemed as a food fish; a good candidate for aquaculture.

FOXFACE
Siganus vulpinus (Schlegel & Müller, 1845)

Pectoral rays 16-17 (usually 16); scale rows above lateral line 16-20; body depth 1.9-2.4 in standard length; snout long, 1.7-1.95 in head, and attenuate; dorsal profile of head concave, the ventral profile very concave; caudal fin slightly forked to nearly truncate; head and a narrow anterior zone of body white with a broad black diagonal band from origin of dorsal fin through eye to mouth and a large triangular black area covering thorax, one apex extending above pectoral-fin base; rest of body and median fins bright yellow. Western Pacific east to islands of Micronesia and New Caledonia; juveniles occur in schools, but begin to form pairs at a length of about 10 cm which are believed to be maintained throughout life; the pairs appear to patrol territories on coral reefs; limited data indicate that the food is benthic algae.

BILLFISHES
FAMILY ISTIOPHORIDAE

This family is well known to game-fishermen and contains the marlins, spearfishes, and sailfishes. These groups are typified by a combination of features including a long bill-like snout composed of the elongated premaxilla and nasal bones; elongate, narrow pelvic fins with three or fewer rays; jaws with teeth; caudal peduncle of adults with two keels on each side; and dorsal fin with a very long base that folds into a groove. Billfishes are primarily oceanic, epipelagic animals that inhabit tropical and temperate seas, periodically entering colder waters. They are active, voracious predators that use the extended "bill" to attack and stun prey, generally fishes and cephalopods. Because of their large size and reknowned fighting ability billfishes are highly prized by anglers. However, the flesh is not particularly tasty. Charter-fishing boat operators are encouraged to promote tagging and release of captured fish rather than participating in their needless slaughter.

INDO-PACIFIC SAILFISH
Istiophorus platypterus (Shaw & Nodder, 1791)
(Plate VI-5)

A tall, long-based, sail-like dorsal fin with 42-49 rays and small second dorsal fin with 6 or 7 rays; 2 anal fins, the first with 12-17 rays and second with 6-7 rays; pectoral rays 18-20; pelvic fins extremely long, almost reaching anus, depressible into a groove; dark blue dorsally, light blue blotched with brown laterally, and silvery white ventrally; about 20 rows of vertical bars on sides, each composed of many light blue round spots; membrane of first dorsal fin dark blue or blackish blue, with scattered, small black spots; remaining fins blackish brown to dark blue. Circumglobal in tropical and temperate seas; undergoes extensive seasonal spawning migration. Grows to 360 cm; all-tackle world record 100.24 kg; Australian record 55.79 kg.

BLACK MARLIN
Makaira indica (Cuvier, 1832)
(Plate VI-1)

Anterior dorsal rays elevated into triangular peak, remainder of fin very low; height of anterior lobe of first dorsal fin smaller than greatest body depth; first dorsal fin rays 34-43; second dorsal fin rays 5-7; first anal fin rays 10-14; second anal fin rays 6-7; pectoral rays 12-20; pectoral fins rigid and cannot be folded close to body; pelvic fins filamentous, shorter than pectoral fins; dark blue dorsally and silvery white ventrally; usually no blotches or dark bars on body in adults; first dorsal fin blackish to dark blue; other fins dark brown tinged with blue. Tropical and temperate Indo-Pacific and eastern Atlantic; densely distributed in northwestern Coral Sea between October and December, believed to represent spawning aggregations. Feeds mainly on various tunas and other pelagic fishes. To 500 cm; all-tackle world record 707.61 kg; Australian record 199.58 kg.

INDO-PACIFIC BLUE MARLIN
Makaira mazara (Jordan & Snyder, 1901)
(Plate VI-2)

Anterior dorsal rays elevated into triangular peak, remainder of fin very low; height of anterior lobe of first dorsal fin less than greatest body depth; first dorsal fin rays 40-45; second dorsal fin rays 6-7; pectoral fin rays 20-23; pectoral rays not rigid and can be folded against side of body; pelvic fins filamentous, shorter than pectoral fins; blue black dorsally and silvery white ventrally with about 15 cobalt-coloured rows of round spots or narrow bars; first dorsal fin blackish or dark blue; other fins blackish brown, sometimes tinged with dark blue. Circumglobal in tropical and temperate seas; undergoes seasonal north-south migrations. Attains 500 cm; all-tackle world record 498 kg; Australian record 275.0 kg.

SHORTBILL SPEARFISH
Tetrapturus angustirostris Tanaka, 1915
(Plate VI-3)

Bill very short, usually less than 15 per cent of total length; anterior dorsal rays elevated into triangular peak, most of remaining part of fin relatively high; height of anterior lobe of first dorsal fin exceeding greatest body depth; first dorsal fin rays 45-50; second dorsal fin rays 6-7; first anal fin rays 12-15; second anal fin rays 6-8; pectoral rays 17-19; pelvic fins slender, filamentous, about twice the length of the pectorals; dark blue dorsally, blue blotched with brown laterally, and silvery white ventrally, without dots or bars; first dorsal fin dark blue; remaining fins dark brown. Tropical and temperate Indo-Pacific, entering eastern Atlantic (via Cape of Good Hope) but not spawning there. To 200 cm.

STRIPED MARLIN
Tetrapturus audax (Philippi, 1887)

Anterior dorsal rays elevated into triangular peak, remainder of fin very low; height of anterior lobe of first dorsal fin about equal to greatest body depth; first dorsal fin rays 37-42; second dorsal fin rays 5-6; first anal fin rays 13-18; second anal fin rays 5-6; pectoral fin rays 18-22; pelvic fins long and slender, about equal to or slightly shorter than pectoral fins in large specimens and slightly longer than pectorals in small individuals; blue-black dorsally and silvery white ventrally, with about 15 cobalt-coloured bars or vertical rows of spots; first dorsal fin dark blue; other fins dark brown, sometimes tinged with blue. Tropical and temperate seas of Indo-Pacific region. Reaches 420 cm; all-tackle world record 498.95 kg; Australian record 275.0 kg.

SWORDFISHES
FAMILY XIPHIIDAE

This family contains a single species, the swordfish, that is closely allied to the billfish family Istiophoridae. The main differences are its lack of jaw teeth, absence of pelvic fins, no scales, and only one keel on the side of the tail base. The swordfish is mainly a warm water species that migrates to temperate and cold waters for feeding in summer and back to warm waters in autumn for spawning and overwintering. Like its billfish cousins, the swordfish uses its beak to stun prey that consists of a variety of fishes, squids, and cuttlefishes. Major sportfishing areas for trolling are located off the eastern United States, western central America, and off eastern Australia and New Zealand.

SWORDFISH
Xiphias gladius Linnaeus, 1758
(Plate VI-6)

Bill extremely long, its cross section flat; no teeth in jaws; adults with a single median keel on each side of caudal fin base; a very tall, short-based dorsal fin with pointed apex; first dorsal rays 34-49; second dorsal and second anal fins very small, second dorsal rays 4-6; first anal fin moderately elevated, falcate with 13-14 rays; second anal rays 3-4; pelvic fins and pelvic girdle absent; pectoral fins situated low on the sides, with 16-18 rays; blackish brown on back fading to light brown or silvery on sides; first dorsal fin dark blackish brown; other fins brown or blackish brown. Circumglobal in tropical, temperate, and adjacent cold seas. Maximum size 450 cm; all-tackle world record 100.24 kg; Australian record 55.79 kg.

TUNAS AND MACKERELS
FAMILY SCOMBRIDAE

The scombrids, or tunas, mackerels, and bonitos as they are commonly known, are well known fishes that form the basis of valuable commercial fisheries in many regions. Worldwide the group contains 49 species. Over the past 10 years world catches have generally fluctuated between about five and six million tonnes annually. These fishes are also highly prized by recreational anglers, and throughout much of the world they support important subsistence fisheries. All species are powerful swimmers and some undergo extensive annual migrations. Scombrids are characterised by two dorsal fins that fold into grooves, and they have distinct finlets behind the second dorsal and anal fins; the pelvic fins have six rays and are situated below the pectoral fins; the scales are small and cycloid; the slender caudal peduncle has at least two small keels on each side, sometimes there is a larger keel in between. Unlike typical "cold-blooded" fishes, some tunas have body temperatures several degrees warmer than the surrounding sea.

Dogtooth Tuna   (*Gymnosarda unicolor*)

WAHOO
Acanthocybium solandri (Cuvier, 1831)
(Plate VII-1)

Dorsal rays XXIII to XXVII-12 to 16 + 8 or 9 finlets; anal rays 12 to 14 + 9 finlets; body covered with small scales; no anterior corselet developed; iridescent bluish green on back; sides silvery with 24-30 cobalt blue bars, some doubled or Y-shaped; a large elongate tuna with a very long snout; teeth strong, triangular, compressed and finely serrate; distinguished from mackerels by its more elongate shape, more numerous spines in the first dorsal fin, and by its banded pattern. All tropical seas; inhabits oceanic waters. Reaches 210 cm; all-tackle world record 67.6 kg; Australian record 46.15 kg.

CORSELETTED FRIGATE MACKEREL
Auxis rochei Risso, 1810
(Plate VII-9)

Two well separated dorsal fins, the first with 10 or 11 tall spines; second dorsal fin followed by 8 finlets; pectoral fins short, not reaching a vertical line from anterior margin of scaleless area on back; anal fin followed by 7 finlets; body scaleless except for the well developed corselet; back dark bluish; 15 or more fairly broad, nearly vertical dark bars in scaleless area above lateral line; belly white. Worldwide in tropical and subtropical seas; inhabits coastal and oceanic waters, forming large schools. Maximum size, 50 cm. Differs from *A. thazard* in having a broader posterior extension of the anterior scaled corselet area (10-15 scales wide under origin of second dorsal fin, compared to 1-5 scale width in *thazard*).

FRIGATE MACKEREL
Auxis thazard (Lacepède, 1800)
(Plate VII-10)

Two well separated dorsal fins, the first with 10-12 spines; second dorsal fin followed by 8 finlets; pectoral fins short, not reaching a vertical line from anterior margin of scaleless area on back; anal fin followed by 7 finlets; body scaleless except for the well developed corselet; back dark bluish; 15 or more narrow, oblique to nearly horizontal dark wavy lines in scaleless area above lateral line; belly white; similar in colour pattern to *Euthynnus affinis* (see below), but differs by having a much wider space between the dorsal fins, a lower spinous dorsal fin and more slender shape. Worldwide in tropical and subtropical seas; inhabits coastal and oceanic waters, sometimes forming large schools. To 58 cm and 4.5 kg.

LEAPING BONITO
Cybiosarda elegans (Whitley, 1935)
(Plate VII-8)

Dorsal fins close together, the first high anteriorly, with 16-18 spines, the second with 17-19 rays, followed by 8-10 finlets; anal fin with 15-17 rays, followed by 6-7 finlets; pectoral fins very short, with 22-24 rays; body mostly scaleless except for the well developed corselet, band of scales along the bases of dorsal and anal fins, and patches of scales around the bases of the pectoral and pelvic fins; deep blue on back with many elongate black spots; belly whitish with several dark stripes; first dorsal fin mainly jet black except posteriormost part white; anal and second dorsal fins yellow. Widely distributed around Australia (except south coast); inhabits coastal waters, sometimes entering estuaries, often in large schools. Reaches 54 cm and 1.15 kg.

MACKEREL TUNA
Euthynnus affinis (Cantor, 1849)
(Plate VII-7)

Dorsal fins close together, the first with 10-15 spines, the anterior spines much higher than those posteriorly, giving the fin a strongly concave outline; second dorsal fin much lower than first and followed by 8-10 finlets; pectoral fins short, reaching to about level of middle spines of first dorsal fin; dark blue on back with a patch of broken, oblique stripes on back extending forward to below middle of first dorsal fin; lower sides and belly silvery white; a few dark spots usually present on lower sides between pelvic and pectoral fins. East Africa and Red Sea to the Hawaiian Islands; forms schools in coastal waters and near offshore reefs. To 100 cm; all-tackle world and Australian record 12.0 kg. Also known by the Polynesian name Kawakawa.

SHARK MACKEREL
Grammatorcynus bicarinatus (Quoy & Gaimard, 1824)
(Plate VII-13)

Dorsal fins close together, the first with 11-13 relatively low spines; second dorsal fin falcate, slightly higher than first dorsal fin, with 10-12 rays followed by 6-7 finlets; anal fin with 11-13 rays followed by 6-7 finlets; pectoral rays 22-26; gill rakers on first arch 14 or 15; 2 lateral lines, first from opercle to caudal keel, second branching from first below anterior dorsal spines and plunging to lower side, eventually rejoining first below the last dorsal finlet; back and upper sides metallic blue-green; belly sil-

very white with a golden tinge; frequently with small dark spots along ventral surface of body. East and west coasts of Australia; inhabits offshore waters in the vicinity of reefs. Maximum size, 130 cm and at least 11.5 kg.

DOUBLE-LINED MACKEREL
Grammatorcynus bilineatus (Rüppell, 1836)
(Plate VII-14)

Dorsal fins close together, the first with 11-13 spines, the anterior ones moderately high; second dorsal fin falcate, about same height as first dorsal fin, with 10-12 rays followed by 6-7 finlets; pectoral rays 22-26; gill rakers on first arch 19-24; 2 lateral lines similar in position to that described for the Shark Mackerel above; back and upper sides metallic blue-green; lower sides and belly silvery white; similar to Shark Mackerel, but has more gill rakers and larger eye (7-9 per cent of fork length versus 3-4 per cent). Red Sea to Australia and the Marshall Islands, ranging north to the Ryukyu Islands; found mainly near coral reefs. To 100 cm, common to 40 cm.

DOGTOOTH TUNA
Gymnosarda unicolor (Rüppell, 1838)
(Plate VII-12)

Dorsal fins close together, the first relatively low and long-based, with 13-15 spines; the second about same height as first and short-based, followed by 6-7 finlets; pectoral rays 25-28; gill rakers on first arch 11-14; a single lateral line that is strongly undulating, particularly the posterior half; body naked posterior to corselet except for lateral line, dorsal fin base, and caudal keel; upper jaw with 14-31 large conical teeth, 10-24 in lower jaw; back and upper sides brilliant blue-black; lower sides and belly silvery; anterior edge of first dorsal fin dark, other fins greyish. Indian Ocean to central Pacific; frequently sighted adjacent to outer reef dropoffs. Reaches 180 cm; all-tackle world record 131 kg.

SKIPJACK TUNA
Katsuwonus pelamis (Linnaeus, 1775)
(Plate VI-12)

Dorsal fins close together, the first with 14-16 spines, the anterior ones relatively tall, giving fin a falcate outline; second dorsal fin falcate, shorter than first dorsal, followed by 7-9 finlets; pectoral rays 26-27; gill rakers numerous, 53-63 on first gill arch; body scaleless except for corselet and lateral line; dark purplish blue on back;

443

PLATE VI

1 **BLACK MARLIN** (*Makaira indica*)

2 **INDO-PACIFIC BLUE MARLIN** (*Makaira mazara*)

3 **SHORT BILL SPEARFISH** (*Tetrapturus angustirostris*)

4 **STRIPED MARLIN** (*Tetrapturus audax*)

5 **INDO-PACIFIC SAILFISH** (*Istiophorus platypterus*)

6 **SWORDFISH** (*Xiphias gladius*)

7 **ALBACORE** (*Thunnus alalunga*)

8 **YELLOWFIN TUNA** (*Thunnus albacares*)

9 **BIGEYE TUNA** (*Thunnus obesus*)

10 **SOUTHERN BLUEFIN TUNA** (*Thunnus maccoyii*)

11 **NORTHERN BLUEFIN TUNA** (*Thunnus tonggol*)

12 **SKIPJACK TUNA** (*Katsuwonus pelamis*)

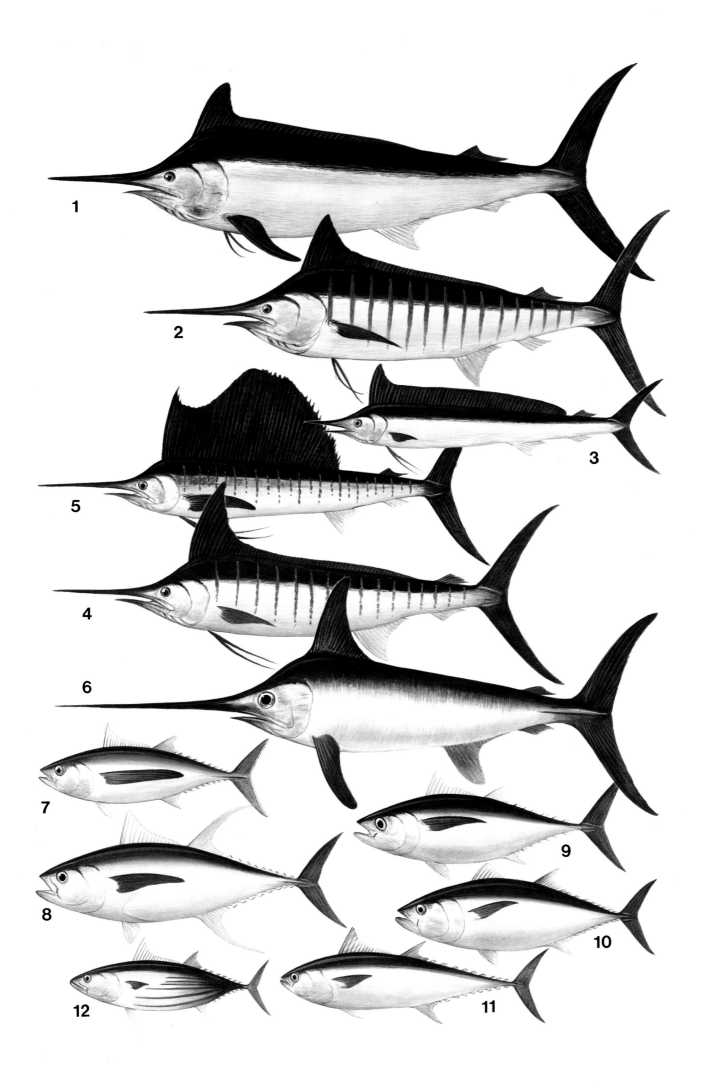

PLATE VII

1 **WAHOO** (*Acanthocybium solandri*)

2 **NARROW-BARRED SPANISH MACKEREL** (*Scomberomorus commerson*)

2 **BROAD-BARRED SPANISH MACKEREL** (*Scomberomorus semifasciatus*)

4 **AUSTRALIAN SPOTTED MACKEREL** (*Scomberomorus munroi*)

4 **QUEENSLAND SCHOOL MACKEREL** (*Scomberomorus queenslandicus*)

6 **ORIENTAL BONITO** (*Sarda orientalis*)

7 **MACKEREL TUNA** (*Euthynnus affinis*)

8 **LEAPING BONITO** (*Cybiosarda elegans*)

9 **CORSELETTED FRIGATE MACKEREL** (*Auxis rochei*)

10 **FRIGATE MACKEREL** (*Auxis thazard*)

11 **LONG-JAWED MACKEREL** (*Rastrelliger kanagurta*)

12 **DOGTOOTH TUNA** (*Gymnosarda unicolor*)

13 **SHARK MACKEREL** (*Grammatorcynus bicarinatus*)

14 **DOUBLE-LINED MACKEREL** (*Grammatorcynus bilineatus*)

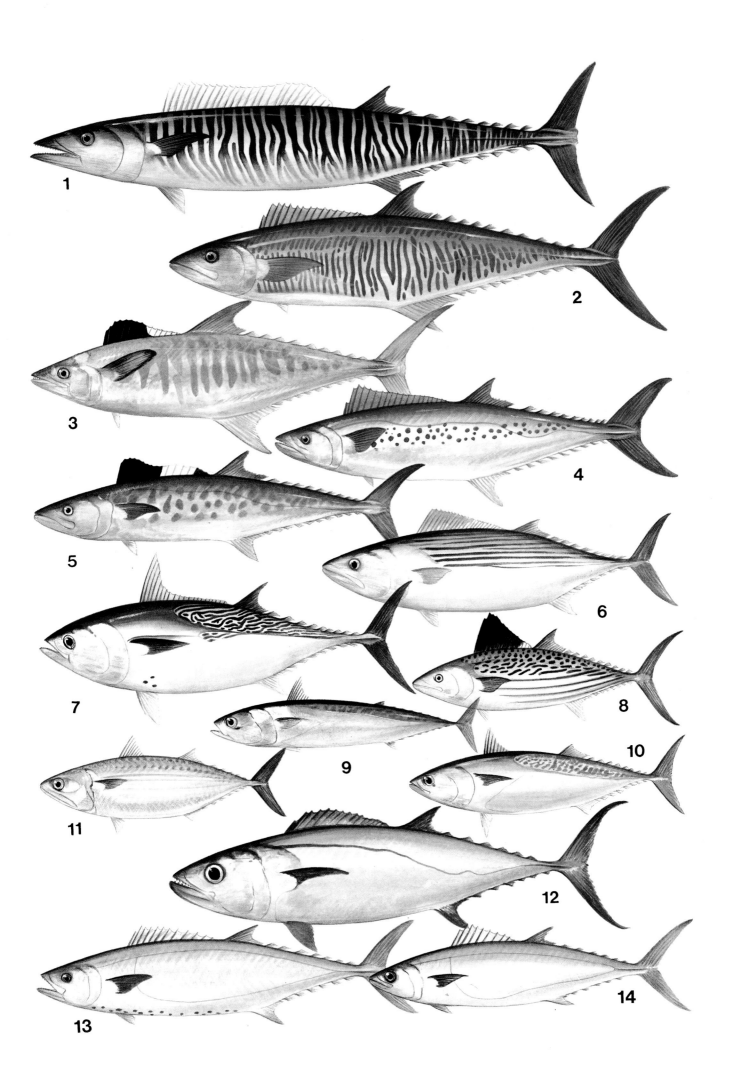

lower sides and belly silvery, with 4-6 conspicuous wavy stripes or discontinuous lines of dark blotches. Circumglobal in seas warmer than about 15 degrees C; makes up about 40 per cent of world tuna catch. Attains 110 cm; all-tackle world record 18.93 kg; Australian record 9.3 kg.

LONG-JAWED MACKEREL
Rastrelliger kanagurta (Cuvier, 1817)
(Plate VII-11)

Dorsal fins well-separated, the first triangular with 8-11 spines; second dorsal and anal fins with 12 rays, followed by 5 finlets; pectoral fins very short with 19-20 rays; gill rakers very long, visible when mouth is open, 30-46 on lower limb of first arch; front and hind margins of eye covered by adipose eyelid; scales behind head and around pectoral fins larger and more conspicuous than those covering rest of body, but no well-developed corselet; generally silver; narrow dark to golden stripes on upper part of body; usually a double longitudinal row of small dusky spots on upper back; a prominent black spot on body under lower margin of pectoral fin; dorsal fins yellowish with black tips; caudal and pectoral fins often yellowish. East Africa and Red Sea to Samoa, north to Japan; feeds on plankton in schools near reefs. To 35 cm. Also known as the Indian Mackerel.

ORIENTAL BONITO
Sarda orientalis (Temminck & Schlegel, 1844)
(Plate VII-6)

Dorsal fins close together, the first without prolonged spines anteriorly, its outline sloping in a straight line posteriorly, with 17-19 spines; second dorsal fin lower than first with 15-16 rays followed by 7-8 finlets; anal fin with 14-16 rays followed by 5-6 finlets; pectoral rays 23-26; gill rakers on first arch 8-13; lateral line wavy; body entirely covered with minute scales except on the well-developed corselet; caudal peduncle with a prominent lateral keel between two smaller keels on each side; back and upper sides steel blue, with 5-11 dark, slightly oblique stripes; lower sides and belly silvery; first dorsal fin entirely black. Indo-Pacific and eastern Pacific. To 102 cm; all-tackle world record 10.65 kg.

NARROW-BARRED SPANISH MACKEREL
Scomberomorus commerson (Lacepède, 1800)
(Plate VII-2)

Dorsal fins close together, the first relatively low with 15-18 spines; second dorsal higher than first with 15-20 rays, followed by 8-10 finlets; anal fin with 16-21 rays, followed by 7-12 finlets; lateral line abruptly bent downward below end of second dorsal fin; back iridescent blue; sides silver with bluish reflections and numerous, thin, wavy bars; juveniles frequently spotted. Somewhat resembles the Wahoo, but has much shorter snout and fewer dorsal spines (15-18 versus 23-27). East Africa and Red Sea to Australia and New Caledonia, north to Japan; frequents coastal seas, often near reefs. To 235 cm, all-tackle world record 44.9 kg; Australian record 44.2 kg.

AUSTRALIAN SPOTTED MACKEREL
Scomberomorus munroi Collette & Russo, 1980
(Plate VII-4)

Dorsal fins close together, the first relatively low with 20-22 spines; second dorsal higher than first with 17-20 rays, followed by 9 or 10 finlets; anal fin with 17-19 rays, followed by 8-10 finlets; lateral line gradually curving down toward caudal peduncle; back iridescent blue, silvery white on sides and belly; sides with numerous small dark spots in poorly defined longitudinal rows; inner surface of pectoral fin dark blue; first dorsal fin steely blue. Northern two-thirds of Australia from Abrolhos Islands, Western Australia to central New South Wales, also southern New Guinea. Attains 104 cm and at least 10 kg.

QUEENSLAND SCHOOL MACKEREL
Scomberomorus queenslandicus Munro, 1943
(Plate VII-5)

Dorsal fins close together, the first relatively low with 16-18 spines; second dorsal higher than first with 17-19 rays, followed by 9-11 finlets; anal fin with 16-20 rays, followed by 9-11 finlets; lateral line gradually curving down toward caudal peduncle; back iridescent blue; sides silvery with about three irregular rows of large, bronze-grey blotches; membrane of first dorsal fin black with large contrasting areas of intense white between sixth and last spine. Tropical and subtropical seas of Australia from Shark

Bay, Western Australia to Sydney, New South Wales, also found in southern New Guinea; inshore coastal waters. Maximum size 100 cm and at least 12 kg.

BROAD-BARRED SPANISH MACKEREL
Scomberomorus semifasciatus (Macleay, 1884)
(Plate VII-3)

Dorsal fins close together, the first relatively low with 13-15 spines; second dorsal tall and falcate, much higher than first dorsal, with 19-22 rays followed by 8-10 finlets; anal fin similar in shape and height to second dorsal, with 19-22 rays followed by 7-10 finlets; lateral line gradually curving down toward caudal peduncle; bronze-green to greenish blue on back, silvery white on lower sides and belly; series of dark grey bars on sides; anterior half of first dorsal fin jet black, posterior half white; pectoral fins dusky. Northern Australia from Shark Bay, Western Australia to northern New South Wales; also southern New Guinea. Attains 120 cm and at least 8.4 kg.

ALBACORE
Thunnus alalunga (Bonnaterre, 1788)
(Plate VI-7)

Dorsal fins close together, the first with prolonged spines anteriorly, giving fin a strongly concave outline; first dorsal with 13 or 14 spines; second dorsal and anal fins falcate, each followed by 7-10 finlets; pectoral fins remarkably long, usually 30 per cent of fork length or longer, extending well past rear of second dorsal and anal fins; pectorals somewhat shorter in juveniles and hence may be confused with Yellowfin and Bigeye, but differs from them in having a white rear border on the caudal fin; small scales on body; corselet of larger scales developed, but indistinct; back metallic dark blue; lower sides and belly whitish; first dorsal fin yellow; second dorsal and anal fins pale yellow; posterior margin of caudal fin white. Worldwide in tropical and temperate seas; important commercial fisheries exist mainly in cooler seas. Attains 150 cm; all-tackle world record 40 kg; Australian record 15 kg.

YELLOWFIN TUNA
Thunnus albacares (Bonnaterre, 1788)
(Plate VI-8)

Dorsal fins close together, the first with prolonged spines anteriorly, giving a strongly concave outline; first dorsal with

13 or 14 spines; second dorsal and anal fins becoming extremely tall in large specimens, well over 20 per cent of fork length; 7-10 finlets behind second dorsal and anal fins; pectoral fins moderately long, usually reaching beyond second dorsal fin origin, but not beyond end of its base, usually 22-31 per cent of fork length; body with very small scales; corselet of larger scales present, but not very distinct; back metallic dark blue, becoming yellow to silver on sides and belly; belly may be crossed by about 20 broken, nearly vertical whitish lines; dorsal and anal fins, including finlets, bright yellow, the finlets with a narrow black border. Worldwide in tropical and subtropical seas; an important commercial species. Reaches 210 cm; all- tackle world record 176.4 kg; Australian record 97 kg.

SOUTHERN BLUEFIN TUNA
Thunnus maccoyii (Castelnau, 1872)
(Plate VI-10)

Dorsal fins close together, the first with prolonged spines anteriorly, giving fin a strongly concave outline; first dorsal with 12-14 spines; second dorsal and anal fins falcate, each followed by 7-10 finlets; pectoral fins relatively short, not reaching to rear of first dorsal fin; very small scales on body; a well-developed corselet of larger scales, but not conspicuous; dark blue on back, lower sides and belly silvery white; fresh specimens with transverse rows of narrow white lines alternating with rows of white dots on lower sides; first dorsal fin yellow or bluish; lateral keel yellow in adults. Southern Hemisphere seas, usually in temperatures between 20 - 26 degrees C; important fisheries are located off Tasmania, New Zealand, and South Africa. Reaches 240 cm; all-tackle world record 158 kg; Australian record 71.2 kg.

BIGEYE TUNA
Thunnus obesus (Lowe, 1839)
(Plate VI-9)

Dorsal fins close together, the first with prolonged spines anteriorly, giving fin a strongly concave outline; first dorsal with 13-15 spines; second dorsal and anal fins falcate, each followed by 8-10 finlets; pectoral fins moderately long, 22-31 per cent of fork length, extending to end of first dorsal fin or beyond; very small scales on body; corselet of larger scales well-developed, but not conspicuous; back metallic dark blue, lower sides and belly whitish; a lateral iridescent blue band running along sides of live fish; first dorsal fin yellow; second

dorsal and anal fins pale yellow; finlets bright yellow, edged with black. Circum-global in tropical and temperate seas; an important commercial species. Maximum size, 240 cm; all-tackle world record 197.2 kg; Australian record 37.13 kg.

NORTHERN BLUEFIN TUNA
Thunnus tonggol (Bleeker, 1851)
(Plate VI-11)

Dorsal fins close together, the first with prolonged spines anteriorly, giving fin a strongly concave outline; first dorsal with 11-14 spines; second dorsal and anal fin falcate, each followed by 8-9 finlets; pectoral fins relatively short to moderately long, 22-31 per cent of fork length in fish under 60 cm and 16-22 per cent of fork length in larger individuals; very small scales on body; corselet of larger scales well-developed, but not conspicuous; dark blue or black on back, lower sides and belly silvery white; colourless oval spots in horizontal rows on lower sides. Southern Red Sea across northern Indian Ocean to Australia and north to Japan. To 150 cm; all-tackle world record 35.9 kg; Australian record 31.26 kg.

LEFTEYE FLOUNDERS
FAMILY BOTHIDAE

The lefteye flounders are recognised by their flattened shape with both eyes positioned on the left side of the body. The dorsal fin originates either above or ahead of the eye, and both dorsal and anal fins contain numerous segmented rays and are separated from the caudal fin. There are many species of bothids and other types of flatfishes occurring in coastal

and shelf waters of Australia including a few commercially valuable species. They typically inhabit soft bottom areas, and are sometimes common on trawling grounds. Relatively few flatfishes are encountered around coral reefs. The other families, Soleidae and Pleuronectidae, that are sometimes seen on the Great Barrier Reef and in the Coral Sea differ from the bothids by having the eyes on the right side. Lefteye flounders, like other flatfishes, have "normal" larvae with an eye on each side of the head, but with increased growth one eye migrates over the top of the head. Their coloration blends remarkably well with the bottom and they have the capability of rapidly changing colours to match their surroundings. The diet consists mainly of fishes and crustaceans.

FLOWERY FLOUNDER
Bothus mancus (Broussonet, 1782)

Dorsal rays 96-104; anal rays 74-81; pectoral rays 10-13; lateral-line scales 76-90; greatest depth of body 1.7-2.0 in standard length; sexual differences develop at about 23-25 cm, characterised by the male having very elongate pectoral fin (on eyed side), tentacles on eyes, wider interorbital space, and spines on snout and above eye; eyed side with numerous variable-sized white to pale blue spots, some arranged to form small partial circles, and small dark brown spots; usually three diffuse dark blotches on lateral line. East Africa to eastern Pacific; often found on sand patches within coral reefs, sometimes on hard substrata. Grows to 42 cm.

Bothus mancus

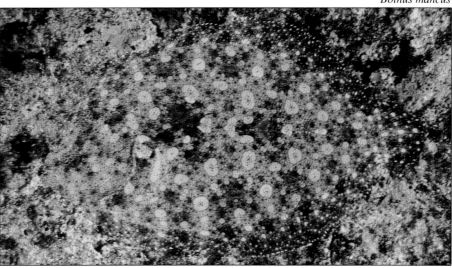

PANTHER FLOUNDER
Bothus pantherinus Rüppell, 1828

Dorsal rays 84-97; anal rays 61-73; pectoral rays 9-12; lateral-line scales 74-87; greatest depth of body 1.6-1.9 in standard length; each eye with 1-3 tentacles; males larger than about 13-16 cm develop an elongate pectoral fin (eyed side), spines on snout and edge of eyes, and broader interorbital; eyed side brown with numerous small dark-edged whitish spots and irregular rings and orange spots of variable size; blotches and rings extending onto median fins; usually a single large diffuse dark blotch on middle of straight section of lateral line. East Africa to Hawaii; usually not found in coral reef environment, but may be on adjacent sand or silty sand flats. Reported to 30 cm.

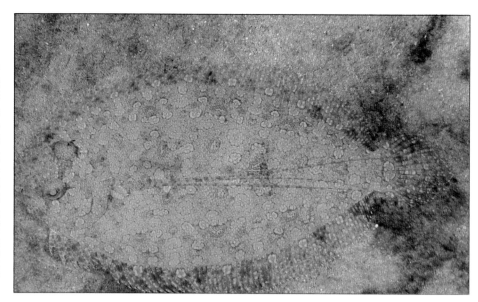

RIGHTEYE FLOUNDERS
FAMILY PLEURONECTIDAE

This flatfish family is characterised by having the eyes on the right side in most species, the dorsal fin origin above or in front of the eyes, no fin spines, and numerous dorsal and anal fin rays. It is distinguished from the right-eyed soles (Soleidae) by its distinct preopercle (cheek) margin (the cheek margin of the soles is hidden by skin and scales). The Pleuronectidae contains about 100 species that are scattered worldwide, but only one is regularly encountered on reefs in our area.

THREESPOT FLOUNDER
Samariscus triocellatus Woods, 1966

Dorsal rays 62-70; anal rays 47-56; pectoral rays 5 (eyed side), a single rudimentary ray on blind side; lateral-line scales 71-76; greatest body depth 2.4-3.1 in standard length; body subrectangular with relatively tall dorsal and anal fins; brown, mottled with irregular light and dark markings; 2-3 dark-edged ocelli along lateral line; outer tip of pectoral fin blackish. East Africa to Society Islands and Hawaiian Islands; occurs on sand, frequently under ledges. Maximum size, 7 cm.

SOLES
FAMILY SOLEIDAE

Soles are flatfishes that have the eyes on the right side of the body, the dorsal fin origin above or in front of the eyes, no fin spines, and numerous dorsal and anal rays. Unlike the righteyed flounders (Pleuronectidae), the margin of the cheek (preopercle) is hidden by skin and scales. They are inhabitants of sandy or mud bottoms, occurring worldwide in tropical and temperate seas, but are rarely seen around coral reefs.

PEACOCK SOLE
Paradachirus pavoninus (Lacepède, 1802)

Dorsal rays 66-70; anal rays 50-53; caudal rays 18; lateral-line scales 75-82; eyes small and close together; pectoral fins absent; overall brown or light grey with numerous large, dark-edged white spots, each surrounding one or more dark markings; also small yellow spots present. Sri Lanka to Samoa and Tonga; has special glands that produce a milky toxin which is distasteful to predators, including sharks. Reaches 25 cm.

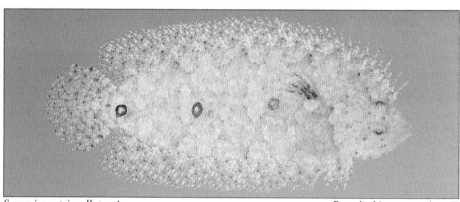

Samariscus triocellatus ▲

Paradachirus pavoninus ▼

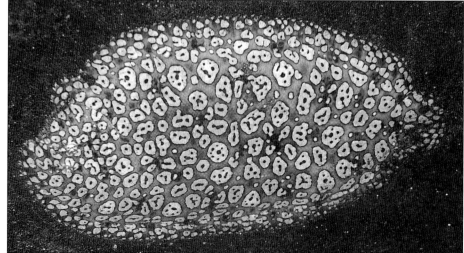

TRIGGERFISHES
FAMILY BALISTIDAE

The triggerfishes have a stout first dorsal spine which can be locked in an erect position by the small second spine (the "trigger", for if it is pressed down the first spine can be "unlocked"), hence the common name for the family. These fishes have relatively deep compressed bodies with the eye set high on the head, a long tapering snout but small mouth, the gill opening a short slit above and in front of the pectoral-fin base, two dorsal fins (the first of III spines, the second consisting of soft rays), an anal fin only of soft rays, and no pelvic fins (replaced by a single spinous knob at the end of a long depressible pelvic bone). The teeth are chisel-like and very close-set, eight in the outer row and six in an inner row which serve to buttress the outer teeth. The skin is tough and rough to the touch, comprised of nonoverlapping scales, each with a broad area of small tubercles in the centre; most species have a patch of enlarged modified scales behind the gill opening; some have rows of curved spines posteriorly on the side of the body. Triggerfishes are usually solitary. They swim by undulating the second dorsal and anal fins, bringing their tail into action only when speed is needed. When frightened, they seek refuge in a favorite hole in the reef with a small entrance; inside they lock themselves in place by erecting their first dorsal spine and depressing the pelvic bone. At night they sleep in the same or a similar hole. The majority of balistid fishes are carnivorous; a few feed in part on benthic algae. They eat a great variety of animal life from zooplankton to crabs, mollusks, and sea urchins. Although their mouth is small, the jaws are powerful and the teeth strong and sharp, enabling them to render large prey with hard parts to small pieces. Therefore they are not compatible with certain invertebrates in an aquarium; also they can be damaging to other fishes in the tank. Triggerfishes lay demersal eggs which are aggressively defended by the female. Some species make a nest by excavating a shallow crater in sand; the eggs are deposited in the centre of the crater. Divers should be careful not to venture close to the guarding female of the larger triggerfishes. Usually the guarding fish will rush rapidly at an intruder but turn before contact is made. If this threat is not heeded and one comes closer to the nest, there is a risk of being bitten. Pectoral-ray counts below include the upper rudimentary ray.

Yellow-Spotted Triggerfish
Pseudobalistes fuscus Juv.

STARRY TRIGGERFISH
Abalistes stellatus (Lacepède, 1798)

Dorsal rays III+25-27; anal rays 24-25; pectoral rays 15-16 (rarely 16); caudal peduncle slender, much longer than deep (as deep or deeper than long in other balistid fishes); a diagonal deep groove before eye; second dorsal and anal fins not elevated anteriorly; caudal fin double emarginate, the lobes longer with growth; grey-brown to olivaceous on back, pale below, with small pale blue or yellow spots dorsally and larger yellow spots ventrally (sometimes faint); three whitish blotches on back (faint or absent in large individuals) and often a broad whitish streak posteriorly from gill opening; juveniles with close-set brown spots dorsally and more widely spaced yellow ones below. Western Pacific to East Africa and the Red Sea; usually found on mud or silty sand bottoms. Reaches 60 cm.

ORANGE-LINED TRIGGERFISH
Balistapus undulatus (Park, 1797)

Dorsal rays III+24-27 (rarely 24 or 27); anal rays 20-24; pectoral rays 13-15 (usually 14); no groove before eye; two rows of strong forward-curved spines on and slightly in front of caudal peduncle; second dorsal and anal fins not elevated anteriorly; caudal fin slightly rounded; dark green to dark brown with diagonal curved orange lines on posterior head and body; a diagonal band of narrow blue and orange stripes from around mouth to below pectoral fin; a black area around peduncular spines; caudal fin orange-yellow. Indo-Pacific; occurs in a variety of reef habitats; diet extremely varied: live coral, algae, sea urchins, crabs and other crustaceans, fishes, mollusks, brittle stars, tunicates, polychaete worms, sponges, and hydrozoans. Reaches 30 cm.

CLOWN TRIGGERFISH

Balistoides conspicillum (Bloch & Schneider, 1801)

Dorsal rays III+25-27; anal rays 21-23; pectoral rays 14-15; a deep groove anterior to eye; region around lips fully scaled; three or four short rows of small forward-curved spines posteriorly on side of body; second dorsal and anal fins not elevated anteriorly; caudal fin rounded, the corners acute; black with very large round white spots on ventral half of body, a yellow network on back centred below first dorsal fin; a white band across snout in front of eye; lips and adjacent zone around mouth orange-yellow, edged posteriorly by a black line and white submarginal line; juveniles with smaller white spots (but most as large or larger than eye) over all of head and body. East Africa to Samoa and Line Islands in the Central Pacific; usually found in outer reef areas. Attains 50 cm. Sometimes identified as *B. niger* (Bloch), but this name invalid due to homonomy. Also known as the Big-spotted Triggerfish in Australia.

TITAN TRIGGERFISH

Balistoides viridescens (Bloch & Schneider, 1801)

Dorsal rays III+25-26; anal rays 22-24; pectoral rays 15; a deep groove before eye; a scaleless area around lips, continuing and narrowing posterior to corner of mouth; small forward-curving spines in about five rows on side of and a short distance anterior to caudal peduncle; second dorsal and anal fins slightly elevated anteriorly; caudal fin rounded to double emarginate; yellowish, often paler posteriorly, the centres of scales broadly dark brown or greenish; a broad blackish zone containing yellow spots extending from dorsal part of head to pectoral base (enclosing eye); a broad blackish band containing a pale line from above mouth to half way across cheek; second dorsal, anal, and caudal fins with broad blackish borders. Indo-Pacific; feeds mainly on sea urchins, coral, crabs, molluscs, and tube worms. The largest of the triggerfishes; reaches 75 cm. A wary fish except when a female is guarding her nest; the three of us were all independently attacked by a large female, and Steene was bitten on the arm; on another occasion Randall was bitten on the leg.

PINKTAIL TRIGGERFISH
Melichthys vidua (Solander, 1844)

Dorsal rays III+31-35; anal rays 27-31; pectoral rays 14-16; scale rows from corner of mouth to lower end of gill opening 28-32; a deep groove before eye; second dorsal and anal fins strongly elevated anteriorly; caudal fin usually truncate; dark brown to nearly black; scaled basal part of caudal fin white, the outer naked part pink; second dorsal and anal fins whitish with a black border; prejuvenile or transforming stage with black lines radiating from eye and longitudinal black lines in second dorsal and anal fins. Indo-Pacific; omnivorous; limited food habit data indicate heavy feeding on benthic algae and detritus (70% of the diet); animal material from stomachs included crustaceans, octopuses, sponges, and fishes. Largest specimen, 35 cm. The prejuvenile stage can reach a length of at least l6 cm, which is extraordinarily large for a postlarval fish.

REDTOOTH TRIGGERFISH
Odonus niger (Rüppell, 1837)

Dorsal rays III+33-36; anal rays 28-31; pectoral rays 15-16 (rarely 16); a deep groove anterior to eye; mouth upturned, the chin protruding; two upper teeth prolonged, visible when mouth closed; about seven longitudinal rows of small spines on posterior half or more of body; anterior part of second dorsal and anal fins very elevated; caudal fin lunate, the lobes prolonged in adults; blue to purplish blue; margins of the second dorsal and anal fins and posterior margin of caudal fin light blue; teeth red; head can be altered to yellowish. Indo-Pacific; feeds mainly on zooplankton, often well above the substratum; may be locally abundant on steep outer reef slopes. Attains 40 cm (including long caudal lobes).

YELLOWMARGIN TRIGGERFISH
Pseudobalistes flavimarginatus (Rüppell, 1829)

Dorsal rays III+24-27; anal rays 23-25; pectoral rays 15 or 16 (usually 16); a deep groove anterior to eye; shallow horizontal grooves on cheek above level of mouth; a broad area above, below, and posterior to mouth scaleless in adults; small spines in five or six horizontal rows posteriorly on body; second dorsal and anal fins slightly elevated anteriorly; caudal fin rounded in young, becoming emarginate in adults, the lobes prolonged in large adults; light greyish yellow, the scale centres darker yellowish grey; anterior and ventral part of head orange-yellow; margins of second dorsal, anal, and caudal fins usually orange-yellow; juveniles with small black spots. Indo-Pacific; most often found in sheltered reef areas with much sand; a wary fish; nest-guarding females less aggressive than *B. viridescens* or the following species. Reaches 60 cm.

YELLOW-SPOTTED TRIGGERFISH
Pseudobalistes fuscus (Bloch & Schneider, 1801)

Dorsal rays III+25-27; anal rays 21-24; pectoral rays 15-16 (usually 15); a deep groove anterior to eye; lower cheek with shallow horizontal grooves; broad region around mouth without scales; no spines on caudal peduncle; second dorsal and anal fins elevated anteriorly; caudal fin of young rounded, of adults emarginate, the lobes prolonged in large adults; deep blue to greyish blue with small yellow spots, these often cojoined to form irregular bands; outer margins of second dorsal, anal, and caudal fins light blue; juveniles brighter blue with fewer and relatively larger yellow spots or broader irregular yellow bands. Samoa and islands of Micronesia to East Africa and the Red Sea; occurs in a variety of reef habitats; females guarding nests aggressive; divers have been bitten. Reaches 55 cm.

WHITEBANDED TRIGGERFISH
Rhinecanthus aculeatus (Linnaeus, 1758)

Dorsal rays III+23-26; anal rays 21-23; pectoral rays 13-14; dorsal and ventral profiles of head nearly straight (true of all *Rhinecanthus*); no deep groove before eye (also characteristic of the genus); three horizontal rows of small forward-curving spines on caudal peduncle, the upper two rows extending anterior to peduncle; second dorsal and anal fins not elevated anteriorly (generic); caudal fin rounded, the corners angular; white with a large blackish area over much of side of body containing four diagonal bluish white bands from midside to anal fin; four blue lines across interorbital and three from eye to pectoral base; an orange-yellow area around mouth enclosing a blue line at base of upper lip, the yellow continuing as a narrowing band to below pectoral base; peduncular spines black, edged in pale blue; anus black. Indo-Pacific; typical habitat, lagoon reef flat where dominated by sand; omnivorous, feeding on algae, detritus, and a wide variety of benthic invertebrates. Reaches 25 cm. Also known as the Lagoon Triggerfish.

HALFMOON TRIGGERFISH
Rhinecanthus lunula Randall & Steene, 1983

Dorsal rays III+25-26 (usually 26); anal rays 22-24; pectoral rays 14; snout long, 2.7-2.8 in standard length; caudal peduncle slender; three horizontal rows of small forward-curving spines posteriorly on body, the upper row ending at front of caudal peduncle, the lower two extending to caudal-fin base; caudal fin slightly double emarginate; yellowish grey on back, shading to white ventrally, with a large blackish area on lower side centred above anus; a broad blue-edged black bar across caudal peduncle with a curved blue band containing a black line anterior to it; four narrow blue bands with black interspaces across interorbital, continuing as three blue bands to pectoral base; a blue and yellow line at base of upper lip, the yellow continuing as a narrow band nearly to pectoral base; anus in a black spot; a black crescent in caudal fin preceded by a yellow area; first dorsal fin black; juveniles lack the black caudal crescent and large blackish area on lower side. South Pacific from Pitcairn Group to Queensland; lives in outer reef reas, generally at depths greater than 10 m; rare. Attains about 28 cm.

WEDGE-TAIL TRIGGERFISH
Rhinecanthus rectangulus (Bloch & Schneider, 1801)

Dorsal rays III+22-25; anal rays 20-22; pectoral rays 13-14; four (rarely five) horizontal rows of small forward-curving spines posteriorly on body; caudal fin rounded, the corners acute; brown dorsally, white ventrally on head and abdomen, with a broad diagonal black band from eye, enclosing pectoral base, to anal-fin base, the part on head preceded by two narrow blue bands; a wedge-shaped black area posteriorly on body, edged anteriorly in gold and preceded by a parallel gold band; four narrow blue bands with black interspaces crossing interorbital; a blue line at base of upper lip and a red bar at pectoral base. Indo-Pacific; common in the shallow outer reef environment exposed to surge; omnivorous, feeding on algae, detritus, and a wide variety of benthic animals, most of which are small; difficult to approach underwater. Attains 25 cm. Also called the Reef Triggerfish.

BLACKPATCH TRIGGERFISH
Rhinecanthus verrucosus (Linnaeus, 1758)

Dorsal rays III+23-26; anal rays 21-23; pectoral rays 13-14; three rows of small black forward-curving spines posteriorly on side of body, the upper row short; caudal fin broadly rounded centrally, the corners distinctly acute in adults; greyish brown dorsally, white ventrally, with a very large black patch on lower side centred above anus; a broad yellowish brown band with four blue lines across interorbital space, continuing with three blue lines below eye to gill opening; a blue zone above upper lip bordered above by a red line which extends to lower pectoral-fin base. Western Pacific, east to the Caroline Islands and west to the Chagos Archipelago; a shallow-water species more inclined than others of the genus to enter turbid silty areas (but always with some form of shelter nearby). To 23 cm.

SCIMITAR TRIGGERFISH
Sufflamen bursa (Bloch & Schneider, 1801)

Dorsal rays III+27-30; anal rays 24-27; pectoral rays 13-15; dorsal and ventral profiles of head nearly straight (true of other *Sufflamen*); a deep groove before eye; a series of longitudinal ridges posteriorly on body following scale rows; dorsal and anal fins not elevated anteriorly; caudal fin truncate to slightly rounded; greyish brown, abruptly pale below a white line from above upper lip to origin of anal fin; a scimitar-shaped dark brown band from in front of pectoral base through posterior part of eye and a second slightly oblique band passing dorsally from top of pectoral base (these two bands may be altered to yellow by the fish); pelvic terminus and edge of pelvic flap black. Indo-Pacific; omnivorous but feeds more on benthic animals than algae; these include crabs and other crustaceans, sea urchins, mollusks, polychaete worms, peanut worms, and tunicates. Attains 24 cm.

FLAGTAIL TRIGGERFISH
Sufflamen chrysopterus (Bloch & Schneider, 1801)

Dorsal rays III+26-28; anal rays 23-26; pectoral rays 13-15; deep groove before eye; longitudinal rows of small spines following scale centres on about posterior third of body; second dorsal and anal fins slightly elevated anteriorly; caudal fin truncate to slightly rounded with acute corners; dark brown with a greenish yellow streak from lower pectoral base to hind edge of eye; lower part of head and abdomen often deep purplish blue; caudal fin yellowish brown with a broad pure white posterior border and narrower white upper and lower margins; capable of altering its colour to light yellowish brown. Micronesia and Samoa to East Africa; usually seen in sheltered back reefs or lagoons. Reaches 22 cm. Sometimes called the Black Triggerfish in Australia.

BRIDLED TRIGGERFISH
Sufflamen fraenatus (Latreille, 1804)

Dorsal rays III+27-31; anal rays 24-28; pectoral rays 14-16; a deep groove before eye; horizontal rows of small spines following scale centres posteriorly on side of body; second dorsal and anal fins slightly elevated anteriorly; caudal fin rounded in young, truncate to slightly emarginate in adults; brown with a yellow band on lower lip; males with a narrow pale yellow to pink band under chin linking behind corner of mouth with a diagonal narrow band of the same colour which continues across lower cheek; juveniles dark brown on back and dorsally on head, abruptly whitish below, with irregular longitudinal yellowish brown lines on body. Indo-Pacific; known from the depth range of 8 to over 100 m; feeds mainly on sea urchins and heart urchins, fishes, mollusks, tunicates, brittle stars, and crabs and other crustaceans; occasionally ingests small amounts of algae. Reported to 38 cm. *S. capistratus* (Shaw) is a synonym.

GILDED TRIGGERFISH

Xanthichthys auromarginatus (Bennett, 1831)

Dorsal rays III+27-30 (the third dorsal spine very small); anal rays 25-27; pectoral rays 13-15; a deep groove anterior to eye; chin slightly protruding; five horizontal grooves separating scale rows on cheek; longitudinal rows of small spines forming ridges along centres of scales of body except anteriorly; front of second dorsal and anal fins strongly elevated; caudal fin emarginate; brownish to purplish grey, the scales of body with a small white spot (spots very small or absent dorsally); margins of second dorsal, anal, and caudal fin of females dark reddish brown, of males yellow, the border broadest centroposteriorly on caudal fin; males with a large bright blue patch on lower side of head. Indo-Pacific, but recorded only from insular localities; occurs on deep outer-reef slopes from depths of 15 to at least 70 m (not common in less than 30 m); feeds on zooplankton, mainly calanoid copepods. Largest specimen collected, 22 cm.

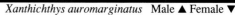

Xanthichthys auromarginatus   Male ▲ Female ▼

459

LEATHERJACKETS
FAMILY MONACANTHIDAE

Leatherjackets, also known as file-fishes in some regions, are close relatives of triggerfishes (Balistidae), but differ from them by having more compressed bodies, generally a more pointed snout, a longer first dorsal spine, a very small second spine (sometimes absent), and no third spine; the teeth are similar, but not as stout, and there are six instead of eight in the outer row and four in the inner row; the scales, which are not conspicuous, have small setae that gives the skin its coarse texture. Unlike the triggerfishes, most species are able to change their colour to match their surroundings, and some develop small skin flaps or tassles which further enhances their camouflage. They tend to be secretive, often hiding in seagrass, thick algal cover, gorgonians, or coral. Most exhibit omnivorous food habits, feeding on a great variety of benthic animal and plant life. Australia has more leatherjackets than any other region in the world with about 60 of the estimated total of 85 species being represented. However, the majority are confined to cooler waters of temperate and subtropical seas. The flesh of many of the larger species is good eating, and in Australia and Japan they are important commercial fishes.

RADIAL LEATHERJACKET
Acreichthys radiatus (Popta, 1901)

Dorsal rays II-26-29; anal rays 25-27; pectoral rays 10 or 11; a small deep-bodied leatherjacket with skin flaps on body and dorsal spine; light mottled brown with narrow white bars and slanted lines. Western Pacific. To 7 cm.

UNICORN LEATHERJACKET
Aluterus monoceros (Linnaeus, 1758)

Dorsal rays II-45-51; anal rays 47-53; pectoral rays 14; a large, highly compressed leatherjacket with a very thin dorsal spine; caudal fin rounded in young, emarginate in adults; tan to grey, often with numerous brown spots on upper sides of body; soft dorsal and anal fins pale yellowish to brownish; caudal fin membranes blackish brown; juveniles with reticulate pattern of pale lines enclosing grey blotches and brown spots, this pattern sometimes persisting on small adults; similar to *A. scriptus* (below), but has a convex dorsal head profile and bulbous ventral head profile; also a much shorter caudal fin. Circumtropical; uncommon in our area. Attains 75 cm.

SCRAWLED LEATHERJACKET
Aluterus scriptus (Osbeck, 1765)

Dorsal rays II-43-49; anal rays 46-52; pectoral rays 13-15; body elongate and very compressed; snout long, the dorsal and ventral profile concave; mouth small and upturned; caudal fin long and rounded, the posterior edge often ragged; olive brown to grey with irregular blue spots and short lines and small black spots; similar to *A. monoceros* (see above). Circumtropical; occasionally seen in lagoons or on outer reef slopes to depths of about 20 m. Feeds on a wide variety of benthic life, including algae, seagrasses, hydrozoans (such as stinging coral), gorgonians, colonial anemones, and tunicates. To 75 cm. Also known as the Scribbled Leatherjacket.

BRUSH-SIDED LEATHERJACKET
Amanses scopas Cuvier, 1829

Dorsal rays II-26-29; anal rays 22-25; pectoral rays 12 or 13; snout short, the dorsal profile straight; first dorsal spine over eye; males with a patch of numerous long spines in front of caudal peduncle, females with a toothbrush-like patch of bristles; dark brown with several narrow, incomplete, black bars on middle of side and blackish caudal fin. East Africa and Red Sea to Tuamotus and Marshall Islands. Attains 20 cm.

YELLOWEYE LEATHERJACKET
Cantherhinus dumerilii (Hollard, 1854)

Dorsal rays II-34-39; anal rays 28-35; pectoral rays 14-15 (usually 15); dorsal profile of snout nearly straight; two pairs of forward-curved spines on caudal peduncle (males have longer, stouter spines); greyish brown, often with series of incomplete darker bars on posterior half of body; iris and caudal fin orange; males with caudal fin and peduncular spines more orange; juveniles and subadults with white spots scattered on body. East Africa to tropical eastern Pacific; to depths of 20 m; feeds on tips of branching corals, also on algae, sponges, sea urchins, and molluscs. Reaches 35 cm.

HONEYCOMB LEATHERJACKET
Cantherhines pardalis (Rüppell, 1837)

Dorsal rays II-32-36; anal rays 29-32; pectoral rays 12-14; dorsal profile of snout slightly concave; males with a large brush-like patch of setae on side of caudal peduncle; bluish grey with close-set orangish-brown spots on body and faint narrow stripes on head; a small white spot on upper edge of caudal peduncle behind soft dorsal fin. East Africa and Red Sea to southeastern Oceania; usually seen on outer reefs to depths of about 15 m. To 20 cm.

LARGE-SCALED LEATHERJACKET
Cantheschenia grandisquamis Hutchins, 1977

Dorsal rays II-39; anal rays 36; pectoral rays 13; red-brown with a broad yellowish streak below dorsal fin extending onto base of caudal fin; blue spots along lower edge of head, a blue stripe along base of dorsal and anal fins, and broad blue upper and lower margins on caudal fin. Capricorn Group to New South Wales. Grows to 26 cm.

LEAFY LEATHERJACKET
Chaetoderma penicilligera (Cuvier, 1817)

Dorsal rays II-25 or 26; anal rays 23 or 24; pectoral rays 12 or 13; body deep and rhomboidal; numerous branched and fringed tentacles on head and body; first dorsal spine short, behind eye, also with branching fleshy filaments; yellowish brown with slightly irregular longitudinal dark brown lines; median fins transparent with black dots. Indo-Malayan region to Australia, north to Japan. To 31 cm.

FAN-BELLIED LEATHERJACKET
Monacanthus chinensis Osbeck, 1765

Dorsal rays II-28-30; anal rays 27-30; pectoral rays 12; body very deep; dorsal profile of snout concave; a large fan-like pelvic flap; a filamentous extension from upper corner of caudal fin; overall tan or yellowish with large irregular brown blotches and mottling; several irregular brown stripes radiating from eye; small light blue spots on head. Malay Peninsula to Samoa, north to Japan. Reaches 38 cm.

BEAKED LEATHERJACKET
Oxymonacanthus longirostris (Bloch & Schneider, 1801)

Dorsal rays II-32-35; anal rays 29-32; pectoral rays 11 or 12; body relatively elongate; snout long and pointed, the dorsal and ventral profiles concave; mouth small and upturned; green with numerous, small, dark-edged orange spots and a black blotch on caudal fin. East Africa to Samoa, north to Ryukyu Islands; often seen in pairs amongst branched or tabular corals; feeds on coral polyps. Attains 9 cm.

MIMIC LEATHERJACKET
Paraluteres prionurus (Bleeker, 1851)

Dorsal rays II-25-28; anal rays 22-25; pectoral rays 10 or 11; first dorsal spine bound by membrane to back, only slightly erectile; two pairs of curved spines posteriorly on caudal peduncle; whitish with four prominent dark brown diagonal bars on back, the two middle ones extending narrowly onto lower side. East Africa to New Caledonia and Marshall Islands, north to Japan; a mimic of the small pufferfish *Canthigaster valentini*, a poisonous species; the colour patterns and shapes of these species are nearly identical, but the two can be distinguished by the lack of the first dorsal fin in the puffer and its shorter-based dorsal and anal fins. Reaches 10 cm.

JAPANESE LEATHERJACKET
Paramonacanthus japonicus (Tilesius, 1809)

Dorsal rays II-24-30; anal rays 24-30; pectoral rays 10-13; body of male oblong, the dorsal profile of snout straight; female deeper-bodied, the profile of snout concave; upper corner of caudal fin of male prolonged as a filament; movable pelvic terminus; mottled brown, effective in blending with the weedy and sandy habitats which it frequents. Western Pacific. Attains 10 cm. *P. oblongus* (Temminck & Schlegel) is a synonym.

YELLOW-EYED LEATHERJACKET
Pervagor alternans (Ogilby, 1899)

Dorsal rays II-31-34; anal rays 27-31; pectoral rays 12 or 13 (usually 13); snout pointed, its dorsal profile concave; caudal peduncle short and deep; first dorsal spine over eye with a row of prominent curved spines on each side; pelvic terminus spiny and movable (the last four characters true of genus, in general); brown with black longitudinal lines on side; caudal fin orange-yellow with a solid blackish submarginal bar; usually a bright yellow ring around eye. Great Barrier Reef, Coral Sea, New Caledonia, New South Wales, Lord Howe Island, and Marshall Islands; usually in rich coral areas and on rocky reefs; not common in our area. To 16 cm.

ORANGETAIL LEATHERJACKET
Pervagor aspricaudus (Hollard, 1854)

Dorsal rays II-31-35; anal rays 28-32; pectoral rays 12 or 13 (usually 12); brown grading to orange posteriorly; numerous tiny black spots on head and body, often arranged to form irregular longitudinal lines; caudal fin orange to yellow with one or more dark submarginal bands; similar to *P. alternans* but lacking solid black lines on body and yellow around eye . Antiequatorial distribution: Mauritius to New Caledonia and Taiwan to Hawaiian Islands; lagoons and outer reef slopes to 25 m. Attains 12 cm.

GILL-BLOTCH LEATHERJACKET
Pervagor janthinosoma (Bleeker, 1854)

Dorsal rays II-29-34; anal rays 26-30; pectoral rays 11-13 (usually 12); a dark blotch over gill opening and extending above it; caudal fin orange to red; similar in appearance to other species of *Pervagor* (above), but lacks the yellow eye ring of *P. alternans*, and has narrow black lines on the sides rather than tiny spots as in *P. aspricaudus*. East Africa to Samoa and Mariana Islands; shallow coral reefs to 20 m depth. To 14 cm.

BLACK-HEADED LEATHERJACKET
Pervagor melanocephalus (Bleeker, 1853)

Dorsal rays II,30-33; anal rays 27-30; pectoral rays 12 or 13 (usually 12); head and nape dark brown, rest of body bright orange; caudal fin orange with ornate submarginal band consisting of several vertical dark lines. Sumatera to Fiji and Tonga, north to Ryukyu Islands. Maximum size 10 cm.

POT-BELLIED LEATHERJACKET
Pseudomonacanthus peroni (Hollard, 1854)

Dorsal rays II-30-36; anal rays 27-33; pectoral rays 11-13; distinguished by expanded belly flap (but much smaller than that of *Monacanthus chinensis*); tan with brown spots on head, body, and caudal fin, often two enlarged brown blotches near base of upper and lowermost caudal rays. Northern Australia. Attains 40 cm.

DIAMOND LEATHERJACKET
Rudarius excelsus Hutchins, 1977

Dorsal rays II-22-24; anal rays 20-22; pectoral rays 10; body depth 1.1-1.2 in standard length; spinules at front of first dorsal spine directed upward, those at side downward; extremely long bristles on caudal peduncle of males; distinguished by its extremely deep body and tiny size; green to brown, very difficult to detect in its weedy habitat. Queensland only; originally described from 2 specimens trawled near Lindeman Island; has been sighted in weed beds on the northern Great Barrier Reef on rare occasions. To 2.5 cm; becomes mature at 1.5 cm.

MINUTE LEATHERJACKET
Rudarius minutus Tyler, 1970

Dorsal rays II-26-28; anal rays 23 or 24; pectoral rays 11 or 12 (usually 11); body depth 1.7-1.9 in standard length; extremely long bristles on caudal peduncle of males; mottled brown; similar to *R. excelsus* (above), but is less deep-bodied and has broader and fewer skin flaps on body. Queensland and Borneo; known from relatively few specimens collected from mixed sand-coral habitats in 2-15 m depth. Reaches 3 cm.

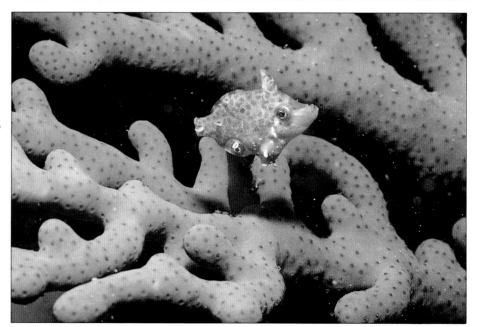

BOXFISHES
FAMILY OSTRACIIDAE

The boxfishes, sometimes called trunkfishes, are unique in possessing a bony carapace of polygonal plates with gaps for the mouth, gill opening, anus, caudal peduncle, and fins. It may be triangular, quadrangular, pentagonal, hexagonal, or nearly round in cross-section; its surface is usually rough due to the presence of small bony tubercles. The species of the genus *Lactoria* have a pair of sharp horn-like projections from the front of the head, the obvious basis for their common name of cowfishes. Boxfishes have no spines in the fins, no pelvic fins, and a single dorsal fin posterior in position but somewhat anterior to the anal fin; they have a small mouth, which is low on the head, and thick lips; the teeth are conical to incisiform with rounded tips, yellowish brown, and in a single row in the jaws; the gill opening is a near-vertical slit extending dorsally from in front of the pectoral-fin base. Boxfishes are slow swimmers, propelling themselves by a sculling action of the dorsal and anal fins; the caudal fin is brought into action when they want to move faster. They feed on a wide variety of benthic animals, particularly sessile forms such as tunicates, sponges, and alcyonarians; many also ingest large amounts of algae. Although the bony carapace alone would seem to be enough to discourage most predators, some species, at least, have another defence, a skin toxin called ostracitoxin which is secreted when the fish is under stress. If a boxfish is placed in a small volume of water with other fishes and harrassed, the other fishes will die; if the concentration of the poison is high enough, it will kill the boxfish too. Pectoral fin-ray counts given below include the rudimentary upper ray.

LONGHORN COWFISH
Lactoria cornuta (Linnaeus, 1758)

Dorsal rays 8-9; anal rays 9; pectoral rays 10-11; a pair of sharp horns about twice eye diameter in length extending anteriorly and often slightly upward from front of head at level of upper part of eye; a second pair extending posteriorly, one from each side of rear of carapace; dorsal profile of head nearly vertical; caudal fin very long, its length about 1.5-2 in standard length, and truncate (though often ragged on its trailing edge); colour variable, but usually olive to yellowish grey or brown with pale blue spots on side; ventral part of carapace orange-yellow; caudal fin often with pale spots and sometimes indistinct dusky spots. Indo-Pacific; not common; generally seen in weedy areas near rocks or reefs. Reported to 46 cm.

467

ROUNDBELLY COWFISH

Lactoria diaphana (Bloch & Schneider, 1801)

Dorsal rays 9; anal rays 9; pectoral rays 10-11; a pair of sharp horns usually a little less than eye diameter in length extending anteriorly from head at level of upper edge of eye; a second short pair posteriorly, one from end of each lower lateral ridge of carapace; a short thorn-like spine middorsally on back; ventral part of carapace strongly convex; dorsal profile of head about 65° to the horizontal; caudal fin rounded; usual colour grey to brown with indistinct dark spots and blotches. Indo-Pacific, but from scattered localities. Attains 25 cm. Possibly more than one species classified under this scientific name.

THORNBACK COWFISH

Lactoria fornasini (Bianconi, 1846)

Dorsal rays 9; anal rays 9; pectoral rays 11-12 (rarely 12); carapace basically quadrangular in cross-section but with a median ridge and large thorn-like spine in middle of back; bottom of carapace slightly convex; anterior and posterior horns similar to those of *L. diaphanus*, but shorter; dorsal profile of head about 45°; caudal fin rounded; light brown with blue spots or narrow irregular blue bands; fins pale. Indo-Pacific; observed more on sand, rubble, or weedy areas than on coral reefs. Maximum length, 15 cm.

YELLOW BOXFISH
Ostracion cubicus Linnaeus, 1758

Dorsal rays 9; anal rays 9; pectoral rays 11; carapace quadrangular in cross-section, the sides concave, broader at base than top, without spines and without a median dorsal ridge (characteristic of the genus); body becoming more elongate with growth (carapace depth of very small juveniles about 1.5 in standard length, of large adults about 3); large adults with a bump anteriorly on snout; caudal fin rounded; small juveniles yellow with round black spots nearly as large as pupil; with growth, black spots more numerous and relatively smaller; still larger fish brownish yellow with one white spot edged in black or rimmed with small black spots on each polygonal plate; largest fish purplish brown, the spots on carapace faint or absent, the grooves between polygonal plates yellow, especially ventrally and on cheek; fins with small dark spots on rays. Indo-Pacific. Reported to 45 cm. *O. tuberculatus* Linnaeus is a synonym.

Ostracion cubicus   Adult ▼ Juv. ▲

Ostracion meleagris   Male ▲ Female ▼

SPOTTED BOXFISH
Ostracion meleagris Shaw, 1796

Dorsal rays 9; anal rays 9; pectoral rays 11; caudal fin rounded in females, truncate with rounded corners in males; juveniles and females brown with small white spots; males brown with white spots dorsally on carapace like females (but spots larger and less numerous), blue elsewhere with dark-edged orange-yellow spots on side, these spots sometimes coalescing along upper lateral ridge to form an irregular band; a large pinkish white area on cheek below eye. Indo-Pacific and tropical eastern Pacific; the most common species of the genus. Reaches 18 cm. *O. sebae* Bleeker and *O. lentiginosum* Jordan and Evermann are synonyms.

STRIPED BOXFISH
Ostracion solorensis Bleeker, 1853

Dorsal rays 9; anal rays 8-9 (usually 9); pectoral rays 9-10 (usually 10); top of carapace nearly flat, the bottom slightly convex, the four ridges sharp; caudal fin rounded; top of carapace of females dark brown, dotted with gold, the upper side with dark brown stripes separated by gold lines, the lower side with irregular dark brown spots within a reticulum of gold lines; cheek brownish yellow with small dark brown spots; top of carapace of males black with a fine light blue-green network; the upper side with a broad black stripe containing two light blue-green lines and a few spots, the rest of side purple with small black spots and larger light blue-green spots broadly edged in black; a black-edged L-shaped light blue-green mark on cheek. Philippines and Indonesia to northern Great Barrier Reef. To 11 cm.

Ostracion solorensis   Male ▲ Female ▼

SHORTNOSE BOXFISH
Rhynchostracion nasus (Bloch, 1785)

Dorsal rays 9; anal rays 9; pectoral rays 11; carapace pentagonal in mid cross-section, deeper than wide, all surfaces concave; middorsal and upper lateral ridges sharp; a distinct small protuberance at front of snout just above mouth; a pronounced rounded ridge over each eye, hence interorbital deeply concave; caudal fin slightly emarginate; juveniles and subadults whitish with round black spots slightly smaller than pupil dorsally on body and caudal fin, and a scattering of smaller black spots on side of carapace; adults darker with more numerous smaller black spots. Western Pacific to East Africa; not common. Attains 30 cm. The related *R. rhinorhynchus* (Bleeker) also has a protuberance on the snout but it is much larger and broad-based; also the top of its carapace is essentially flat (although there is a median dorsal ridge).

SMALLSPINE TURRETFISH
Tetrosomus concatenatus (Bloch, 1786)

Dorsal rays 9; anal rays 9; pectoral rays 11; carapace triangular, the dorsal ridge with two thorn-like spines; three spines along each ventrolateral ridge; a small spine (two in juveniles) at front of ridge above eye (spines on ridges diminish in size with age); a very small median protuberance on cara- pace above upper lip; caudal fin rounded; light yellowish brown with pale blue mark- ings. Western Pacific to East Africa. Reaches 30 cm. *T. tritropis* (Snyder) and *T. reipubli- cae* (Ogilby) are synonyms.

HUMPBACK TURRETFISH
Tetrosomus gibbosus (Linnaeus, 1758)

Dorsal rays 9; anal rays 9-10 (usually 9); pectoral rays 10-11; carapace triangular in cross-section, the three ridges sharp, the median dorsal ridge strongly elevated in middle of body, ending in a large thorn-like spine; four to five lesser spines along each ventrolateral ridge; a small spine on ridge above eye; caudal fin slightly rounded; yellowish grey to brown, often with small pale blue spots and diffuse dark markings. Western Pacific to East Africa and the Red Sea; usually found in seagrass beds or algal flats. Attains about 25 cm.

PUFFERS
FAMILY TETRAODONTIDAE

The puffers, also known as blow-fishes, are named for their capacity to inflate themselves. They are characterized by having tough scaleless skin (often with small spinules), beak-like dental plates with a median suture, a slit-like gill opening in front of pectoral-fin base, no spines in fins, a single short-based dorsal fin posterior in position, a comparable anal fin below or behind the dorsal, no pelvic fins, and no ribs.

When attacked, these fishes draw water into a highly distensible diverticulum from the ventral part of the stomach, thus greatly expanding the size of their bodies. Puffers are well known for producing a powerful poison, tetraodontoxin, in their tissues, especially the liver and ovaries; serious illness, and not infrequently death, have resulted from eating these fishes. The degree of toxicity varies greatly with the spe-

cies and apparently also with geographical area and the season. The family is divisible into two subfamilies, the Tetraodontinae and the Canthigasterinae; the latter group consists of the small, often colourful tobies (also known as sharpnose puffers); they enjoy some freedom from predation as a result of their repelling skin toxin. Puffers are often called toadfishes in Australia.

Black-saddled Tobies (*Canthigaster valentini*)

SUBFAMILY TETRAODONTINAE

STARS AND STRIPES PUFFER
Arothron hispidus (Linnaeus, 1758)

Dorsal rays 10-11; anal rays 10-11; pectoral rays 17-19; small spinules on head and body except snout and posterior caudal peduncle; nostril consisting of two fleshy flaps from a common base (characteristic of the genus); caudal fin rounded; greyish to greenish brown with small white spots dorsally, shading to white below with curved dark stripes; pectoral base and gill opening alternately circled by narrow black and white bands. Indo-Pacific and tropical eastern Pacific; diet highly varied: algae, mollusks, tunicates, sponges, corals, anemones, crabs, tubeworms, sea urchins, brittle stars, starfishes (including the crown-of-thorns), hermit crabs, and hydroids. Largest, 48 cm.

STRIPED PUFFER
Arothron manilensis (de Proce, 1822)

Dorsal rays 9-11 (usually 10); anal rays 9-10 (usually 10); pectoral rays 16-19; head and body largely covered with small spinules (may be embedded); anal-fin base posterior to dorsal-fin base (true of other *Arothron*); caudal fin rounded and very long, its length 2.25-3.2 in standard length; brownish grey to greenish on back, whitish to pale yellowish ventrally, with 8-20 narrow dark stripes on body (reddish brown to black dorsally, brownish yellow to light reddish ventrally), the upper stripes curving downward on head to be continuous with lower stripes on body; caudal fin broadly edged in blackish. Western Australia and western Pacific east to Micronesia and Samoa.; generally found in shallow protected waters on silty sand or mud substrata.

Largest recorded, 31 cm. Often misidentified as *A. immaculatus* (Bloch & Schneider), a species which lacks dark stripes and has a shorter caudal fin on the average.

MAP PUFFER
Arothron mappa (Lesson, 1830)

Dorsal rays 11-12; anal rays 10-11 (usually 11); pectoral rays 17-19; heavy-bodied for the genus; head and body covered with small spinules except for region around mouth, base of fins, and caudal peduncle; caudal fin slightly rounded; about upper two-thirds of body light yellowish grey with highly irregular black bands, many forming a reticulum; a large irregular black blotch around gill opening and pectoral-fin base; lower third of body white with a faint reticulum of yellow and a large irregular black blotch or group of smaller blotches below pectoral fin; irregular black lines radiating from eye. Micronesia and Samoa to East Africa; usually found on coral reefs; not common. Attains 60 cm.

473

Arothron nigropunctatus Normal phase ▲ Bicolour phase ▼

BLACKSPOTTED PUFFER
Arothron nigropunctatus (Bloch & Schneider, 1801)

Dorsal rays 10-11 (usually 10); anal rays 10-11 (usually 11); pectoral rays 17-19; head and body covered with small spinules except middle of back, around mouth, and side of caudal peduncle; caudal fin slightly rounded; colour variable, grey to dark brown dorsally, whitish to bright yellow ventrally, but always with widely scattered black spots of different size and usually with a transverse pale band dorsally on snout separating dark areas around eye and mouth. Islands of Micronesia and Samoa to East Africa; a coral-reef species; feeds heavily on live coral and other coelenterates; also ingests sponges, tunicates, and algae. Attains at least 25 cm.

STAR PUFFER
Arothron stellatus (Bloch & Schneider, 1801)

Dorsal rays 11-12; anal rays 11; pectoral rays 17-20; small spinules on head and body except top of snout, base of fins, and side of caudal peduncle, the spinules most evident ventrally; caudal fin slightly rounded; adults white with small black spots on head, body, and median fins, those on pectoral base and around gill opening largest (spots relatively smaller and more numerous with growth); ventral part of head and body largely free of spots except a black area around anus; juveniles orange with small black spots, the abdomen with broad irregular diagonal black bands. Indo-Pacific; limited food habit data indicate a highly varied diet including sea urchins, sponges, coral, stinging coral (*Millepora*), starfishes, crabs, hermit crabs, and algae (*Halimeda*). Reaches 90 cm.

474

MILKSPOTTED PUFFER
Chelonodon patoca (Hamilton, 1822)

Dorsal rays 10; anal rays 8; pectoral rays 15-16; a patch of spinules on back from behind interorbital nearly to dorsal fin and another on throat and abdomen; nasal organ a depression with a low rim and anterior and posterior flaps; origin of anal fin below midbase of dorsal fin; caudal fin slightly rounded; grey to brown on back with large round to ovate white spots (sometimes with dark centres), shading to white ventrally; a broad streak of yellow on lower side; often exhibits three narrow dark bars on back. Western Pacific to the Persian Gulf; generally found inshore, frequently in brackish areas. Recorded to 33 cm.

SUBFAMILY CANTHIGASTERINAE

AMBON TOBY
Canthigaster amboinensis (Bleeker, 1865)

Dorsal rays 11-12 (usually 12); anal rays 10-11 (usually 11); pectoral rays 16-17 (usually 17); a ridge of skin middorsally (characteristic of the genus); snout conical and attenuate (also generic); caudal fin slightly rounded (generic); brown dorsally on head and body, shading to whitish ventrally, with small pale blue spots on body and basally on caudal fin, small dark brown spots on lower side mixed with the blue, and blue lines radiating from eye; cheek with numerous close-set small pale blue spots or irregular lines. Indo-Pacific and tropical eastern Pacific; occurs in shallow outer reef areas, often in the lower reaches of the surge zone; omnivorous, about half the diet algae, the rest a variety of benthic animals such as polychaete worms, sea urchins, brittle stars, tunicates, and molluscs. To 14 cm.

BENNETT'S TOBY
Canthigaster bennetti (Bleeker, 1854)

Dorsal rays 9-10; anal rays 8-10 (usually 9); pectoral rays 15-16 (usually 15); caudal fin slightly rounded; a broad diffuse dark grey-brown stripe on upper side of body, the back above brownish yellow with numerous small orange spots and a scattering of small pale blue spots and lines, the body below white with red, orange, and pale blue dots; region around eye orange-yellow with blue lines; a blue-edged black spot at dorsal-fin base. Indo-Pacific; usually seen in shallow protected waters on sand-rubble bottoms near reefs or in sea grass or algal beds; stomach contents of three from New Guinea 85% algae. Attains 10 cm.

THREE-BARRED TOBY
Canthigaster coronata (Vaillant & Sauvage, 1875)

Dorsal rays 9-10 (usually 10); anal rays 9-10 (usually 9); pectoral rays 16-17 (usually 17); whitish with a dark brown band across upper interorbital and three triangular dark brown bars on upper half of body (the first vertical, the second oblique, and the third on caudal peduncle very oblique), these bars with orange-yellow and blue markings along their edges; scattered small orange-yellow spots on lower side; region around eye orange-yellow with blue lines. Hawaii and Micronesia to East Africa; known from 6 to over 100 m; most often observed below 15 m on open bottoms of low relief; feeds on algae and a variety of benthic animals such as mollusks, crabs and other crustaceans, polychaete worms, peanut worms, brittle stars, bryozoans, tunicates, and sea urchins. Reaches 13.5 cm. *C. cinctus* Jordan & Evermann is a synonym.

LANTERN TOBY
Canthigaster epilampra (Jenkins, 1903)

Dorsal rays 10; anal rays 9; pectoral rays 16-18 (usually 17); whitish with numerous blue dots on body; a large blackish spot usually present at base of dorsal fin and extending a short distance anteriorly; snout yellow with dark-edged blue spots and lines; region around eye yellow with dark-edged blue lines radiating from eye; a small yellow spot, narrowly edged in black and blue, often present above pectoral-fin base; caudal fin yellow with pale blue longitudinal bands. Islands of central and western Pacific and Christmas Island in the eastern Indian Ocean; usually found on reefs at depths greater than 25 m. Attains 11 cm.

GREEN-SPOTTED TOBY
Canthigaster janthinoptera (Bleeker, 1855)

Dorsal rays 9-10 (usually 9); anal rays 9-10 (usually 9); pectoral rays 16-18 (usually 17); brownish orange with close-set pale blue-green spots on head and body and blue-green lines radiating from eye; a dark ocellus sometimes present at base of dorsal fin; fins largely unmarked. Indo-Pacific; a cryptic reef-dwelling species usually found in caves. Reported to 9 cm. Closely related to the Hawaiian endemic *C. jactator* (Jenkins) and the tropical eastern Pacific *C. punctatissima* (Günther).

SHY TOBY
Canthigaster ocellicincta Allen & Randall, 1977

Dorsal rays 9; anal rays 9; pectoral rays 16; orangish brown, paler ventrally, with two dark brown bars anteriorly on body extending onto upper abdomen, separated by a narrow white band, the first bar preceded by a similar band; upper part of body with blue lines (faint in zone of dark bars), the lower part with pale blue spots and short lines, most evident on caudal peduncle; snout and cheek with vertical blue lines, and blue lines extending upward from eye; a dark brown ocellus at base of dorsal fin. Known from the Philippines, Indonesia, islands of Melanesia, and the Great Barrier Reef; very secretive; rarely observed underwater, then only fleetingly as it moves from one hole of the reef to another. A small species; attains 6.5 cm.

SOLANDER'S TOBY
Canthigaster solandri (Richardson, 1844)

Dorsal rays 8-10 (usually 9, rarely 8); anal rays 8-9 (rarely 8); pectoral rays 16-17 (usually 17); orangish brown, paler on abdomen, shading to orange on head, with numerous small dark-edged pale blue spots on head and body and dark-edged blue lines radiating from eye; a blue-edged black spot at base of dorsal fin; caudal fin orange with small dark-edged pale blue spots. Indo-Pacific; the most common species on shallow rocky bottom and coral reefs at many localities. Individuals at islands of Oceania are a little different in colour from those of the western Pacific; the latter lacks the yellow or white ventral part of the body, has a few longitudinal blue lines on the nape and dorsally on the caudal peduncle, and the snout and caudal fin are more orange (sometimes orange-red); this form was named *C. papua* (Bleeker), currently regarded as a synonym of *solandri*.

BLACK-SADDLED TOBY
Canthigaster valentini (Bleeker, 1853)

Dorsal rays 9; anal rays 9; pectoral rays 16-17 (usually 16); whitish with small yellowish brown spots (except ventrally), a dark brown bar from behind eye across nape, and three on body, the two anterior ones narrowing as they reach upper abdomen, the posterior one on caudal peduncle short and broad; blue lines extending posteriorly from eye; caudal fin yellow, the upper and lower edges blackish; base of dorsal and anal fins with an orange bar. Indo-Pacific; a shallow-water coral-reef species, and one of the most comon of the genus; mimicked by the small filefish *Paraluteres prionurus* to gain the protection the model enjoys from its skin toxin. Reaches 9 cm.

PORCUPINEFISHES
FAMILY DIODONTIDAE

The porcupine fishes share with the puffers the ability to inflate themselves by drawing water into the abdomen; they have the added protection of formidable sharp spines on the head and body. These may be three-rooted, hence fixed, as seen on the species of *Chilomycterus* and *Cyclichthys* (called burrfishes) or two-rooted and movable, as in *Diodon*. Normally the spines of the species of *Diodon* lie against the body, the tips pointing backward, but when the fishes expand their bodies, the spines are erected approximately perpendicular to the surface of the body – an obvious deterrent to a potential predator. Porcupinefishes differ further from the puffers in having broader pectoral fins (often with the posterior margin emarginate), lacking a median suture on their stout dental plates, and in having larger eyes. Most are nocturnal; usually they hide in small caves or beneath ledges by day. Their strong dental plates and powerful jaws are admirably suited to crush the hard tests of sea urchins, the shells of gastropod molluscs and hermit crabs, and the exoskeletons of crabs; these animals, which are active mainly at night, are the principal prey of diodontid fishes. Porcupine fishes have been reported as harboring tetraodontoxin, though much less frequently than some of the puffers. Care should be taken in handling these fishes, not only because of their sharp spines but because they have the capability of inflicting a severe bite.

SPOTTEDFIN BURRFISH
Chilomycterus reticulatus (Linnaeus, 1758)

Dorsal rays 12-14; anal rays 11-14; pectoral rays 19-22; head and body with short immovable spines, about 8-10 in an approximate row from snout to dorsal fin; median fins small, the caudal rounded; grey on back with scattered round blackish spots of variable size, shading to white ventrally; a diffuse dusky bar below eye, one posteriorly on head, one beneath end of pectoral fin, and often a faint one just anterior to dorsal and anal fins; median fins with numerous small black spots. Circumglobal; rare; more often found in subtropical and warm temperate than tropic seas. Reported to 55 cm; the young remain in the pelagic realm until a length of about 20 cm. *C. affinis* Günther is a synonym.

ORBICULAR BURRFISH
Cyclichthys orbicularis (Bloch, 1785)

Dorsal rays 11-13; anal rays 10-12; pectoral rays 18-21; spines short and three-rooted, hence not erectile; a small movable spine below and behind corner of mouth; about 8 spines in an approximate row from snout to origin of dorsal fin; no spine on caudal peduncle; no fleshy tentacles; brown, shading to white ventrally, with black spots (most about pupil size), often in clusters, the most conspicuous forming a bar on side in front of a vertical through origin of dorsal fin; spines within white or yellow spots. Western Pacific to East Africa; usually found on sand or rubble substrata. To 15 cm.

FRECKLED PORCUPINEFISH
Diodon holocanthus Linnaeus, 1758

Dorsal rays 13-15; anal rays 13-14; pectoral rays 22-25; long erectile spines on head and body (true of all *Diodon*); 12-16 spines from top of snout to dorsal fin; anterior middle spines on top of head longer than longest spines posterior to pectoral fins; no spines on caudal peduncle; two small barbels on chin; light olive to light brown, shading to white ventrally, with small black spots dorsally and anteriorly; a brown bar from above to below eye; a broad transverse brown band on occipital region of head and another across middle of back; a large oval brown blotch above each pectoral fin, and one around dorsal-fin base; fins without spots. Circumtropical, but distribution spotty; may be found on coral reefs but also occurs on open bottoms far from the shelter of reefs or rocky substrata; recorded from the shallows to at least 100 m. Maximum length, 29 cm.

PORCUPINEFISH
Diodon hystrix Linnaeus, 1758

Dorsal rays 14-17; anal rays 14-16; pectoral rays 21-25; 16-20 spines in an approximate row from top of snout to dorsal fin; spines anteriorly at front of head shorter than longest spines posterior to pectoral fins; one or more small spines dorsally on caudal peduncle; no small spine below eye pointing downward; no barbels on chin; olive to light grey-brown dorsally with small black spots, shading to white ventrally; fins yellowish with small black spots. Circumtropical; generally found on coral or rocky reefs; feeds mainly on mollusks (especially gastropods), sea urchins and heart urchins, crabs, and hermit crabs. Largest collected, 71 cm.

BLACK-BLOTCHED PORCUPINE-FISH

Diodon liturosus Shaw, 1804

Dorsal rays 14-16; anal rays 14-16; pectoral rays 21-25; 16-21 spines from top of snout to dorsal fin; spines on front of head much shorter than those behind pectoral fins; a short downward-pointing spine below front of eye; no spines on caudal peduncle; two small barbels on chin; brown with black spots on upper part of body, shading to white ventrally, with large white-edged black blotches as follows: above and passing ventrally from eye; across rear of head, in front of gill opening, above each pectoral fin, middle of back, and around base of dorsal fin; fins yellowish. Indo-Pacific; found mainly on reefs. Reaches 50 cm. *D. maculatus* Dumeril and *D. bleekeri* Günther are synonyms.

LONGSPINE BURRFISH

Tragulichthys jaculiferus (Cuvier, 1818)

Dorsal rays 12; anal rays 12-13 (usually 12); pectoral rays 21-22; head and body with spines of variable size, most short and two-rooted, but five or six on side behind axil of pectoral fin extremely long and movable; snout very short, the mouth barely anterior to eye; caudal fin rounded; olivaceous brown, shading to white ventrally, with a row of three black spots smaller than pupil of eye, one on head before lower end of gill opening, one beneath outer part of pectoral fin, and one on side between dorsal and anal fins; fins unmarked. Australia and New Zealand except in the south; usually seen in less than 20 m. Reported to 60 cm.

GLOSSARY

Adipose eyelid: immovable transparent outer covering or partial covering of the eye of some groups of bony fishes, such as mullets and trevallies, which performs protective and streamlining functions.

Adipose fin: a small fleshy fin without rays found on the back behind the dorsal fin of some primitive teleost fishes such as the lizardfishes.

Alcyonarian: animal of Subclass Anthozoa (corals, sea anemones) of Phylum Coelenterata; polyps with eight tentacles; includes soft corals and gorgonians.

Allopatric: in reference to species with different geographical distributions; the opposite of sympatric.

Antrorse spine: a small bony projection directed anteriorly (present on the lower preopercular margin of some serranids).

Anus: the posterior external opening of the digestive tract from which wastes are voided; sometimes called the vent.

Axil: the acute angular region between a fin and the body; usually used in reference to the underside of the pectoral fin toward the base. Equivalent to the armpit of man.

Band: an oblique or irregular marking (compare 'bar' below).

Bar: an elongate colour marking of vertical orientation, the sides of which are usually more-or-less straight (although they need not be parallel).

Barbel: a slender tentacle-like protuberance of sensory function which is often seen on the chin of some fishes such as goatfishes and some of the croakers.

Benthic: referring to the benthos, the fauna and flora of the sea bottom.

Bifurcate: divided into two branches.

Biserial: arranged in two separate rows.

Bommie: an isolated coral head; Australian term.

Branched tubules: refers to lateral-line scale tubules which divide into two or more branches.

Canine: a prominent slender sharp-pointed tooth.

Carapace: a rigid shield encasing the body.

Carnivore: a flesh-eating animal.

Caudal fin: the tail fin. The term tail alone generally refers to that part of a fish posterior to the anus.

Caudal peduncle: the part of the body between the posterior basal parts of the dorsal and anal fins and the base of the caudal fin. The usual vertical measurement is the least depth; the length measurement herein is horizontal, generally from the rear base of the anal fin.

Cephalic flaps: the forward-directed projections on either side of the mouth of manta or devil rays (Mobulidae).

Ciguatera: an illness resulting from eating a fresh fish with ciguatoxin in its tissues (see Introduction to Lutjanidae).

Circumnarial groove: a cleft or groove around the nostril openings found in some sharks.

Circumpeduncular scales: the transverse series of scales that completely encircle the caudal peduncle.

Cirrus: a small slender flexible fleshy protuberance; the plural is cirri.

Claspers: rod-like grooved processes attached to the pelvic fins of male sharks, skates, rays, and guitarfishes. Used to transmit sperm during copulation.

Cloaca: cavity into which the intestinal, urinary, and reproductive canals open.

Coelenterate: an aquatic animal of the Phylum Coelenterata which is characterized by a central mouth usually surrounded by tentacles bearing stinging cells, and no anus; includes sea anemones, corals, and jellyfishes.

Community: the assemblage of animals and plants living in one habitat.

Compressed: laterally flattened; often used in reference to the shape of the body - in this case deeper than wide.

Crenulate: wavy or scalloped, in reference to the shape of an edge (as of a lip).

Crustacean: an animal of Class Crustacea, Phylum Arthropoda; includes crabs, lobsters, shrimps, and copepods.

Ctenoid scales: scales of bony fishes which have tiny tooth-like projections along the posterior margin and part of the exposed portion. Collectively these little teeth (or ctenii) impart a rough texture to the surface of the scales.

Cuspidate: bearing a pointed projection (cusp); generally used in reference to sharks teeth with more than one cusp.

Cycloid scales: scales of bony fishes, the exposed surfaces and edges of which lack any small tooth-like projections; they are, therefore, smooth to the touch.

Demersal: living on the sea bottom.

Denticles: tooth-like projections such as the scales which cover the bodies of cartilaginous fishes.

Depressed: dorsoventrally flattened. The opposite in body shape of compressed.

Depth: vertical measurement of the body of a fish; most often employed for maximum height of body excluding fins.

Distal: outward from the point of attachment; the opposite of proximal.

Dorsal: toward the back or upper part of the body; the opposite of ventral.

Dorsal fin: a median fin along the back which is supported by rays. When there are two or more dorsal fins the most anterior one is designated the first.

Echinoderm: an aquatic marine animal of the Phylum Echinodermata; radially symmetrical with a skeleton composed of calcareous plates (may be reduced to spicules); many move via their numerous tube feet; includes starfishes, brittle stars, sea urchins, and sea cucumbers.

Elasmobranch: a subclass of cartilaginous fishes including sharks, skates and rays.

Elongate: extended or drawn out.

Emarginate: concave; used to describe the posterior border of a caudal fin which is inwardly curved.

Endemic: native; in reference to an animal or plant restricted to a certain area.

Epipelagic: pertaining to the surface layer of the open sea.

Esca: the bait or lure of lophiiform fishes (see illicium).

Falcate: sickle-shaped; used to describe the shape of fins.

Family: a major entity in the classification of animals and plants which consists of a group of related genera. Family words end in 'idae', such as Gobiidae for the goby family; when used as an adjective, the 'ae' is dropped, thus gobiid fish.

Fork length: the straight-line distance from the front of the snout to the distal end of the shortest middle caudal fin ray.

Forked: inwardly angular; used in describing the shape of a caudal fin which is divided into two equal lobes, the posterior border of each of which is relatively straight.

Fusiform: spindle-shaped; used in reference to the body shape of a fish which is cylindrical or nearly so and tapers toward both ends.

Gas bladder: a tough-walled gas-filled sac lying in the upper part of the body cavity of many bony fishes just beneath the vertebral column, the prinicipal function of which is to offset the weight of the heavier tissues, particularly bone. The organ is also called the swim bladder.

Genus: a group of closely related species; the first part of the scientific name of an animal or plant. The plural is genera.

Gill arch: the bony and cartilaginous support for the gill filaments and gill rakers. Normally there are four pairs of gill arches in bony fishes.

Gill opening: the opening posteriorly and often also ventrally on the head of fishes where the water of respiration is expelled. Bony fishes have a single such opening on each side whereas cartilaginous fishes (sharks and rays) have five to seven. The gill openings of sharks and rays are called gill slits.

Gill rakers: stout protuberances of the gill arch on the opposite side from the red gill filaments; they function in retaining food organisms. Gill rakers vary greatly in number and length and are important in the classification of fishes.

Gonads: reproductive organs.

Gorgonian: a sessile animal of the Subclass Alcyonaria, Class Anthozoa, Phylum Coelenterata; includes sea fans and sea whips.

Head length: the straight-line measurement of the head taken from the front of the upper lip to the membranous posterior end of the operculum.

Herbivore: a plant-feeding animal.

Homonym: the scientific name of an organism which is the same as that given to another organism; the second of these two identical names is invalid.

Illicium: the 'fishing pole' and 'lure' of lophiiform (pediculate) fishes which is used to attract prey close to the mouth.

Incisiform: chisel-like; used to describe teeth which are flattened and truncate with sharp edges like the front teeth of some mammals such as man.

Inferior tail ridge: a bony ridge along the lower edge of the tail in pipefishes.

Inferior trunk ridge: a bony ridge along the lower edge of the trunk of the body in pipefishes.

Interdorsal ridge: a tough fold of skin that runs along the middle of the back between the dorsal fins of some sharks.

Interopercle: one of the bones comprising the operculum; bordered anterodorsally by the preopercle and posterodorsally by the opercle and subopercle.

Interorbital space: the region on the top of the head between the eyes; measurements may be taken of the least width, either fleshy (to the edges of the orbits) or bony (between the edges of the frontal bones which rim the orbits).

Interradial membrane: the membrane between fin rays.

Invertebrate: an animal lacking a vertebral column; includes the vast majority of animals on earth such as the corals, the worms, and the insects.

Isthmus: the throat region of a fish which extends forward from the ventral part of the chest (thorax) and narrows anteriorly.

Keel: a lateral strengthening ridge posteriorly on the caudal peduncle or base of the caudal fin; typically found on swift-swimming fishes with a narrow caudal peduncle and a broadly lunate caudal fin.

Labial furrows: grooves around the outer edges of the lips that are prominent in some sharks.

Lanceolate: lance-shaped, hence gradually tapering to a point; used to describe a caudal fin with very long middle rays. An unusual fin shape most often seen among the gobies.

Lateral: referring to the side or directed toward the side; the opposite of medial.

Lateral line: a sensory organ of fishes which consists of a canal running along the side of the body and communicating via pores through scales to the exterior; functions in perceiving low frequency vibrations, hence provides a sense which might be termed 'touch at a distance.'

Lateral-line scales: the pored scales of the lateral line between the upper end of the gill opening and the base of the caudal fin. The count of this series of scales is of value in the description of fishes. Also of value at times is the number of scales above the lateral line (to the origin of the dorsal fin) and the number below the lateral line (to the origin of the anal fin).

Lateral trunk ridge: a bony ridge along the middle part of the anterior body of pipefishes.

Leptocephalus: the elongate, highly compressed, transparent larval stage of some primitive teleost fishes such as the tarpon, bonefish and eels.

Lower limb: refers either to the horizontal margin of the preopercle or to the ventral part of the gill arch.

Lunate: sickle-shaped; used to describe a caudal fin which is deeply emarginate with narrow lobes.

Maxilla: a dermal bone of the upper jaw which lies posterior to the premaxilla. On the higher fishes the maxilla is excluded from the gape, and the premaxilla bears the teeth.

Medial: toward the middle or median plane of the body; opposite of lateral.

Median fins: the fins in the median plane, hence the dorsal, anal, and caudal fins.

Midlateral scales: refers to the longitudinal series of scales from the upper edge of the operculum to the base of the caudal fin. Generally used for fishes without a lateral line.

Molariform: shaped like a molar, hence low, broad, and rounded.

Mollusc: an animal of the Phylum Mollusca; unsegmented with a muscular 'foot' and visceral mass; often protected by one or two shells; includes gastropods (snails and nudibranchs), pelecypods (bivalves such as clams and oysters), cephalopods (such as squids and octopuses), and amphineurans (chitons).

Nape: the dorsal region of the head posterior to the occiput.

Nasal barbel: tentacle-like protuberance located close to the nasal opening.

Nasal fossa: cavity or pit containing the nasal organ.

Nasoral groove: a cleft or furrow between the nostril and mouth in some sharks.

Nicitating eyelid: a movable transparent membrane which serves to protect the eye of elasmobranch fishes.

Ocellus: eye-like marking with ring of one colour surrounding spot of another.

Omnivore: an animal which feeds on both plant and animal material.

Opercle: the large bone which forms the upper posterior part of the operculum; often bears one to three backward-directed spines in the higher fishes.

Operculum: gill cover; comprised of the following four bones; opercle, preopercle, interopercle, and subopercle.

Orbital: referring to the orbit or eye.

Order: a major unit in the classification of organisms; an assemblage of related families. The ordinal word ending in the Animal Kingdom is 'iformes'.

Origin: the beginning; often used for the anterior end of the dorsal or anal fin at the base. Also used in zoology to denote the more fixed attachment of a muscle.

Oviparous: producing ova (eggs) that hatch after leaving the body of the mother; the mode of reproduction of the great majority of bony fishes.

Ovoviviparous: producing eggs which hatch within body of mother; mode of reproduction of most sharks and rays.

Paired fins: collective term for the pectoral and pelvic fins.

Palatine: a paired lateral bone on the roof of the mouth lying between the vomer and the upper jaw; the presence or absence of teeth on this bone is of significance in the classification of fishes.

Papilla: a small fleshy protuberance.

Pectoral fin: the fin usually found on each side of the body behind the gill opening; in primitive fishes such as herrings, this pair of fins is lower on the body than in more advanced forms.

Pelagic: pertaining to the open sea (hence not living inshore or on the bottom); oceanic.

Pelvic fin: one of a pair of juxtaposed fins ventrally on the body in front of the anus; varies from abdominal in position in primitive fishes such as herrings to the more anterior locations termed thoracic or jugular in advanced fishes. It is sometimes called the ventral fin.

Perinasal groove: cleft or furrow around the nasal opening in some sharks. Also called circumnarial groove.

Pharyngeal teeth: opposing patches of teeth which occur on upper and lower elements of the gill arches. Vary from sharp and piercing to nodular or molariform; may be modified into a grooved grinding apparatus (or pharyngeal mill), such as is seen in the parrotfishes.

Plankton: collective term for pelagic animals and plants that drift with ocean currents; many are motile but are too small or swim too feebly or aimlessly to resist the sweep of the current. By contrast, animals of the nekton are independent of water movement.

Polychaete: an animal of Class Polychaeta of Phylum Annelida; a segmented worm with setae (bristles), which may move about freely or live permanently in a tube. Polychaete is from the Greek meaning many hairs or bristles.

Polyp: the sedentary form of coelenterate animals consisting of a tubular body with one external opening (the mouth) rimmed with tentacles; may be one of a colony; the soft part of a living coral.

Precaudal pit: the dorsal depression or notch just in front of the caudal fin of sharks.

Predorsal scales: the series of scales along the middorsal line extending anterior to the origin of the dorsal fin.

Premaxilla: the more anterior bone forming the upper jaw. In the higher fishes it extends backward and bears all of the teeth of the jaw. It is this part of the upper jaw which can be protruded by many fishes.

Preopercle: a boomerang-shaped bone, the edges of which form the posterior and lower margins of the cheek region; it is the most anterior of the bones comprising the gill cover. The upper vertical margin is sometimes called the upper limb, and the lower horizontal edge the lower limb; the two limbs meet at the angle of the preopercle.

Preoral length: measurement used for sharks taken between the snout tip and front of the upper jaw.

Preorbital: the first and usually the largest of the suborbital bones; located along the ventroanterior rim of the eye. Sometimes called the lachrymal bone.

Principal caudal rays: the caudal rays which reach the posterior, terminal border of the fin; in those fishes with branched caudal rays, the count includes the branched rays plus the uppermost and lowermost rays which are unbranched.

Produced: drawn out to a point; lengthened.

Protrusible: capable of projection as in some jaws.

Proximal: toward the centre of the body; the opposite of distal.

Radii: small (often microscopic) grooves on the margin of scales; radiate from the focus (centre of origin) of the scale, hence cut across the circuli (growth rings).

Ray: the supporting bony elements of fins; includes spines and soft rays.

Rhomboid: wedge-shaped; refers to a caudal fin in which the middle rays are longest and the upper and lower portions of the terminal border of the fin are more-or-less straight; essentially the opposite of forked. It is an uncommon fin shape.

Rounded: refers to a caudal fin in which the terminal border is smoothly convex.

Rudiment: a structure so deficient in size that it does not perform its normal function; often used in reference to small nodular gill rakers at the ends of the gill arches.

Seta: a bristle or bristle-like structure; the plural is setae.

Scute: an external bony plate or enlarged scale.

Segmented rays: the soft rays of the fins which bear cross striations, at least distally.

Serrate: notched along a free margin; like the edge of a saw.

Sexual dichromatism: a condition wherein the two sexes of the same species are of different colour.

Simple: not branched.

Snout: the region of the head in front of the eye. Snout length is measured from front of the upper lip to the anterior edge of the eye.

Soft ray: a segmented fin ray which is composed of two closely joined lateral elements. It is nearly always flexible and often branched.

Spatulate: flattened with a rounded end, sometimes used to describe tooth shape.

Species: the fundamental unit in the classification of animals and plants consisting of a population of individuals which freely interbreed with one another. The word 'species' is both singular and plural.

Spine: unsegmented bony process consisting of single element, usually rigid and sharply pointed. Those spines which support fins are never branched.

Spinule: a small spine (but not used to refer to the spines in fins).

Spiracle: an opening between the eye and the first gill slit of sharks and rays which leads to the pharyngeal cavity.

Standard length: the straight-line length of a fish from the front of the upper lip to the posterior end of the vertebral column (the last element of which, the hypural plate, is somewhat broadened and forms the bony support for the caudal fin rays).

Stripe: a horizontal straight-sided colour marking.

Subopercle: an elongate flat dermal bone which is one of the four comprising the operculum; lies below the opercle and forms the ventroposterior margin of the operculum.

Suborbital depth: the distance from the lower edge of the eye to the nearest edge of the upper lip.

Suborbital stay: a bony ridge across the cheek found in scorpaeniform fishes.

Subterminal notch: indentation near the tip of the posterior edge of the upper caudal lobe of many sharks.

Supraorbital: the region above the upper edge of the eye.

Supraorbital ridge: bony crest above eye.

Supraorbital tentacle: a slender flap of skin above the eye.

Symbiosis: the living together in close association by two dissimilar organisms. This term includes commensalism whereby one organism derives benefit from the association but the other does not (though it is not harmed), parasitism where the association is disadvantageous to one of the organisms, and mutualism where both organisms exist to mutual advantage.

Sympatric: in reference to species which live in the same major geographical area; the opposite of allopatric.

Synonym: invalid scientific name of an organism proposed after accepted name.

Tail: that part of an animal posterior to the anus (disregarding the hind limbs of quadrupeds).

Teleost: refers to the Teleostei, the highest superorder of rayfin bony fishes. The other superorders are the Chondrostei (surgeons and paddlefishes are living representatives) and the Holostei (the bowfin and true gars are contemporary forms). Teleosts represent about 96% of extant fishes.

Tholichthys larva: the pelagic stage of butterflyfishes (Chaetodontidae) characterized by external bony plates covering the head.

Thoracic: referring to the chest region.

Total length: the maximum straight-line length of a fish; generally taken from the front of whichever jaw is most anterior to the end of the longest caudal fin ray.

Transverse scales: series of scales in a vertical row, often counted between the dorsal and anal fin bases.

Truncate: square-ended; used to describe a caudal fin with a vertically straight terminal border and angular or slightly rounded corners.

Uniserial: arranged in a single row.

Upper limb: refers either to the vertical free margin of the preopercle or the upper part of the gill arch

Ventral: toward the lower part of the body; the opposite of dorsal.

Vertical scale rows: see midlateral scales.

Villiform: like the villi of the intestine, hence with numerous small slender projections. Used to describe bands of small close-set teeth, particularly if slender. If the teeth are short, they are often termed cardiform.

Viviparous: producing living young which develop from nourishment directly from the mother.

Vomer: a median unpaired bone toward the front of the roof of the mouth, the anterior end of which often bears teeth.

Zooplankton: the animals of the plankton.

FAMILIES BY AUTHOR

John E. Randall

Introduction
Acanthuridae
Albulidae
Atherinidae
Balistidae
Blenniidae
Carapidae
Cirrhitidae
Creedidae
Diodontidae

Excocetidae
Holocentridae
Labridae
Microdesmidae
Mullidae
Muraenidae
Ostraciidae
Pempheridae
Pinguipedidae
Priacanthidae

Scaridae
Serranidae
Siganidae
Synodontidae
Tetraodontidae
Trichonotidae
Uraniscopidae
Zanclidae

Gerald R. Allen

Acanthoclinidae
Alopiidae
Antennariidae
Aplodactinidae
Apogonidae
Atherinidae
Aulostomidae
Batrachoididae
Belonidae
Bothidae
Bythitidae
Caesionidae
Callionymidae
Caracanthidae
Carangidae
Carcharhinidae
Centriscidae
Centropomidae
Chaetodontidae
Chandidae
Chlopsidae
Clupeidae
Congridae
Coryphaenidae
Dactylopteridae
Dasyatidae
Echeneidae
Eleotridae
Ephippidae

Exocetidae
Fistulariidae
Gerreidae
Ginglymostomatidae
Gobiesocidae
Gobiidae
Haemulidae
Hemigaleidae
Hemiramphidae
Hemiscyllidae
Heterodontidae
Hexanchidae
Istiophoridae
Kuhliidae
Kyphosidae
Lamnidae
Lethrinidae
Lobotidae
Lutjanidae
Malacanthidae
Mobulidae
Monacanthidae
Monocentridae
Moringuidae
Mugilidae
Myliobatidae
Nemipteridae
Odontaspidae
Ophichthidae

Ophidiidae
Opistognathidae
Orectolobidae
Platycephalidae
Plesiopidae
Pleuronectidae
Plotosidae
Polynemidae
Pomacanthidae
Pomacentridae
Pseudochromidae
Rhincodontidae
Rhinobatidae
Scombridae
Scorpaenidae
Scyliorhinidae
Sharks – General
Soleidae
Solenostomidae
Sparidae
Sphyraenidae
Sphyrnidae
Stegostomatidae
Syngnathidae
Teraponidae
Torpedinidae
Trypterygiidae
Xenisthmidae
Xiphiidae

INDEX

493